As a theologian, Karl Rahner, S.J., has been distinguished by his breadth of scholarship, originality of thought and practicality of purpose. Any one of these qualities could lift a theologian to prominence; the combination of them in Father Rahner assures him of an influence beyond his century, even though it is for his own century that he writes—with a relentless integrity.

In *Nature and Grace* Father Rahner is concerned with dangers in contemporary Catholic thought and practice — dangers against which too few voices have been raised. There is the danger, first, that the individual will be submerged in what Rahner calls the mass-Church—wherein it is possible to be a Catholic by custom, convenience, nationality, social status—by almost any title, in fact, except that of personal faith and commitment.

There are the threats to the Christian conscience posed by an extreme situation—ethics which would "baptize" Sartre as Aquinas did Aristotle, and a sin-mystique, seen in some modern Catholic novelists, which would hold that only the sinner really knows God.

There is the even greater danger that the enlarging role of the laity will be looked on as rooted in pragmatic need rather than theological necessity. Father Rahner's tracing of the sacramental roots of the layman's role are among the finest pages to be found in the yet inchoate theology of the laity.

Yet, despite the seriousness of its subjects and profundity of treatment, this present volume is informal in tone and simple in style. For Father Rahner is a pastoral theologian, who knows that theology is light for the many, not a luxury for the few.

Readers of *Free Speech in the Church* or *The Christian Commitment* will welcome another timely, non-technical volume from the author's pen. Readers encountering Father Rahner for the first time will marvel that a theologian of such high renown can make wisdom seem like common sense. With lesser thinkers, it's the other way around.

NATURE AND GRACE

NATURE AND GRACE

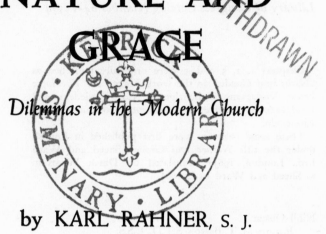

Dilemmas in the Modern Church

by KARL RAHNER, S. J.

CATHOLIC SCHOOL OFFICE
4140 LINDELL
ST. LOUIS, MO. 63108

SHEED AND WARD · NEW YORK

© Sheed and Ward, Inc., 1964

Library of Congress Catalog Number 64-13574

Chapters 1, 2, 3 and 5 were originally published as
"Natur und Gnade," in the work *Fragen der Theologie
heute,* Verlagsanstalt Benziger & Co., Einsiedeln, and
Grefahren im heutigen Katholizismus, Johannes-Verlag,
Einsiedeln.

These same chapters were first published in English
under the title *Nature and Grace* (Sheed and Ward
Ltd., London, 1963), translated by Dinah Wharton.
© Sheed and Ward Ltd., 1963.

Manufactured in the United States of America

Contents

Contents

Abbreviations

NATURE AND GRACE

I. Dangers in Catholicism Today

Introduction

The greatest dangers are always so particularly dangerous
because they go unnoticed. It is the same in the Church.
She is always threatened by dangers. The greatest are those
from within; all those from outside only become dangerous
to her if they touch upon a weakness within. The promise
that the gates of hell will never prevail against the Church
does not promise her constant visible, "empirical" strength
and immunity, but promises the power which is God's alone
in the weakness and vulnerability of the men who are her
members. When men feel safe and assured because "nothing
can ever really happen to the Church," then they always
find out sooner or later that indeed nothing can "happen"
to the *Church,* who is in God's hand, but quite a lot can
happen to the men who out of idleness or timidity do nothing and rely on this.

The dangers to the Church are often unnoticed—the
spirit of an age, for example, which is taken for granted
everywhere, and so also in the heart and instincts of the
good and faithful Christian before he can control it with

an understanding armed with the truths of the Faith; the
spirit of an age, which can even secretly be at work in those
who are protesting against it. (For example rationalism is
fought very rationalistically, because one must "fight one's
opponent with his own weapons.") These dangers can
always only be overcome by the saints and prophets of
the Church. For only they can conquer through the ever-
new (and ever-ancient) Holy Spirit, the spirit of a new
age "non in persuasibilibus humanae sapientiae verbis, sed
in ostensione spiritus et virtutis." They overcome this spirit
not by arguing against it (even though in the household
of the Church this, too, is unavoidable), but by bringing
and manifesting to it in themselves the eternal Holy Spirit
of the Church so powerfully that he becomes the living
Spirit of the day. (How little and humble these beginnings
often are, and how old-fashioned and outdated they can
seem!) We others, in our fight against these dangers, use
the weapons of human wisdom; we argue in a harassed way
about this and that; we try to immunize against diseases
without being able to get out of the country in which the
disease is endemic; we fight with the weapons of our opponents and we can count ourselves lucky if they don't do
us more harm than the enemy; we fight for God's truth
(we do really), and in doing so always defend a little (unnoticed and against our will) our own error, which is of
yesterday, against the error of today. And when we are
finished we find with shame that we have been God's unprofitable servants. But we can comfort ourselves that even

this fight by humble servants and miserable sinners was also God's will, as long as we realize that it is not a question of our saving his Church but of his saving us in her.

The three chapters gathered together here are not the call of a prophet. They do not claim to point out *the* dangers—either all of them or the most important—to the Church today or to strike down the greatest and most widespread dangers by the manifestation of the Spirit and his power. They are three essays which originally appeared in different places, and no effort has been made to disguise their origin. They are essays of a theology teacher. A little abstract, therefore, and pedantic, as befits his subject (today at any rate). They approach their common subject in different ways; in one the danger is reviewed by setting out some positive principles; in another the danger in question is described mainly *a posteriori* and a little said about how to deal with it; in the third the danger is in a sense deduced *a priori* and not much said about fighting it.

At any rate, here are three dangers which it is perhaps worth the trouble of thinking about. They hang closely together. The danger in the first chapter is the opposite to that in the second chapter: in the one the danger of the individual taking refuge in the collective and thinking that to be a good and mature Christian it is enough to march willingly and stoutly with all the rest in the mass of the "people of the Church"; in the other, the danger of making moral decisions only as a unique individual and thinking one has no obligation to obey the universal law which the

Church is and which she preaches (as a law of love and true freedom). The third chapter turns from the general danger of a false idea of individuality to the individual case of the Church's teaching and speaks of the danger of esoteric theories about this which are against the very nature of the Church's faith and her teaching authority.

1

The Individual in the Church

Anyone who has to speak about the individual in the Church today has a difficult task before him. He may well still be able to say something "quite correct." But will he be able to say the *decisive* thing for the time in which we live? We are in the midst of a tremendous battle between an individualism which is centuries old, and the new collectivism which is advancing victoriously, secure in the knowledge that the future is in its hands. And we Christians are divided against ourselves; for the noise of our own arguments against individualism, subjectivism, the individual and his independent rights, is still ringing in our ears and now a new age is upon us which has laid the old world in its grave, and we regretfully remember what a good time we had in that world which we fought so hard against. And when we carefully take up a middle position between the two, a polemical "neither-nor" and a synthetic "both-and," don't we perhaps have an uneasy feeling that our formula is very nice—but very theoretical?

We can't say that this difficulty is about things which do not concern us, that we are not concerned with the individual and the community in general, but with the individual and the religious community of the Church. It is true that in this case we can have a surer knowledge of the theoretical relationship between them. It is true that here it could at least seem that the practical difficulty for actual living people were only onesided: the question of the Christian and his rights as opposed to the rights of the Christian community, so that we should be back to our apologetics for the social against the individual.

But if we look more carefully we find that the atmosphere of the general conflict between individual and community is the same as in our conflict. When, in the last three hundred years, the individual would have nothing to do with the Church, this was because of a general basic attitude of individualism which he, who had absorbed the intellectual life of the preceding three hundred years, would share and which would make him passionately defend the rights of the individual against the claims of the community. And so it comes that our problem shares in the general uncertainty of the whole field. The latest statements, with their formal "both-and" and "partly-partly," may be clear. They are clear. This is important and encouraging. But can we be so completely certain that the individualism of the past few centuries—perhaps since the end of the Middle Ages—has not also done its work—even when all basic principles have been adhered to—in the Church and among good and faithful Christians, work which was permissible, perhaps even right, for the time, and yet also, perhaps, here and there exaggerated, even harmful? Can we be sure that we know how to strike the exact balance between the individual and the community, even if we *are* agreed on the theoretical principles? Are we certain that the actual daily life of the Church, past and present, has not ever laid a burden on the individual of today which we have no right to ask him to bear?

Finally, aren't we now seeing a failure of the individual good practising Catholic in his duty to make decisions which is his precisely *as* an individual, while he looks inquiringly to the Church for directives which are either, unfortunately, in fact not given, or which could not be given at all and so should not be expected, a passive do-nothing attitude because no directive has been given from above? And doesn't this force us to realize that in the Church too there is a sheep-like submissiveness and anti-individualistic self-effacement which we, who battled so fiercely against individualism, did not bargain for, and which should terrify us? And are we not already witnessing here and there among faithful Catholics a decline in private religious practices, moral self-discipline, ascesis, etc., even though they take part wholeheartedly in the communal religious life of the Church? And so isn't there a need for an examination and defence of the individual in the Church, of his rights and above all his duties in relation to the Church as a body? Aren't we, then, involved within the Church in a war on two fronts? How to conform the individual to the Church and the Church to the individual? Isn't the situation here

just as confused and difficult as in the general conflict between the individual and society in the secular sphere?
What is the right thing for us to concentrate on *today?*

What follows does not claim to give the final answer to
these questions. Its purpose is more modest. It is limited to
the theoretical, abstract and general. It speaks theoretical
truths, and sometimes only theoretical opinions, in the hope
that for a start even this may be of some use.

I. THE INDIVIDUAL

The first point to be made is twofold: There is, and
there should be, an individual in the religious sphere. What
does this mean and why is it so?

1. Philosophical and Dogmatic View of the Individual

It is impossible to elaborate here a metaphysic and ontolo-
gy of the individual, and even if we did, it could not hope
to obtain general acceptance. For as long as there is a
philosophia perennis it will remain at variance on this question. Only a brief general outline can be sketched, which,
although its Thomist origin is still evident, is so preliminary to an exact philosophical statement and system, that it
will be acceptable to any Christian philosophy.

The concept "individual" is difficult to define. It is not
the genuine, exclusive opposite to "common," but, rather,

correlative to it, and increases and decreases *with* it. All the
mistakes in this field arise from the failure to realize the
analogical and correlative character of these concepts. They
only conflict and exclude each other when individuality
on a certain level declares itself an absolute, and is opposed
to a correlative "community" which is on a completely different level of being. If, for example, individuality on the
spiritual-personal level raises itself to an absolute ideal, and
from this pinnacle on which it has set itself decides what
community may still keep on the level of society or the
group (the correlative to individuality on the material level),
then you have individualism. Or, when individuality on the
material-biological level is rightly seen (for it does exist),
but then correlated to community on the spiritual-personal
level, then you have collectivism. Individuality does not
always mean the same thing; what makes a thing an individual being, a being existing for itself which cannot be
substituted or exchanged, is by no means always the same.

At the lowest end of the scale is the merely individuated
single being which must pay for being "in itself" by being
enclosed within itself, excluding everything else, and which
cannot go out from itself without ceasing to possess even its
own action, making it into something outside itself which
it acts *upon*. At the highest is the greatest mystery of our
Faith, the most perfect individuality, who, in the fullest
sense, exists for his own sake and is immutable, but nevertheless excludes nothing of the perfection of any other
being, having all reality within himself; who gives himself
totally and yet for this very reason possesses himself most

completely; in whom perfect individuality and perfect community do not conflict but *are* each other.

Between these two extremes, the one the "death" of lifeless matter and the other the infinite life of the Blessed Trinity, is man. He is rooted in earth, individuated, and thus separated from others, by matter, in which there is neither true individuality nor true community, because the individuality is the same kind as every other man's and the community merely the sum total of all its component individuals. But through the liberating individuality of a spiritual personality he can also come to share in the life of the Trinity, that most perfect community and most radical individuality which belong to the Father, the Son and the Holy Ghost. And because man is body, spirit and grace, and because he is all this in his individuality, neither he nor it can be reduced to a rigid formula. He has the individuality of all levels of being; he contains within him all the Protean changeableness of the world itself.

He is an individual by *matter*, that is, an individual by demarcation from many more like him; *a* man, one individuated human being (for only mankind can be man as a whole); and he is merely an individual who is one among many more, one example of countless others, so common that he is just one more like the rest, of no particular importance, and so all by himself and lonely.

However, he is at the same time a *spiritual* personality. That is, he is more than an individual example of many more the same, more than one individuation of a common kind. He is a genuine individual, who is truly unique and irreplaceable, and who, when he comes into contact with another, does not form a society or group of like beings, but a community of different, unique beings. For in spite of, or rather because of his spiritual-personal uniqueness and "unexchangeability," he is open to infinite reality by knowledge and love, and by this knowing and loving-valuing openness he can *become* all things—even the other *as* other—and, vice versa, he can only become all things in so far as he becomes spiritual and personal, that is, a unique individual.

Furthermore, man is a *son of God*. That is, if we may bring theology into this examination of the analogy of individuality, God his creator values him so highly as a unique individual, that he has given him the power to enter the community of the most perfect individuality; by grace he can become the beloved child of the Father together with his only-begotten Son, and with the Son call the Father *his* Father; and with the Holy Ghost he can lovingly embrace both Father and Son, and thus receive an individuality in grace and glory which is a supernatural sharing in the individuality of the Trinity. In other words, individuality (the *unum* of scholasticism) is a transcendental concept, and goes together with the concept of "existing being" and, like this concept, has analogical meanings. If, then, an existing being's measure of individuality is determined by its analogical degree of being, the degree of being of a man in grace and glory can only be determined by uncreated grace, that is, by the communication to him, by grace but really, of God himself in his own reality; and so this is man's highest and finally determining individuality, and it is itself determined from within by the individuality of the three divine persons of the Trinity. He shares by grace in the individuality of God, which is a perfect community in possession of an identical reality.

But these three levels of individuality must be seen as they belong together united in the one man. Each of these descriptions of one level is only true if it is seen in union with the others, each of these three levels becomes a reality only when, in the unity of the human person, it comes into contact with the others. Man becomes a member of the species when he gets his spiritual personality, and he only gets this by becoming a member of the species. The same goes for the relationships to others corresponding to each of these three levels of individuality, society or group which correspond to material, biological individuality; community which is the correlative to spiritual, personal individuality; union in Christ (as we can say, following Gal. 3.28), which is the correlative to theological individuality—none can ever be isolated from the other levels, above or below. And because of this, the group, for example, is not just a herd; although it belongs ontologically to the sphere of material-biological individuality with its corresponding multiplicity of like beings, it can, through man's spiritual, personal action, be made truly human. And likewise, man's spiritual-personal community is not an angel-like heavenly hierarchy, but needs, in order to be itself, the media which belong to the material-biological sphere and so to the group.

If individuality and membership of a community are not conflicting but complementary concepts, then the real problem is not whether man is an individual or a member of a community, nor is it really that human individuality, and so human community, are themselves on three levels, to which the one word "individual" applies only in an analogical sense. The really difficult problem is to find the right balance and the true recognition of each other between individuality on one level and community on the *other* levels. We shall see more clearly what this means when we consider the concrete case of the relationship between the Church as a society, on the level of the group, and the individual as a spiritual-personal being who also possesses a supernatural life.

2. Religious View of the Individual

The Christian religion recognizes the individual. In fact, it was the first, in the true sense, to discover him. Ancient classical philosophy regarded only the universal and eternally unchanging as eternal and of any real importance. And so when pagans thought most deeply about their gods, they saw even them as no more than unseeing representations of universal norms subordinate, in the last resort, to the impersonal *dike* and *heimarmene*. Christianity, on the other hand, recognizes the individual. He *as* an individual has a unique, eternally important destiny; during a limited space of time with a real beginning and a real end, he makes himself what he will be for eternity. In the Christian religion, *each man* can call the Infinite One *his* God, a God who in his turn calls each man by name and in spite of his infinity acts in each case in a free, unrepeatable and incalculable way; for universal norms are not finally decisive with him, but to each of his creatures, in that private, unrepeatable dialogue which we call grace, he gives a unique love which is for him alone. Each man is to go into his room and shut the door and pray to him in secret as his God; he gives himself by grace to each directly, without anything whatever coming between, and this in spite of, or rather *because of*, the mediation of all grace through Christ the mediator and his church, whose purpose is not to come between God and man in the manner of the neo-Platonic or Areopagitical cosmic hierarchy of mediators, but to give each man immediate access to God. When Paul says, "He loved me and gave himself for me"; or when Pascal speaks of the Lord saying, "J'ai versé telle goute de sang pour toi"; or when Newman speaks continually of "God and myself," this is just common Christian knowledge of the absolute eternal importance of each individual.

3. *Ethical and Moral-Theological View of the Individual*

If the ontological structure of a being determines how it should behave, then a human being is morally bound to be and become by the exercise of his free choice the individual he is. As a spiritual-personal being and a sharer by grace in the life of the Trinity he has an individuality which is really unique and unexchangeable, never accidental or conformed to a set pattern. This spiritual and personal uniqueness is not subject to universal norms, laws and rules, but nevertheless, like everything else, is still under the binding will of God, which in this case is not for the individual as one of a common kind, but from person to person, from God to each single man.

Thus there is a sphere of individual morality and religion, a sphere of moral duties and religious objectives which, while it never conflicts with the universal moral law, nevertheless has the decisive word over and above it and can no longer be contained within it. Of course there is not, and must not be, an individual morality which sets itself up against the universal moral law; but there is an individual morality which is binding on the individual as uniquely for him, and this cannot be called a mere application of a universal principle to one case. And so there is a "private" sphere of moral and religious life which universal morality and its expounders and guardians do not merely in fact overlook, but which is by its very nature out of their reach.

This private sphere is thus not in the least a sphere of arbitrary choice and freedom from obligations, but is directly subject to the morally binding holy will of God. God of course wills precisely that each man should be a unique individual, and this uniqueness he not only received at his creation but is free himself to achieve throughout his life; it can, and by its nature must, be the object not only of God's creating will but also of his morally binding will. There is a power in man which recognizes this individual morality as its obligatory norm. When we call it conscience we must distinguish between two functions of conscience; the one which tells a man's subjective self the *universal* norms of ethics and moral theology and applies them to his "case," and the one by which the individual hears God's call to him *alone*, which can never be fully deduced from universal norms.

There must therefore be a "technique" or, better still, a *techne*, an "art" in the Greek sense, of apprehending the demands of this strict individual morality, and this is to be clearly distinguished from the theory, the *episteme*, establishing the universally valid norms of moral philosophy and theology. If we were to look for a traditional name for it we would call it the charismatic art of "discernment of spirits," a term which, during the last few hundred years, has in fact usually been misunderstood because the discernment was either expressly or implicitly understood to be limited to the perfection of the casuistical application of theoretical norms to the individual "case." Really it is something quite different; it is the ability to hear and recognize God's call to this man alone among the many voices all calling him in different directions, the "spirits." What follows from this will immediately be seen when we now consider the relationship between the individual we have thus defined and the Church.

II. THE INDIVIDUAL IN THE CHURCH

1. The Church

Before we can state more precisely the relationship between this individual and the Church we must first say a little about the Church's nature as it concerns us here. The Church is the community of the redeemed bound together in spirit in Christ Jesus, and at the same time a visible organized society with rules and founder's charter. Neither truth about the Church should be separated from or confused with the other. If we saw in the Church only the union in Christ by grace of the redeemed, this would be the heresy of a purely invisible Church; if we saw in her only the organized society, the "Ministry of Salvation," this would be ecclesiological Nestorianism, as Leo XIII called it, or, as Pius XII called it, ecclesiological naturalism. Both these realities belong to the Church's fullness; in a certain way the one is a sacramental visibility signifying the other; but nevertheless they do not fully overlap, it is not possible to think of them as strictly two aspects of one and the same thing which cannot exist apart. For, to mention only the least disputable case, under certain circumstances someone can belong to the community-by-grace of the redeemed in Christ without being a member of the visible, organized Church. And—this is in fact dogma—someone can be a member of the visible society of the Church and yet be cut off from the community in Christ through mortal sin, which can even be a purely internal denial of the Faith. And so community by grace and the organized society, although they are ordered to one another and belong together in the fullness of the Church, are distinct realities and in different sociological spheres, and constituted differently. Consequently the relationships of the individual to the Church as a community and to the Church as a society are not the same.

The Church as a community by grace in Christ is in the same sphere as, and is correlative to, spiritual and personal individuality elevated by grace; the Church as an organized society is correlative to the individual as a materially, biologically individuated member of a species, who thus ontologically can and must be subject to a law, which is the same for him and his fellows, authority imposed from without, dominating influences etc.

As we said before, the real difficulty lies only in the relationship between the Church as an organized society and man as a spiritual and personal individual. This is what we must discuss further. We have already made plain and need not repeat that even man's unique and unrepeatable personal individuality is not that of an individualism which would make him alone, but makes him one of the great community of countless unique spiritual persons and one of the union by grace in Christ. In what follows, when we speak of the Church we shall always mean the Church as an organized hierarchical body, the Church who, through laws, commands, general directives etc., guides and supports men in working out their salvation. When we speak of the individual we always mean man in his spiritual and personal individuality, not as just one of the species.

2. The Individual in the Church

We hope that now the essential point which we are here concerned with is clear; in every man there is a sphere of personal individuality elevated by grace which we may call *private* and which cannot and may not be touched by the Church. Not as if this sphere were not also Christian, that is, conformed to Christ and superformed by grace; on the contrary. Not as if this sphere were a sphere of private arbitrary choices and of freedom from moral obligation to God; not as if, for this sphere, laws could not be formulated (right up to the three divine persons whom we "count together") or general and analogical statements be made (and unfortunately must be). Not as if one part of man was out of the Church's reach, for because of his unique nature and the resulting interpenetration of his metaphysical levels of being, she reaches indirectly even his spiritual and personal uniqueness, his "private" sphere. But within the Church he has a truly private sphere, in the sense that this cannot be immediately reached by the Church as a lawgiving society.

This private sphere is, as we said, private *in principle*, essentially private, private by nature. In every society there are some things, some actions of its members, which *in fact*, because of their unimportance, are not objects of the society's authority and are left to the individual, even though (of course this might be very difficult or impossible in prac-

tice) they could be subject to the society's authority. But
this is a private sphere *beneath* the society's authority, as
we might say. It must not be confused with the private
sphere *above* it or secret from it, which it cannot and may
not touch. There is, for example, no ruling by the Church
as to how much incense should be put in the censer; there is
no ruling as to what the individual should say to his God in
his private prayers. But these two cases are fundamentally
different. The word "sphere" must further be guarded
against misunderstanding, because in our ontological analysis we are dealing with *metaphysical* levels of being in man
which are conceptually, not really, distinct (although they
are partly founded on the real distinction between body
and soul). The private sphere is, of course, *not* necessarily a
clearly delimitable real region (the region of "purely internal acts") which is materially and visibly delimited from
the social sphere. But because man is also a unique spiritual
and personal being, elevated by grace, he must have in his
total human activity a private sphere in which spirit and
grace can be actualized and expressed. In other words, because in his *being* he is made up of more than one metaphysical component, and all must be realized and expressed,
in his *doing*, which is always done by his whole self, the
principles of action corresponding to these metaphysical
levels of being, and the organs of these principles, must
forbearingly make room for each other so that they can
all fulfill themselves.

And so it is not to be expected that particular acts of a
man, which are always acts of the whole man, can be clearly

seen beforehand to be out of the reach of ecclesiastical-social authority. And yet the principle is sound that there must be actions which affirm the spiritual-supernaturalized uniqueness of man and the limits which the Church as a society ascribes to herself. Thus there can and should be actions which are the expression of a man's personal and Christian uniqueness, although they are in themselves also accessible to ecclesiastical authority. If the preceding reasoning is sound, then we have shown that this must be true. But we must consider a few facts which will enable us to put it more precisely, illustrate it and show its implications so that we can see what it means in practical pastoral terms.

First we must consider that the Church recognizes and respects this sphere. She claims authority to rule and even to punish the individual. But she has never claimed the right to decide finally his moral standing in the sight of God. We see that this is true not merely because it would in practice be very difficult, but because there is in fact no ecclesiastical "human judgement day" by which a man can finally be judged. (1 Cor. 4.5.) In moral theology there is the famous disputed question, which has not even yet been settled, as to whether the Church can directly command internal acts. However it is eventually settled—as we have shown, this is of no importance for our present question—it at least shows that in moral theology there is the implicit awareness that we may not take for granted that the Church can claim the right to rule and command every part of a man. We could consider the fact that the Church herself forgoes the right to force the Faith and baptism upon the unbaptized, and we could ask ourselves what principles govern her behaviour in this respect which would apply also to the baptized. For the difference between them is not of such a kind that there is no limit to the authority of the Church over the baptized, because without any doubt she has a right to make demands in the name of God on the unbaptized also.

Finally we must consider this: A large part of a Christian's religious life is, at least in fact, outside the official juridical life of the Church. There is, at least in fact, a private religious life. What the Christian thinks, reads and prays, which religious vocations he chooses, which way to Christian perfection he follows etc., is left to his own decision. For Christians in general the religious duties as members of the society of the Church are very light; Sunday Mass, fasting laws, Easter duties etc. Is this merely because it is the Church's policy to restrict the duties she imposes on her members? Is it because the rest belongs to the "private sphere beneath," as we called it? Or can we see from this the fundamental fact that there must be a real, original "private sphere above" in religion too? Without any doubt this last is true. Otherwise we should have to admit that the Church *should* exercise a religious dictatorship or collectivism over this sphere, that she should set up an obligatory ecclesiastical appointments office to decide everyone's vocation in the Church under pain of sin, decide who are to be priests, which women are to be parish helpers, who are to be on the parish council. Or that she should control the length and content of everybody's prayers, even if this were a practical possibility. To ask questions like these is to answer them immediately in the negative. This means that there must be a private sphere in the Church which in principle and by nature cannot be regimented and fulfilled by the Church as a society. We can't say that this is accepted as a matter of course. Are we sure that in our practical dealings we never forget it, so long as we have not also worked it out theoretically?

And so now at last we come to what we actually set out to do; to try and illustrate the abstract principle and bring out its implications so that we can show what it means in practical pastoral terms.

III. CONCLUSIONS AND APPLICATIONS

When we call the private religious sphere the region in which man's spiritual-personal and supernatural individuality must express and realize itself, we can see for ourselves what we need to consider when we speak of the individual in the Church.

(1) Because the individual is a unique spirit-person, in religious matters too he has *the right and the duty to make choices* which cannot be directly governed by the Church's laws. We have already spoken about the individual morality which is a duty for us all, and about the individual function of conscience which does not subject the individual to universal laws but directs the moral choices possible to him through his spiritual individuality, which is not merely that by which he is one of the species. Now we must expressly add that *this individual morality cannot be directly gov-*

erned by the Church. Of course the Church can preach a formal kind of individual morality—become who you are; fulfil God's will for you as an individual—but she cannot tell me what I am actually meant to be. Of course the Church says, be the individual you are in the sight of God. But she cannot tell a man exactly—and in this case exactness is everything—what he is, what he must do to be this individual.

This is not just a negative statement about the Church. When we say the Church may not and does not want, as Dostoievsky puts it in his story of the Grand Inquisitor, to relieve the individual of the burden and the duty of having to be an individual, this implies an imperative for *him;* he is not allowed at all times to take shelter behind the moral rulings of the Church. He is not necessarily clear in his conscience if there is no directive; he is not necessarily justified before God even if he has kept all the laws expressible in abstract terms. Over and above the Commandments preached by the Church he has still to ask: Lord, what do you want *me* to do? He must know that moral theology and casuistry, however necessary they both may be, are no substitute for the gift of discernment of spirits in the sense we explained before; there must be in him and for him a fundamentally private life of prayer and moral decisions. The man who misuses Church and liturgical community as a way of escaping from himself is an ecclesiastical collectivist and belongs to the sheeplike mob described in the story of the Grand Inquisitor, who think they are saved when they are freed *from* themselves—instead of to themselves

—by the Church relieving them of the burden of having to take initiative and make decisions.

At the moment collectivism is the order of the day; but for us it is at its most dangerous not in the compulsory collectivism which assails the Church from outside, but in the collectivism inside the Church, our own weariness and idleness which gladly forgoes the responsibility of making decisions. When we are sometimes surprised at people's good will towards the Church and her directives, the leadership of her priests and youth organizers—at least, peoples who are still in regions sociologically Catholic—we should not always be entirely pleased about it; it can also mean an attitude of collectivism, a good will which is not through the power of faith and a vital, carefully considered personal conviction, but a weakness of will which has so little courage and belief in itself that it is ready to follow anyone who is prepared to lead, and in this case it may be the priest because for purely sociological reasons (family tradition, political loyalty etc.), he may be the most immediately obvious leader. But only brave hearts can really be won for God. Isn't, for example, the noticeable disappearance of a private thanksgiving after Communion such a sign of a collectivist tendency among people who immediately become spiritually breathless when they are left alone to pray? When someone cannot pray by himself at a private Low Mass, this at any rate seems to indicate something of the kind.

A few years ago we were always talking about the "adulthood" of the laity. When this was used to imply that the individualist should be able to do whatever he wanted, when it implied ill-feeling against the many exactly formulated rules of divine and ecclesiastical moral law, when it became a slogan with which to attack an unwelcome clarity and unambiguousness in moral law and casuistry, even when this was obviously possible with practically no difficulty, it was all a big mistake. Where universal norms are possible they cannot be appealed against in the name of individual conscience. If induced abortion or contraception can be universally recognized as morally wrong and are declared to be morally wrong by the Church, then there is no appeal against this in the name of individual conscience; as long as it is something objectively right the universal norm must be repeatedly taught to the individual so that he won't go against it.

But *within* the morally possible and allowable in the abstract, there is a field of individual obligation and individual duty. And this is also the field for the "adult" laity. For example, a certain form of devotion to Our Lady could in certain circumstances not be imposed as a duty for everybody by the Church and yet be an obligation and duty before God and his conscience for an individual. Joan of Arc had a duty to dress in men's clothes and fight for her king and country, without being told so by the Church. And the chief difficulty when her cause was brought forward for canonization was not whether in practice and in theory she was always obedient to the commands of the Church, but whether, even during her trial, she ever fell short of this individual duty. Today the danger of an ecclesiastical collectivism is hard upon us; not by the Church overstepping her limits, but by the individual not being able to hold out and bear his responsibility any longer, and clinging onto the Church's apron-strings; not by the Church wanting to reduce her members to servitude, but by the masters themselves wanting to be enslaved.

It is, of course, not possible in the space of this brief essay to say exactly how these imperatives of individual morality are to be recognized in concrete cases. But after what we have said about the individual one thing at least must be clear; an individual imperative is not necessarily absent if it cannot be exhaustively deduced from the universal moral law. This is an obvious fact which in practice is extremely often forgotten. When, in an important question, we pray to the Holy Ghost, as well as asking the moral theologians, we pray *not only* that the moral theologians may be enlightened by him to apply the right rules rightly to our case—this indeed is a difficult task in itself and needs the help of prayer—but also that he may tell us further what precisely he wants *us* to do within what is morally possible. For very often (in principle, that is, if not in practice always), within this sphere there are several possibilities, of which one is willed by God, and a failure to do this one can have the most grievous consequences. When at some future time it is asked whether we Christians and the Church as she is on earth today have done the right thing, they will not be able to say of us that for the most part we have acted theologically immorally, but perhaps they may not be able to say so easily that we have done the *will of God.*

God has a particular will for each individual but of course each individual will not learn what it is in such an extraordinary way, by a kind of revelation, as did Joan of Arc, Catherine of Siena, Bernadette Soubirous and others like these. How this "call" usually comes, how precisely this spiritual individual instinct works, how it is supported by the guidance of the Holy Ghost through his gifts, how it can be tested by the "art" of discernment of spirits, how more precisely an individual call like this to follow after Christ comes through reading Scripture and meditating on the life of Jesus (so that for us the life of Jesus is more than merely one case exemplifying the fulfilment of the moral law completely independent of him), all this is impossible to go into here.

In this context we can only draw attention to one thing; however much it is for the individual himself to find out what he as an individual is meant to decide and do, we can and should help each other. To put it concretely, the spiritual director or confessor is more—or, in individual cases, should be more—than a practical moral theologian. Of course he must be a moral theologian too, for with good will he can learn moral theology, and God does not usually supply heavenly charismata to make up for our laziness and ignorance; but he should really be more than this; he should seek heavenly enlightenment with his penitent, pray with him to learn the will of God and not imagine he knows it all already just because he has worked hard at moral theology; he should be a sensitive reactor to impulses from God, he should be prepared to share the burden of making decisions, he should, in fact, be an enlightened "spiritual father" (which, of course, no one can become just by having all the trappings of one).

(2) As this unique individuality is also on the level of *grace*, the individual's action is not only personal decision under God's unique will for him, but is itself given by God by grace; this means that it is not only action raised by grace with power to share in God's life, but also *charismatic action*. Each man has his charisma, his gift, his vocation, says St. Paul. We must not always expect this to be something manifestly extraordinary or miraculous. In practice we cannot clearly distinguish it from the level of spiritual-personal individuality, which in itself still belongs to the natural sphere, even though it works itself out in the religious sphere too. And so for practical purposes we have already spoken about this charismatic vocation in what we said before. But we should also speak of it directly because it sheds light on our theme from another direction, immediately biblical.

The charismatic in the Church is what is unique by grace in the Church, the individual's right by grace in the Church and for the Church. In the Church there is not only the institutional, universal and permanent; grace and impulsions to action come not only through the institutional sacra-

ments, commandments and official guidance and ruling.
God doesn't abdicate in favour of the Church and leave her
to rule for him undisturbed. Still today his Holy Spirit is
at work directly in the Church, he is present in ever-new
and unique events, and the direction in which he moves
cannot be certainly predetermined by the law of the
Church. The Church is not just a band of charismatics free
to do whatever they will, but none the less, as Pius XII says
in his encyclical, the charismatic—the element in her, if
we may so put it, of dynamic unrest if not of revolutionary
upheaval—belongs to her very essence. The Spirit of God,
himself this holy unrest making all things new, does not
necessarily come upon the Church in her official rulers.
Children, virgins and the poor in spirit can also become
seers and prophets in the new alliance, and can learn from
God a new way of being a Christian and a new Christian
way of life, and can receive from him a mission to show
this to the Church of their time . . . and the official Church
and we members of the Church would do wrong if we were
to refuse to listen to such a message, if we were to try and
force such messages, impulsions, missions and charismata to
choose strictly between being traditional and being false.

It is a curious thing that those who would like to be
charismatics themselves often immediately appeal to dogma
and tradition when they are confronted with a genuine
charismatic utterance which they ought to listen to, if it
goes against their habits of thinking. Devotion to the Sacred
Heart, as Margaret Mary Alacoque proclaimed it, was,

whatever Richstätter and Hugo Rahner may say to the contrary, genuinely "new" and so right; it met a situation in the Church which was not always there. What is true in big things is true in small; and we should never forget the counsel given by the *Spiritual Exercises* of St. Ignatius to the director of exercises (who in a certain measure is the Church's representative): "He is to allow the Creator to deal with his creature and the creature with his Creator *directly.*" (*Annotatio* 15a.) Wherever we have this "direct dealing," presupposed by Ignatius to be a perfectly normal preliminary, between the Lord and the individual man, there we have the beginning of a genuine charisma, however quiet and simple and unobtrusive its first appearance may be.

(3) A third thing—already partly touched upon—which we have still to say about this private religious sphere in the Church is something about our *relations with others within this sphere,* if we may call it this.[1] The private sphere is not an isolated region which does not come into contact with the social at all. And because of this an individual's private sphere can and should make contact with others. Christians can and should be bound together in a relationship which is not itself part of the social organization of the Church. Where several Christians pray together, where one helps another with good spiritual counsel, or comforts him in the power of the Holy Spirit, there truly Christian and so truly private life is at work. This is not just something that does happen in fact, but something which

ought to happen. This is another thing which may never be replaced or repressed by official ecclesiastical organization, however necessary this too may be. There are, then, in the Church what we may call movements, "free groups" which extend into the social sphere but which do not stem from the Church's official organization, but are formed by individuals.

There have always been charismatics without office in the Church to work at the care of souls, the prophets of the *Didache*, the monks with special graces in the ancient Greek Church, men like St. Benedict and St. Francis, who were not priests. Men like this have not the Church's authoritative mission to work upon other members of the Church; but when a man with such a gift lives a good Christian life and when other Christians feel the power of the Spirit in him and freely attach themselves to him, he should not have too many obstacles put in his way through unenlightened zeal or jealousy or a bureaucratic mania which cannot stand anything not to be officially organized. Otherwise we shall have an ecclesiastical totalitarianism which forgets that the Church, too, is for men and not men for the Church, and that all official ecclesiastical organization and orders, even though they are necessary and have God's authority, are nevertheless subsidiary and may not stifle private religious community life, but must encourage it, protect and nourish it.

When we say that it is possible and right that lay charismatics should exist and work for souls in the Church, we are not saying anything against the ideal of the Latin Church, which does her uttermost to get charismatics with office or charismatic officials, or to put it more simply, holy priests. On the contrary, when official authority and personal charisma are united in one person (an occurrence which is very fortunate and desirable but cannot be brought about at will), when we have the holy official (it is obviously no accident that there is a special mass for confessor bishops, because such a fortunate occurrence must be celebrated in a special way), when a new pentecostal wind blows directly on the official Church, this is the best possible balance between office and spiritual gift, between the charismatic individual and the social organization of the Church.

One day the completed kingdom of God will come. Then there will be only individuals each with his own face and his own destiny which God's purely personal love has given to each one. And these unique beings will be eternal because they were always more than just examples of the universal. But these individuals are loving individuals. And love is both unique and all-embracing. And so these unique beings form the communion of saints, the eternal kingdom of the love of God who is both One and All. And in it he is in everyone because he embraces all. For love unites by the very fact that it sets free and differentiates. Now we still have the Church militant. But in her the future age of liberating and uniting love is already at work. And because of this the visible Church gives the individual his freedom, and he achieves his free individuality in the Church by constantly and selflessly giving himself up to her service in humble and believing love.

Notes

1. For what follows cf. Karl Rahner, "Friedliche Erwägungen über das Pfarrprinzip," *ZKT*, 70 (1948), pp. 169–98.

2

The Appeal to Conscience

Conscience without any doubt belongs to the "eternal in man," to the things in him which are in a certain sense "absolute" and final. His theory of conscience, and, influenced by this, his conscience itself, depend in a peculiar way on the spiritual situation in which he hears its voice and judgment. This is what we are now going to consider. First we must examine certain current tendencies whose theory of the nature and function of conscience seeks to gain the acceptance of Catholics too; tendencies which take their origin from the general spiritual situation of our time and threaten the Christian doctrine of conscience. And, secondly, we must hold up against this theory the true Christian view. In our description of these tendencies we cannot here go into them fully, neither can we give evidence for them or the names of their propounders, nor can we discuss the question whether these tendencies exist or, where they actually exist, are as explicit and systematic as we make them here. It will be enough if we succeed in calling by their right name a few notions which are everywhere present as an anonymous danger.

The two tendencies which we want to describe here
we could perhaps call extreme "situation-ethics" and the
"mystique of sin." Let us try to understand their origin and
nature:

1. The Tendency Towards an Extreme Situation-Ethic

We certainly are living in "extreme" times in moral
matters as in others. That is to say the events and situations
in which we must lead our moral life today make the
morally right thing very often much more difficult than in
former times both to know and to do. The enormously
complex world-wide interdependence and development of
economic and social life, the greater mental and spiritual
differences between people, the constant threat to physical
existence of hunger, war and economic catastrophe, the
ever-present possibility of great encroachments into the private life of even the humblest and most unknown individual
by state or party or economic forces, the over-population,
the lack of accommodation, the subjection of all people to
the influence of a quickly changing, universally advertised
"public opinion," the loosening or break-up of longstanding and stable bonds between the individual and his family,
clan, home country, position in life and profession, the ease
of travel which makes people nomads, the possibility that
any opinion and any idea will be supported and campaigned
for unhindered, everywhere the overstrain on the emotions
through the refinement of the entertainment industry,

which offers people at any moment the ready-made possibility to escape from themselves—these, and many other things, make it extremely difficult today to know clearly and to do the morally right thing.

In former times life was simpler and more straightforward. The right way to behave was for the most part theoretically clear and easy to know, it had been tested and done before any number of times, and from a moral norm had become concretized in the code of behaviour of the society. Life then made the morally right behaviour also the most reasonable by the standards of utility, success and worldly profit, and the individual was to a large extent relieved of the responsibility of finding out and deciding what to do (at least in external actions).

What used to be an extreme borderline case in a moral situation which hardly ever occurred, has now become almost the "normal" case; there are very few things which everyone is agreed about; countless different and contradictory opinions are held about the right way to behave and each man has more or less to sift out the right one for himself; we know "statistically" how little the actual behaviour of people is in accordance with the officially held standards of behaviour; morally right behaviour leads only too easily to economic disadvantages which can even threaten existence; it has become dangerous to confess one's faith; the most normal marriage, even without bad will, only too often runs into the most serious moral difficulties; the unity and indissolubility of marriage are both threatened and family limitation is a very difficult problem; a

political belief can sometimes be held only at the peril of
one's life; today even the least intellectual of men who has
already travelled about and seen foreign countries and
other customs experiences the instability and changeability
of the forms and norms of life today, and the bewildering
extent to which the fundamental principles of religion and
morality and behaviour in economic, social, sexual and
political life are relative to time and place.

Perhaps we are also unconsciously influenced by a kind
of "Protestant" dislike of a material moral norm in Christianity, by an unwillingness to accept that besides (or
within) our trusting faith in God's forgiveness, other
definite attitudes and actions can be of decisive importance
to our salvation and justification in God's sight. Either expressly or involuntarily, our thought is extremely existentialist; where there is spirit, person and freedom, there is
no "essence," no universal nature of man and his moral life,
which can determine in advance, before he makes his free
decision, the rightness or wrongness of his actions; hence
there are no universal and universally binding norms, only
the autonomous individual, who is in no way a "case" or
"example" of the universal, and who alone can know in
his own completely free choices how he must act and
whether he has acted right. Today, much more easily and
more often than in the "good old times," we are likely to
feel that we are involved in theoretically insoluble dilemmas
of conscience; the duty to confess our faith *and* the duty to
care for the earthly wellbeing of our family; the duty not

to kill the child in the womb *and* the duty to preserve the life of the mother; the duty not to commit adultery *and* the right, felt almost to be a duty, not to stunt one's own personal development; the duty to keep sexual life to marriage alone, *and* the assumed right to it even in circumstances where marriage may be impossible.

With such a situation combining all these possible difficulties become chronic and universal, we run the risk of a short circuit; we want to keep the moral law and obey the binding commands of our conscience, we—at least Christians—don't want to give in to a mere moral relativism and scepticism. But admittedly or unadmittedly, we give up hope of being able to clarify and master these overwhelmingly complex situations with definite, universally valid and justifiable—at least in general terms—moral norms. And so consciously or unconsciously, expressly in theory or implicitly in fact, we beat a retreat. We "detach ourselves from the enemy"—that is, we seek a solution which excludes in advance the actual case in which the dilemma occurs, and solves everything once and for all by holding that the difficulties experienced up till now present only apparent problems. We retreat to the "motive" for an action; we give up asking for definite ways of behaving, definite actions. *What* you do is not important, but only the motive for which you do it; if this is good nothing else matters before your conscience and before God. If, for example, we act in "love," then everything is all right, which, of course, implicitly or explicitly, presupposes that this love can realize itself in more or less any action, and so the action itself can be no criterion for whether it is really love.

We retreat to "conscience"; we give up trying to clarify a difficult moral situation, to see it in the light of the universal and always universally binding norms of the natural law and the Christian revelation and thence to determine what is the one right thing, which God wills, to do here and now. We reduce Christianity's moral demands to perform definite actions to a purely formal duty to be faithful to our own conscience and brave enough to do what it tells us. We say (in the difficult and complex situations in which our conscience must make a decision): This is a case where everyone must go by his own conscience; you must decide what to do yourself; the right thing to do, what your conscience tells you, depends entirely on the one concrete situation; it is a decision for one individual about one purely individual case. The norm for the individual conscience is no longer the objective nature of the act concerned, the moral law and the commandments of God, but in a sense, the conscience itself. The conscience is no longer the voice and the interpreter of a binding norm, about which an objective agreement among men is fundamentally possible, but is, as it were, itself the lawgiver, which issues its decrees from which there is no appeal, unique and inscrutable, valid always for the one individual case alone.

There are different theories of how the conscience functions in such an extreme situation-ethic; in so far as people have a theory about their attitude at all, it may be an existentialist theory or a theory of unconditional loyalty to one's own freedom, or it may be more religious, such as a kind of individual inspiration from above (even a pseudo-mysticism), but all these theories have this in common: The conscience is not the mediator of a law, but itself the source of moral decrees which are valid only once, only for me, only in this one situation; if they contradict the Church's teaching on the universal norms of the Christian moral law, this can no longer be adduced as a reason for calling these decrees in question.

This kind of situation-ethic recognizes no moral norm which is universally binding, theoretically justifiable, and originates outside the conscience itself. In the eyes of its upholders, to dispute this extreme situation-ethic is a relapse into Old Testament legalism, an exchange of outward forms for loving faith, a denial of the freedom of the children of God, an exaggerated essence-philosophy, which postulates a definite human nature unchanged throughout all the changing course of history, whereas in fact man is an undetermined existence free at every moment creatively to form himself anew. Much (not all!) of the dislike of moral-theological casuistry prevalent today among Catholics too is a symptom of an implicit situation-ethic of this kind: we should not and cannot try to clarify an individual case theoretically by referring it to general principles; the conscience can and must itself alone decide in the individual case what it thinks is right and what not. When a confessor, because it is too much trouble or because he is uncertain or afraid of a battle with his penitent, does not make the

effort to clarify his penitent's dilemmas of conscience,
which are certainly often very difficult and complex, and
instead in almost every difficult case contents himself with
saying: You must work this out with your own conscience,
do what your conscience tells you; and when a Christian
does not make the effort to confront himself and his actual
behaviour with the moral law of the Church, when he will
no longer recognize this teaching to be binding also on him
in his situation, because he is afraid that this teaching could
condemn his behaviour, when instead of this he explains
that he has a good conscience, that he will take this on his
own conscience, that in this case the Church is just speaking in general terms or too "theoretically," in this case she
and her priests had no idea of the situation and could speak
"lightly"—then we have a situation-ethic, perhaps unrecognized, at work.

II. The Tendency Towards a Mystique of Sin

A second danger to the Christian conscience today—if
we may use a quick catchword to name what we mean—
is a certain kind of mystique of sin. This attitude may
generally be even more latent and unrealized, but there is
no doubt that it is there. What we mean by mystique of sin
is this: Only too often and too easily today in the complex
and burdensome situations which he has to face, man experiences in himself and others guilt and moral failure, the
collapse of his good will to know and to do the right
thing. He knows (rightly) that even in this guilty situation

God's mercy is still with him, calling him to repentance and to faith in the grace of the Redeemer; he knows that the Redeemer has come not to call the pharisaical self-righteous, but sinners who beat their breast and pray, Lord be merciful to me a sinner; he knows (rightly) that when we say we are not sinners we deceive ourselves and God's truth and love are not in us. And today much more than ever the true and earnest Christian feels that if God were to judge us according to his justice not one in a thousand could stand before him. It follows close upon this to think and to write and to act: We are sinners; we remain sinners; even when we have been justified we still can't keep God's commandments; but we are the real Christians just because we know that we are sinners and confess it and just because we do give God's mercy and overflowing grace the opportunity to manifest and fulfil itself; the important thing is not to avoid sin but trustingly to let ourselves be taken hold of by God's grace.

Then comes the almost instinctive feeling that to do right and honestly strive to avoid sin is in the last resort pharisaical hypocrisy and self-righteousness, and the real and only possible way to be a good Christian is not to live a life of faithful observance of God's commandments, but to fall down at his feet in guilt and despair, as it is only when we are in this state of complete collapse that God can really be God to us: incomprehensibly merciful beyond all our deserts and all our hopes. When the Christian is described in modern Christian novels he is the guilty one whose life is broken and wrecked, and he no longer tries to do anything about it by beginning a new life and bringing forth fruits worthy of repentance and asking, "Brethren, what shall we *do*?" (Acts 2.37.) Instead he lets his earthly life hopelessly drain away and at the same time he is taken hold of by God's grace, which does not change him but takes hold of him and saves him unchanged, as it were, just from the outside.

There is the danger that the commission of sins will come to be thought of as a necessary stage in a Christian life, without which the grace of God, which alone makes him a Christian and redeemed, could not exist at all. There is the danger already formulated by St. Paul: "Should we not continue in sin that grace may more abound?" (Rom. 6.1.) From this it is a short step, and logically follows, to teach, at least as a theory, a doctrine of universal salvation, which holds that each and all are in fact saved, and a short step to thinking that the most sublime and "supernatural" kind of cooperation in Christ's redemption is to share in the world's guilt by humbly becoming guilty with it.

Briefly, there is the danger that the man who is in fact sinful and keeps on sinning, who is unstable and a moral wreck, might be idealized into *the* type and the only genuine type of the Christian, and that what is humanly sound and stable and firm, ordered and balanced, might be considered of no importance for actual Christian life. There is the danger that the only point at which the grace of God can take hold might be thought to be the point at which—from the human viewpoint—the man has broken down, the danger that grace might be seen only as forgiving and no longer as healing, redeeming and safeguarding, the danger, in a new form, of the gnostic heresy which holds that the God of the Redemption is not also the God of the Creation and its ordering, but that the earth and the flesh are essentially unredeemable, and only when they prove themselves unredeemable to the very last, from above and remaining above, grace comes. This is what we mean by saying there is this danger which could wreck the true informing and right acting of our consciences, the danger of a morbid mystique of sin.

What should we now say about these two dangers? We shall try simply to hold up against them the Church's teaching. We do not mean to try to give the right answer to the concrete conscience-dilemmas which we used as examples to illustrate what we meant. The answers to these, which are indeed often difficult and in constant need of improvement, must be sought elsewhere. Here we give only basic principles which are necessarily only general.

III. Situation-Ethics

First of all, it goes without saying that a man must obey his conscience. For conscience is the most immediate giver of moral imperatives, and can never be passed over. Even if a conscience were objectively wrong about something, but in the concrete case the error could not be corrected, it would still have to be obeyed, because by its very nature it can never rightly be switched off or set aside or got round. Even in his obedience to his guiltlessly misinformed

conscience, man is being obedient to God and paying
homage to goodness. But it also goes without saying that
the conscience is not automatically infallible; it can easily
make mistakes and it is very difficult to distinguish *its* voice
—the real voice of conscience—from the voice of precipita-
tion, passion, convenience or self-will, or of a moral primi-
tiveness which cannot see the finer distinctions or the more
remote consequences of the act. And so man has a duty to
do everything he can to conform his conscience to the
objective moral law, to inform himself and let himself be
taught and make himself prepared to accept (how difficult
this often is!) instruction from the word of God, the magisterium of the Church and every just authority in its own
sphere.

It is right that there should be a "conscience" which tells
the individual man what he must do *as* an individual.[1] That
is to say: that the individual is not just one member of the
human race with a common human nature (he is this too),
but also unique and irreplaceable, he has a sphere of moral
choices which cannot be clearly decided by universal norms
and laws alone, but need a special individual function of
his conscience. Because the unique individual exists, there
exists also an individual morality and a corresponding function of the conscience. But because the individual does not
take away the universal, but by God's will lies within what
is universally human in him, there is an individual morality
only within a universal normative morality (but it *is* nevertheless there, although it is only too often overlooked);
and there are individual moral imperatives only within the

framework of universal Christian morality; and they can never go outside it.

It is right that the Christian conscience should be mature and of course this applies to the laity, and when it is not mature enough it should be told and encouraged to try and become so, in order to prevent society and the Church suffering severe damage. But this maturity of the Christian conscience is not an emancipation from and casting off of the universal norms preached by the Gospel and the Church by appealing to a unique situation and one's own conscience; it is the ability to apply these norms oneself to a concrete situation without needing help in every case, and the ability to see moral duties and obligations also in cases where the official universal norms are too abstract and general to be applied by their official exponents, either without great difficulty or at all.

But even though there is an individual morality within the framework of universal morality, even though maturity of conscience is an ideal to be worked for, nevertheless there is no genuine situation-ethic in the sense in which we described it above.

First of all, it goes without saying for Catholics, as was made clear at the time of the Reformation, that morality is essential to a Christian and religious life. The fulfilment of the Commandments is an essential part of Christianity as such, and not just an indifferent matter, which is at most a field for faith to manifest itself (which is what a "believing" situation-ethic logically leads to).

Furthermore, the Church teaches these commandments

with divine authority exactly as she teaches the other "truths of the Faith," either through her "ordinary" magisterium or through an act of her "extraordinary" magisterium in *ex cathedra* definitions of the Pope or a general council. But also through her *ordinary* magisterium, that is in the normal teaching of the Faith to the faithful in schools, sermons and all the other kinds of instruction. In the nature of the case this will be the normal way in which moral norms are taught, and definitions by Pope or general council the exception; but it is binding on the faithful in conscience just as the teaching through the extraordinary magisterium is.

It is therefore quite untrue that only those moral norms for which there is a solemn definition (and these are criticized from all sides in the "world") are binding in faith on the Christian as revealed by God, and must be accepted by him as the rule for his own behaviour; and of course it is equally untrue—and this is often unadmittedly expected— that the moral law preached by the Church must necessarily receive the assent (even if it is only theoretical) of the non-Christian world. When the whole Church in her everyday teaching does in fact teach a moral rule everywhere in the world *as* a commandment of God, she is preserved from error by the assistance of the Holy Ghost, and this rule is therefore really the will of God and is binding on the faithful in conscience, even before it has been expressly confirmed by a solemn definition.

A moral norm is by nature universal but, precisely as a universal law, is intended to be the rule for the individual

case. And so when it is fully grasped and rightly understood and interpreted (that is, understood as the magisterium means it, not just as an individual thinks fit to
interpret it), and bears on an individual case, then this
unique individual concrete case is bound by the norm and
obliged to abide by it. When, for example, the Church
teaches that *every* directly induced abortion is morally
wrong, that every sacramentally contracted and consum-
mated marriage between two baptized persons is indissolu-
ble, then this applies to every individual case quite
regardless of the circumstances. In these cases there is no
"situation-ethic" by which, according to the circumstances
(which of course everyone is tempted to regard as quite
unique and extraordinary in his own case), the attempt is
made to see if in this case the conscience—still "recognizing" the universal law, that is, for all other cases except this
one—would not be objectively justified in considering another course of action right. A situation-ethic carried to its
logical conclusion would become an ethical and metaphysical nominalism in which the universal could never
actually bear upon the concrete with binding force.

Of course, there will also often be the guiltlessly mistaken
conscience which thinks, for special reasons in special
circumstances, it may or must act differently from the
moral norm which, without its knowing, is laid down by
the Church. But, if it is not to degenerate into a merely
private subjective voice, the Christian conscience has the
duty to order itself by the objective moral norms. And if
the Christian knows that these objective norms are to be

found in the teaching of the Church, and if he knows that his case too (like every similar case) is meant by the law, then it is not easy to see how a believing Christian can still logically and guiltlessly come to the conclusion that in his situation the "case" is morally other than the universal law judges it to be. If in such cases he would at least admit that from human weakness he had offended against the law, which he was nevertheless bound to keep, then it would be easier to help him. But those who think that in their individual case they can still objectively justify their offence against the law by appealing to their situation with subtle theoretical excuses, or by appealing to their "conscience," or even to a private enlightenment from God, are in very serious and dangerous error. They can only succeed in deceiving themselves, for they are suppressing God's truth.

When a man has once realized (and in this age of psychoanalysis one would expect this realization to be widespread; unfortunately it isn't) how easily and in what refined ways he can deceive himself, how quickly what is desired by him appears also justified to him, how hidden and distorted the final standards are by which he in fact judges and values things, how "obvious" something can seem to us when it is in fact a very dubious and problematic case, then he will be more careful in his appeals to a "good conscience." And anyone who has read the first chapter of St. Paul's Epistle to the Romans has read how God judges the doubtless very "respectable" Jews and Gentiles (and where are there *no* people who think themselves very respectable?); and he will have been dismayed to find that the "good conscience" of respectable people who know at once what God asks of them and what he "naturally" can't expect of us, is only too often just the punishment and result of their blind but still responsible sinfulness: their real conscience has been muted leaving their heart to say what it will unhindered, and the Scripture says the heart of man is evil from his youth.

If we Christians, when faced with a moral decision, really realized that the world is under the Cross on which God himself hung nailed and pierced, that obedience to God's law can also entail man's death, that we may not do evil in order that good may come of it, that it is an error and heresy of this eudemonic modern age to hold that the morally right thing can never lead to a tragic situation from which in this world there is no way out; if we really realized that as Christians we must expect almost to take for granted that at some time in our life our Christianity will involve us in a situation in which we must either sacrifice everything or lose our soul, that we cannot expect always to avoid a "heroic" situation, then there would indeed be fewer Christians who think that their situation requires a special ruling which is not so harsh as the laws proclaimed as God's laws by the Church, then there would be fewer confessors and spiritual advisers who, for fear of telling their penitent how strict is God's law, fail in their duty and tell him instead to follow his conscience, as if he had not asked, and done right to ask, *which* among all the many voices clamoring within him was the true voice of God, as if it were not for God's Church to try and distinguish it in accordance with his law, as if the true conscience could speak even when it had not been informed by God and the faith which comes from hearing.

A man who has learnt—by the grace of God!—to beware of man because he is a liar (*omnis homo mendax*) and so beware of himself because he is a man, will no longer be able to say so lightly: I will make this right with my conscience; what the priests say is just red tape. Must we make the thing right "with our conscience" or in fact—putting it more exactly and more honestly—with God? And doesn't God speak more clearly—precisely in complicated and difficult cases—by his own word through the mouth of his Church?—so we can only be certain that we are really hearing the voice of our conscience and not the voice of our own sinful inclinations when this voice agrees with the Church's teaching. The priests are not erecting red tape when they abide by the teaching of the Church, but they are telling us the word of God. Is it really extraordinary that this word (which is God's) is so "unrealistic" and so "unsuited to the times," when "reality" is against God and the times are evil and the Christian must be prepared to take his stand for God against "reality" and the "times" even unto death?

But if this is the case, what has become of the freedom of the children of God? Does this not put us back under the rule of the letter which kills and is only the law of sin? (Cf. 1 Cor. 15.56.) Isn't it true that we may "love and do what we will"? Is it true that where the Spirit of the Lord, who justifies, teaches and gives us divine life, moves a man, then he is no longer *under* the law, he is free from the law, the letter of which is imposed on him with binding force and reveals in him the helplessness of a man weakened and enslaved by sin; when the Spirit is strong and powerful within a man and binds him immediately to God above all law in a relationship of fully personal love, then the law is "superseded" by the inner law of the heart, the law of Christ in the power of which we not only know within us what is right but can have the strength freely to do it.

But in order to be free like this we must really have the Spirit; this Spirit can be lost; and man the liar can deceive himself that he has this Spirit when he really hasn't. We have not got the Spirit if we do not keep God's laws, and we can only keep these laws in the Holy Spirit in whom God's will and God's power are one, and in whom alone we can have true Christian freedom. He who boasts of the freedom of the children of God, when asked, Do we then overthrow the law? must answer with St. Paul: By no means, on the contrary we uphold the law. (Rom. 3.31.) He must know and live the Scripture; he who fulfils the law shall live (Gal. 3.12); the *doers* of the law will be justified before God. (Rom. 2.13.) The law has come to an end because it has been superseded, not by the arbitrary choices of our human will but by the power of the Holy Spirit. But the only way of knowing whether we have the Holy Spirit in us is precisely by whether we fulfil the law. And even the sinner, who flies to Christ's grace and finds therein salvation and justification, only really flies to Christ in his conversion if he confesses that he has become guilty precisely because the grace, which would have given the power to want and to do the will of God, has through his own fault remained ineffective, only really flies to Christ if he is truly prepared not only to seek forgiveness from God for the things he has left undone, but to do God's will henceforth; for "if any man says that God's commandments cannot be fulfilled even by those who have been justified and given grace, let him be anathema." (Council of Trent, sess. 6, can. 18.)

To the free children of God also it is said (in the eternal freedom of God it will no longer need to be said; but now it must still be said because they are in danger of confusing their true freedom with the desires of their flesh): Do not deceive yourselves, neither the debauched, nor idolaters, nor adulterers, nor sodomites, nor thieves, nor misers, nor drunkards, nor revilers, nor extortioners will inherit the kingdom of God. (1 Cor. 6.9.) We can do "everything" only when we love. But we are not loving if we do evil. Are there not today many "good" Christians who subtly and dishonestly try and make the freedom of Christians a justification for a pact between right living and godlessness, light and darkness, Christ and Belial in their moral life, who do everything they want, good or evil, and then say they still love, instead of really loving (which calls for the greatest renunciation) and then doing everything which a man who really loves God may do?

And so it remains: The commandments of God come truly and plainly out of the mouth of the Church and they require obedience whether in this or that case they are easy to apply or not; they are the will of the living God who has spoken to us through Jesus Christ our Lord—the will of God—which is also for his children who are justified and living in grace and the freedom of the Holy Spirit. The Faith which justifies before God is the loving Faith which does God's will.

IV. The Mystique of Sin

We must now say a little more about that tendency which we called a mystique of sin.

First of all, it goes without saying for Christians that Christianity is salvation also for those who have fallen into sin before God, because without the grace which preserves from sin or saves from sin no man could be sinless in God's sight. Whenever a man, from the depths of his sin, looks up to God in faith and repentance and grace, and longs for him and accepts his gift of salvation in Christ Jesus, there is more joy in heaven over this one sinner than over ninety-nine just men who think they need no repentance. It goes without saying that salvation is nearer to the broken —even if it is their own sins they are broken by—and humble in heart than to the self-righteous, with their miserable respectability which is often only a deceptive façade to cover their inner rottenness. It goes without saying that God's grace has secret ways which we cannot fathom, which are not our ways, of redeeming and saving men who in human eyes can only seem far from God. His grace is beyond our understanding and does not have to give an account of itself to us. He binds us, not himself, to the ways which he has shown us.

But it is true as well that he who honestly says, I have sinned, must also say, I will arise and go to my Father. But in God's country there is no commerce between light and darkness, God and sin. It is a defined truth of the Faith that God's grace makes it possible for the man who has been justified to keep God's commandments, so that if he falls again into sin, he falls although he could have stood firm and he himself is the really responsible, guilty cause of this fall. And so a conscience which tries to comfort the sinner with the thought that he could not avoid sinning, and that this sin was in fact no danger to his salvation, as long as even in his sin he went on trusting in God's forgiveness, is not the voice of grace, but the voice of the man's own self-delusion, which wants an easy compromise between sin and God. "Felix culpa" can only be said by those who through God's grace have overcome sin.

That God writes straight on crooked lines gives the creature no right to draw crooked lines in his book of life. Such an act which actually plans and calculates to make sin a stage in his development is a creature's most hateful *hubris*, which is prepared to outwit God's mercy, which tries to see and calculate human life from God's standpoint, and is arrogance and self-delusion of such a serious nature that God threatens to answer it not with his grace but with his justice. Precisely because sin can be committed not only immediately and expressly in the sphere of faith and trust, but also in the moral sphere in the narrower sense, in the sphere of the Commandments, and because from the creature's point of view there is no way of getting rid of it, no way out, man never has the right to surrender himself "in faith" into this position merely because he imagines he can still hope for forgiveness and that even while he sins God's grace will not abandon him. If God gives his grace to a man who *has* sinned, this is always a new action of God's grace which is in no way due to the man, and cannot be calculatingly relied on before the sin is committed.

It is curious how these upholders of an existentialist mystique of sin all of a sudden fall into an essentialist philosophy, which is quite out of place here and makes the unpredictable miracle of God's forgiving grace suddenly become an essential of man's existence which is always at his disposal and can be counted on in advance.

When—particularly in modern Catholic novels—we hear described for us how grace seeks and finds even him who was lost, we read this gratefully as an echo of the Gospel. But at the same time we must guard ourselves against misunderstanding this echo, as if all Christian existence was contained in this kind of deliverance alone. On the contrary, it is always something more; it is a new life (even when the only thing that has to be done in this new life is to endure a miserable ending to our earthly life), it is the sanctification of the world, it is work in faith and grace, it is bearing fruit in the Holy Ghost, it is the ever-renewed striving (even when in fact it breaks down again

and again) to bring about the reign of the kingdom of God
in ourselves and the world. Whatever is healthy or morally
fine or well ordered and harmonious, even apparently on
the purely human level, is (even when this is not realized)
a manifestation of grace and the divine life which is entrusted to us and demanded of us, because the Word became flesh not to save us *from* the flesh because it had been
corrupted by sin, but to save the flesh *itself*. It does not
make this salvation any the less God's action that it also
comes about, and must do, through our action, for our
action is already his grace.

We are today all threatened by the danger of cultural,
spiritual and moral collapse. But even if this comes upon
us, we shall let God be greater than our collapse and even
in our fall grasp his saving grace in faith. But we shall
not sinfully and morbidly make this possible collapse the
cornerstone of a system in advance, as if it were the only
genuine Christian situation. If we have a breakdown of
this kind we shall only still be able to attain salvation and
blessing through it if we fight against it. And so—not in
naive worldly optimism but in obedience to our Christian
mission and in courage and hope through the grace of God
—even at this late hour in the history of our Western
civilization, we love what is wholesome and hopeful and
good and make it the goal of our striving which *we* must
try and attain, whatever God may do with us, for what he
does is for him and not us to decide. A man with this attitude praises the power and glory of grace better than one

who is obsessed by his possible moral collapse and thinks he can only survive it by regarding it merely as a scheme of victorious grace. The true praise of *sola gratia* does not need the help of a mystique of sin.

Notes

1. Cf. Chapter 1, "The Individual in the Church," pp. 9 ff.

3

A New Form of Heresy

St. Paul says that schisms—heresies—must come. Whatever St. Paul himself may have meant by "heresy," in the
history of the Church the word has always been taken to
mean what we mean by it today; the distortion of the word
of God preached by the Church into a human error, by a
Christian who makes his own fancy and his own standard
a measure of the word of God, and suits it to himself instead
of himself to it, and so sets up his own Christianity against
the Church's. That they "must" come is the natural consequence of the freedom of fallen man, and results from sin
or error or both. But *that* this heresy comes and will come
—although God's greater power and grace never abandons
us—is for the Christian who has been instructed by God's
prophetic word not just a chance surprise which one may
expect soon to disappear because it should not have happened at all, but is something the Christian already knows
about—heresy, like sin and guilt and stress and despair, will
accompany human life and the history of the kingdom of
God till the end of the world. And so there "must" be
heresies, because they are more than just the consequences

of a misused freedom; they belong to those mysterious things which "must" be so that no man, and so no man's truth either, can boast before God.

And therefore the Christian will not be surprised when he encounters heresies. He will even expect them and regard them as inevitable and even as the greatest and highest, and so "necessary," temptation, in which darkness really clothes itself in the garments of light. And when the Christian encounters no heresy, none which could really tempt in this way as a real challenge, he will not consider his peace of spirit something to be taken for granted, but will ask himself in dismay whether perhaps the eyes of his spirit have become so blind and his heart so insensitive to the difference between truth and falsehood that he can no longer recognize a heresy when he meets one; whether the age and country he lives in no longer produce heresies because at bottom, in spite of their formal acceptance of all the truths of the Faith, they have become so indifferent to God's truth that they no longer need to mitigate the remorselessness of revelation by setting up human systems in its stead.

If, then, there must be heresies, today too and "specially for me," where, then, are the heresies which we must guard against? What form will they take today in order to deceive people the more easily? One might think that this question was quickly answered! The world in which Christians live like a flock of scattered and hunted sheep, is full of errors which contradict the Word of God which has come to us in Christ Jesus; this error proclaims itself loudly and with conviction from all the newspapers, shouts out of loudspeakers, dresses up in the works of the poets, and is at work in the business of the world which—as always—is inclined to evil; it is the spiritual atmosphere in which we must live and breathe, day in, day out. In these days a Christian has not far to look for heresies, if he is seeking them because they "must" be.

This answer is right. But it does not describe the whole situation of the Christian in the face of heresy today. For the errors which this answer has in mind no longer claim to be *Christian* truth, a genuine interpretation of the revelation entrusted by God to the Church. They call themselves, openly and honestly, unchristian, and don't set any store by being regarded as the Church's truth. So the Christian who listens to the Church's teaching can make light work of them. True that in his practical life and everyday dealings he will very often live more in accordance with the spirit of the world than the truth of the Church. But nevertheless, if he seeks the truth his spirit is to accept, the principles by which he is to live, he will have little difficulty in distinguishing the errors of the world, which do not pretend to be Christian, from the message of the Gospel. It has never been—at least so it seems—so easy as it is today to draw the necessary fine distinction between what is world and what is Christianity, so long, of course, as one really and unquestionably wants to be a Christian at all. For, as we said, the world of the spirit today no longer always claims to represent only the message of the Gospel, and it has never been so easy to know clearly what Christ and his Church's teaching is as it is in this our modern age when the Church has developed her understanding of herself to the point of formulating precisely and finally the nature of her teaching authority and the way in which it functions.

And so the errors meant by the answer which we criticized are in fact not heresies, not Christian errors. They are clearly "outside." They can no longer tempt us by claiming to be the true Christian faith. They can indeed be a temptation—and naturally a very strong one—to the Christian to leave the Church and Christian truth, and base his spiritual life on something else. But to regard and defend these errors as Christian and Catholic truth is no longer possible for Catholics as it was in former times. This means (to put the same thing in yet another way) that heresy in the form it used to take, which we still wrongly take for granted is the only form for any heresy, is no longer so dangerous a temptation to the Christian as it used to be. Of course, in former centuries too the Christian had to know that Christ's gospel had been entrusted to his Church, and that *she* is the guardian and authoritative exponent of God's word.

But where and how this Church speaks, and where and how to find out what she says, was not so clear then as now. For example, during the Arian controversy, would it have been possible for every Catholic (as it would be today) to tell by a clear, easily accessible principle which was universally recognized beforehand as revealed, *where* the Church was actually speaking? Even today theologians have difficulty in establishing that a council was ecumenical

except by the assent of the Pope to it—that is, by the help
of a principle which in earlier times was indeed objectively
present and in action, but which had not then been expressly and precisely formulated, and so did not belong to
the universally recognized dogmas of the Faith. And so it
happened that on the one hand the true Faith and heresy
could both claim to be Christ's Church, and on the other
hand, the Christian did not have as an indisputable Christian
truth the formal principle by which to distinguish between
these claims.

Today it is different. The magisterium of the Church is
not only (as it objectively always was) present with binding force in the word of the Bishop of Rome, but this fact
is itself a truth of the Faith which must be accepted in
advance by the Catholic Christian; but this was not so clear
in earlier ages. Because today the formal principle of faith
has itself become part of the body of doctrine which the
Catholic must believe, his position is different from that of
a Christian in former times; if in any question under discussion he sets his own opinion up against that of a papal
definition, in doing so he would know that he was setting
himself up against a truth of the Faith, which *he himself*
had already acknowledged as his own faith—that is, that
not only the true Church as a whole (whose voice it is not
always easy to distinguish) but also the Roman See is the
final judge of what is and what is not the true meaning of
revelation. By the very act of holding this opinion which
was against the principle he himself had acknowledged up
till then, this Catholic would be putting himself outside the

Church, which up till then he had acknowledged as the
only true Church of Christ, and he himself could know
clearly that he was doing this. And so today it is not possible to advocate an erroneous doctrinal opinion *in the
Church* which one has acknowledged, in accordance with
the formal definitions, to be the only true Church of Christ.

Is there then no more heresy *in* the Church? Is heresy
now only possible outside the Church, because on the one
hand the true Church, as guardian of the truth, points out
heresies as soon as they arise, and on the other hand, the
Catholic knows clearly in advance *where* the Church is
and where she speaks, without a general council or some
other means of discovering the universal consensus of
bishops being necessary to establish or support it? Or are
there still heresies *in* the Church today because they "must"
be, and so must be in the Church, because being threatened
and assaulted by heresy is a necessary element of Christian
existence in the world?

Let us accept for the moment—if only as a working
hypothesis—that there "must" also be heresy *in* the Church.
Then because of what we have said, it is clear in advance
that this heresy will have to assume a different form from
that of previous heresies. In former times heresy existed
undisguised and open, even *in* the Church (by "Church"
meaning, of course, not her objective essence in its reality,
but the actual group of people whom the men of those
days could have thought of as this reality), because the
formal principle of faith had not become expressly and
bindingly part of the content of faith by which the bound-

aries of the Church could be clearly defined. Today, on
the other hand, an *open* heresy (that is, one which is clearly
and precisely formulated) held by a Catholic is shown to be
against the teaching of the Church immediately the Pope
condemns it, and this by principles which the Catholic
himself has already expressly owned and acknowledged;
he must either give up the heresy or leave the Church,
which would be to deny a doctrine which up till then he
had expressly acknowledged as a truth of his own faith.

If in spite of this there is still heresy *in* the Church today,
it can no longer be open but must have become covert and
hidden. It must (if it exists) have become a sort of crypto-
gam. If it is not to die out, the disease of heresy cannot be
plainly visible, and easy to diagnose from its formulated
teaching in opposition to the teaching of the Church; but
it must now be a hidden, nameless sickliness which saps the
spiritual life-force, a "creeping" sickness.

If we take our *a-priori* hypothesis a little further and ask
what, more precisely, will this hidden heresy be like (if it
exists), we must consider again the reason why it can no
longer come out in the open. The reason is that open heresy
would immediately come up against the Church's magisterium in the form which, unlike a general council, is
always there in readiness to react quickly and clearly to
the whole Church—the teaching authority of the Pope—
and the fact of this authority has already been acknowledged as part of his faith by the would-be heretic. The
heresy would have to be hidden and covert, cryptogamic,
so that in practice it would be more or less impossible for

the papal magisterium to get at it. But this magisterium can only pronounce judgement on a heresy if it is openly formulated in clear intellectual terms above the level of mere feeling and attitude. If the heresy is not thus formulated, the magisterium clutches at air, for this is the only kind it can cope with. Hence this latent heresy has two principal methods: on the one hand it avoids coming into conflict with the magisterium by avoiding clear statements in books, official teaching etc., and taking refuge in the private and esoteric domain reserved for the initiated only; on the other hand, it keeps to the vague and approximate, the undefined attitude, and in writing concerns itself only with the doubtful, with "attempts," and with the exposition of unsolved problems (but in fact meaning more than this), passing over truths which contradict it in silence. To put it more briefly: Heresy in the Church today (if it exists) must and can take cover, and by being indifferent in theory and in fact to the truths of the Faith which contradict it, can remain latent in the Church.

Before we now go on to ask whether this new[1] form of heresy, which we have built up *a priori*, really exists in the Church, we must first say a little more about it in order to avoid misunderstandings. When we speak of the methods employed by heresy in the Church we must *not* think only or first and foremost of conscious heresy, which its advocate incurs guilt in holding. Of course *contumacia* belongs to the Church's *legal* concept of heresy, because only thus can it be guilty and matter for the Church's right to punish. But this is not the point for us at the moment. For in the

sense we mean here every error which in fact is contradictory to God's revelation, every distorted notion and
every false interpretation of the Faith, which stems from
an unchristian mental attitude, is heresy and a man who in
the daily course of his life does not live by the truth, and
does not even reckon with it—as friend or enemy—in his
behaviour, is a heretic. At least it is material heresy and we
should notice that in our case this material heresy is not
formulated, but is expressed in a way of behaving, an attitude, a vague and general feeling which can permeate all
a man's thought and behaviour.

Here we should observe that heresy is not only dangerous to salvation in so far as it is disobedience of the will, but
independently of this question of guilt in the will, it is also
dangerous in so far as it is a lack of truth and reality in the
understanding. Because the man who is in error is missing
the truth which means salvation to him, his error is dangerous whether he holds it in good will or in bad.[2] It is also not
true that a heresy in the sense we mean could not exist in a
man together with an earnest will to believe right. For the
mind of man contains and lives by far more than what it
consciously adverts to, and can be moved at the same time
by different "spirits."

And it is not true that this heresy can only exist in the
men of the *hearing* Church. It can exist in all the members
of the Church. If we are all sinners and are all affected in
some measure by self-opinion, arrogance, spiritual sloth
and indifference which (beginning in our will) spreads to
our understanding and to what we teach with it, then it is

only to be expected that this vague heresy can exist also in the members of the *teaching* Church. Of course the Spirit of truth, who has been promised to the Church, will guard the holders of the magisterium from ever solemnly defining an error to be of faith. And it is also certain that over and above this the help of the Spirit is at the disposal of the Church's official teachers in full measure. But when there is narrowness of spirit, self-will and obstinacy, when people go in for hair-splitting and rivalries between schools—and this is also possible in the teaching Church—truth and understanding, and so the teaching of it, cannot be as it should be. There are distortions and narrowings which one can go on thinking for a long time are an integral part of truth as it is revealed, believed and taught.

This existential "colouring" of the truths taught (if we may so put it) can in some way reflect the sinful individuality of the holders of the magisterium, even if nothing positively false is taught. Because of the hardness of heart and indifference of the Church's teachers the truth of the Gospel can be preached in a way which makes the men who hear the teaching at that time unable to grasp it sufficiently and really make it their own. Who could deny *a priori* that there have been times (and perhaps there still are) when, at least by way of failure to realize the living import of the truth, there has been error in the teaching Church and in this sense "heresies"? Could anyone deny (if he believes in the "Church of sinners") that the light of the Gospel too, not only the love, has not always and at all times shone so brightly in the earthly lamp of the Church as God would have it shine? If we now ask whether the hidden heresy we have been considering *a priori* actually exists in the Church today, and exists more prevalently than in former times (because then heresy could more easily remain in the Church, at least for a time, in open form), we mean heresy in the widest sense, to cover all the forms of spiritual unawareness which are the sign or the result of a man not holding onto God's truth with all his heart and strength.

We have postulated these hidden heresies, in the widest sense, *a priori;* heresies must be and must be in the Church because she is a Church of sinful men. But do they in fact exist in the Church? We think they do. In the encyclical *Spiritus Paraclitus* Benedict XV says there are people, even teachers of the sacred sciences, who attack in secret some of the teachings of the Church. (*DB*, 2186.) This "occulta oppugnatio" which Benedict XV says does happen in the Church of our time, is the most enormous form of the hidden heresy we are referring to. And there is no doubt that it is not yet dead. Think, for example, of the books published by Mensching and Mulert before the last war, advocating a "Reformed Catholicism"; they did, of course, contain open heresies (open, that is, if we don't count the anonymity of the authors), and so could be condemned as heretical by the Church, but these heresies were the reflection of an attitude and a teaching which could be called covertly heretical, because the authors, while admitting that their theories were against the Church's teaching, nevertheless did not want to be expelled from the Church and so chose to remain anonymous.[3]

But the most enormous kind of hidden heresy, which clearly took shape for the first time in the history of modernism, is not the only kind or the most important or the most dangerous. Much more frequent (although difficult to pin down) is an attitude of mistrust and resentment against the Church's magisterium, a widespread feeling of being suspiciously and narrowly controlled by it in research and teaching, the feeling that "one can't say what one thinks" (but one is nevertheless justified in thinking it in "good" conscience). Doesn't one come across the feeling that one can say more (at least among friends) than one can write? Or the attitude that one should be glad that this and that has been said by Protestant theologians outside the Church, and one has to go to them to read it because one could not say it without risk oneself?

One sometimes gets the impression that the theoretical opinions of a theologian are hidden under the form of his historical research to make them more acceptable because less evident. Isn't there here and there something like an esoteric teaching which is only spread by word of mouth? Isn't there unformulated heresy which avoids clear exposition in print and works by omissions and one-sided perspectives, overstepping explanation and going straight from the wrong attitude to wrong practice? How often, for example, do people purposely avoid mentioning hell, or pass over in silence, or with at most a few uncertain and embarrassed

mumblings if it can't be avoided, the evangelical counsels,
consecrated virginity and the celibacy of the clergy? How
often does the preacher preach to the educated people in
his congregation about temporal punishment for sin, indul-
gences, angels, fasting, the devil (at most he will talk about
"the demonic" in man), purgatory, prayer for the Holy
Souls and other old-fashioned things? When "inner freedom" is recommended "to develop positively in the Church
and to treat the confessional in its present state as incompetent so long as it exercises the sacrament of forgiveness in
the service of sexmolochism,"[4] then the practice of this
hidden heresy has found its formal theory, namely the
express recommendation to live heresy in secret.

But there is yet another form of this hidden heresy, and,
paradoxically, it can affect those who are proudest of their
longstanding and unimpeachable orthodoxy; heresy in the
form of indifference. God's truth is always one and the
same and final; it is preached by the Church's magisterium.
When this magisterium has defined the truth entrusted to
her by Christ in a form which is binding in conscience on
the Christian, then this truth is true and valid in this form
for all time; the Church's preaching and theology will always refer back to these formulations of the truth made in
the course of the Church's history in the sure knowledge
that in them the truth concerned really is rightly expressed
(although, of course, any formulation of a truth of the
Faith, because it is in human words, can never express it
adequately, and at least in principle, could be replaced by
a still better and fuller formula); a formulation in intellec-

tual concepts is never just an attempt to put into words an
experience of the Faith which is in itself nonrational (as
in the modernist misconception of the intellectual element
in the Faith).

But this truth of God in human words is not meant
merely to go on being monotonously repeated in stereotyped phrases in theology textbooks. It is meant to come
into living contact with the individual Christian, to take on
flesh and blood, penetrate his heart and mind and bring
him the truth. Each man anew has to make it his own. Each
man, with his own experiences, his own vocation and his
whole spiritual situation, which is not only that of Catholic
Christianity but the general spiritual situation of his time,
must individually hear God's message anew. And because
a man's faith is not the message that could be heard but the
message he *does* hear, and because the truth of revelation
cannot exist on earth in one eternally static and valid form
but only as it is actually believed by men, the plain unchanging truth of the Gospel, as it is actually heard and
understood by men of every age, must bear the mark of
that age upon it. If it doesn't, or doesn't sufficiently, this
does not make it timeless and universally valid; it is much
more likely to mean that it wears the garb of another age,
which men have become used to, and because it is ancient
and customary have falsely come to think of it as *the* expression of the eternally unchanging truth of the Gospel.
This freezing of the form in which the truth of the Gospel
is expressed is in fact a dangerous symptom of indifference,
whether conscious or not, to the truth, the symptom of a

lack of power to assimilate it existentially and express it in new terms. Who could doubt that this form of heresy also exists in our time—heresy in which dead orthodoxy is only the expression and the result of a secret indifference to the truth, in which a thing is left unchanged because men are so indifferent that they do not want to have to go to the trouble of getting rid of it or questioning it?

If anyone thinks that all this has been said so that we should now go about smelling heresies everywhere and ferreting them out, he has not understood the point. We only referred to the signs of the actual existence of this hidden heresy by way of *a-posteriori* support for the *a-priori* thesis that today there must be this changed form of heresy. Anyone who wants to draw practical consequences from this theological speculation should first of all look to himself. For the kind of heresy we mean here cannot be guarded against merely by the good will to believe rightly and be obedient to the Church's magisterium.

From all this it follows naturally that the usual methods of dealing with heresy up till now are of relatively little use against this latent kind. The Church can preach the truth, she can herself conceptually formulate heretical tendencies (as Pius X did for the first time in his encyclical against modernism) and then refute them in this form. But she can do little against mute heresy, she is for the most part helpless against heresy which only speaks in correct statements and keeps silent on those which do not suit it, against the heresy of indifference and a theologically sterile integralism. She is inevitably tempted today to make the difficulty even greater. And for the same reason as that which has caused this changed form of heresy. Because (since the First Vatican Council) the magisterium of the Church knows that it is itself an object of faith it is more likely now than in former times to be tempted to suppress heretical opinions with its formal authority alone, without ensuring that they are pulled up by the roots. There is the temptation to fight heresy only by *administrative* measures (by putting books on the Index, removing suspect teachers etc.) instead of by actual *magisterial* measures (by positively formulating the true doctrine so that the error is really uprooted); the temptation to impose silence without also speaking out the truth or allowing someone else to, and speaking it out in a way which is not only true but which can penetrate mind and heart. The temptation is not insuperable, as we said, but it is present (that is not to say, given in to), and belongs in the situation of this changed form of heresy, because it is caused by the same thing. Wasn't there, for example, too long a silence over many questions of biblical theology in the time of modernism?

At any rate, today there is unavoidably a greater danger than ever before that by officially suppressing hasty unripe theological theses and opinions heresy will not be killed but only changed into its new form, which will really enable it to resist the measures of the magisterium against it. For, so it seems to us, the development of the Church and the knowledge of her formal teaching authority as itself an object of faith "must" bring with it a form of heresy which, in this context, has not existed up till now.

Notes

1. Of course only relatively "new." We don't deny that there could have been fairly similar phenomena for different reasons earlier in the Church's history. We only mean that this form of heresy is "typical" today, for the reasons we have given here.

2. The modern Christian has almost completely ceased to realize the danger to salvation of error in belief. He thinks of error in matters of faith as a threat to salvation only as the expression of the bad will of the man who holds it; it is not knowledge of the truth as such which is important, but the moral disposition. If the ancient Christian conviction that error is dangerous to salvation (whether the will is good or bad) is right, and nevertheless there can be guiltless error which does not destroy salvation, it is only possible to reconcile the two by saying that even in and with this error a man can still attain, according to his knowledge, what is necessary of the reality upon which salvation depends; and vice versa, if he cannot do this, then there must be guilt, and it is not possible that every (existential) error could be guiltless.

3. It is beyond the scope of this essay to answer the question why Christians who know that their theories are against the Church's official teaching nevertheless want to stay in the Church. Besides the reason we have already mentioned—that by leaving the Church they would also be contradicting a defined truth about the Church and her magisterium—there are other reasons too; a man of today is no longer as ready to trust his own opinion as he was in the times of self-conscious individualism and liberalism; he is no longer so convinced of it that he could easily set up a religious community himself, without getting lost in sectarianism and enthusiasm, etc. When people have this feeling and yet cannot bring themselves to believe unconditionally in the Church then we get—since the time of modernism—the attempt to build a private little chapel within the big Church, an esoteric sect within the big community.

4. Ernst Michel, *Die Ehe*, Stuttgart, 1949, p. 128.

II. Faith Seeks Understanding

4

The Sacramental Basis of the Layman's Position in the Church[1]

The subject of the sacramental basis of the layman's position in the Church is a theme with a direct bearing on Catholic dogmatic theology. Of its very nature, it presupposes Christian faith on the part of the listeners. Yet it is not a theme fit only for the pulpit—one which can be considered only as hortatory, as an appeal to Christians to live up to what they have long since understood through their faith. There are many themes in the area of dogmatic theology which are not controverted, which every Christian accepts in faith and in a definite sense as true and which even appear to him as self-evident in terms of his conscious belief, whenever there is express mention of them.

These, nevertheless, exist for the most part far too remotely within his conscious belief; they are too little reflected upon and are unduly crowded out of the ordinary perspective in which the normal Christian is accustomed to see the reality of his faith. And so these themes fail to constitute a truly formative and determining power in the concrete conduct of Christian life. There is something like

a heresy of forgetfulness, inattention, and complacency
which can exist to a formidable degree within the Church
itself. To speak expressly of such truths and realities of our
faith, to proclaim them with proper conceptual exactness,
is not only the aim of preaching but also and much more
that of reflective theology itself. Such a theological consideration is not only the business of theologians but also of all
those Christians whose general spiritual consciousness is
such that they either bring their faith to reflex consciousness
or else run the risk of living as though they did not have it.
It seems to me that the present topic has to do with truths
and realities of this class.

Background of Recent Discussion of the
Layman's Role in the Church

Let us be honest and objective. In the last four decades
much has been said about an awakening of the Church
within the minds and hearts of the faithful; it has been
pointed out that Christians *are* the Church and not only
her charges. To be sure, Catholic Action and the liturgical
movement came into being and still continue to do good
work. These movements, however, if they are to be significant and effective, presuppose a revision in the ordinary
understanding of the relationship between the Church and
the laity. Since the end of the patristic period of the Church,
not so much in theory nor in her innermost conscious belief but to a great extent in her average consciousness, the

Church has become a mere institution, a clerical organization for whom the remaining people, i.e., the laity, are objects of direction and care, of instruction, of guidance, of possible sanctification, but not really subjects engaged in a joint enterprise. We can hardly expect that a mentality resulting from 1500 years of history should have radically changed in the space of the four decades since the end of the First World War.

During the centuries of barbarian invasions the Church met the invaders as the superior cultural force, but it was practically impossible to get these peoples to live up to their tasks as responsible members of the Church. During the time of the investiture controversy and similar occurrences, the Church had to set herself off as a hierarchic element from profane civil society, and in this manner overcome the Caesaro-papist danger which was already a factor during ancient times. In the time of the Reformation she was compelled (tragically so) to check the call of the laity to an actualization of the common priesthood of all Christians—a call which was in itself in order at the dawn of modern times. It was necessary to channel the laity's vocation into the confines set for it by divine law by virtue of the hierarchic structure of the Church. These limits become even more evident if we do not confuse the secular movement of the democratic and social-reform forces at the beginning of modern times, as expressed in the Renaissance, the peasant wars, the Anabaptists, etc., with the contemporary and parallel but still essentially different tendency for the laity to assume consciously a responsible role in the Church.

Let us not allow ourselves to be deceived or astonished. The awakening of all Christians to an effective, concrete consciousness of their active function in the Church is still just beginning. May God grant that the realization of this consciousness, in which the Spirit of God within the Church is palpably at work, may not have to take effect by the reduction of the Church to a very little flock. In such a group close brotherly union comes easily, and each person, even among the clergy, is aware that the Church is everybody's concern; a role of active cooperation within the Church is open to all since there are only too few who will opt for a dignity and honor which entails such hardship, danger, and a readiness to make the supreme sacrifice itself.

What then is the actual situation when we look objectively and realistically at the normal consciousness of men in the Church? We would have to respond as follows: (1) The Church is still an institution borne by the clergy who, through the mediation of the truths of divine revelation and sacramental grace, care for the eternal salvation of all the other members, called the laity. (2) The term "layman" is still generally understood in the Church as meaning the non-experts, the non-specialists in the Church. The word communicates nothing but the merely negative information that such a one is excluded from all office, dignity, and functions which belong to those who form the Church and represent it vis à vis the laity.

Fundamental Theme To Be Investigated

Naturally this common consciousness does not say with any kind of reflex decisiveness or clarity that the situation is this and this alone. That would indeed be heretical. But what still remains to be said concerning the laity remains unexpressed and hazy and without any real force in the consciousness of the faithful and the clergy. Only when the laity is needed for some urgent reason do we recall these *other* truths which are valid *also* for the laity in any adequate Catholic ecclesiology. We then suddenly announce them to the laity, only to be amazed that they do not make the urgent practical application—which is the only thing that interests the harassed clergy—as quickly and effectively as anticipated. But we ought not be amazed at this, if these truths concerning the call of the laity towards a responsible role in the Church are unintentionally and without malice allowed to relapse to their former level of consciousness at a time when the threat to the Church is no longer so imminent.

Not because it is new or unheard of but because the old truth has scarcely begun to penetrate our minds and hearts, we must declare and substantiate this single proposition: *Through sacramental consecration and empowerment every Christian in the Church is constituted, qualified, and in duty bound to a position and task of active co-responsibility and work inside and outside the Church.* This one proposition and it alone must therefore be explained and substantiated.

It will be simplest to deal simultaneously with two questions: *to what end* every Christian is empowered and commissioned and *by what means* this vocation and empowerment takes place, i.e., by reception of the sacraments. Otherwise too many repetitions would be necessary.

Baptism and Membership in the Church

A person becomes a Christian and a member of the Church through Baptism. Baptism is the first sacrament of forgiveness of sin, of the communication of divine grace, of sharing in the divine nature, and of interior, lasting capacity for faith, hope, and love towards God and men. But this interior, abiding, personal sanctification of man, who is made just from being a sinner, takes place in Baptism *inasmuch as* this rite of initiation incorporates the baptized into the community of those who believe and confess the salvation of God in Christ. God gives grace to man for his own individual salvation by incorporating him in the *Church*.

This attachment to the Church, this membership in the Church, is the first and most immediate effect which every Christian receives from this sacrament of initiation. It is for all the foundation of every aspect of their Christian life, including even such hierarchic, sacramental, and priestly powers as they may subsequently receive, for the unbaptized cannot validly receive any other sacrament and can possess no juridical power in the Church.

In Baptism a man receives grace for his own salvation insofar as he becomes a member of the Church. But this proposition ought not be rendered innocuous by imagining that this membership in the Church, which is granted only through Baptism, is given only for this precise purpose, i.e., that these other remaining gifts are given to the baptized for his individual justification and sanctification and for no other purpose. That this is completely false is manifested by the fact that this merely individual justification and sanctification in a case of necessity can be gained by faith and love alone without any sacrament, as is the case indeed with many unbaptized. Baptism must, therefore, possess a positive significance which is prior to this individual salvific effect and is not confined to the latter. Membership in the Church is not only a means towards the end of personal salvation but has its own significance by virtue of Baptism. This is already implicit in the meaning and function of the Church as a whole. And when we inquire into this meaning, then the consideration just presented must be repeated.

Baptism and the Mission of the Church

The Church has for its purpose and significance more than merely to render it possible or easier for many individuals to achieve their individual salvation; to this end the Church could indeed be considered useful and significant, but not unconditionally necessary, since this end is often reached without any tangible intervention on the part of the Church, however strictly this salvation is ordered toward the Church by God's command and by the necessity of a desire for the sacrament which is also commanded. But one thing is concretely impossible without the Church (even though we can still abstractly conceive of this Church under different aspects and juridical forms): namely, that the grace of God in Christ should be present as an event, an abiding and historically tangible event, in an incarnational body in the world. For God wished his self-communication to be the redemptive salvation and the divinization of the world in a supernatural "all-in-Godness" (if we may be permitted to speak so presumptuously) only in the Incarnation of His Word and presumably only could want it in this manner.

From this it follows that the spatio-temporal appearance, the presence in history in the here and now, the emergence from mere interiority of conscience into *all* the dimensions of mankind, in man's history, society, comportment, science, and art—all these belong to the essence of this grace and to the innermost nature of this self-communication on the part of God, which divinizes the very core of man's being in his most personal free decision. Because salvation comes in the flesh of Christ and because man is to be saved in and through all the dimensions of his existence, it is necessary for grace to become corporeal, historical, and social. And if it becomes so then it is called the Church. Anyone who is sanctified through Baptism, in which he is incorporated in this Church as the historical and social reality of Christ's grace in the world, receives necessarily with the grace of the Church a status, a commission, and a power to share in this function of the Church as a tangible historical embodiment of God's grace in the world. Stated in other terms: If this grace is actively formative of the Church because it is in the form of Christ and therefore incarnational, this must be true whenever grace is given—even though in many cases this property of grace is realized in a very rudimentary way. If therefore this grace itself is given ecclesially, that is, sacramentally, then this Church-forming function must impel and capacitate man to a fuller realization of this property. It must therefore so incorporate a man in the Church that he becomes a true member and so attains an active operative role in this community and shares in its basic functions.

In the concrete, precisely what is there in the nature of the Church, the historical manifestation of God's grace in the world, in which every baptized person shares through Baptism? Why does grace constitute a quasi-sacramental reality in the world? Because grace comes from Christ, the incarnate Word of God. It exhibits itself in this way most clearly and unchangeably in its very essence as God's free act, which comes not from below and from the powers of creation, but from God's sovereign initiative. Grace can best be grasped in its true nature if it is not simply always and everywhere diffused throughout the world and inseparably united to it, but if it possesses a definite historicity, so that it can historically encounter man in his being as a free, corporeal, and historical person.

The Church is not merely a mediator of grace, so that she would become superfluous as soon as this grace of God had penetrated into the interior of man and had become, so to speak, absorbed. Her function is rather to pour out grace into the world, into history, and into human society. She has the function of incarnating grace in the Word, in the sacraments, in law, and in the concrete experiential life of the sanctified, in order that this grace may reach these areas, so that they may all be incorporated into the Kingdom of God and into the body of the Word. The Church is the quasi-sacramental word, in which this grace, everywhere at work, becomes manifest in history and calls out to the individual, proclaiming its own victorious presence. And everyone who is baptized shares in this function.

Once we look upon Christianity from this point of view, the reality itself is not altered but the perspectives under which it can be seen are vastly changed. The Christian is then no longer so much one who possesses grace (as if it were more or less certain that this were not the case with non-Christians) but one in whom grace wishes to reveal itself historically. In fact, can we say of any man, even if he is unbaptized, that he certainly lacks the grace of God and the remission of sins? No. By what, then, are the express and the "anonymous" (i.e., the justified but unbaptized) Christians distinguishable from one another? Precisely in this, that the baptized Christians are evident in the dimension of history, public life, the Word and the sacraments, whereas the others are so only in the silence of their innermost believing state of conscience, without perhaps knowing it reflexively. And what the express (i.e., the baptized) Christians are in this dimension of the historical and social, this they *ought* to be. They are commissioned, by their very nature, to be bearers of the function of the Church as the visible and social manifestation of grace, and to do so by a personal decision to take up, accept, and realize this manifestation in their whole life. What is true of the Church is also true of the individual baptized Christian. He is commissioned through Baptism to be the bearer of the Word, the witness of truth, the representative of the grace of Christ in the world. The unbaptized is the object to which the Church applies her sacred powers to redeem and sanctify. At the very instant in which this power is applied, the *object* of the Church is changed into a *member* of the Church, into an *element of the active subjectivity* of the Church. He is no longer set over against the Church, but stands with the Church over against the world. He is one who is called, chosen, selected; he ought to shine forth as the stars in the heavens in the midst of a lost and dark generation.

With respect to the baptized the Church of course retains a relationship of subject, standing over against those who receive from her, are directed by her, and in turn look to her as recipients. But if the Church exercises a role of subject toward these members as objects, inferiors, pupils, and followers, still she treats them differently from unbaptized persons, over whom she also makes claims. This difference of attitude would have no basis unless the baptized person were also her own member, a fellow subject within her, and a joint bearer of her active function.

This status accrues to him precisely through Baptism, and not only when he becomes a priest, bishop, or bearer of hierarchical power in the strict sense. For the peculiar quality of the Church's relationship to the baptized is partly determined by this active membership of his, even in cases when the Church encounters him in the name of Christ. Paul once said: Those who are outside, God alone will judge. The Church is the judge only regarding those who are within. Not because they are handled in a worse manner, but because they are of greater worth. They are worth more because they have a function which is the Church itself. The Church therefore watches over her own witnessing function in the world precisely when she instructs her own members, calls them to order, and sanctifies them.

The Church's relation to her members is in all aspects affected by the function which she herself represents and exercises in the world precisely through her members. If Paul quite nonchalantly accepts the fact that commerce and intercourse is had with non-Christians and yet forbids such relations with the sinful Christian, if he reacts much more vigorously to a slight deviation from the Gospel proclaimed within the Church than against error outside the Church, if he is very sensitive to the impression which a gathering of the community and its divine worship makes on non-Christians, if the pastoral letters make no mention of the clergy's apostolic activity towards those outside the Church, if the "propaganda" toward the outside world appears therefore not at all organized and if no special necessity for this was experienced, all of these phenomena and many others which we will pass over rest upon a conviction that every Christian is evidently co-responsible for and engaged with the Church and her mission, precisely because he is a member of the Church.

For this reason he is treated otherwise than an outsider if he sins. By deviating from his own task he compromises his commission to further the holiness of the Church as the visible manifestation of the victorious grace of God in the world, and he likewise compromises the Church and her task. The Church separates herself from the sinner by a kind of interdict or excommunication because otherwise she herself would betray her own purpose. Thus the primitive Church took it for granted quite nonchalantly that the missionary work of the Church would continue without a great deal of apparatus and organization, for each Christian must in his own life bear witness to the fact that God's grace has taken hold of his life, redeeming and transforming it. Baptism, therefore, in giving the Christian a position in the Church, initiates him into the basic function of the Church itself, to be the incipient advent of God's kingship in his victorious grace. And even in the case where he is the object of the Church's solicitude for his salvation, the Church cannot forget that the baptized is an object of her solicitude in an entirely different way from the unbaptized. In her care for the baptized the Church is mindful that he can effect his own salvation only if and when he exercises his active function in the Church and with her gives testimony to God's truth and grace for the salvation of the world.

Nature of the Layman's Mission in the Church through Baptism

It may well be that Baptism assigns to the laity no new position in the world like the hierarchical offices in the Church. The official emissaries of the Church's hierarchical apostolate will in normal circumstances be only those who by their vocation are summoned forth from their profane station within the world in order to go to all nations. But if the baptized layman in the normal course of events remains in the world in his own prescribed, secular sphere of existence, he nonetheless receives through Baptism a new and different task in this precise situation. For the Church becomes present at this very place through him. In saying "Church" here, we do not mean to denature the concept, restricting it to the external organization of the Church, to her merely juridical structure, or to her own historically palpable influence as an organization, as a "complete society."

When we say "Church" in this context we mean: the grace of God, God's power appearing as faith, hope, love, and trust in the meaning of existence and in its infinite manifestation in God's deeds. We here mean "Church" in the sense of the Truth that liberates all human truth by exposing it to the infinitely superior truth of God's mystery. We mean imperishable courage, the gamble of love, in which without counting the cost a man suddenly casts his entire life into the incomprehensible Abyss which we call God. When we say "Church" we mean all this, inasmuch as the grace of God embraces, transforms, and liberates every earthly reality. For this grace does not alight at any point whatever, in some secret recess of consciousness, which scarcely dares make contact with this infinite mystery of existence. Rather it takes on bodily form, spontaneously bears witness (even without benefit of Sunday pulpit oratory). It is joyfully lived, lovingly communicated to others, and through life and death acquires a habitation in all the dimensions of existence. This is the Church of which we are speaking. And concerning it we say that it should be made visibly present wherever *this particular Christian* finds himself.

The mission of the baptized layman in the task of the Church does not mean simply a pious Sunday amusement, a Corpus Christi procession with the local dignitaries of the community or party or with good Catholics, nor does it mean just voting for Catholic candidates, or patiently paying church taxes. Rather it involves the radical, all-revolutionizing consciousness of the fact that the baptized, when he remains and lives in his completely normal occupation, in his family, community, nation, and state, in his human and cultural milieu, has precisely in these situations an infinite task as a Christian, namely, to make the truth, selflessness, and love of the Kingdom of God win out and thus allow the Church to be present in her most essential nature where he is present and where he alone can be, where no one else can represent the Church, not even the clergy, and yet where the Church must be.

Of course, the layman, when he stands at this post conscious of his task, will experience the fact that this Church of truth, goodness, selflessness, uprightness, bravery, quiet harmony with the dark secret of existence, this Church that knows how to face death without despair and fulfil her duty soberly even without hope of reward—this Church, he will find, is also represented by some who do not know that this community to which they belong is precisely the people of God, maintaining in the Church of Jesus Christ its social unity, historical identity, and quasi-sacramental visibility in accord with the will of God and of Christ. But this "anonymous" Christianity, consisting of those who only think that they are not and should not be Christians, lives in reality from the unique grace of Christ and furthers the grace which finds in the Church its historical tangibility and bodily existence.

If we speak thus of a Church of interior grace, of real love and faithfulness, of calm death (wherein faith and charity are always perfected), we are not substituting for the customary conception of the Church another concept by a kind of conceptual sleight of hand. No, we are not speaking of some "invisible Church" but precisely of that which appears in the concrete visible Church or which, even where it does not appear in the societal form of the Church, still belongs to the Church and is directed to her in all truth. We are not depreciating the visibility of the concrete, tangible Church, for it is and ought to be called the social and historical manifestation of God's truth, grace, and Spirit, which can be and are, according to the teaching of this same Church, powerfully at work in places where the historico-social reality of the Church is not yet clearly perceptible.

We say then that the Christian, because and insofar as he is a member of the Church by virtue of his baptism, has to represent at his station within the world the victory of grace, love, and faith and the advent of the Kingdom of God, and that he has to bear responsible witness to these eternal salvific truths in the world. But this is not to deny that there are "anonymous" Christians where he is stationed —not merely perhaps, but certainly—in whom this same power of grace to which the official Christian must bear witness has already begun to take effect. The fact that these others are Christians without even knowing it may make it harder for the express Christian at his place in the world, in his family, his job, or his secular business, to distinguish himself so markedly that this Church which he represents can become clearly distinct from the world in this particular milieu. But this changes nothing in the task and the special responsibility of baptized Christians to let the Church be present there where they themselves are stationed in the world as baptized persons.

God's sovereign freedom in the distribution of talents and graces, the breathing of the Spirit through all the thoroughfares of the world, frequently (if we may be permitted to express it in this way) makes competition for His own Church. For He prepares His church of sanctified humanity outside of *the* Church. This sanctified people is not yet visibly and officially incorporated in the Church and perhaps will not be until the end of time has come and all that is good and true is gathered into the Church of everlasting life. But nevertheless this is no reason for the baptized to be any less conscious of his mission and radical responsibility. Whenever he encounters in the world law, order, love, fidelity, courage, comfort in life and strength in the face of death, then he knows that there the grace of Christ is at work, since without it natural virtues do not remain intact for any length of time; and therefore, where these realities are manifested in all the gloom and guilt of this world, they testify to the grace of Christ even without knowing it.

Where the Christian encounters such virtue in the world, he cannot say to himself: "Look, one can apparently get along without Christianity and the Church." Rather he must say to himself: "Here is being accomplished that for which you have been commissioned, sent, and empowered by the finger of the living God, who has branded into your being and life the indelible seal of Baptism." Woe to you if this seal is less brilliant, less eloquent, and less convincing in your life than in that of Albert Schweitzer, Simone Weil, or Wolfram Siewers and the many others on whose brows we may believe the sign of Christ shines, even though they do not seem to be aware of it. Precisely because the official baptized Christian is so often sent to "anonymous" Christians of inner, unnoticed grace, the mission in the service of the Church which is given with Baptism frequently becomes an act of blind unconditional obedience in which one bears witness to God even though the testimony seems

so unconvincing that the witness himself can take no pride
in it.

The Baptized Christian's Role in the
Church Not as Opposed to the
Cleric's Role but as an Expression of the
Very Nature of the Church

At any event it is clear that through Baptism a person not
only becomes a subject of the Church, bound to her norms
and sharing in her blessings, but also a member of the
Church who has to take part in her function of bearing
witness to the advent of the eschatologically victorious
grace of God, in which God Himself becomes the Savior
of the world. And thus the baptized Christian in the Church
receives a position which does not merely consist in his
being the object of the activity of the hierarchy or being
distinguished from the clergy by the fact that he is *non-*
clerical. It ought to be quite evident that when we have to
speak of the Church and her nature, we should not at the
very beginning speak of something which concerns the
inter-relationship between elements within the Church. The
relationship of the individual members of the Church to one
another is not in place in a preliminary description of the
Church's nature because the proper determination of the
relationship between two elements of a totality to one
another presupposes an understanding of the totality itself.
The establishment of the precise powers, tasks, and obliga-

tions of the guiding organ in the Church and the other duties of the other members and organs emanating from and subordinate to this guiding organ cannot pass for a description of the nature of the Church, no matter how essential, beneficial, and indispensable the functions of this hierarchy of sacred powers may be. If however we say that the Church is the body of Christ, the enduring, historical presence of His truth and grace in the world, the continuing efficacy of the Incarnate Word in the flesh, and if we say that every baptized person shares in this because he is a member of this body, then we have said everything if we have really understood the sentence we have uttered.

We could naturally develop in many respects the statements made above. We would then have to point out that this function of the Church is not at all exhausted in the function of the powers in the Church which are of a juridical nature and which can be discharged by officials. We would also have to point out that there is a charismatic element in the Church which belongs as much to her nature as do the institutional and official elements.[2] We would also have to show that there is a development of the consciousness of faith in the Church directed by the Holy Spirit and not by the plans of human officials, and that there is and must be an unplanned progress of the experience of faith through the fortunes of the Church on which the magisterial authority in the Church is dependent, not indeed *de jure* but *de facto*. We would then have to indicate that for this charismatic element in action, belief, and love under the immediate influence of the Spirit (who does not always and necessarily proceed through channels), the so-called layman by reason of his baptismal membership can be and often enough really has been, no less than the clergy, the gateway and the antenna, and that he therefore has the obligation to develop in himself a proper receptivity in order to fulfil his position within the Church.

We could recall that, according to the words of Pius XII, there is and must be something like public opinion in the Church (without which both the pastor and his flock would be the poorer) and that the laity are and must be to a great extent the carriers of this necessary public opinion in the Church.[3] We could point out that there is necessarily something like a supernatural *existential-ethic*, even though what is commonly known as situation ethics is a heresy: for while the particular decision of the individual Christian must of course be standardized in his life by the general principles which the Church proclaims in her magisterium, the decision cannot be adequately deduced from this source alone; hence at this point every man and Christian has an immediate relationship to God which remains in the visible Church but cannot be borne by her visible magisterium (however important this magisterium may be as a negative norm against deception). This immediate relationship of every Christian, including the layman, to God (an immediacy which must be thought of as resting totally on the grace of Baptism) has immense significance not only for the private life of the individual but also for the Church.

The role of the layman in the Church originating in Baptism is therefore not primarily to be viewed from the aspect of the clergy but rather from the nature of the Church. Naturally there must be in any socially constituted community of man a directive organ and its incumbents. This power of leadership in Christ's Church is, of course, founded on Christ and not democratically constituted from below. This is true, moreover, because the Church and therefore the dignity, task, and function of every member of the Church which Christ established come from above. In civil society it is evident that the political organization of a people or nation does not primarily arise from the fact that the political structures are at hand, but rather the civic apparatus shapes into a society an existent historical human mass, a people, a culture and community life developed in the course of history. Furthermore, the life of the politically organized people does not consist solely, or primarily, or ultimately in the function of its own directive organs; rather these basically have a role of service toward the life of the people.

The same is true of the Church. What is juridically organized from above is a previously existing community of the redeemed, of believers, of those impelled by the Spirit of God, loved by God, and called to eternal life. In all these operations the life of the Church is contained. And the governing office of the ecclesiastical hierarchy has the function of promoting this very life. Finally, what really matters in the Church and for the Church as a living entity is that there be faith, hope, and love, that the grace of God be received as God's life, that witness be borne to the Truth of God, to God's fidelity, and to the hope of eternal life.

Everything else in the Church, including every juridical constitution involving subordination and superiority, office and authority, is given and ordained only as a means to this end, because, while the Church and her really prime task are essential, it is not intended that the Church fulfil her existence in these functions themselves. We could say, therefore, in a very true and pregnant sense that the clergy exists because there are laymen. And "laity" is no belittling term but means the same thing as membership in the Church, which is made up of these laymen and fulfills herself in them as Christ's presence in the world.

Confirmation and the Layman's Vocation

All that we have said of Baptism as the sacramental foundation of the layman's status in the Church, whereby the baptized by God's call and institution is raised to a new station, to a permanent, ineradicable form of life involving active cooperation in the realization of the Church's essence and definition—all this is even more true of Confirmation. Ultimately it is not decisive when and with what understanding we received this sacrament of spiritual adulthood. What is far more important is whether we, as confirmed, sometime or other in our life take note of what objectively took place and what we subjectively have to fulfil.

It is difficult for the dogmatic theologian to draw a sharp line between the two sacraments in reference to their meaning and effects. They form together the one initiation into Christian life; they sacramentally represent from two aspects in two sacraments the one totality of the Christian vocation. Thus we do not have to try here to differentiate the two sacraments very explicitly from one another. It is sufficient to say here that Confirmation is more evidently the sacrament of witness to the Faith, of charismatic plenitude, of the Holy Spirit, of the apostolic mission of those sealed with the Spirit on behalf of the world, to subject it to God's rule. More evidently than Baptism it is the sacrament of fortitude in Faith in the face of the powers and forces of this world, the power of lies and disbelief, of daemonic striving for self-redemption. This sacrament makes it clear that the Christian as confirmed layman is not a mere object of education and direction by the Church as a hierarchical organization, but rather one who has been raised by his Christian initiation to a position, a mission and task, and hence to a personal responsibility towards the world.

Penance and the Layman's Role in the Church

It could be shown for all the other sacraments that they have an ecclesiastical dimension, that they are not merely events of private concern for salvation or personal reception of salvation, but rather self-realization of the Church. They dispose their recipients not only towards God but also towards the Church. And thus all the sacraments, including those which every layman receives, are a progressive initiation into the active work of the Church. Penance as the sacrament of reconciliation with God and the Church is the sacrament of the renewed fulfilment of Baptism and Confirmation, reactivating in some measure the initiation. And this renewal will differ according to a man's assigned position within the Church. Whoever receives the Spirit anew, receives Him (as the Fathers of the Church have expressly said) as the Spirit of the Church through being reconciled with the Church. And therefore he receives Him as the Spirit who desires to transform and heal the world by means of the community of believers in whom He dwells, and thus to fill the world with God's own life and bear witness to this intention of His by the very existence of the Church.

The Eucharist and the Layman's Mission

That the sacrament of the Eucharist is a sacrament of the Spirit-inspired unity of the Church itself and is not first of all the sacrament of a private audience with God; that it is the bread of the Church's unity in love is already well known. Whoever therefore receives this bread of life cannot do otherwise (as long as he knows what he is doing) than accept from the Spirit (which this body of Christ gives) the power of unity of this Church in love. And *all* Christians receive in like manner this sacrament of supreme unity, this manifestation of the supreme unity of eternal life. No one has any preference over another in this highest sacramental symbol of Christianity's complete essence. To be sure, from the very nature of this sacrament, because it symbolizes and effects in ever greater measure the unity of the Church, the hierarchical constitution of the Church must likewise manifest itself in the manner of its administration. The Lord's Supper, in which all participate, because all are loved and redeemed in the same manner, must be celebrated in an orderly fashion, i.e., according to Christ's will, with the bishop or priest presiding. If it were not conducted by one officially ordained, the Lord's Supper could not possibly be a function of the Church.

But precisely this orderly Lord's Supper supposes from the very beginning Christ's intention towards all Christians, the whole Church. Christ offers this meal of eternal life through the ordained official, but He offers it to all, and even the man holding office in the hierarchy reaches the consummation of his own Christian existence not by the fact that he administers but rather by the fact that he receives, like every one else, the Body of the Lord and thus is filled with the Lord's Spirit. Here he performs the greatest activity of his own life, which is likewise similar to that of all Christians inasmuch as he believes, hopes, and loves.

Marriage and the Lay Christian

The fact that Marriage immediately assigns a social and ecclesiastical function to the Christian, a position founded both in the world and in the Church, no longer needs amplification. Marital society is consecrated by the sacrament of Marriage as an efficacious sign of the unity between Christ and the Church and thereby becomes formative of the Church. And if Matrimony does not imprint an indelible character like Baptism, Confirmation, and Orders, nevertheless, as long as it lasts in this life between two Christians (i.e., till the death of one of the marriage partners), Marriage remains a lasting symbol of grace which is continually being offered to the marriage partners as the grace of Christ. Marriage, moreover, is an enduring state within the Church; as the initial, permanent, and sacramentally consecrated human community, it incorporates the partners into the most intimate local church in existence, i.e., the two-in-oneness of two married people. And this community is provided with a Christian grace and a Christian salvific task.

The Sacrament of the Sick and the Layman's Position in the Church

If it is true that the death of a Christian (including the enduring of the approaching threat of death, even where this yields again to health) is a dying together with Christ, a believing, hoping, and loving acceptance of death as the final reality of life, which Christ took upon Himself and redeemed, and if it is true that the death of Christ was not the most private event of His life (in spite of the fact that He died in the most agonizing loneliness conceivable) but rather a cosmic event in which everything is saved and all sin expiated, then our death also must have a universal significance as a dying with Christ. We suffer to the end, with all and for all, the fate in which all are made equal, i.e., death, which gives birth to life because death is secure in Christ.

Hence it is not surprising that even in this moment of extreme loneliness the Church does not allow man simply to fall into this death, a private death so irrespective of persons, but rather the Church accompanies man in the Sacrament of the Sick, the sacrament of the approaching threat of death, inasmuch as he, sanctified and strengthened by this prayer of faith, produces once again an effective action which is of value to the entire Church. When a person "dies in the Lord," he has also died with the Lord for all who are of the Lord. Therefore the Christian never leaves his own sacramentally assigned position within the Church and for the Church until everything is completed.

Significance of Our Conclusions

At the beginning of this chapter we formulated this proposition: by sacramental consecration and empowerment every Christian in the Church is constituted, qualified, and in duty bound to a position of active co-responsibility inside and outside the Church. The narrow framework of this short essay did not permit us to give anything more than the most general substantiation and interpretation of this proposition. But at least this one point should have become evident: "laity" means in the Church the opposite of what it means in secular usage, for instance, in the sentence, "He is an utter layman in the field of criminal law." In the secular sphere "laity" means those who cannot have a voice, who have nothing to say, who are excluded from a certain area of life and responsibility. "Laity" means just the opposite in the area of theology.

Of course, it may be true, in accordance with the latest studies, that the application of this word to the baptized, believing Christian, in order to connote his difference from the clergy, is not immediately derived from the biblical concept of "the people of God" (from the *laos theou*, with which it is *linguistically* connected) but rather that from the very beginning it carried with it a suggestion of "layhood." However it would be and actually is catastrophic if the Christian has merely one realization concerning his own Christian position, i.e., that he is not a cleric and therefore must play a totally subordinate and more or less passive role in the Church. Every Christian is indelibly sealed by his Baptism; every Christian through Baptism is an anointed and consecrated person, a temple of God, a chosen, elect soul, one who is called to the community of those who know and confess that God has had mercy on the world and has called it into His life. Every Christian is the sharer in an active function inside and outside the Church. The word of God is also placed on his lips, even if he has no mission or power to preach in the official assemblies of the community. For he ought to carry the message of the Gospel from the community assembly to the very place where it should proceed if it has any meaning and power, namely, where life is being lived, a life which yearns to be illumined and redeemed by God's Word. The baptized Christian may articulate this word primarily—

though he should not confine himself to this—by the sincere activity of his own life and not through his own words. He can apply to himself, as a divinely sealed member of the Church of the Word, the saying: "Woe to me if I did not preach and did not bear witness."

Every Christian is through Baptism and all the other sacraments co-responsible for the task of the Church: that through the Church the grace of God become tangible and convincing in the world which has been redeemed by God's love and still has to be redeemed by continuing to experience and perceive the fact of her redemption. This is always an activity within and without. Within because we who are Christians must always become Christians anew; without because by far the greater part of the world has not yet *com*prehended what it has already *ap*prehended in the depths of its consciousness and what can be understood as the grace and promise of being definitively taken over by God's grace.

It remains true and ought not be hushed up, since there is no need to do so, that the unordained Christian who is not charged with a mission of Orders and leadership in the Church clearly differs from a cleric. In this respect a subordination and difference of rank in the Church exists according to Christ's will. But this gradation and distinction of dignity is totally directed to certain definite ecclesiastical-social functions in the structure of the Church's life and has no relevance with reference to holiness, the embrace of God's love, or even necessarily the objective salutary value of the function itself. For a free charism received by a layman in the Church with respect to the salvation of men and the world can be effectively of greater significance than the exercise of an institutional, official, or even a sacramental power. Nor does this difference of rank result in a division of classes as regards the radical demands of God or the inescapable duty to keep and preserve the world in all its dimensions as the reality of God's creation and to bring it to the reality of the Redemption.

If we mull over all these points and look for a very simple formula which would summarize everything, then we might say: through the sacraments the layman in the Church is not, of course, a cleric (since both have different tasks within the Church which mutually condition one another). But having seen and said this we might well say: the layman in the Church is not a layman—but a Christian. And each layman is asked whether he wishes to be what he already is.

Notes

1. This essay, which was not included in the English edition, was translated specially for this book by G. Richard Dimler, S.J.

2. Cf. Chapter 1, "The Individual in the Church," Part I.

3. Cf. the author's *Free Speech in the Church* (New York and London, Sheed and Ward, 1959).

5

Nature and Grace[1]

By and large nowadays only "specialist circles" concern
themselves with the subject "nature and grace." But at least
it *is* again being talked about, and not disregarded except
when mention of it cannot be avoided. It is a subject which
arouses passionate discussion. Views differ over it and the
controversy is not merely academic. This is splendid. For
since the controversy between Catholic and Protestant
theology died down and became sterile in the eighteenth
century, and the traditional scholastic theology was won
back in victory over the thin-blooded theology of the
Enlightenment in the nineteenth century, for a short time
it was generally thought that the subject "nature and
grace" was closed, that everyone was agreed about it and
more or less everything worth knowing was now known.

If we are going to try and describe this standard view
of nature and grace in post-Tridentine and neo-scholastic
theology, we must emphasize that we really do mean
standard. Of course the theology of today possesses all the
riches of yesterday and all past ages. In the Church nothing
is ever completely forgotten. And the truth expressly stated

contains within it, unexpressed, depth upon depth of implications. And so it is easy to make mistakes in a description of the standard view of a subject in current theology.
And yet this standard view does exist. And it is often more
important in the Church's life than the sublimer insights of
the few.

What was neo-scholasticism's standard view of the
relationship between grace and nature? In order to see it
as it really was (although it did not fully realize this itself),
we must start from a problem in the doctrine of grace
which is apparently only a peripheral problem. The supernatural grace through which man is justified and can do
just works was regarded as something in itself beyond
consciousness. This is a theological opinion which has
always been in dispute. But it is the prevalent one and has
determined the standard view of the subject: Supernatural
grace is a reality which we know about from the teaching
of the Faith, but which is completely outside our experience and can never make its presence felt in our conscious
personal life. We must strive for it, knowing as we do
through faith that it exists, take care (through good moral
acts and reception of the sacraments) that we possess it,
and treasure it as our share in the divine life and the pledge
and necessary condition for life in heaven. But the conscious
sphere in which we experience ourselves is not itself filled
by this grace. We cannot experience what difference being
supernaturally "elevated" has made to our spiritual and
moral acts (the acts themselves as opposed to the objects,
distinct from the acts, which they are intentionally directed

towards). Thus, in this most widespread view of it, grace is
a superstructure above man's conscious spiritual and moral
life, although it is, of course, also an acknowledged object
of his faith and recognized as the highest, the divine, life in
him which alone has power to bring him salvation. It looks
as if this conception must be the right one; we can know
nothing about our supernatural state (or only conclude
something about it with some degree of probability from
certain indications), we cannot "see" anything of the action
of grace (or at most only those helps of "healing grace,"
which are in themselves natural, to fulfil the natural law).
The simplest experience and the teaching of the Council of
Trent[2] (*DB*, 802, 805, 825, 826) seem to endorse this view
almost as a matter of course.

Once one has this view, then of course the sphere of our
spiritual and moral actions, within which we are present to
ourselves, seems to be identical with "nature" in the theological sense. And this sphere is even made a definition of
what we mean by nature; nature is what we experience
of ourselves without revelation, for this is nature and
nature *only*. And vice versa, only nature and its acts constitute that life which we experience as ours. We make up
from the elements of our natural powers, habits etc., those
acts in which we intentionally direct ourselves towards
God's revealed mysteries and which we know to be "essentially" (but only "essentially") supernaturally raised.
Supernatural "enlightenment," moral "impulsion" and "inspiration" to do good, the "light" of faith, the working of
the Holy Spirit—scriptural and traditional terms like these

are reduced to this purely entitative elevation of our natural
moral acts, or to natural psychological influences (which
are, however, regarded as being, under God's providence,
directed towards our supernatural salvation). In short, the
relationship between nature and grace is thought of as two
layers laid very carefully one on top of the other so that
they interpenetrate as little as possible. And accordingly,
nature's orientation towards grace is thought of as negatively as possible. Indeed, grace is in fact the most perfect
fulfilment of nature; indeed, God the Lord of this nature
can require man to submit himself to his will that man
should have a supernatural life and destiny, and to open
himself to grace; but nature in itself has only a *potentia
obedientialis* to do this, thought of as negatively as possible;
the mere absence of a contradiction in such an elevation of
nature. Nature itself can be fulfilled in a purely natural
destiny, content and harmonious in its own sphere, without
direct contact with God in the Beatific Vision; when it
turns in on itself in its immediate self-awareness (as it is in
the nature of spirit to do: *reditio completa in seipsum*) it
is aware of itself as if it were a "pure nature." In its present
fallen state it differs from "pure nature" only, in the words
of the well-known phrase (which is an opinion, not a
definition), *sicut spoliatus a nudo*—as the man who has lost
his clothes differs from the man who has never had any.
The lack of grace is only thought of as a deprivation because of a decree of God (which "demands the possession
of grace") and an event in the past (Adam's sin); it is not
as if the lack itself were any different in the two cases.

This standard view cannot be acquitted of a certain "extrinsicity," as it has been called—granted, of course, that when formulated with proper precision it can be shown not to go against any teaching of the magisterium on the relationship between nature and grace. Neither can we deny (although we sometimes may not like hearing this said) that in practice it is not without danger. For if it is the true view, then all that man can experience of his spiritual life takes place within the bounds of nature alone, and this nature is divided into two sectors: the "purely natural," which (with its supernatural elevation considered as completely above consciousness) is the life of nature alone, and then those acts (e.g., faith or the desire to serve God) which are (subjectively) constituted of purely natural elements and are only directed towards the supernatural as their object. If this is so, then it is not surprising (although of course not always justified) when a man takes very little interest in this mysterious superstructure of his being; this grace is not present where he is present to himself, in his immediate self-awareness. One can get the impression (although it may not be objectively justified) that during the course of the theological development in the Middle Ages, what had originally been called grace came to be thought of as the act of nature performed with natural powers (e.g., the power to love God above all things), and in order to get round this, what was basically the same thing was superimposed upon nature and called "supernature," and then, of course, it was pushed away into the region above the consciousness and became an unconscious modality of the spiritual and moral in nature, and it was hard to see what further use it could be. Think, for example, of the distinction— right, of course, in a certain sense—between natural and supernatural "love of God above all things"; how can these two loves differ *as love*, i.e., spiritual, when the supernaturalness of the supernatural love only rests in an entitative "elevation"? Would one be completely mistaken in seeing a connection with modern naturalism of this theory too? If it is true that the modern lack of interest in the supernatural could only have developed on the basis of this conception of grace (which is of course in some measure nominalistic)?

Theological controversy has again become strong over the question of the correctness or adequacy of this conception. There are several reasons for this.

Philosophically the kind of scholastic philosophy connected with the work of J. Maréchal[3] was involved. In his intellectual, transcendental dynamism, Maréchal sees man (in so far as he is spirit, thus in his "nature") as in his very essence "desiderium naturale visionis beatificae" (to give him St. Thomas's phrase). This desire is, of course, conditional and so it does not take away the freedom of his actual vocation to the direct vision of God through grace, and it is fundamentally present in every spiritual act in the form of a longing for the absolute Being (without therefore being explicitly and conceptually formulated). It is the *a priori* condition of every affirmation and acceptance of any finite thing. In this recourse to the doctrine of a natural desire for the direct vision of God we can see already how from a minor corollary (or so it seems) in St. Thomas, it became for Maréchal the key to the understanding of a spiritual nature. It is understandable that in the thirties there was a long debate over the meaning attached by Maréchal and his school to this natural desire, and whether it could be squared with the Church's teaching that the direct vision of God is supernatural and gratuitous.[4] At any rate, it began to be understood that the orientation of man as a spirit towards God is not an "extra," but it is what makes him what he experiences himself to be and he cannot finally deny and repress it without sin, because it is affirmed (even if only as an implicit, transcendental *a priori*) in every act of his spirit.

In the field of history of theology[5] the main concern was with the history of theological reflex knowledge of the supernatural, and how it differs from the natural. It was realized that the modern theological concept of the supernatural (and the natural as its counterpart) only developed slowly and the application of these terms to the many individual theological problems was only slowly worked out (problems, for example, like the necessity of strictly supernatural and internal grace for every act profitable to salvation; the possibility of distinguishing between natural and supernatural morality and defining the boundaries between them; the difference between supernatural actual and habitual grace; the impossibility of positive preparation for justification through moral acts performed without saving grace; whether a purely natural destiny for man after death is conceivable). On the whole it is true to say that the de-

velopment has been legitimate and a true unfolding of the
facts given in revelation; it has not been a false development.
It is also true that with St. Thomas it had already progressed
far enough to make what comes later clearly visible in him
(which is not to say that he reached the point reached by
Cajetan and post-Tridentine theology). But now we are
getting a picture of the process of development itself. We
see more clearly that we cannot read all the later insights
and distinctions into the earlier theology. And because we
can see this we are in a better position to inquire whether
during the process of development earlier valuable knowledge has not been lost, whether the gain has not been at the
cost of the loss of other knowledge, and that there is, therefore, much to be regained which theology once possessed.
It may be that there is a tendency to overrate the difference
between medieval (especially St. Thomas's) and post-
Tridentine theology of grace. It may be that in the grace
theology of the seventeenth- and eighteenth-century "Au-
gustinians" there are elements which should not be considered tenable today simply because Benedict XIV declared
them free of hidden Jansenism. When we realize the special
nature of the history of thought on a subject, and when we
realize that it cannot simply be divided up into the history
of thought on the clear unchanging truth never disputed
by really orthodox theologians, and the history of wicked
heretical teachings, our historical study not only shows us
how we arrived at the final form of modern theology, but
enables us to rediscover the intentions and preoccupations
of earlier theologians which have been forgotten in modern

textbook theology, always in danger, as it is, of making the manageable and simplified the criterion of the truth and of hallowed tradition. We discover (to give just a few examples from our own subject) that the concept of the "natural desire for the Beatific Vision" in St. Thomas is not merely a left-over, to be explained "historically" from the time when theology was not yet so explicit about the supernatural and gratuitous nature of the direct vision of God (which, of course, it *is* in this case); that behind the hesitation to postulate a strictly supernatural actual grace (as well as habitual) lies not *only* a faulty terminology only slowly to be put right, which does not grasp that the saving acts, which are done before justification and yet cannot be done without grace, necessarily require the existence of actual grace;[6] that we can learn something today from St. Thomas about the relationship between sacrament and personal act which was forgotten or simplified in later theology; that medieval theology thought much more deeply about "uncreated grace" than post-Tridentine official theology, which thought of the "indwelling of the Spirit of God" more or less exclusively in terms of "created grace," and in its anti-Protestant zeal was too ready to call created grace simply "grace."

A third incentive to reapproach the question of the relationship between nature and grace has come from the revival of the dialogue between Catholic and Protestant theology.[7] In the nature of the case Protestant theologians are bound to be concerned with this problem too (al-

though, of course, from different points of view). And
they have recently re-examined it, taking as their starting-
point the Bible, Luther, and controversy with modern
humanism and Anglo-Saxon-American optimism. They
were bound to ask what else is man besides a sinner, how
far does he remain a sinner when he has been justified. We
find in early Protestant doctrine that in man without grace
there is absolutely nothing good (which serves toward
salvation). But this teaching (which, rightly understood,
is held also by Catholics) is only the beginning of the investigation; and this is where there are new possibilities of
discussion with Catholic theologians. And these opportunities have already been partially made use of. And, vice
versa, Catholic theology has been driven to examine afresh
(even though only a few Catholic theologians may actually
be doing so) what is right in the Protestant doctrine and
how it can be made more clearly valid for us; we must
see Christ as the centre of the whole existing world and
economy of salvation; we must show that the supernaturalness of grace does not mean that man in his "natural" being
is a closed system complete in itself with grace as a pure
superstructure which leaves what is beneath unchanged;
we must investigate whether and in what sense a Catholic
can hold the axiom "simul justus et peccator"; we must
make our own the idea of existential, personal "moments
of grace," which is also implicit in and proper to the Catholic doctrine of grace, and we must clear up the misunderstanding which leads people to think that the idea of a

"state" of grace, when grace is "present" but not necessarily "active," is an aberration from the true biblical doctrine of grace.

We need not waste much time in saying that the "modern mentality" has stimulated theological thought in this direction. We want a single complete picture of man, we want a synthesis of all the different things we know about him. We think "existentially." And so we want as far as possible to "experience" the reality of grace in our own existence where we experience ourselves; we want to see and feel its power at work in us. And in accordance with other modern tendencies, we shall not only want to see grace as it concerns the individual, but also consider more explicitly its ecclesiological aspects, grace in the history of salvation not only within the Church, the possibility of grace and its highest manifestations in the world of non-Christian religions.

When in what follows we give the "findings" of these theological investigations, of course this does not mean that they have already been officially accepted or already become *sententia communis*. The development of the Church's teaching does not progress so quickly. Especially when, as at the moment, immediate problems of the day (particularly moral problems) and Mariology demand even more attention than these more complex problems, which inevitably need a long time to ripen. And so here we can do no more than tentatively outline the main line of development of these investigations.

We may hold that the problem of "uncreated grace"

can be carried further.[8] Piux XII said in his encyclical
Mystici Corporis that there are questions here still open
and purposely left open by the Church's magisterium. If
(as Pius XII says) grace and glory are two stages of the
one process of divinization, and, as classical theology has
always held, in glory God communicates himself to the
supernaturally elevated created spirit in a communication
which is not the *efficient* causal creation of a creaturely
quality or entity distinct from God, but the quasi-formal
causal communication of God himself, then this can also be
applied to *grace* much more explicitly than it commonly
has been in theology up till now. "Uncreated grace" will
then no longer be regarded as merely the consequence of
the creation of "infused" grace, constituting the state of
grace, as a "physical accident"; but rather as the very
essence of grace (which also explains much better how
grace can strictly be a mystery, for a purely created entity
as such can never be an absolute mystery). God communicates himself to man in his own reality. That is the mystery
and the fullness of grace. From this the bridge to the
mystery of the Incarnation and the Trinity is easier to find.

The theory (already held by Petavius, Scheeben and
others) seems to be gaining ground that in grace a relationship is established between man and each of the three divine
persons which is not an appropriation but a *proprium* of
each divine person. If the direct vision of God can only be
founded on the quasi-formal causal self-communication of
God and not (adequately) on a created quality in the spirit
of man, and if (as is self-evident) the three divine persons

are the object of this direct vision each *as* a single Person,
then the essential (ontic) quasi-formal communication of
God, which replaces the *species impressa* as the ontological
ground of man's knowing possession of God, must also
imply a non-appropriated relationship of each of the three
divine persons to man. And thence the relationship between
the "immanent" Trinity and the Trinity in the economy
of salvation could be rethought, and the highest mystery of
the Christian faith be seen more clearly as a reality with
which man has to do not only intellectually (and through
the incarnation of the Word), but also actually in the living
of his life of grace. It would be realized that God is not
only tri-personal in himself, but also communicates himself
tri-personally (in grace which is not only an external
efficient causality of God as *creatio ex nihilo*), although, of
course, it always remains true that wherever God exercises
his *efficient* causality this is always the work of the whole
Trinity as one single cause.

Perhaps we should go even further. The connection between the Incarnation and the order of grace is usually
regarded as purely factual.[9] In fact God willed that the
order of grace should be dependent on the incarnate Word.
It is tacitly presupposed that it could have been otherwise.
Is this presupposition clearly and certainly right? The
order of grace and the Incarnation both depend on a free
gift of God. But does it follow that these two objects of
his free gift, in both of which he communicates his very
self to man (although of course in different ways), are *two*
acts of his loving freedom? Isn't it possible (on Catholic

principles) to hold with the Scotists that the original act
of God (which settles everything else) is his emptying of
himself, Love giving up himself, in the Incarnation, so that
with the Incarnation the order of grace is already *there*
and without this decision of God to give up himself it
would be quite inconceivable? And who can produce fully
convincing arguments to refute the man who holds that
the *possibility* of the Creation depends on the possibility of
the Incarnation, which is not to say that the reality of the
Creation (as nature) necessarily involves that the Incarnation should happen. If this is accepted (its very simplicity
recommends it even apart from other more positive indications, e.g., pre-Nicene and pre-Augustinian Logos-theol-
ogy), then grace takes on a much more radically christo-
logical character; the incarnate Word come into the world
is not only the actual mediator of grace through his merit
(which is only necessary because Adam lost this grace),
but by his free coming into the world he makes the world's
order of nature his nature, which presupposes him, and the
world's order of grace his grace and his *milieu*. And from
this point, as we said, it would be possible to reach a much
deeper understanding of the inner life of the Trinity. The
Word would not then be only one of the divine persons
any of whom could become man if he wanted to, but *the*
person in whom God communicates himself hypostatically
to the world; the Incarnation mirrors the unique personal
character of the second divine person, the Word. From the
Trinity's external work we can get a glimpse into their
inner life. This cannot be impossible because the axiom

that the efficient causality of God in his external acts is a causality of the three persons acting together as the one God cannot be applied to quasi-formal causality. At this point the speculation of pre-Nicene and Greek theology needs to be reexamined. It will appear that in this Augustine understood too little of the earlier theology, that precisely the Logos is the one who appears and must appear if God wants to show himself personally to the world.

From a more precise understanding of "uncreated grace" we can also see more clearly that because of the very thing which distinguishes the Catholic theology of grace (that grace is not only pardon for the poor sinner but "sharing in the divine nature"), the idea that it holds grace to be merely a created state in the order of being, and so merely "ontic" and unexistential—a "physical accident"—cannot be maintained.[10] Grace is God himself, his communication, in which he gives himself to us as the divinizing loving kindness which is himself. Here his work is really *himself*, as the one communicated. From the very first this grace cannot be conceived as separable from God's personal love and man's answer to it. This grace must not be thought of "materialistically"; it is only put "at man's disposal" by letting itself be used as is the way with the freest grace of all, the miracle of love. We only think here in ontic categories (also Catholic) because a Catholic theology has got to think of the real (and what more real and more powerful than the love of God?) as "real" and "existing," has got to express the highest things in the most abstract words, and so God's act of love to us, precisely because it is God's and

not our act (although of course it frees us not only to have
things done to us but to do things), must be thought of as
coming before our act of love and faith and making this
act possible, and thus, inevitably, it must be thought of in
categories of being—state, accident, habit, infusion etc.
These expressions do not lead anyone astray who under-
stands them and never forgets that grace is always the free
act of God's love which man can "dispose" of *only* in the
measure in which he himself is at this love's disposal. We
must of course always remember that God does not thereby
become smaller but man greater. And finally we must
realize that Christianity is not a religion based only on the
feelings; our praise of the greatness to which God has
raised us, and thus our praise of God, must come from our
minds too, and not only our grateful hearts. This is true of
Mariology and it is true of the doctrine of grace, of which
Mariology is only the most beautiful part.

Grace also penetrates our conscious life, not only our
essence but our existence too. The teaching of St. Thomas[11]
on the specific object of the entitatively supernaturally
elevated act, an object which (*qua* formal) cannot be
reached by any natural act, must be rethought and made
prevalent again. Here "object" does not mean "objectively
given, distinguishable from others through reflection and
seen together *with* others." A formal object is neither an
object of knowledge nor just the bringing together of
what is common to many individual objects by abstracting
it afterwards; it is the *a-priori* "mental horizon," which
we are conscious of in being conscious of ourselves, which

is the context for all our knowing and recognizing of
a-posteriori individual objects. If we take the ancient
scholastic teaching of the formal object as the "light" by
which and in which all other objects are seen, then we
can't object to the Thomist doctrine of the supernatural
formal object on the grounds that it cannot be "experienced." We must, moreover, remember that the *a-priori*
formal object of an act is conceptually different from another formal object clearly distinguishable from it on reflection afterwards. There is no particular difficulty for a
metaphysic of knowledge in seeing that transcendence to
being at all, the natural openness to being as a whole, is not
clearly distinguishable in reflection afterwards from the
supernatural transcendence, by grace, of the Spirit, in
every one of its supernaturally elevated acts, to the God of
eternal life and to the immediate experience of (threefold)
Being, although both kinds of transcendence (formal object of the natural spirit and formal object of the supernaturally elevated spirit) are conscious. From these very
brief considerations on the metaphysics of the spirit we can
see St. Thomas's doctrine to be fully defensible. And it
recommends itself further by being the metaphysical-
theological translation of the conviction expressed in Scripture. For if one honestly and unprejudicedly reads Scripture as it is and does not correct it by tacitly assuming that
it can't be saying this because it is "wrong," then one has to
admit that Scripture does not think of the gift of the Spirit
(the divine *pneuma*) as only an entitative "elevation"
above man's consciousness of his acts, which in his con-

sciousness and existentially remain the same and are only
changed through the Faith which comes from hearing; it
is rather "life," "anointing," "comfort," "light," "inter-
ceding for us with unutterable groaning," *pneuma,* which
is more than *nous,* inner impulsion, witness of the Spirit etc.
It would be good if the teaching of Scripture was confronted point by point with this scholastic controversy.
Then we should be rid once and for all of the tacit assumption that in a serious and weighty religious question we can
take it for granted *a priori* that we shall get no more clear
help from Scripture if the question is being debated among
theologians, because if this were the case it would have
been decided long ago. If all theological opinions were to
recognize that supernatural actual graces are to be qualified
as "enlightenments" and "inspirations," then this teaching
of tradition would have to be taken seriously. It could not
have an anti-Thomist interpretation put on it which would
take away all its meaning. For an entitatively elevated act,
which on the conscious level remains a natural act, cannot
(without making the words meaningless) be called an inner
enlightenment and inspiration. The very fact that the anti-
Thomist—i.e., Molinist—thesis seeks to keep these words
and find a meaning for them shows how strong is the conviction of tradition that the supernatural act performed
through grace is also different spiritually, i.e., consciously
and existentially and not only entitatively, from every
natural act.

At this point we can note, and should be able to see more
clearly than usual, that not only the justified perform super-

natural acts. There are impulsions by grace which precede the acceptance of justification in free faith and love. And there is grace outside the Church and her sacraments. If we think of God's invitation by grace to the man compelled towards the possibility of making an existential decision in his immediate spiritual development not as intermittent grace, "actual" in the sense that it is temporary and is only given in special circumstances (and there is no theological reason which forces us to do so), but mean by "actual" only that the grace is specially given for an existential decision, as an "invitation" and as a "possibility" (to act freely for salvation), if we consider that in this sense man's moral freedom is not curtailed but continues to be at his disposal even when he has been given by grace the possibility of performing supernatural acts,[12] then we can say that this supernatural transcendence exists in every man who has reached the use of reason. He is not necessarily thereby justified, he can be a sinner and an unbeliever; but in so far as he has the concrete possibility of doing morally good actions he is open to transcendence to the God of supernatural life, whether his free action accords with or contradicts this potentiality of his supernaturally elevated spiritual existence. *If* in each moral act he takes up a positive or negative position towards the *totality* of his actual existence (and this we do not need to go into here), then we should have to say that every morally good act done by a man is in the order of salvation also a supernatural act of salvation. Then we should have come to the well-known opinion of Ripalda. This need not dismay us.

For in the first place, although Ripalda's thesis has not often been advocated, it has never been forbidden; and in the second place, we could give up the supposition (that we do take up a positive or negative position in each moral act) which leads us to Ripalda's conclusion, without having to give up our basic position. We have shown this by the line of argument which we have outlined; it is perfectly acceptable to hold that man's whole spiritual life is permanently penetrated by grace. Just because grace is *free and unmerited* this does not mean that it is rare (theology has been led astray for too long already by the tacit assumption that grace would no longer be grace if God became too free with it). Our whole spiritual life takes place within God's will for our salvation, his prevenient grace, his call making itself heard; all this is going on, perhaps unrecognized (if it is not recognized from the message of Faith coming from outside), in our conscious sphere of existence. Man lives consciously even when he does not "know" it and does not believe it, i.e., cannot make it an individual object of his knowledge merely by introspection. This is the inexpressible but existing ground of the dynamic power of all spiritual and moral life in the actual sphere of spiritual existence founded by God, i.e., supernaturally elevated, a "merely *a-priori*" existing ground, but still existing, something which we are conscious of in being conscious of ourselves, not as an object, but nevertheless existing.

We do not need to explain that this supernatural *a priori* in our spiritual existence, even though it can only be clearly brought to light and turned into objective knowledge through interpretation by revelation coming from without, nevertheless manifests itself in a thousand ways as a secret entelechy of individual and collective life, which would not happen if it were not at work. It follows from this that the history of religion, even outside the official history of revelation, is not just the result of natural reason and sin but the result of natural spirit, grace and sin (also in its *conscious* history, in its objective spirit). When a man is called by the message of faith of the visible Church, this call does not come to a man who is brought by it (and by his conceptual knowledge) for the first time into contact with the reality proclaimed; but it is a call which makes him reflect on and realize (and of course makes him take up a position towards) what was before the unrealized but truly existing grace present in him as an element of his spiritual existence. Preaching is the awakening and making explicit of what is already there in the depths of man, not by nature but by grace. Grace which enfolds man, the sinner and the unbeliever too, as his very sphere of existence which he can never escape from.

At this point we have now at last reached and can properly formulate the actual problem[13] "nature and grace" in the narrower sense. It is clear that in the living of his mental and spiritual life man is aware of his "nature," even in the theological sense in which it is the opposite to grace and the supernatural. For when he reflects on himself, he experiences himself in every judgement of himself in which he looks at himself as an object and sees himself in his transcendence towards the infinite as something which he

is necessarily, a unity and a whole, which cannot be dissolved into unknown quantities, and which exists as a whole
or not at all; he grasps his metaphysical essence, spirit in
transcendence and freedom. And from this transcendental
analysis of what is said implicitly about man in every human
act, he must then go on to see many other things as "essential" to man; his being in the world, his bodiliness, his belonging to a community of fellow men. In short, there is a
metaphysical knowledge of man's essence, primarily here,
of his nature, by the light of his reason, meaning independent of revelation; but also through a means (his reason)
which is itself a part of the essence thus grasped. But for
the theological reasons already given, it is also true that the
actual human nature which is here experiencing itself need
not, and cannot, regard all that it thus experiences as "pure"
nature, as distinct from supernatural (particularly if this
self-experience of man is seen in the context of the whole
of human history, without which it cannot reach full awareness). Actual human nature is *never* "pure" nature, but
nature in a supernatural order, which man (even the unbeliever and the sinner) can never escape from; nature
superformed (which does not mean justified) by the supernatural saving grace offered to it. And these "existential
facts" of his concrete (his "historical") nature are not just
accidents of his being beyond his consciousness but make
themselves apparent in his experience of himself. He cannot
clearly distinguish them by simple reflection (by the light
of natural reason) from the natural spirituality of his
nature. But when once he knows through revelation that

this order of grace exists, which is given to him unmerited
and does not belong to his nature itself, then he will be
more careful; he must take into account that perhaps many
things which he concretely experiences in himself and
ascribes almost involuntarily to his "nature" are in fact due
to the working in him of what he knows from theology to
be unmerited grace. Not as if he now no longer knew what
was nature in him. The nature of a spiritual being and its
supernatural elevation are not like two things laid one beside the other, or one against the other, which must either
be kept separate or the one exchanged for the other. The
supernatural elevation of man is the absolute (although
unmerited) fulfilment of a being which, because of its spirituality and transcendence towards infinite being, cannot
be "defined," i.e, "confined," like sub-human beings. These
are "defined" through its being of their very essence to be
limited to a particular sphere of reality. (It would therefore
be impossible, for example, for them to be "elevated" to a
supernatural fulfilment; this elevation would take away
their essence which essentially "confines" them.) The
"definition" of the created spirit is its openness to infinite
being; it is a creature because of its openness to the fullness
of reality; it is a spirit because it is open to reality *as such*,
infinite reality. So it is not surprising that the greatness of
the fulfilment—the openness does not of itself *require* this
absolute and unsurpassable fulfilment and has a meaning
without it—cannot be immediately recognized as either
"owing" or "unmerited." Nevertheless, in spite of the difficulty in distinguishing what is "nature" and what isn't,

nature is not thereby overthrown. The beginnings of this fulfilment already exist—the experience of infinite longing, radical optimism, discontent which cannot find rest, anguish at the insufficiency of material things, protest against death, the experience of being the object of a love whose absoluteness and whose silence our mortality cannot bear, the experience of fundamental guilt with hope nevertheless remaining etc. Because these beginnings are brought to absolute fulfilment by the power of God's grace, this means that in them we experience *both* grace *and* nature. For we experience our nature where we experience grace; grace is only experienced where by nature there is spirit. And vice versa, in fact, as things are, when spirit is experienced it is a supernaturally elevated spirit.

As long as we keep these remarks about the relationship between nature and grace to the general and formal, no particular difficulty arises, although we are saying that we can only encounter nature as spirit in the supernatural order and never the spirit as "pure nature." But it becomes more difficult when we try and make precise statements on the concrete and individual level. What, precisely, in this nature is nature, and what would not be there but for its elevation to the supernatural order? For example, is the resurrection of the body part of man's natural destiny as a spiritual person, or does it only happen through grace? Or what would the final destiny of a pure nature be like in the *concrete*? These are questions which could only be answered if we could experiment with pure nature, and use our results as the basis of a theory of its final destiny.[14] But as things are we cannot go beyond an essentially formal doctrine of a "natural" final destiny which—as from what has been said is naturally to be expected—is merely an abstract formalization of the concrete doctrine of a supernatural final destiny. This goes to show that medieval theology did well not to bother too much about a natural beatitude. Not only because there is in fact no such thing, but also because it is basically only the abstract formalization of the actual supernatural final destiny taught by theology (and not so very helpful), and because if an attempt is made to make it concrete, it is bound to borrow unjustifiably from theology.

In fact this "pure" philosophy of man's natural essence is not even necessary. If we are talking to a non-Catholic we have only to remember not to base our argument on revealed facts which he does not accept. If in this conversation we refer to a man's experience of himself, we must note at once what the non-Christian does not accept in this experience. If he will not accept it on a certain point then it may be that he himself is not capable of a legitimately "natural" experience, either because he has been badly instructed or because in spite of good instruction he cannot grasp it by reflection (although he has it), or it may be that *we* are speaking of an experience which was in fact through grace, and the non-Christian's experience is not as clear as ours (he has it, though, in some measure, as we said above) and so he cannot understand our argument. Because both cases are possible, because it is not easy even for a Christian to distinguish clearly between them,

and because a supernatural argument can be meaningful
and successful even with a non-Christian (when an argument from revelation is not possible), the question whether
a metaphysical (i.e., pre-theological) argument has as its
real starting-point "pure" nature or historical nature is in
the concrete case of no great importance.

The concept of pure nature is a legitimate one. If someone says: I experience myself as a being which is unconditionally directed towards the immediate possession of God,
he has not necessarily said anything untrue. The statement
is only untrue if he says that this unconditional longing
belongs to "pure" nature or if he says that this pure nature
(which does not exist) *can't* exist. When a man knows
through revelation that the Beatific Vision is through grace,
and experiences it in his longing for it as a miracle of God's
gratuitous love, he has to say that it is a free gift, not due
to him by nature, not pledged to him by his creation (so
that our creation, which was a free act of God, not due to
us, and the free gift of grace to the already existing creature,
are not one and the same gift of God's freedom). The concept of "pure nature" is implicit in this statement. It is not
just a meaningless extravagance of idle theological speculation, but it is the necessary background against which to
see the Beatific Vision as free grace, not due to us; not due
to us either as sinners or as creatures.

The attempt to work out more clearly the way in which
nature is ordered to grace (in the sense of a *potentia
obedientialis*) is still meaningful when we realize that grace
is not due to nature, whether sinful or not. This does not

make it necessary to think of this *potentia obedientialis* for grace more or less as the mere lack of contradiction to it, with the resulting "extrinsicity" already spoken of. Being ordered to grace and being directed to grace in such a way that without the actual gift of this grace it would all be meaningless, are not the same thing. Even though a spirit (i.e., openness to God, freedom and conscious and free self-possession) is essentially impossible without this trancendence, whose *absolute* fulfilment is grace, yet *this* fulfilment does not thereby become due; supposing, of course, that the conscious self-possession in freedom is itself meaningful in God's sight (and not just a means, a mere phase on the way, towards possessing the Beatific Vision). This supposition is perfectly legitimate. For the absolute (not infinite) worth and validity in itself of every personal act makes this supposition. If it is legitimate, then this is how things stand: Without transcendence open to the supernatural there is no spirit; but spirit itself is already meaningful without supernatural grace. Its fulfilment through grace is not, therefore, an exigency of its nature, although it is open to this supernatural fulfilment. And when this is clear we are no longer in danger of forgetting the supernaturalness of grace, and can proceed without further hindrance to work out with all due precision the exact meaning of this transcendence of the spirit towards the supernatural. We can only fully understand man in his "undefinable" essence if we see him as *potentia obedientialis* for the divine life; this is his *nature*. His nature is such that its *absolute* fulfilment comes through grace, and so nature *of itself* must reckon with the *meaningful* possibility of remaining without absolute fulfilment. The attempt can even be made to see the Hypostatic Union in the line of this absolute fulfilment of what man actually is. Going into all this in order to try and get a metaphysical anthropology as close as possible to the teaching on grace and to see the higher as the gratuitous fulfilment of the lower,[15] is not just idle playing about. If we don't do this it will not be possible in the long run to awaken in people an existential interest in that mysterious life which is given with supernatural grace. In the working out of the full and precise meaning of the term *potentia obedientialis* we should not confine our attention too one-sidedly (as often happens) to human *knowledge*. In Scripture God is love and not *gnosis gnoseos;* we can therefore only fully understand man and his absolute fulfilment (through grace) if we see him as freedom and love—and this not only as the complement and emotional accompaniment of knowledge. For reasons already given it is not at all a bad thing that in this analysis of man as *potentia obedientialis* there has been no "chemically pure" description of pure nature, but mixed in with it there are traces of elements of historical nature, i.e., nature possessing grace. Who is to say that the voice heard in earthly philosophy, even non-Christian and pre-Christian philosophy, is the voice of nature alone (and perhaps of nature's guilt) and not also the groaning of the creature, who is already moved in secret by the Holy Spirit of grace, and longs without realizing it for the glory of the children of God?

There is still much more to be said on the subject of the present state of the theology of grace, what it is and what it should be. We should discuss grace in its relationship to the Church,[16] what it means and how it is ordered to society; the current textbooks tend to treat it with a curiously individualistic narrowness. And we should mention the renewed interest in the relationship between grace and man's personal action. But there is no more room for this here.

Little advances and shifts in the field of the theory of any science are often not of immediately evident importance. At first these changes may look like mere passing fashions or scholarly quibbling. But if we realize that these new insights enter the common consciousness and become the unquestioned suppositions which are the basis for our action, then we may begin to see that a great deal, sometimes everything, depends on them. It is a strange thing that we Christians are often convinced enough of the power of "theory" to produce very practical results; but by "theory" we are not so likely to mean theology as Church politics, social questions, propaganda methods and suchlike. Living theology itself is not very highly thought of. Many people in the Church often have the impression that it goes on fussing superfluously with questions which were settled long ago, causes disturbances and keeps people from attending to more important things. These people do not realize that a lively and inquiring theology of today is working to make tomorrow's preaching reach mind and heart. This work of theology's may often look inconse-

quential and fruitless. But it is necessary. Even though
heart and grace are the only things which we cannot do
without.

Notes

1. It goes without saying that the bibliographical references
given here can only represent a very limited and inevitably arbitrary selection of the dogmatic and historical literature on grace.
And in general it will have to be confined to the last two centuries.
2. On this teaching cf. A. Stakemeier, *Das Konzil von Trient
über die Heilsgewissheit*, Heidelberg, 1947; V. Heynck, "Das
Votum des Generals der Konventualen Bonaventura Costacciaro
vom 26. Nov. 1546 über die Gnadengewissheit," *Franz Stud.* 31
(1949), pp. 274-304, 350-95; Fr. Buuck, "Zum Rechtfertigungs-
dekret. Die Unterscheidung zwischen fehlbarem und unfehlbarem
Glauben in den vorbereitenden Verhandlungen"; Fr. J. Schierse,
"Das Trienter Konzil und die Frage nach der christlichen Gewiss-
heit": both in Georg Schreiber, *Das Weltkonzil von Trient*,
Freiburg, 1951, Vol. 1, pp. 117-167; G. M. Lachance, "L'Homme
peut-il savoir qu'il a la grâce?" *Rev. Univ. Ottawa*, 24 (1954), pp.
65-92; M. Guérard des Lauriers, "St. Augustin et la question de la
certitude de la grâce au Concile de Trente" in *Augustinus Magister*
(Congrès International Aug. 1954), Communications vol. 2, pp.
1057-67; L. M. Poliseno, "I Carmelitani e la certezza dello stato di
grazia nel Concilio Tridentino," *Carmelus*, I (1954), pp. 111-45.
3. In this short theological essay no bibliography will be given
of this philosophical trend which was of great importance in the
meeting of scholastic and modern philosophy. Many Catholic
philosophers of today are indebted to a greater or lesser extent to
the teaching of Maréchal, e.g., Hayen, A. Grégoire, Siewerth,
Max Müller, K. Lotz and many others.
4. Cf., for example, E. Brisbois, "Désir naturel et vision de Dieu,"
NRT, 54 (1927), pp. 81-97; H. Lennerz, "Kann die Vernunft die
Möglichkeit der beseligenden Anschauung Gottes beweisen?",

Schol., 5 (1930), pp. 102–8; H. Lennerz, "Ist die Anschauung Gottes ein Geheimnis?", *Schol.*, 7 (1932), pp. 208–32; M. Corvez, "Est-il possible de démontrer l'existence en Dieu d'un ordre de mystères strictement surnaturels?", *RT*, 37 (1932), pp. 660–67; R. Garrigou-Lagrange, "La possibilité de la vision béatifique peut-elle se démontrer?", RT, 38 (1933), pp. 669–88; further literature in *Bull. Thom.*, 1932, pp. 745–69; 1935, pp. 896–907; *Bull. Thom.*, V (1937 ff.), pp. 632–43; 728; P. Descoqs, *Le Mystère de notre élévation surnaturelle*, Paris, 1938; further literature in Z. Alszeghy, *Greg.*, 31 (1950), pp. 444–6. Bound up with this whole problem is the question whether or not this orientation towards God held by Maréchal can demonstrate at the least the possibility of the Beatific Vision. We cannot go into it here.

5. Only a small selection of the literature of the last twenty-five years can be given here. Biblical theology will be omitted, because on the whole it has, unfortunately, had little influence on the dogmatic theology of the schools during this period. First must be mentioned the survey of the whole history of the theology of grace by H. Rondet, then a few works on patrology, then medieval and modern history of the theology of grace: H. Rondet, *Gratia Christi. Essai d'histoire du dogme et de théologie dogmatique*, Paris, 1948; H. Rahner, "Die Gottesgeburt. Die Lehre der Kirchenväter von der Geburt Christi im Herzen der Gläubigen," *ZKT*, 59 (1935), pp. 333–418; E. Mersch, *Theology of the Mystical Body*, New York, 1951. A. Lieske, *Die Theologie der Logomystik bei Origenes*, Münster, 1938; J. Gross, *La Divinisation du chrétien d'après les pères grecs*, Paris, 1938; A. Lieske, "Zur Theologie der Christusmystik Gregors von Nyssa," *Schol.*, 14 (1939), pp. 408–514; J. Loosen, *Logos und Pneuma im begnadeten Menschen bei Maximus Confessor*, Münster, 1941; A. Mayer, *Das Bild Gottes im Menschen nach Clemens von Alexandrien*, Rome, 1942; H. Urs von Balthasar, *Présence et pensée. Essai sur la philosophie religieuse de Grégoire de Nysse*, Paris, 1942; J. B. Schoemann, "Gregors von Nyssa theologische Anthropologie als Bildtheologie," *Schol.*, 18 (1943), pp. 31–53, 175–200; J. Daniélou, *Platonisme et théologie mystique. Essai sur la doctrine spirituelle de saint Grégoire de*

Nysse, Paris, 1944; H. du Manoir, *Dogme et spiritualité chez saint Cyrille d'Alexandrie*, Paris, 1945; P. Galtier, *Le Saint-Esprit en nous d'après les pères grecs*, Rome, 1946; A. Lieske, "Die Theologie der Christusmystik Gregors von Nyssa," *ZKT*, 70 (1948), pp. 49–93, 129–68, 315–40; J. Grabowski, "St. Augustine and the Presence of God," *TS*, 13 (1952), pp. 336–48; E. Braem, "Augustinus' leer over de heiligmakende genade," *Augustiniana*, I (1951), pp. 7–20, 77–90; II (1952), pp. 201–4; III (1953), pp. 328–340; IV (1954), pp. 196–204; H. Merki, *Homoiosis Theo. Von der platonischen Angleich-ung an Gott sur Gottähnlichkeit bei Gregor von Nyssa*, Freiburg, Switzerland, 1952; H. Doms, *Die Gnadenlehre des seligen Albertus Magnus*, Breslau, 1929; J. Schupp, *Die Gnadenlehre des Petrus Lombardus*, Freiburg, 1932; F. Stegmüller, *Zur Gnadenlehre des jungen Suarez*, Freiburg, 1933; F. Stegmüller, *Francisco de Vitoria y la doctrina de la gracia en la escuela salmantina*, Barcelona, 1934; F. Stegmüller, *Geschichte des Molinismus I: Neue Molinaschriften*, Münster, 1935; E. Köster, *Die Heilslehre des Hugo von St. Viktor*, Emsdetten, 1940; H. Bouillard, *Conversion et grâce chez saint Thomas d'Aquin*, Paris, 1944; R. C. Dhont, *Le Problème de la préparation à la grâce. Débuts de l'école franciscaine*, Paris, 1946; M. Flick, *L'Attimo della giustificazione secondo S. Tommaso*, Rome, 1947; Z. Alszeghy, "La teologia dell'ordine soprannaturale nella scolastica antica," *Greg.*, 31 (1950), pp. 414–50 (survey of recent literature); S. Gonzalez Rivas, "Suarez frente al misterio de la inhabitacion," *Estud. Ecl.*, 24 (1950), pp. 341–66; J. Auer, *Entwicklung der Gnadenlehre in der Hochscholastik mit be-sonderer Berücksichtigung des Kardinals Matteo d'Aquasparta* I, Freiburg, 1942, II, Freiburg, 1951; A. M. Landgraf, *Dogmenge-schichte der Frühscholastik*, Part I, vols. 1–2: *Die Gnadenlehre* Regensburg, 1951–1952; H. Lais, *Die Gnadenlehre des hl. Thomas in der Summa contra Gentiles und der Kommentar des Franziskus Sylvestris von Ferrara*, Münich, 1951; J. Alfaro, *Lo natural y lo sobrenatural. Estudio historico desde santo Thomas hasta Cayetano (1274–1534)*, Madrid, 1952; O. Lottin, *Psychologie et morale aux XIIe et XIIIe siècles*, Louvain, 1942–54, I, II, III, 1–2, IV, 1–2; W. A. van Roo, *Grace and Original Justice according to St. Thomas*,

Rome, 1955; Z. Alszeghy, *Nova creatura. La nozione della grazia nei commentari medievali di S. Paolo*, Rome, 1956.

6. St. Thomas considered the actual acts of "preparation" for justification as acts of justification "taking over," done with the grace of justification already present; and so he did not need to concern himself very much with the acts of preparation which precede justification in time; he has thus something new to tell *us*, not only we him.

7. Out of the Catholic works we will mention here only the following: H. Urs von Balthasar, "Deux Notes sur Karl Barth," *RSR*, 35 (1948), pp. 92–111; J. Hamer, *Karl Barth*, Westminster, Md., 1962. H. Volk, *Emil Brunners Lehre von dem Sünder*, Münster, 1950; H. Urs von Balthasar, *Karl Barth. Darstellung und Deutung seiner Theologie*, Cologne, 1951; A. Ebneter, *Der Mensch in der Theologie Karl Barths*, Zürich, 1952; H. Küng, *Justification: The Doctrine of Karl Barth with a Catholic Reflection*, New York, 1964.

8. We mention only the most recent works on all the problems connected with the question of uncreated grace and appropriated or unappropriated indwelling of the divine persons: H. Kuhaupt, *Die Formalursache der Gotteskindschaft*, Münster, 1940; H. Schauf, *Die Einwohnung des Heiligen Geistes. Die Lehre von der nichtappropriierten Einwohnung des Heiligen Geistes als Beitrag zur Theologiegeschichte des neunzehnten Jahrhunderts unter besonderer Berücksichtigung der beiden Theologen Carl Passaglia und Clemens Schrader*, Freiburg, 1941; "The Inhabitation of the Holy Spirit: A Solution According to De la Taille," *TS*, 8 (1947), pp. 445–70; J. Trütsch, *SS. Trinitatis inhabitatio apud theologos recentiores*, Trent, 1949; S. J. Dockx, *Fils de Dieu par grâce*, Paris, 1948; C. Sträter, "Het begrip 'appropriatie' bij S. Thomas," *Bijdr.*, 9 (1948), pp. 1–41, 144–86; J. H. Nicolas, "Présence trinitaire et présence de la Trinité," *RT*, 50 (1950), pp. 183–91; J. Fitzgerald, *De Inhabitatione Spiritus Sancti Doctrina Sancti Thomae Aquinatis*, Mundelein, 1950; R. Morency, *L'Union de grâce selon saint Thomas d'Aquin*, Montreal, 1950; P. Galtier, *L'habitation en nous des trois personnes*, Rome, 1950; H. P. C. Lyons, "The Grace of Sonship," *Eph. Th. Lov.*, 27 (1951), pp.

438–66; C. Kaliba, *Die Welt als Gleichnis des dreieinigen Gottes. Entwurf zu einer trinitarischen Ontologie*, Salzburg, 1952; P. de Letter, "Sanctifying Grace and Our Union With the Holy Trinity," *TS*, 13 (1952), pp. 35–58; P. J. Donnelly, "Sanctifying Grace and Our Union with the Holy Trinity: A Reply," *TS*, 13 (1952), pp. 190–204; F. Bourassa, "Adoptive Sonship. Our Union with the Divine Persons," *TS*, 13 (1952), pp. 309–35; P. de Letter, "Current Theology. Sanctifying Grace and the Divine Indwelling," *TS*, 14 (1953), pp. 242–72; F. Bourassa, "Présence de Dieu et union aux divines personnes," *Sc. Eccl.*, 6 (1954), pp. 3–23; K. Rahner, "Zur scholastischen Begrifflichkeit der ungeschaffenen Gnade," in *Schriften zur Theologie*, 1.

9. Cf. N. Sanders, "Een bovennatuurlijke orde mogelijk zonder Christus?," *Stud. Cath.*, 29 (1954), pp. 152–8; K. Rahner, "Zur Theologie der Weihnachtsfeier," *Schriften zur Theologie*, III (Einsiedeln, 1956), pp. 35–46; K. Rahner, "Die ewige Bedeutung der Menschheit Jesus für unser Gottesverhältnis," *Schriften zur Theologie*, III (Einsiedeln, 1956), pp. 47–60.

10. J. Auer, "Um den Begriff der Gnade," *ZKT*, 70 (1948), pp. 341–68.

11. This is not the place to quote the textbooks which deal with this question. Let us only note in passing that it is also of great importance for the problem of the foundation of faith. Cf. A. Lang, *Die Wege der Glaubensbegründung bei den Theologen des 14. Jahrhunderts*, Münster, 1930; F. Schlagenhaufen, "Die Glaubensgewissheit und ihre Begründung in der Neuscholastik," *ZKT*, 56 (1932), pp. 313–74, 530–95; G. Engelhardt, *Die Entwicklung der dogmatischen Glaubenpsychologie in der mitttelalterlichen Scholastik vom Abälardsstreit bis zu Philip dem Kanzler*, Münster, 1933; R. Aubert, *Le Problème de l'acte de foi*, 2nd edition, Louvain, 1950; cf. also K. Rahner, "Über die Erfahrung der Gnade," *Schriften zur Theologie*, III (Einsiedeln, 1956), pp. 105–9.

12. The necessary condition of being able to believe at all. In Straub's theory everyone who has reached the use of reason can have this as "fides stricte dicta sed virtualis."

13. We can only give here a somewhat arbitrary selection of the

literature about this controversy, which centres mainly on the historical and theological works of H. de Lubac. We then mention several articles on the teaching of the encyclical *Humani Generis,* for as is well known, this encyclical also took up a position on this question. Further articles on *Humani Generis* are listed in, e.g., *Revista Espagnola de Teologia,* 11 (1951), pp. 173–6, 311–39; H. de Lubac, "Remarques sur l'histoire du mot 'surnaturel,'" *NRT,* 61 (1934), pp. 225–49, 350–70; J. Martinez-Gomez, "Notas sobre unas notas para la historia de la palabra sobrenatural," *Arch. T. Gran.,* 1 (1938), pp. 57–85; H. de Lubac, *Surnaturel. Études historiques,* Paris, 1946; H. Rondet, "Nature et surnaturel dans la théologie de St. Thomas d'Aquin," *RSR,* 33 (1947), pp. 379–95; C. Boyer, "Nature pure et surnaturel dans le 'Surnaturel' du Père de Lubac," *Greg.,* 28 (1947), pp. 379–95; G. de Broglie, *De Fine Ultimo Humanae Vitae. Pars prior, positiva,* Paris, 1948; H. Rondet, "Le Problème de la nature pure et la théologie du XVI siècle," *RSR,* 36 (1949), pp. 80–121; P. J. Donnelly, "The Gratuity of the Beatific Vision and the Possibility of a Natural Destiny," *TS,* 11 (1950), pp. 374–404 (bibliography); W. Brugger, "Das Ziel des Menschen und das Verlangen nach der Gotteschau," *Schol.,* 25 (1950), pp. 535–48; M. J. de Guillou, "Surnaturel," *RSPT,* 34 (1950), pp. 226–43; R. Paniker, *El concepto de naturaleza. Analisis historico y metafisico de un concepto,* Madrid, 1951; G. Weigel, "Historical Background of the Encyclical *Humani Generis,*" *TS,* 12 (1951), pp. 520–49; J. Simon, "Transcendance et immanence dans la doctrine de la grâce," *Rev. Univ. Ottawa,* 21 (1951), pp. 344–69; L. Renwart, "La 'Nature pure' à la lumière de l'encyclique *Humani Generis,*" *NRT,* 74 (1952), pp. 337–54; E. Gutwenger, "Natur und Übernatur" *ZKT,* 75 (1953), pp. 82–97; H. Urs von Balthasar-Gutwenger, "Der Begriff der Natur in der Theologie," *ZKT,* 75 (1953), pp. 452–64; J. Ternus, "Natur-Übernatur in der votridentinischen Theologie seit Thomas von Aquin," *Schol.,* 28 (1953), pp. 399–404; M. R. Gagnebet, "L'Enseignement du magistère et le problème du surnaturel," *RT,* 53 (1953), pp. 5–27; L. Malevez, "La Gratuité du surnaturel," *NRT,* 75 (1953), pp. 561–86; K. Rahner, "Über die Verhältnis von Natur und Gnade," *Schriften zur Theologie,* I (Einsiedeln, 1954), pp. 323–

45; R. Bruch, "Das Verhältnis von Natur und Gnade nach der Auffassung der neueren Theologie," *Th. Gl.*, 46 (1956), pp. 81–102.

14. If this nature's infinite openness *could* have a final destiny at all and not be, in the concrete, either the free limitation by God to a finite end, determined by him but which could not have been deduced *a priori* from the nature itself, *or* absolute fulfilment.

15. Everywhere in the hierarchically constructed universe of real differences without "jumps"—with the many and different coming out of the one—"fulfilment" and "gratuitousness" both in one are the characteristic mark of the relationship between two realities.

16. H. de Lubac, *Catholicism. A Study of Dogma in Relation to the Corporate Destiny of Mankind*, trans. Lancelot Sheppard (from the 4th edition of *Catholicisme. Les Aspects sociaux du dogme*, Paris, 1947), New York, 1958.

Missing Persons

Missing
Persons

STEPHEN WHITE

WHEELER
WINDSOR
PARAGON

This Large Print edition is published by Wheeler Publishing, Waterville, Maine USA and by BBC Audiobooks, Ltd, Bath, England.

Published in 2005 in the U.S. by arrangement with Dutton, a member of Penguin Group (USA) Inc.

Published in 2005 in the U.K. by arrangement with Time Warner Book Group UK.

U.S. Hardcover 1-58724-983-9 (Hardcover)
U.K. Hardcover 1-4056-1150-2 (Windsor Large Print)
U.K. Softcover 1-4056-2137-0 (Paragon Large Print)

The text of this Large Print edition is unabridged.
Other aspects of the book may vary from the original edition.

Set in 16 pt. Plantin by Carleen Stearns.

Printed in the United States on permanent paper.

British Library Cataloguing-in-Publication Data available

Library of Congress Cataloging-in-Publication Data

White, Stephen, 1951–
    Missing persons / by Stephen White.
        p. cm.
    ISBN 1-58724-983-9 (lg. print : hc : alk. paper)
    1. Gregory, Alan (Fictitious character) — Fiction.
2. Psychotherapist and patient — Fiction.   3. Paranoid schizophrenics — Fiction.   4. Clinical psychologists — Fiction.   5. Missing persons — Fiction.   6. Boulder (Colo.) — Fiction.   7. Large type books.   I. Title.
PS3573.H47477M57 2005b
    813′.54—dc22   2005004964

for Lynn Nesbit

. . . Peace is poor reading.
— Thomas Hardy

A girl was missing.

In any other town it would have been local news. Even here, on any other day, it might have been just local news.

But it wasn't any other town.

It was Boulder.

It wasn't any other day.

It was Christmas.

And a girl was missing.

Again.

God.

1

The fact that I was sitting with Diane behind Hannah Grant's office at 6:30 on a mid-December Thursday evening meant that I'd already lost the argument we'd been having since she yanked me out from behind my desk five minutes earlier. She killed the ignition on her Saab and summed things up for me anyway. "We can't leave in the morning if we can't reach Hannah. It's that simple."

She was right.

With only nine shopping days until Christmas, Diane Estevez and I were scheduled to make the short flight over the Rockies to Las Vegas for a weekend professional workshop — Diane, I suspected, was pretending to be much more enamored of EMDR than she really was — and Hannah was generously providing coverage for our clinical psychology practices while we were away. Without coverage, we couldn't go.

Diane had switched our Frontier flight the next day from noon to the cusp of

dawn so that she could cram in a few additional hours getting intimate with some dice, and Hannah needed to consent to the slight change in plans. But Hannah — whose adaptive lassoing of her myriad OCD symptoms typically dictated that an unreturned phone call caused her a degree of psychological discomfort equivalent to the physical distress of a sharp stone in her shoe — had failed to return three different messages from Diane since breakfast.

"Is that her car? Do you know what she drives?" I asked. The only other car in the tiny lot was a silver Volkswagen Passat.

"Looks like hers." Diane offered the comment with a slightly sardonic lilt, and I assumed that she was referring more to the car's pristine condition than to either its make or model. In stark contrast to the spotless Passat, Diane's Saab was covered in the gray-beige film that adheres to virtually every moving vehicle in Colorado after any slushy late fall snowstorm, like the one we'd had the previous weekend.

I stepped out of Diane's car and peered into Hannah's. No clutter on the console. No errant French fries on the floor. No empty Diet Coke can in the cup holder. In fact, the only indication that the vehicle hadn't just been hijacked from a dealer's

showroom was a copy of *Elle*, still in its plastic sleeve, on the backseat.

The mailing label on the magazine read "H. Grant," and was addressed to the Broadway office. The code in the corner indicated that the subscription would terminate the following April. "It's hers," I said.

Diane had joined me beside the Passat. "Hannah reads *Elle*?"

My own reaction was a little different; I was thinking, *Hannah leaves magazines in her car? Shame!* I said, "I think you're missing the point. It means she's inside with a patient. She'll return your call when she gets a minute."

"I don't know about that. I'm getting a feeling," she said. "And not a good one."

"About Hannah?"

"A little, but more about Vegas." Diane's tone was somber. She took her craps seriously. "Let's go inside," she said.

Hannah was a clinical social worker and her therapy practice was in one of the old houses aligned on the side of Broadway closest to the mountains, only a few blocks from the Pearl Street Mall. The cumulative force of more than a decade of migration by psychotherapists had allowed mental-health types to usurp most of that partic-

11

ular urban habitat from sundry lawyers and accountants who had previously set up shop in the houses — some grand, some not — in the row. The uprooted professionals had moved to less charming but eminently more practical spaces in the modern buildings recently erected to fill parking lots a few blocks away on Canyon Boulevard.

The back door of the single-story house was locked. Diane and I followed a flagstone path down the side past a hedge of miniature lilacs that stood naked for winter. We made our way to the front of the building and strolled up a few stairs into a waiting room that had probably been the home's original parlor. On the far side of the lamp-lit room a thirties-something woman with an astonishing quantity of frizzy hair was sitting on a green velvet settee reading a copy of *Yoga Journal* while munching from a bag of Cheetos. I noted that she checked her wristwatch after she glanced up at us.

I also noted that her fingertips were almost the exact same color as her hair.

"Which office is Hannah's?" I whispered to Diane. I'd never been in the building before. Hannah was one of Diane's close friends; I had no doubt that Diane knew

which office she occupied.

"Down that hall on the left. The one on the right is Mary's."

"Mary" was Mary Black, M.D., a psychiatrist who without benefit of fertility concoctions had given birth to triplet boys only a few weeks before, on Thanksgiving eve. Both Mary's extended maternal adventure and her extended maternity leave were in their earliest stages, which meant that Hannah was without doubt going to be working alone in the building for a while.

Diane stepped down the hall toward the offices. "Look," she said.

Stuck into the jamb of Hannah's office door were four folded notes. Two were addressed to "Hannah," one was addressed to "H. Grant," and one was intended for "H. G." Diane picked the one addressed to "H. Grant." It appeared to have been written on the back of a page from a daily calendar of unintentionally humorous quotations by the second President Bush.

"What are you doing, Diane?" I blurted. "Those are probably from patients. You can't read them."

Without even a microsecond of indecision Diane rejected my protest. "Of course they're from patients. That's the point,"

she said. She glanced at the first note, handed it to me, and said, "Look, Hannah missed her one o'clock." Next, she grabbed the paper that was addressed to "H. G." "And see? She missed her four-thirty, too. How come she's missing all her appointments if her car's here? Huh? How the hell do you explain that?"

I didn't know how to explain that.

The other two notes were from patients whose therapist had stood them up earlier in the day. Hannah had apparently been missing her clinical appointments since at least nine o'clock that morning.

The woman with the orange Roseanne Roseannadanna hair appeared behind us in the narrow hallway. Despite the fact that she was balancing on tall, chunky heels, she still had to gaze up at an acute angle to look Diane in the eyes. "Are you here to see Hannah?" she asked. "I have a six-fifteen appointment. Every Thursday. She's never late."

The woman's voice was part annoyed, and part something else. Concern? Fear? I wasn't sure. But her point about Hannah's reliability was well taken. Hannah's obsessiveness was legendary among her friends and colleagues. She was never late.

Never.

I'd begun tasting acid in my throat; I had a bad feeling, too. Though, unlike Diane's, mine had absolutely nothing to do with dice. I tapped lightly on Hannah's office door with my knuckles. My cautious incursion was apparently way too timid for Diane; with an NHL-quality hip-check she moved me aside and grabbed the knob.

The door slid right open.

2

Hannah's classic black patent-leather purse, as unscuffed as the day it had been crafted, rested on the floor in the middle of the room. It stood up neatly, its arched handles perfectly vertical. But the bag was on the floor.

It shouldn't have been on the floor.

Diane apparently had the exact same reaction I had to the presence of the purse in the middle of the room. But since the distance between her cortex and her mouth was much shorter than mine, she verbalized her conclusion first: "Hannah would never put her purse there."

Diane meant on the floor. *Nope.*

In the middle of the room. *Never.*

What was certain was that Hannah had a place for her purse. A specific place. A correct place. I didn't know where she kept it. Probably in a drawer in her desk. Maybe someplace more esoteric, in her filing cabinet under "P." But in any circumstance

that approached ordinary, she absolutely wouldn't put it on the floor in the middle of the room.

The rest of the office was neat. OCD neat, with one exception: Hannah's coat was tossed carelessly over the top of the desk. I noted the swirled torn paper from an open roll of LifeSavers licking out of one of the coat pockets.

Hannah's 6:15, the woman with the cheddar-colored locks, was trying to peer past us into the office, but she was too short to manage a look over our shoulders. I felt her hand on my back and turned toward her.

I said, "Hello, I'm Dr. Alan Gregory, one of Ms. Grant's colleagues. Why don't you have a seat in the waiting area while we try to figure out what's going on?" Not overconfident about her emotional stability, I'd adopted a voice that was as comforting as a hot-water bottle wrapped in fleece.

Neither my words nor my tone had the desired effect, though. "This is *my* time," the woman protested, tapping the crystal of a garish purple Swatch on her wrist. I detected more than a little pout in her retort, considered the bag of Cheetos, and gave a momentary thought to the clinical

17

regression that Hannah was confronting in her therapy with this woman.

"I know," I said even more gently. "I know. But the circumstances today are a little unusual. If you want to leave your name I'll make sure that Ms. Grant gives you a call as soon as we straighten all this out. I'll tell her you were here. I promise."

She wanted none of it. "I'll just wait," she said. "It is my time. Though I do hope I'm not being charged."

I sighed, pausing a moment as the woman retraced her steps and resumed her perch on the velvet settee in the waiting room. As she lowered herself to the sofa her fingertips left bright orange imprints on the forest green velvet upholstery. Once I was sure she was settled, I joined Diane inside the doorway to Hannah's office.

I said, "I think you should go check the bathroom, Diane. Maybe Hannah fell or something."

"Oh God!" she said. "Of course. Why didn't I think of that?" She rushed past me and down the hall.

I'm not sure why I did what I did next. Maybe it was because I was standing by myself in the hallway feeling lost and stupid. Maybe it was intuition. Maybe it was because I thought the Cheetos lady

might be back and I was looking for a place to hide. I don't really know.

What I did was that I took half a step across the narrow hall and tried the knob on Mary Black's office door. To my surprise I discovered it unlocked. Immediately after I let go of the knob the door began to swing open on its own, as though the old building was listing just the slightest bit in that direction.

One look inside and I knew Hannah was dead.

I knew it because living people's flesh is never that shade of gray and living people can't, or don't, hold the posture that Hannah was in. Her body was splayed backward over a leather cube ottoman, her head only a yard from the edge of the open door. Her legs were spread immodestly, her torso twisted forty-five degrees at her waist. A dark pool stained an area the size of a basketball on the dhurrie rug below her legs. My gut reaction was: blood. But my nose said urine.

Hannah's right arm was bent at the elbow and the thumb of her right hand was hooked in the fabric of the silk blouse near her armpit, as though she'd been thinking about hitchhiking someplace when she died.

Oddly, the left front tail of Hannah's blouse was tucked up under the front of her bra, exposing a few inches of pale abdomen. Why a woman would tuck her blouse up under her bra, I couldn't begin to guess.

Hannah's mouth was open, as were her eyes, and her fine dark hair spilled down, perfectly filling the eight- or nine-inch space that existed between the back of her head and the worn finish of the old pine floor.

I dropped to one knee and touched the smoothly stretched skin on Hannah's neck with the tips of three fingers. I tried not to look into her dark brown eyes but they drew me in like pools of still water. Despite shifting my fingertips a few times I couldn't find a carotid pulse. It didn't matter; the chill of Hannah's flesh on my own had already confirmed to me that I wouldn't.

Hannah had been dead a while. I recalled the four notes that had been stuck in the jamb of her office door, and figured that she had fallen into her current posture sometime that morning. The arithmetic was simple. My watch said 6:45 p.m. Hannah's first known missed appointment had been almost ten hours earlier, at 9 a.m. A

brief stint as a coroner's investigator earlier in my career had taught me the usually trivial fact that, after death, human bodies at room temperature yield core temperature at the rate of about one degree an hour. Ten hours meant ten degrees. I guessed that the flesh that my fingers had just touched was probably a good ten degrees cooler than my own.

But I knew it could have been cooler than that, or warmer than that. My experience touching the flesh of dead people was, admittedly, limited. I allowed for the possibility that Hannah had been dead since the night before and I tried to recall how long a body needed to be dead before the stench of death became apparent. Couldn't.

I began inhaling slowly and self-consciously, as though I hadn't already been breathing the air in the room. I thought it tasted stale and sour, but the only foreign odor I detected was that spill of urine.

I knew that medical examiners working to determine time of death also did calculations about flying insects and their eggs and the life cycle of maggots, but I quickly decided that I would leave that entomological arithmetic to them.

I was also self-aware enough to know

21

that I was doing all the distracting contemplating so that I wouldn't be forced to confront the fact that I was unexpectedly alone in an office with a friend's dead body.

Behind me I noted the sound of a toilet flushing, followed by the timbre of water running, the click of a door opening, and the cadence of familiar footsteps down the hall. Diane, apparently forgetting that she and I were not alone, called out, "Hannah's not there, but I really had to pee."

I backed out of the room and saw Diane retracing her steps down the hallway from the bathroom. Her eyes caught mine, registering wariness that quickly disintegrated into shock as she digested my expression. I blocked her path and took her into my arms before she could reach the entrance to Mary Black's office. I whispered into her hair, "Your friend is dead. I'm so, so sorry."

The sound that came from Diane's throat as she processed my words was plaintive and poignant. Resignation and denial and the first disbelieving chords of grief were all mixed into one long, sad wail.

When I looked up I saw the Cheetos lady standing at the other entrance to the

hallway, tears streaming down her face. A bright orange smudge across her cheeks marked the spot where she'd tried to wipe away her grief.

And failed.

3

Neither Diane nor I was going to get home in time for dinner.

It had taken all of my physical strength to keep Diane away from her friend's inert body — I was far from being able to consider it a corpse — and it had taken all my powers of persuasion to get both Diane and the Cheetos lady out of the house while we waited for the police to arrive.

I was staggered by Hannah's death, but my loss was nothing compared to the loss that either Diane or Hannah's patient was feeling. I kept telling myself that I could freak out later.

Diane needed to freak out now.

Outside the house, after I'd called 911 on my cell, I was standing helplessly with Diane on the front walk when she said, "I don't want to leave Hannah alone. She shouldn't be alone. Let me go in and wait with her. Please. What can it hurt?"

My arm was firmly around her shoulders

and I know I whispered replies to her pleadings, but I don't recall exactly what I said. My tight grasp on Diane reinforced my words: I didn't think she should go back inside.

Had Hannah died at home after an illness I would have led Diane to her friend's bedside, not held her back. But Hannah had apparently died in strange circumstances in her colleague's office. Until those circumstances became clear, I knew from my coroner's experience that the environment around Hannah's body should stay uncontaminated.

Three things kept replaying in my brain.

Hannah had been in Mary Black's office, not in her own.

Hannah's purse had been in the middle of her office floor.

Her shirt was pulled up and tucked under her bra.

Why, why, and why?

The lady with the frizzy hair had moved away from Diane and me and taken off her shoes. She was sitting, almost immobile, her chin in her hands, on one of the steps leading up to the wooden porch at the front of the house. Her tears had stopped flowing, her expression a blank mask of shock.

"Are you sure she's dead?" Diane demanded more than once in those first few moments. I explained that I'd felt for a pulse and told her that Hannah's skin was already cold. And then I explained it again.

I didn't say anything about the dark stain of urine.

"She hates being cold," Diane protested. "Hannah shouldn't be cold. She doesn't like winter. Maybe a blanket. I could find a blanket. I have one in the car. Raoul makes me keep one in the car in case . . ."

It wasn't easy but I was able to get Diane settled on a kidney-shaped concrete bench that sat amidst some wild grasses beside the front walk about halfway to the street. I stepped a yard away from her, pulled out my cell phone, hit the speed dial and reached Lauren, my wife, who had probably just walked in the door from her job as a prosecutor for Boulder County.

"Hey, it's me. I'm glad you're home."

"What's wrong?"

She could tell something was.

"Hannah Grant?" I said. "You remember her?"

"Diane's friend."

"She was going to cover for us while we were in Vegas. She's dead. We just found

her body in her office. We're waiting for the cops."

"My God. Are you all right?"

"We're okay. Call Raoul, okay? Tell him Diane's going to be late. I don't know how late, but you know how these things go. It's probably going to be a while." Raoul Estevez was Diane's husband. "Diane's very upset. They were close friends."

Lauren set her empathy aside for a moment and got down to business. Her business. Cops and courts and lawyers and bad guys. "Do you and Diane need lawyers?"

"No, nothing like that. Hannah wasn't returning Diane's messages about coverage for our trip. We were concerned. We just walked in and . . . found her body. That's all."

"You're sure? Don't just say yes. I want you to think before you answer me."

I thought. "Yeah, that's all."

"How did she die?"

"No idea. There was no blood I could see. Could be natural causes, but my gut says not. Her body's in a funny position." I was still thinking, too, about that black patent-leather purse in the middle of the floor and about the blouse tucked up under the front of her bra. "Is there any reason a woman would tuck her shirttail

up under the front of her bra?" I asked.

"What? The front tail?"

"Yes."

"No, not that I can think of."

From the south side of the Pearl Street Mall I heard the piercing intrusion of a siren approaching, fast.

I said, "The cops are here, babe. I should go."

"I'll make some calls. Stay in touch. I love you."

"Me, too," I said. Diane walked up next to me. I said, "Lauren's going to call Raoul and let him know what's going on."

"What is going on?" she asked me. "Do we know?"

The first of what would become four squad cars rolled up over the curb and then slowly powered up onto the sidewalk, blocking the path. A couple of patrol cops I didn't know jumped out of the car. The look on their faces was either that they didn't believe whatever the dispatcher had told them about why they were rolling to the Broadway address, or that they were hoping the dispatcher had gotten the story wrong. I stepped forward, introduced myself, told them I had called 911, and I explained what we had found inside.

One cop marched to the front door to check out my story. The other one stayed outside with his three witnesses. A minute later a couple of EMTs arrived in their bright, boxy wagon. They too went inside to confirm what I already knew. Everything everyone did, it seemed, was preceded and followed by whispers into radios.

To me it all felt like slow motion. I was thinking: *Somebody is dead. We should hurry.* The reality was, of course, different. The reality was: Somebody was dead. What was the point of hurrying?

More patrol cops arrived in the next few minutes, and after a brief consultation with the two first responders a couple of them strung a perimeter of crime-scene tape that reached all the way to the big trees along the front curb and included the larger houses and yards on each side. Gawking drivers quickly brought traffic to a virtual standstill.

Call it bad luck, call it a side effect of being married to a prosecutor, or of being best friends with a cop, but I'd been around enough crime scenes to know what to expect and wasn't at all surprised that Diane and the Cheetos lady and I were soon separated from one another.

The women were each offered a seat in

the back of different squad cars while I was shuttled to the front porch of the elegantly restored Victorian next door. From there I watched the cluster of uniformed cops disperse. Two headed to the back of the house clutching a fat wheel of crime-scene tape. The ones who'd stayed in front were trying to look like they had something important to do, something besides wait. The EMTs waited for something, too.

We were all doing indeterminate time in the wake of unexplained death, a sentence that would endure until the arrival of an unmarked car bringing detectives to the scene.

Part of me wanted to see my friend, Sam Purdy, step out of the detectives' sedan.

That was the selfish part.

The generous part of me hoped that he had the evening off.

4

Sam had the evening off.

As soon as the two detectives who were catching new felony cases on that shift climbed out of their car, I recognized them. One was a buff, square-jawed, tight-eyed man named Jaris Slocum. Over a year before, while I'd been visiting Sam in the detective bureau in the Public Safety Building on 33rd Street, he had introduced me to Slocum as we passed each other in a long hallway. Once we'd paced out of eavesdropping range on our way to lunch somewhere, Sam had added, "Slocum's kind of an asshole."

I recognized Slocum's partner, too, though until that moment I hadn't known he was a cop. He was, like me, an avid recreational bicyclist. We ran into each other a few times a year on Boulder's back roads or in the nearby mountain canyons. The previous September we had ended up in an impromptu posse that had done a couple

of memorable training climbs together up Four Mile. He was a pleasant, not-too-competitive guy who had legs and lungs that were designed for steep inclines. He was younger than me, stronger than me, and better looking than me. I knew him simply as Darrell.

The two detectives ambled across the sidewalk and checked in with the patrol cop who was manning the log. I watched him point at me seconds before the detectives climbed the slope of the front lawn toward my solitary aerie on the neighboring building's front porch.

Remembering Sam's caution about Slocum, I greeted the bicyclist detective first. "Hi, Darrell. What a night." I held out my hand. "Alan, Alan Gregory. Remember me?" He didn't. "We climbed Four Mile together a few months back? I see you occasionally when you ride."

It took Darrell a second but he finally recognized my face. "Alan? Yeah, hi. You're, um, part of this?" He waved his left arm in the general direction of Hannah Grant's dead body.

"Unfortunately. I was the one who found her. Hannah. She's a colleague. Was. I'm a psychologist." The last sentence felt like a complete non sequitur to me. I imagined

that it did to Darrell, too. I added, "Hannah was a social worker."

"You're the RP?" He caught himself using cop vernacular and added, "The one who called this in?"

RP. Reporting party. "Yes."

Slocum stepped up and took charge. His intrusion had all the subtlety of a belch during grace at Thanksgiving dinner. "Sit right there, sir. Yes, on those steps behind you. Don't speak with anyone until we're ready to interview you. Do you understand my instructions, sir?"

For some reason — possibly the vice-principal tone in his voice — I found myself questioning the sincerity of his repeated use of "sir."

Jaris Slocum either didn't recognize me, which wouldn't have been surprising, or — and this was a more worrisome possibility — had recalled our prior introduction and decided that any friend of Sam Purdy's deserved an additional bolus of hard-ass attitude.

Fifty feet or so away from me a damn good woman lay dead. During traffic lulls I could hear Diane weeping from the backseat of the patrol car where she had been stashed. The Cheetos lady was still looking like she'd just lost her only friend

in the world. The sum of those parts? I was in absolutely no mood for any I'm-the-boss-and-you'll-do-what-I-say cop crap from Detective Jaris Slocum.

"And you are?" I said. My tone wasn't exactly a model of I'd-love-to-cooperate-Detective.

Detective Darrell's badge wallet was hanging on his belt for all to see. Slocum's wasn't. Wisely, Darrell chose to answer my question even though it had been addressed to his partner. He was busily trying to douse the lit matches that Slocum and I were slinging at the kindling in each other's pants. To me, he said, "This is Detective Jaris Slocum. And this is Alan . . . ?"

"Gregory," I said.

"He and I ride together sometimes," Darrell explained to Slocum.

"That's nice. Now sit, Alan Gregory. We'll be back to talk to you. Wait for us, understand?"

"I still haven't seen a badge," I said. I shouldn't have said it. But I did.

Slocum couldn't find his badge wallet. He checked all his pockets, and then he patted them all a second time. Finally, after an exasperated exhale he barked, "It must be in the car."

If Slocum had wanted to transport the annoyance that he packed into those few words he would have needed a wheelbarrow, or a tractor-trailer.

"I can wait," I said. "Go ahead and get it. I'd like to see some ID. I think that's my right."

Slocum and I both knew he wasn't about to slink back to his big Ford and fish around for his detective shield at my behest. He gave me an icy blue-eyed stare. "I said to have a seat."

I said, "I'm fine standing."

He took a step toward me. "And I said to sit."

I came so close to saying "fuck you" that my lower lip actually came together with my bottom teeth.

Darrell sensed what was developing as though he knew either Slocum or me real well. I knew the person he knew real well wasn't me.

"Enough," he said.

He was talking to both of us.

I had to cool my heels for almost an hour before the detectives got back to me. From what I could see, they'd spent most of the time either singly or together with the Cheetos lady and with Diane. For a

while I was perplexed why they didn't go inside the offices and start detecting in there where Hannah and the evidence were, but then I realized they were probably waiting for a search warrant to arrive at the scene.

In the meantime, I was cold and exhausted and hungry and sad and angry and impatient and would have been much more comfortable sitting on the stoop than walking in circles on the front porch.

But I stood. It was a point of honor. Or a badge of stubbornness. One of those things.

The story I had to tell about discovering Hannah's body wasn't complicated and once things had calmed down a little bit between Slocum and me, it was simple to discern from the detectives' questions that Slocum and Olson — his cop ID had revealed not only bicyclist Darrell's last name, but also a double dose of middle initials, C. and R. — were primarily interested in two specific areas of my narrative.

The first? Why had I decided to reach across the hall and try to open the door to Mary Black's office? I stuck with the truth on that one — I didn't know. I just didn't know. It was one of those things that I had just done.

The truth, however, didn't set me free. One of the detectives — either Darrell Olson playing good cop, or Slocum naturally taking on the role of bad — revisited the question of me opening Mary Black's door at least five times during our relatively brief discussion. They seemed as dissatisfied with my fifth reply as they had been with the first. I told them I wished that I had a better explanation, but I didn't.

The second focus of the detectives' interest was more concerning to me. They wanted to know what I had been doing the rest of the day — minute-by-minute, hour-by-hour — up until the moment Diane dragged me from my office to her Saab to drive to Hannah's office.

"What? You mean from the moment I got out of bed? That early?" I asked in a futile attempt at levity when Slocum pressed me on my day's itinerary for the second or third time.

"Sure," he replied. "Assuming you have a witness for that part of your day, too." His cold eyes weren't smiling at all but his cheekbones had elevated just enough to let me know that he was enjoying whatever temporary advantage he thought he had.

Not for the first time that evening I

thought, *God, Sam, you're right. Slocum is an asshole.*

"As a matter of fact, I do have a witness. I want you to be sure to write this name down. Are you ready?"

He glared at me as though he'd rather beat me with a long stick than do what I suggested, but he brought his pen down so that the nib hovered just above the page in his notebook.

Stressing each syllable for his benefit, I said, "My witness, for this morning's events, is Deputy DA Lauren Crowder of the Boulder County District Attorney's office." I slowly dictated the ten digits of our home phone number, and then added Lauren's office number for emphasis. "Give her a call. Please. I'm sure she'll be thrilled to tell you what time her husband crawled out of bed this morning."

Slocum stopped writing.

Darrell Olson took a step back so that his partner wouldn't spot the smile that was forming on his face.

I said, "I'm going home now, Detective. I think you know how to reach me if you have any more questions."

Slocum made a quick move toward me — or at me — but Darrell stepped forward and spoke before his partner could do

something he would regret. "Warrant's here, Jaris. Come on, let's go inside and see what we have."

I didn't go right home. I found Raoul, Diane's husband, pacing outside the crime-scene tape and filled him in on all that had happened late that afternoon. He was almost too agitated to attend to my words. Raoul Estevez had a roster of relatives who had not survived Franco's reign in Spain, and the sight of his wife squeezed into the back of a squad car being peppered with questions from law enforcement authorities wasn't sitting particularly well with him.

"She is not under arrest?" he demanded, his words causing little cartoonish puffs of steam in the cold air. Although it's his second language — actually, his fourth or fifth — Raoul's English is better than Prince Charles's, but the American legal system still perplexed him at times. English is my only language, isn't in Prince Charles's league, and the American legal system still perplexed me at times, too. Still, since I was the natural-born citizen, I assumed the responsibility of translating the proceedings for Raoul.

"No, they're just questioning her about

what happened, what she saw, that's all. She'll be done soon. She didn't see much; I found Hannah's body."

As if on cue, Slocum, who had not taken his partner's advice about going inside and looking around, hopped out of the cruiser and, I thought, reached in to help Diane from the backseat.

"See?" I turned to Raoul. "It looks like she's done."

Diane suddenly yelled, "Get your goddamn hands off me!"

Raoul's voice grew hard. "It doesn't look that way to me."

I turned back to the cruiser. Slocum had Diane completely out of the car and was twisting her ninety degrees so he could shove her face-first up against the rear fender of the black-and-white. Instantly he had her legs spread past shoulder width and in seconds he had her arms behind her back and handcuffs on both her wrists.

I was shocked. "Don't, Raoul." I had to stand in my friend's path to keep him from crossing the yellow tape and joining the fray. I planted my feet on the ground and both my hands on Raoul's hard chest. Finally, he stepped back.

Ten seconds later I had Lauren on the phone. "Get Cozy down here fast. I think

Jaris Slocum just arrested Diane for something."

Lauren said, "Slocum? God help us, he's such an asshole lately."

The verdict, it appeared, was unanimous.

5

Cozier Maitlin lived, literally, around the corner.

From my sentry position just outside the crime-scene tape, I spotted Cozy on the sidewalk as he was descending the final steep section of hill that drops down from Maxwell toward Broadway. Despite the crowd of gawkers gathered around the yellow police tape, he wasn't that hard to spot. Cozy stood six-feet-nine.

I checked my watch — no more than seven or eight minutes could have passed since Jaris Slocum had cuffed Diane and shoved her rudely back into the rear seat of the black-and-white.

Pointing toward the corner, I said to Raoul, "That's the defense attorney Lauren called."

"That was fast. He's tall."

"He's good. He helped Lauren with that thing, you know, a few years ago. Hey, Cozy!"

Cozy didn't break stride as he approached, or wave. Maybe he elevated his chin an additional millimeter or two, but that was the only indication that he'd heard me calling his name. He was wearing the same suit I imagined he'd worn to his downtown office that morning — the blue was a navy that shared a lot of DNA with black, and it was lined with the palest of gray pinstripes. His white shirt appeared freshly starched and his black shoes were the shiniest things on the block.

A nice, full-length umbrella or a walking stick would not have been out of place accessorizing his outfit.

We shook hands. "Good evening, Alan. At least the location is convenient this time. And the weather is delightful for December. No blizzard. I can't tell you how grateful I am for that."

"Thanks for coming so quickly, Cozy. This is Raoul Estevez. Raoul, Cozier Maitlin."

"A pleasure, Mr. Estevez. I'm aware of your work." That was Cozy's way of communicating that he wasn't worried about his fee. "It is your wife who is being detained?"

"In that car." Raoul pointed at the squad that was parked at an angle on the lawn in front of the building where Hannah lay dead.

43

"Do you want to know what happened?" I asked.

"I understand someone died here under suspicious circumstances. Beyond that, not really. If either of you was an intimate of the deceased, please let me offer my condolences," Cozy said, insincerely. He lifted one of his long legs, stepped over the crime-scene tape, and somehow managed to adopt an even more imperial deportment as he moved out onto the lawn. He paused, turned back to Raoul, and said, "Give me a moment or two to sort this out. Everything will be fine. It will." After one more step, Cozy looked back over his shoulder at me. "Lauren said I'd be speaking with Jaris Slocum. That's true?"

I nodded. I considered the wisdom of editorializing about Detective Slocum's apparent personality flaws, but decided that I didn't need to do anything to inflame the situation any further.

"Slocum is . . . difficult," Cozy said. He said it in such a way that it sounded more damning than Sam Purdy informing me that Slocum was an asshole, or than Lauren concurring.

"That's been my experience so far this evening," I replied.

I was feeling a million things. Grief,

anger, frustration, fear, even some relief, now that Cozy was there. Still, my anticipation of what was to come next was so sharp that I would have yanked out my wallet and maxed out all my credit cards for a ticket to the production I was about to get to witness for free.

Cozy immediately marched over to the cruiser and confronted the patrol cop assigned to keep watch on Diane, who was continuing to fume in the backseat. Cozy's approach wasn't tentative, and didn't have any excuse-me-please in it. He moved in until he stood toe-to-toe with the cop, a young black man who was about six-two, 210.

Cozy dwarfed him.

Cozy's introductory gambit to the officer consisted of a few words that caused the man to react by trying to step back to create some breathing room. But since the cop was already leaning against the car there was no place for him to go and he had to crane his neck upward to even see Cozy's face. I imagined that the view was like gazing up from below Mt. Rushmore.

The patrol cop listened to Cozy for only another beat or two before he raised his voice and barked, "Step back, sir! Step *back!* Now! That's a warning!"

The cop's hand gravitated ominously toward his holster.

I held my breath and instinctively grabbed Raoul's arm so he wouldn't do something valiant, and stupid. I'd known him a long time, and knew that Raoul was capable of both.

Cozy, of course, didn't step back an inch. He was daring the cop to get physical with him. And if the young cop preferred to do loud, Cozy could do loud just fine. With volume that matched the patrol cop's do-what-I-say voice and then raised a few decibels for good measure, Cozy announced, "I am her attorney and I would like to speak with my client, officer. Officer" — Cozy leaned back at his waist so that he could read the cop's name tag — "Leamer. It's a pleasure to meet you. My client — that is she, by the way, that you are *protecting* — won't, will not, be answering any more of the detectives' questions tonight."

The volume of that soliloquy drew virtually everyone's attention to the cruiser, including Jaris Slocum's. He was up on the front porch and immediately began a march toward the car with long strides, his hands tightened into fists. Cozy must have felt him coming. He spun away from the

patrol cop and greeted Slocum with, "A pleasure seeing you, as always. Is my client actually in custody, Detective?"

Slocum stopped five feet from Cozy. I don't know why he kept his distance — maybe so that he wasn't close enough to shake Cozy's outstretched hand. Slocum's mouth opened and closed about a centimeter as he tried to process the latest developments: A large, imperial criminal defense attorney had penetrated the perimeter and he seemed to be making speeches for the benefit of the dozens of gathered citizens.

Not good.

"Haven't decided? Is that it? Perhaps I can help," Cozy taunted. His words were polite, his tone was even doing a clever masquerade as respectful. But everyone, especially Slocum, knew it was a taunt.

Slocum opened his mouth again, but still no words came out. Finally he was able to mutter, "I'm trying to investigate a suspicious death here."

Cozy's reply was immediate. "Good for you. As a taxpayer, I applaud your . . . conscientiousness. But that is neither here nor there at the moment, is it? The question at hand is, you see, quite simple." Cozy leaned over and smiled at Diane in the

backseat of the cruiser before returning his attention to Slocum. "Is my client in custody? Yes or no?"

Cozy's voice carried through the heavy December air as though he were a thespian center stage at the Globe.

"She is not under arrest."

"Ah, but I didn't ask you that, did I?" He was doing his best to sound like Olivier doing Henry IV. "I asked you if my client was in your custody — yes, or no."

I could barely discern Slocum's response. I thought he said, "For now, she is . . . um, being detained for questioning."

"I appreciate that clarification. As of now she is officially declining your invitation for further questioning, so I assume, then, that she is free to go." Cozy leaned over and made quite a show of staring into the backseat of the cruiser. With mock horror he added, "Has she been handcuffed, Detective Slocum?" He included Jaris's name so that the assembled citizenry would know who was responsible for the travesty. Had he next recited Slocum's badge number — had Slocum been wearing a badge — I would not have been surprised. "Is that possible? Is she really handcuffed and locked in the backseat of a police cruiser? Are you planning on taking

her to the jail and *booking* her?"

"She was not being cooperative."

Cozy held out his own wrists and used the full power of his baritone. "Was she? Like my client, I too am planning to be uncooperative if this is the way the Boulder Police Department is choosing to behave toward its law-abiding citizens."

"Mr. Maitlin," Slocum implored.

At that moment I actually had just the slightest sympathy for Jaris Slocum. Cozy's performance had gone more than a little over the top.

Cozy ignored Slocum's plea and made a great show of holding out his French-cuffed wrists to see if Slocum would dare put a slightly less elegant pair of cuffs on them. "Would you like to handcuff me, as well? Is that the current policy of the department when citizens exercise their constitutional prerogatives to grieve silently?"

I could tell that Jaris Slocum would have loved nothing better at that moment than to handcuff Cozier Maitlin, but the presence of fifty or so civilian witnesses served to deter his more primitive impulses.

Darrell Olson's primary role in his detective partnership was, apparently, to sense what was about to go wrong between Slocum and one of Boulder's citizens.

Once again, Darrell did his job with aplomb. He rushed up, grabbed Slocum's arm, pulled him closer to the house — and much farther from Cozy — and went nose to nose with him for about half a minute. I couldn't hear a word of their argument but my respect for Darrell C. R. Olson expanded exponentially as he barked whatever he was barking. When the tête-à-tête between the two detectives was over, Slocum climbed the porch and marched into the old house where Hannah lay dead.

Olson returned to Cozy. He used a low voice to address him, modeling for him, hoping to reduce the inflammation. As he spoke he spread his hands in conciliation, palms up, like a don trying to pacify a peer. I couldn't tell what he was saying, but it took him a minute or more to get through it.

Cozy's reply wasn't a whisper; his tone remained floridly oratorical. "No, Detective. Not in a few minutes. Right now. I want the cuffs off my client and I want her released. Now. There is no point whatsoever in prolonging her agony. She is despairing over her friend's death. I guarantee you that this interview is over for tonight."

Olson dipped his head a little and spoke

again. It was apparent that he was still determined to try to be deferential, to try to lower the temperature of the conflict a little, but that he was also trying not to roll over to Cozy's demands.

Cozy listened to Darrell's continued plea, thought for a moment, and decided that he wanted none of it. He said, "Now, Detective." Cozy gestured toward the old house and Jaris Slocum, and in a much lower, tempered voice added, "That man is your problem, not mine. You have my sympathy, but nothing more. Now, please."

Olson shook his head, scratched his ear, stuffed his hands in his pockets, and mumbled something to Officer Leamer. Without so much as a nod, the detective walked away from Cozy and the patrol car.

Leamer opened the back door of the cruiser, helped Diane to her feet, and removed the handcuffs from behind her back. The fire in her eyes, if focused, could have ignited candles across the street.

Cozy introduced himself to his client and said something to her so quietly I couldn't discern a word. Diane had fresh tears on her face. She said, "Thank you, thank you." Then, as though she'd somehow forgotten, she cried, "My God, Hannah's dead."

Raoul said, "That's it?" Actually, what he said was, *"C'est finis?"*

I said, "For now."

6

Diane and I didn't make it to Vegas.

Hannah Grant's ashes were interred the following Tuesday after a sentimental service in one of the downtown churches. I had never before seen so much of Boulder's mental health community present in one place.

I was in a pretty good position to know that the police were flummoxed by the case. The local media was already reporting that the cops had no active leads. Lauren confirmed to me that after a week the investigation was spinning its wheels. My friend Sam Purdy, the Boulder police detective, usually wouldn't talk out of school about important cases with me, but he did roll his eyes when I mentioned Hannah.

That told me a lot.

During one late-night phone conversation he went way out on a limb. "We got crap," was what he said.

Lauren swore me to secrecy but revealed that Slocum and Olson had located no witnesses to anything that supported a finding of homicide. No one had seen Hannah leave her south Boulder condo the morning of her death, but she'd arrived at Rallysport Health Club early enough to work out before driving away just before 8:30. The time was almost certain. Two different witnesses recalled an incident in the locker room — Hannah had tripped over another woman's gym bag on the way back from the shower and both women had fallen hard to the floor. The witnesses were confident that they knew what time Hannah had dressed after her workout before heading to her car.

They were confident about one other thing, too. As she fell, Hannah had definitely hit her head on the tile floor. Someone had offered to go get ice. Hannah had declined; she said she was fine and had to get to work.

No one reported seeing her arrive at her office building. The few of Hannah's patients who had shown up for appointments on the day she died and who had voluntarily come forward to speak with the police reported nothing that provided any direction for the investigation.

The detectives weren't able to develop any motive for an assault. Hannah's personal life revealed no promising leads. Her finances were pristine. Her professional record was free of formal complaints.

The cops had no physical evidence that a crime had been committed. Actually, the truth was that they had way too much physical evidence. The little office building was chock-full of fingerprints and trace evidence. Dozens of different patients made their way through the space every week.

Hair, fibers? All the police could want, and more. Apparently Hannah's obsessive-compulsive tendencies had lacunae in the terrain where "neat" stopped and "clean" began. For investigators, Hannah's housekeeping weakness created a problem. To use trace evidence to rule in the presence of an intruder in the building, Jaris Slocum and Darrell Olson had to rule out the presence of any and all routine visitors to the building, which meant — minimally — obtaining exemplar prints and DNA samples from all of Hannah's patients and all of Mary Black's patients and from any other routine visitors to the building, including the woman who delivered the mail, the guys from UPS and FedEx, and the various tat-ted and pierced kids who delivered

takeout from restaurants on the nearby Pearl Street Mall.

Mary Black, the psychiatrist and mother of three who shared office space with Hannah, declined to make her patient roster available to the police, citing doctor-patient confidentiality. Diane, whom Hannah had entrusted with the clinical responsibility of closing her practice in the event of her death, also declined to make Hannah's patient roster available to the police, citing the same doctor-patient confidentiality issues. When the police pressed the issue, she'd enlisted Cozy Maitlin to run interference for her.

Diane was ambivalent about keeping the information to herself. After what Jaris Slocum had done to her the evening Hannah's body was discovered, Diane wasn't, of course, particularly inclined to cooperate with him. But she was eager to do anything she could to help identify anyone who might have had anything to do with Hannah's death. As far as Hannah's patient roster was concerned, though, Diane had decided that was information to which Slocum wasn't entitled.

Hannah's death officially remained "suspicious" until the Boulder County coroner issued his report eight days after her death.

The medical examiner had identified two discrete blows to Hannah's head, and he identified her cause of death as traumatic head injury resulting in cerebral hemorrhage. He specified the manner of her death as "undetermined." The ME's opinion was that the damage inflicted by a flat surface, possibly the tile floor at Rallysport, had not been sufficient to cause Hannah's death. Hannah's death was directly attributable to the second head trauma, origin unknown.

The dual traumas either had been unintentional blows suffered during the fall in the gym the morning she died — one impact caused by the tile floor, one by something else — or had been the result of two blows to her head intentionally inflicted by an assailant. Sam pointedly reminded me that a third possibility existed: One blow had been suffered during the fall at the health club, and the second blow, the fatal one, had been inflicted by an assailant at Hannah's office.

Diane heard the coroner's findings first. Diane always tended to hear gossip first. What source she might have in the medical examiner's office eluded me, but she found me on Friday morning at the office at a moment when we were both between pa-

tients and stunned me with the news.

"Somebody may have killed her, Alan. My God, somebody may have killed her. Why would somebody want to kill Hannah?"

I held her while she wept. I'd lost count of how many times I'd held Diane while she wept since Hannah's death. The tears weren't endless, but they were frequent. Diane's grief arrived in short, intense bursts, like the August monsoons. Clear skies before, clear skies after.

I asked myself the same question Diane was asking a dozen times a day for a while after that. *Why would somebody want to kill Hannah?*

I couldn't provide an answer. I used the fact that I couldn't answer it to console myself with the likelihood that Hannah's death had been accidental. Nothing more than a freak reaction to a silly accident in a health club locker room.

But the police were left with a buffet of anomalies that they couldn't explain. Why was Hannah's purse on the floor of her office, a place she would never leave it? Why was Hannah's body found in Mary Black's office, a place she had no reason to go? And why was Hannah's blouse tucked up under the front of her bra?

★ ★ ★

Hanukkah had arrived and Christmas was growing ever closer.

The effort to determine the manner of Hannah's death turned colder along with the weather.

Media interest in the case declined quickly, and Hannah's very public death soon became what, perhaps, it really had been all along — a private tragedy.

7

If you don't happen to be an inveterate shopper intent on milking the swollen teat of post-holiday sales — I am not — and if you aren't required to be at work — it was a Sunday, and I wasn't — the day after Christmas is a sleep-in day.

Or maybe — if the snow gods have conspired with the ski gods to dump ten powdery inches of flash-frozen Dom Perignon on the upper reaches of Beaver Creek and one of your wife's friends has generously offered two free holiday season nights at her Bachelor Gulch ski villa — the day after Christmas is most definitely a play day.

Lauren and I had packed our ski stuff and winter clothing and an immense quantity of three-year-old paraphernalia the night before and were out of bed well before dawn in an almost certainly futile attempt to beat the pre-ski traffic that seemed to always clog I-70 West into the

Colorado Rockies during the winter months. She was fixing some breakfast for our still-sleeping daughter, Grace; I was loading the car. While I was on a trip into the kitchen to grab a cooler to lug to the garage, Lauren said, "See that?"

"What?"

She pointed at the tiny kitchen TV, which was tuned to a local channel so we could hear the ski-traffic report. Why? I wasn't sure. If the traffic was awful, we'd take I-70 into the mountains. If the traffic was light, we'd do the same thing. She said, "That thing at the bottom of the screen."

I assumed she meant the crawl, the strip of text that I always seemed to be reading when I should be watching the screen and that I never seemed to be reading when news about some important update was moving across the screen that I should probably be reading. From the time that crawls first appeared on TV screens, I'd decided that I was genetically incapable of reading the moving words and simultaneously attending to what was happening on the rest of the screen. I'd long ago concluded that I did not possess a twenty-first-century mind.

I lifted the heavy cooler laden with God-knows-what and took a lumbering step to-

ward the door. "Nope, didn't see it."

"It said that —"

"We have breaking news from our Boulder bureau," interrupted one of the morning anchors. With that preamble I turned my attention back toward the TV, but my eyes immediately found the crawl and I couldn't have told you which of the two anchors was speaking. "Apparently — and details are sketchy — apparently, and this is truly hard to believe, another little girl has disappeared on Christmas night in Boulder. We have a reporter on the way to the scene right now and should have more information momentarily. June?"

June said, "You're right: This is so hard to believe, that it's happening again. For those of our viewers who aren't familiar with Boulder, it's even the same neighborhood as last time. That was what, eight, nine years ago? We'll get those details for you and we'll be back with more right after a break."

Lauren said, "I'm going to check on Grace."

"I checked her when I got up, sweets. She's fine."

"So did I. I'm going to check on her anyway."

She hustled toward Grace's room. I set

the cooler on the floor.

Another little girl has disappeared on Christmas night in Boulder.

Lauren was breathless when she tiptoed back into the kitchen. "Grace is fine," she said.

"Yes." I put my arms around her and planted my hands on her ass. Lauren and I were parents of a little girl who hadn't disappeared on Christmas night. Somewhere else in Boulder another pair of parents couldn't say the same.

"Are you catching? You're not catching, right?" I asked. One of Boulder County's prosecutors was always on call for legal emergencies that might require the presence of a representative from the DA's office. Infrequently, that meant that she was called to crime scenes. Like to the location of the disappearance of a girl.

"No, no," she said, pulling away from my hug. "I couldn't leave town if I was on call. You know that. Should I wake Grace?" she asked.

"Let me finish loading the car first. We'll both get much more accomplished if she stays asleep until the last possible moment."

An hour later we were climbing through

Mount Vernon Canyon on I-70 into the mountains, sharing the freeway with at least a million other vehicles. Maybe two million other vehicles. Every one of the other vehicles carried skiers or snowboarders who had, like us, crawled out of warm beds before dawn in order to beat the traffic. I searched for irony, knowing it was there somewhere.

In back, secure in her high-tech car seat, Grace was flipping through a fat cardboard book about erudite dogs and talking to herself, while next to me Lauren was flipping through radio stations trying to find the latest news about what was going on with the missing girl back in Boulder. I wasn't really listening to the radio, partly because Grace's almost incomprehensible monologue was too cute to ignore, but mostly because none of the radio reporters seemed to know much about what was happening with this year's missing girl, so they were using their airtime to talk about the other missing girl, the one who had disappeared eight Christmases before.

I'd long before decided that I despised hearing rehashes of that dreadful story.

"It's a teenager. They think she's fourteen," Lauren summarized for me as the Denver station she was listening to faded

64

away, its signal lost hopelessly in the mountain canyons. "Her father went to check on her early this morning. She wasn't there. They were going to go skiing today, just like us. We did the exact same thing with Grace."

I thought, *But at our house Grace was in her bed,* and felt a chill crawl up my spine and goose flesh spread across my shoulders and neck. *What would it be like if she hadn't . . . ?* I tried comforting myself with the fact that it wasn't really as bad as the last time a girl went missing on Christmas night in Boulder. It wasn't.

The last time the girl they couldn't find was only six years old.

The last time a terrifying note was discovered on the stairs.

And I soothed myself with the obvious, the obvious being that six-year-olds don't often run away from home, not for real, and certainly not on Christmas night. I reminded myself that a fourteen-year-old girl might run away.

Fourteen-year-olds do run away. Maybe this girl had just run away. Probably this girl had just run away.

Numerals representing the ages of the two missing girls lined up in front of my eyes as though they were symbols spinning

on a slot machine. As the numbers came to rest, I did the math. Today's fourteen-year-old missing girl was the same age — had been born the exact same year — as the tiny blonde who went missing eight years to the day before. If that other little girl had survived, the two children might be classmates, or friends, or sleep-over mates. They might go skiing on Christmas holidays with each other's families.

I felt another chill.

"Their house is only a few blocks away from, you know," Lauren said. She meant from the other house, the one where the little beauty queen's dead body had been found by her father on the day after Christmas in an unused room in the basement, her head smashed, her neck cruelly cinctured with a homemade garrote.

"Where exactly?"

"On Twelfth, they said."

Three blocks away. Just three blocks and eight years separated two little girls gone missing on Christmas nights in Boulder.

At that moment we were passing an overhead digital highway sign, the kind that in winter usually cautions motorists of icy and snowpacked conditions ahead. But this one had an even more sobering message — an Amber Alert. All concerned citi-

zens were supposed to be on the lookout for a missing blond-haired, 115-pound, five-foot-six fourteen-year-old. No name was given.

My first reaction? Selfish. I hoped I didn't know her. I hoped she wasn't the daughter of any of my friends, or any of my patients. I wanted to feel the relief of insulation. I wanted her to be a stranger.

"Amber Alert," I said to Lauren. "Look."

She stared in the direction of the highway sign until we passed below it, then turned on her seat and faced our daughter. She said, "Your parents really love you, Gracie."

Gracie laughed.

Obliviousness, I thought, *can be a very, very good thing.*

My detective friend, Sam Purdy, told me later on that it was as though a giant warehouse had been surreptitiously constructed nearby when the other case of the missing girl had finally faded into near oblivion and that all the satellite trucks, and all the microwave trucks, and all the flimsy network pop-up tents, and a few hundred cameras and microphones had simply been secreted away so they'd be

ready for the next time.

The next time had turned out to be the massacre at Columbine and the time after that had been the Kobe Bryant circus up in Eagle County. After the Kobe invasion, all the equipment had apparently been returned to the secret warehouse to await the next, next, next time the almost-tabloid media would mobilize for a full-scale assault on a Colorado town. That was the only explanation Sam could concoct for how quickly the equipment reappeared on the streets of Boulder on the day after Christmas.

I was determined to miss it all.

By noon on that Boxing Day, Grace was either enjoying or enduring her first day ever in ski school and I was busy chasing Lauren, who was a much better skier than me, and a much, much better powder skier than me, through untracked down on the forest edges of the Golden Eagle run at the top of Beaver Creek.

In Boulder, three thousand feet below us in altitude — based on what Sam would tell me later — the cameras were already in place, the high-tech satellite and microwave trucks were bouncing signals around and through the atmosphere, and producers had already begun choosing loca-

tions for the stand-ups the on-air talent would do for that night's news.

Some of the reportorial faces would be familiar from the last time Boulder had endured this invasion. Others were recognizable because of what the country had endured in the intervening years because of the tragedies that had befallen Chandra Levy, or Elizabeth Smart, or Laci Peterson. Or because of the innocent lives ended by the Beltway snipers. Or because of Kobe Bryant and whatever happened at Cordillera. Or because of whatever Michael Jackson was accused of lately. Or because of some other crime du jour.

Or.

In America, there were always plenty of candidates.

As each fresh tragedy was anointed a mega-news event, I'd quickly grown fatigued of the relentless television and newspaper and Internet and magazine coverage afforded, or foisted upon, all the previous victims and all the previous perpetrators, and upon the unsuspecting but apparently ravenous populace.

Somebody had to be watching all this coverage, right?

I suspected that I'd fatigue of this latest criminal/media extravaganza, right in my

hometown, even faster. I really was determined to miss it all.

I was. Honestly.

Lauren and I grabbed a late lunch at Spruce Saddle, the big mid-mountain restaurant at Beaver Creek. It wasn't lost on me that I was only a couple of ridge tops away from the elegant resort where Kobe and a young woman had crossed paths, and was within shouting distance of the courthouse where that diseased melodrama played itself out.

Lauren chose a table close to an overhead television so she would immediately know if there were any updates being broadcast about the missing girl in Boulder. I was silently trying to discern whether her acute interest in the case was an indication of parental empathy — or a counterintuitive way to stem the flow of understandable parental dread — or whether it was a more uncomplicated professional prosecutorial curiosity. I was trying to grant her the benefit of the doubt and not even consider the possibility that my wife's interest might be simply voyeuristic. Unsure, I headed for the bathroom. When I returned I spied Lauren folding up her cell phone. I took a chair that left my

back to the television.

Which left me facing in the general direction of Cordillera.

"Who'd you call?" I asked.

"The office."

"Yeah, what did you learn?" I didn't really want to know, and wasn't sure why I'd asked. Probably the same reason that I tried the door on Mary Black's office.

"This is my job. I could be involved later on. I need to . . . you know, whether . . . the girl . . ."

Not too bad, only slightly defensive. "I know," I said. I leaned across the table and kissed her lightly on her lips, tasting the waxy gloss of a fresh application of sunblock. "So, what did you learn?"

I'd done it again; I'd once again asked a question that I didn't really want to know the answer to. I convinced myself that my question was an act of marital generosity: Lauren needed to talk.

"They don't know what they have. But because of what happened last time — you can imagine — they're being extra, extra cautious. They're treating it like a crime scene, even though no one's really sure what it is exactly. The girl's family is cooperating, totally. So far the crime scene techs don't think anything's been unduly

71

contaminated. That's all good, considering."

She meant, of course, considering what a total mess the crime scene had been the last time. The time with the little blond beauty queen, the one who sang and danced into our homes over and over and over again in her little sexy cowgirl getup.

"What do the police think? Was it an abduction of some kind?"

"Some of what they're seeing says yes, some says no." She gazed around to see if anyone in the crowded cafeteria was paying attention to our conversation, and she prophylactically lowered her already hushed voice a few additional decibels. "There hadn't been any threats, and they didn't find a note or anything like that. Nobody's called the family about ransom. There's no evidence of forced entry at the house. But there is some blood."

"A lot?"

"More than a couple of drops. I'm just telling you what I heard from the office. It's thirdhand, or fourth."

"Could she have run?"

"It's a possibility, apparently. The cops are trying to track down all her friends, to see what they know. Since the schools are on break, it's complicated. Some of her

best friends are out of town."

"But her family thinks it's possible?"

"I guess. Apparently, the family situation is complicated. The girl has had some emotional issues in the past. I don't have those details."

I couldn't look my wife in the eye when I asked the next question. With the edge of my hand I moved salt that had been spilled on the table by an earlier diner into one long sodium mogul and pushed it to the side. "And they checked all the little rooms in the basement that nobody ever goes into?"

That's where the other girl's body had been found eight years before. In a rarely used room in a dingy basement. Her tiny body had been discovered by her distraught father, who had carried it up the stairs for all to see.

"Yeah, twice at least. It's different this time. The circumstances. It sounds like it's a nice house, but it's not huge and fancy like the other one. And it only has a small basement, a partial, like ours; underneath it's mostly crawl space. They checked."

"Twice?"

"Three times." She smiled sadly.

"Who's on it?"

"From my office? Andy."

"From the cops?"

"It's a big team for now. And, yes, it includes Sam and Lucy."

"Sam won't be happy. It was one of his claims to fame that he never had a thing to do with the other one."

"I doubt if any of them are happy," Lauren said. "There're so many reporters chasing everyone around that they've had to block off the street. You know that all the detectives will be under a microscope."

Or a microphone. "Is Jaris Slocum on it?"

She slapped my wrist to shush me. "Babe, we're on vacation. Let's not go back there." She held up her cell. "I want to call and see how Grace is doing in ski school. Am I crazy?"

"You're a mother. You get special dispensation."

She made the call. Grace, it turned out, was enjoying ski school. I wasn't surprised. As she aged and I got a chance to experience the wonder of really beginning to know her, I was learning that my daughter rolled well with the punches.

Lauren closed up the phone. I asked, "How's your energy?" That's as close as I would get to finding a safe way to inquire about the current state of Lauren's multiple sclerosis. I knew from experience that

on rare good days a couple of hours of skiing was often all that she could manage before her legs began to feel like over-cooked asparagus. We'd already done a long drive up to the mountains and spent a couple of energetic hours cutting powder.

For Lauren, that was an awful lot of activity.

"Good, I'm fine. I'll wriggle out of these boots and put my feet up over lunch. That will help."

Was I convinced? Hardly. "We can go down the hill and eat if you want. We have all day tomorrow to ski, you know. And Tuesday morning, too. No need to press it today."

"I'm good, Alan. I want to do the top of Bachelor's Gulch before all the powder is skied off. I love it up there."

Arguing with her was an option. Prevailing was not. Across the room, the food-court lines were long. I stood. "You rest, I'll go get you something to eat. What would you like for lunch?"

We drove down the hill to Boulder after a late breakfast two days later, on Tuesday.

The skiing had been a joy, Lauren's atypical stamina on the slopes was a holiday gift, and by late Monday in ski school

tiny Grace had managed — for about eleven horizontal feet of a two percent grade — to comport her stubby little legs into something resembling a snowplow. Lauren and I gladly forked over $24.95 for a DVD that proved our daughter had accomplished the dubious feat.

Midday mountain traffic wasn't bad over Vail Pass, and the Eisenhower Tunnel approach was merely aggravating, not paralyzing. On the eastern side of the Divide I kept my eyes peeled on my rearview mirror for out-of-control big-rig truckers who had already fried the air brakes on their rigs on the highest stretches of the seven percent grades.

Grace and Lauren both slept all the way from Copper Mountain to Golden.

For the forty-eight hours plus we'd been up skiing I had managed to avoid — almost completely — the media saturation coverage about the girl who had disappeared on Christmas night. Lauren had told me a few new things, but with concerted effort on my part I knew almost nothing about what had transpired while we were gone.

And I was proud of it.

But as I-70 bent to follow the final contours of the Front Range, and as the beige

winter haze of the Denver metropolitan area became visible in the distance, it was clear that my brief holiday was coming to an end, and I decided, reluctantly, to re-enter the real world. I killed the Otis Redding CD and tuned to KOA, a Denver AM station with enough brash watt-power to push its often dubious signal up into the crevices of the Front Range foothills. I didn't have to listen long to hear an update — "the absolute latest on the tragedy in Boulder" — that informed me that the girl, Mallory Miller, was still missing and that the Boulder Police continued to refer to the event as a "disappearance," not a "kidnapping."

Fifteen minutes later, as I drove Highway 93 just shy of the entrance to Coal Creek Canyon, Mallory Miller's father — his first name was William — came on the air — LIVE! — with a plea for his daughter to come home, or for whoever had her to release her, or both. Whatever the problem is, he told his daughter, we can solve it.

His plea was poignant, but I didn't hear too much of it. I was distracted by something else: his name.

Gosh, I was thinking, *I once knew a guy in Boulder named Bill Miller.*

8

Details dribbled out the way they inevitably do. I'd continued to learn a few things from my conversations with Lauren. She wasn't due back in her office until after the first of the year but was staying in touch with her colleagues daily. According to my wife the detectives working the case were apparently split into two camps during those crucial early days: those who believed that Mallory had run away and those who believed that she'd been abducted. Not surprisingly, public opinion was divided along the same fault line.

Lauren's reading of the shifting winds within law enforcement was that the runaway viewpoint was prevailing.

TV and newspapers provided background. Hour after hour of background. Given the paucity of public facts, way too much background. But apparently that was only my opinion. Four thousand reporters and camera people and producers can't be wrong.

Right?

Mallory lived in the Twelfth Street house on the Hill with her father and little brother, Reese, who was twelve years old. The Millers were separated; the children's mother had moved away from Boulder when the children were much younger. The police had been in touch with Mrs. Miller — apparently, and surprisingly, the media had not — and were confident that she could add nothing pertinent to the investigation of her daughter's disappearance.

What was known publicly about the Christmas-night events in the Miller household?

On Christmas evening Mallory had been home by herself. The Miller family had been invited to a holiday dinner at a friend's house, but Mr. Miller and Reese had gone to the celebration alone after Mallory complained about a stomachache. Mr. Miller had offered to cancel the plans, but she had insisted that they go on without her.

The physical evidence in the Miller home sounded screwy. Although a casement window near the back door was unscreened and unlocked, the family maintained that it had been that way for as long as any of them could remember. The po-

lice were not convinced that the rear window had been used to gain entry to the house, and there were no other possible indications of forced entry.

A trail of tiny blood drops ran from Mallory's second-floor bedroom down the stairs. The drops stopped abruptly a few feet from the door that led into the family room/kitchen at the rear of the house. Although DNA testing on the drops was pending, initial examination of the blood indicated that it was probably Mallory's. The upstairs bathroom that Mallory shared with Reese was a mess, and reportedly Reese had told the police that the mess was severe, "even for her."

Did the blood drops and the messy bathroom constitute evidence of a struggle? It depended, apparently, on whom you asked.

The record of incoming and outgoing phone calls indicated that Mallory had likely been home from the time her family left for dinner until the last time her father had called to check on her about ten minutes before nine. He had called a total of four times during the few hours that he and his son had been away from their home. Mr. Miller and Reese arrived back home at 9:20 or so.

Mallory had left a note on the kitchen counter thanking Santa Claus for a great Christmas. The note said she'd already gone to bed so that she could be fresh for their ski trip the next day.

In the note, Mallory didn't make mention of her stomachache.

Both Mr. Miller and his son agreed that the note had been written hurriedly. Mallory, known for flowers and hearts flourishes on all her correspondence and many of her school papers, and for generous helpings of XXXs — kisskisskiss — to accompany her signature, had signed the note with a single cursive M instead of her usual florid, all lowercased "mallory," or her self-deprecating, ironic, all lowercased "mall."

Reese retired to his room, and Mr. Miller closed up the house, turned off the lights on the Christmas tree, and was in bed before ten.

The next morning, Bill Miller went into his daughter's room early — he said 4:30 — because the Millers were planning to drive all the way to Steamboat Springs the next morning and Reese had insisted that he wanted to be in line when the lifts opened to try his new Christmas snowboard in some fresh powder. But Mallory

wasn't in her room. Since she hadn't actually made her bed since mounting a brief public-relations campaign to extend her curfew the previous summer, there was no easy way to know if her bed had been slept in.

Her clothes for the ski trip were neatly packed in a duffel on the floor.

Mr. Miller's initial suspicion was that his daughter had snuck out the night before — it wouldn't be the first time — and for some reason hadn't been able to sneak back in before dawn. He guessed she had fallen asleep at a girlfriend's house, and was about to phone her closest buddy, a girl named Kara, when Reese noticed the trail of blood that seemed to start in the hallway between her bedroom and the bathroom they shared.

While Bill Miller was searching for Kara's phone number, it was Reese who called 911.

Mallory's teardrop-shaped backpack, which according to her good friends, Kara and Tammi — they were both more than willing to be interviewed by anyone with a camera — functioned more as a purse than a book-bag, wasn't in the house. Missing along with the backpack were Mallory's cell phone, her wallet, and her school

planner. The school planner was important because Mallory apparently used it as an all-purpose notepad. It was where she was most likely to jot down friends' phone numbers, weekend plans, and any musings about current romantic infatuations. The girls also assured police that Mallory kept a diary — they'd both read parts of it, though not recently — but it was never located.

The absence of the school planner and the diary meant that detectives were missing a treasure trove of information about Mallory's current life. The cell phone was crucial because the memory contained the numbers of everyone Mallory considered significant.

The neighbors across the street, the Crandalls, reported that they saw a man "loitering" on the Millers' sidewalk early that Christmas evening, before the snow had started falling. He was bundled up against the cold, they said, and walked back and forth down the block. They couldn't provide a better description.

An interesting and curious sidelight to the grand scope of media coverage of what was, at face value, nothing more than the case of a likely teenage runaway, was Mr. Miller's refusal to do interviews with any

of the national media luminaries who were desperate to do a two-shot with him. He limited his on-camera time to a pair of brief appearances with a local TV reporter, Stephanie Riggs — they'd previously become acquainted on a committee that was organizing a charity run — and to occasional solo stand-ups in the front yard of his home. Each time he professed his love for his daughter and urged her to come home, or at least to call.

If someone out there has her, he'd add, please let her go. Please.

I found that I was admiring his decision not to become a media slut.

I thought he sounded like someone who thought his daughter had run away.

The lead detectives on the case were a couple of senior people that Sam liked. I didn't know either of them. A few other teams were assisting.

Jaris Slocum and Darrell Olson were assigned to interview neighbors.

Another pair of detectives was assigned to put together a detailed time line of events. That pair consisted of Sam Purdy and his partner, Lucy Tanner.

9

Diane had covered my practice while Lauren and Grace and I were up skiing.

Once I'd finished retrieving the dogs from vacation doggie-camp at our neighbor Adrienne's house, and after I'd finished unloading the car and stowing our ski gear, I phoned Diane to let her know that we were home and that I was on the clock. "We're back from the mountains. You're free to go play. No calls, I hope," I said.

"No calls. Your patients are always well behaved. How was it?" she asked perfunctorily.

"Perfect — great snow, terrific weather. Too short. You and Raoul have a good Christmas?"

"Yeah, you have a minute?"

"Sure," I said. I was already wary. Diane's tone was a few degrees too serious. A few as in almost 180. I guessed that we were about to talk, once again, about

Hannah, and why someone would want to kill her.

"I need a consultation," she said.

"Like a clinical consultation?"

"Exactly."

"Okay."

"This isn't a casual thing. It's a formal consultation, Alan. You can't tell anyone what I'm about to tell you."

I was standing in the kitchen and I found myself searching behind me for a stool. Something about Diane's manner screamed that this was going to be one of those why-don't-you-sit-down conversations.

"Of course."

Yowsa, I was thinking. *What is this about?*

"It's a consultation about a consultation. In a way."

"I'm ready, Diane."

"Did you know that every once in a while Hannah talked to me about her cases? When she wanted an opinion about something she was a little unsure about, she'd run it by me."

"I'm not surprised. You're good."

"I am, but that's not the point. A few days before she died she asked me out for a glass of wine after work. No big deal, we probably did it about once a month."

"Okay."

"She had a specific case she wanted to discuss — a kid she'd seen the previous Friday. I didn't know the girl's name at the time, of course. Still don't, not for sure."

What Diane was describing was far from unusual. Collegial consultations between psychotherapists are often casual, and usually conducted in a way that protects the patient's anonymity.

"Yes?"

"The strange thing — the thing that Hannah wanted my consultation about — was that this kid had come in on her own. Her parents didn't arrange the session. Kid just showed up in her office, sat in the waiting room, and wanted to talk."

"A walk-in?" I asked. I didn't know a single private-practice psychotherapist in Boulder who saw patients without appointments.

"A walk-in."

Diane didn't treat adolescents. Occasionally I did. I said, "Usually a parent makes the contact, and comes to the first session. That should have been a red flag."

Diane cleared her throat as a way of letting me know that my unfortunate propensity toward platitudes was interfering with her narrative. She added, "I know that." Her tone was not only scolding me for

being condescending, but was also making clear that even if she didn't eat foie gras she knew what a goose was.

I tried to remember Colorado mental health law. I thought the age threshold when a child could seek treatment without a parent's consent was fifteen, but I wasn't totally certain. I'd have to check.

"How old was the kid?"

Diane answered, "Fourteen, fifteen — I'm not a hundred percent sure. I'm pretty sure Hannah said 'teenager' but . . ." I suddenly guessed where we were going. And I didn't like the road map I was seeing. At all. I feared that Diane was intimating that Hannah Grant had seen Mallory Miller for psychotherapy less than a week before Hannah died, and only two weeks before Mallory had disappeared. I said, "You're not thinking Hannah's mystery patient was Mallory Miller, are you?"

"Everything fits."

Other questions began making soft landings in my head like a platoon of paratroopers. Why would Mallory seek treatment without consulting her father? And why with Hannah? Had she made a second appointment? Had Hannah made a diagnosis? Was Mallory fearful? Had Hannah said anything about Mallory

thinking of running away?

And the most important question: Is there any way I can avoid hearing any more about this?

But Diane had an agenda that was quite different from insulating me from becoming more complicit, and she had a line of inquiry that I wasn't anticipating. She said, "I can't tell anybody about this, right? That's what Hannah had wanted my consultation about. I told her that I thought she had to sit on it, had to wait and see what developed with the kid. Now, I want to hear from you if I was right."

I hesitated while I considered the peculiar circumstances she was describing. While I pondered, Diane filled in the dead air. "You have the craziest practice within a thousand miles of here. I figured that if you don't know what to do about something like this, then nobody does."

I ignored the accusation, or compliment, or whatever it was. I said, "You probably can't tell anybody anything. But it ultimately depends on what the girl told Hannah during the appointment. And on her age. For legal purposes I think you have to assume that right now you're Hannah — you have the same confidentiality responsibilities that she had when she

saw the kid. Are you wondering about talking to the police? Is that it?"

"Sure, but I'm wondering about going to Mallory's father, too. I'm sure he'd love to know —"

"You probably can't talk to him. Other than the usual child-abuse exceptions to the privilege, your hands are tied. Even if you were sure it was Mallory — and it doesn't sound like you are — I don't think you could tell anyone about the girl's session."

Because it was Diane I expected her to argue with me. She didn't. She asked, "You want to know what she said? Why she was there?"

"To give you any useful guidance, I probably have to." That was my way of saying, "No, not really."

Diane paused before she said, "I don't really know that much. The girl was depressed about the holidays. And she misses her mom."

10

Despite its cosmopolitan airs, Boulder is, at its core, a small town. As would likely have occurred in any other small town, it seemed that everyone knew someone who knew someone who had some connection to the missing girl. In the week between that season's Christmas and New Year's celebrations many hours were lost, probably way too many, in informal parlor sessions intended to identify the precise arcs of those degrees of separation.

My friend and neighbor Adrienne, a Boulder urologist, made it clear that one of the key players in the drama — someone connected to the Miller family, or to one of the public faces of the law enforcement team — was one of her patients. I had two biking buddies who had daughters who played on the missing girl's U-15 club soccer team. Lauren's legal assistant's teenage son's best friend used to cut the grass at the missing girl's house.

Like that.

As I'd suspected when I first heard that Mallory's father's first name was Bill, it turned out that I, too, had a tangential tie to the Miller family. It was tangential only because of the passage of time. Years before — I would have to check my records to put a precise number on the question of how many years, but I was guessing somewhere around eight or nine, maybe even ten or eleven — I'd seen the missing girl's parents for a solitary couples therapy session. Just one. Given the time lag since that session, my recall of the intervention was surprisingly clear, probably because of how disheartening my clinical appraisal was at the time.

Mr. Miller had dragged his reluctant wife in for the evaluation. It had been clear to me from the moment the introductions started that Mrs. Miller did not want to be in my office. Her demeanor had reminded me of a child who would gladly promise never, ever to eat candy again if she could only avoid the dentist's drill *this* time. All that was absent was a foot stomp.

My clinical antennae were further tuned by her appearance. Any professional who has spent enough hours with people suffering acute mental illness would have rec-

ognized that Mrs. Miller's physical appearance was just the slightest bit off. Her hair, her makeup, her clothes — everything was just a degree or two away from ordinary. My session with the Millers was on a lovely Indian summer September day, and Mrs. Miller came dressed in a wool suit, carrying a straw bag, and wearing scuffed white pumps. On her eyes she wore big, bright Jackie O sunglasses. All the pieces, individually, were fine. Acceptable, at least. But together on a fine autumn day they totaled a sartorial sum that I guessed only Mrs. Miller could fully comprehend.

For his part, Mr. Miller was in something close to full-blown denial about the extent of the daunting challenges he faced. He appeared to have convinced himself, at least temporarily, that a few heart-to-heart sessions of some old-fashioned talking therapy would be just the trick to help lead his wife away from the middle of the field where she'd been aimlessly wandering and ease her back onto the straight and narrow marital tracks where she belonged.

Where exactly was Mrs. Miller doing her figurative wandering?

Into another man's bed? No. Drugs? Alcohol? Nothing so pedestrian.

Mrs. Miller, it turned out, attended wed-

dings. Usually two or three ceremonies a month, but during prime nuptial season she would do more. "Ten one month," Mr. Miller had reported to me over the phone when he'd called for the initial appointment. "That's her record. This past June. The truth is she'd do ten a week if she could fit them in."

She dressed elegantly for each one of the ceremonies. Her collection of wedding outfits numbered in the dozens, and she had an enviable assortment of spring and summer hats — Mr. Miller called them hats; Mrs. Miller referred to them as "my bonnets." She bought nice gifts for every one of the happy couples. Many of the outfits and all of the wedding gifts were purchased from cable TV home shopping channels. She stayed away from registries — "Who needs to be told what to buy? My Lord," she asked aloud during our session — and apparently her gifting tendencies leaned toward ceramic figurines of animals. Puppies and kittens mostly, but occasional angels and young children.

The wedding presents were always pricey things. "It's her only vice," Mr. Miller had said in admirable defense of his wife's largesse. During one particular month of nuptials every newlywed couple

received — after a one-hour this-is-it closeout sale on QVC — a beautiful shiny chrome home espresso machine from Italy. The piston kind. The total tab for the machines was almost two thousand dollars.

The UPS guy and the FedEx lady who drove the routes that included the Millers' home were on a first-name basis with everyone in the household.

Other than the sheer number of weddings, and the accumulating expense, what was the problem? The problem was that Mrs. Miller had never been invited to any of the ceremonies. None. Still, she fervently believed that she was an honored guest at every one of them, and if challenged could concoct an elaborate though ultimately nonsensical explanation for her attendance.

Her typical pattern was to arrive at the church or synagogue with some breathless flair just moments before the festivities began. She'd edge herself into a prime seat for the service, usually in the second or third row right behind the family, always on the bride's side, center aisle, and she'd smile and wave at the other guests as though she knew them quite well.

She always cried during the vows.

On more than one occasion after the

nuptials were complete she'd exited the church along with the bride's family and joined the wedding party for the limousine ride to the reception.

Psychotherapists are trained to ask the question, "Why now?" Why is this man, or this woman, in my office seeking help *today?* Why didn't she come in last week, or last month, or next week, or next month? The answer to the question yields what we like to call the "precipitating event."

For the Millers the precipitating event for seeking psychological assistance was crystal clear. The previous weekend Mrs. Miller had, at the insistence of an irascible groom and an implacable bride, been removed from a festive wedding reception at the Hotel Boulderado by the police. The immediate precipitant for her removal was Mrs. Miller's dubious decision to break into the celebratory dance between the newlyweds and politely, but firmly, demand her turn to waltz with the groom.

"Excuse me? I think you forgot your dance with *me,*" she'd said to him with a sad smile as she tapped the groom on the shoulder. "You'll excuse us?" she'd added for the benefit of his befuddled bride.

Then Mrs. Miller held up her silk-draped arms, waiting her turn to be swept away.

The groom, it turned out, was a Boulder sheriff's deputy. Half the guests at the wedding were Boulder sheriff's deputies. Not one of them recognized the woman in the yellow silk dress. Most importantly, the bride, who knew the detailed logistics of her wedding day as intimately as a chef knows the contents of his larder, didn't recognize the woman in the yellow silk dress.

Later that day, at the police department across town, the authorities released Mrs. Miller to Mr. Miller's custody with the strong suggestion that a mental health consultation might be in order.

Enter *moi*.

My appraisal?

Based on the brief history the Millers provided, Mrs. Miller's descent into schizophrenia had been gradual. By history, I was guessing that she'd suffered her first psychotic break at around age twenty-three — she and her husband had celebrated their own wedding when she was twenty-two — and she had begun to display more intransigent symptoms of psychosis shortly after the birth of her

daughter. Mrs. Miller was twenty-four at that time. The symptoms worsened once again after the birth of her son two years later. I suspected that over the intervening years her family had consistently minimized her growing list of eccentricities, and that the reclusive behavior she demonstrated — reclusive when she wasn't attending weddings, that is — had been rationalized away one way or another. Evidence of her frank psychosis had, at times, been blatantly denied by everyone in her limited orbit.

The severe mental illness was Mrs. Miller's. The conspiracy to pretend it didn't exist, however, was most definitely a family affair. Her husband, Bill, was a nice guy. After five minutes in my office, I realized that he was a relentless cheerleader and a determined advocate for his wife. "Whatever I can do to help, I'll do," he said. "Anything."

It was my unpleasant task to suggest to Mr. and Mrs. Miller that before they focused on issues in their marital relationship — perhaps — Mrs. Miller should seek some individual treatment for the difficulties she was having distinguishing things that were real from things that were not.

"Is it that bad? Really?" Mr. Miller said

in mutual self-defense after I'd asked how he felt about what was going on in his marriage. "I love Rachel. In the grand scheme of things this is a small problem, right? I mean, we're talking weddings. It's not cancer. There are many, many times when she seems just fine."

During my internship, while I was spending a rotation in an acute adult psychiatric inpatient unit, I had become extremely frustrated by one of my patients. He was a huge Samoan man, a schizophrenic whose communication abilities had devolved to the point where his speech consisted solely of multiple repetitions of a deeply baritone "hoho," sometimes singly, more often tendered in multiple repetitions. Despite his severe psychopathology and his immense size — the man outweighed me by at least 200 pounds — he was congenial and cooperative. We would sit for brief one-to-one "psychotherapy" sessions a few times a week. Each meeting lasted five minutes, max. He would listen to me — I doubted at times that he comprehended the intended meaning of a single word I said — gesture in the air with his fat hands, and say, "Hoho, hoho," occasionally interrupting my otherwise useless intervention, sometimes waiting po-

litely until I was done.

Infrequently he would smile or open his eyes wide in apparent wonder. More often his face would yield no expression at all.

My Samoan patient was already receiving enough Haldol to sedate an elephant, yet his mystifying psychotic process seemed immune to my best, though admittedly inexperienced and ultimately ineffective, attempts to be helpful.

I confessed to my supervisor, who knew the situation well, that I felt incompetent to treat the man. The supervising psychiatrist said two things that have stuck with me ever since. First, he told me that there are some people who are better at being crazy than I will ever be at being therapeutic. The Samoan, he said, was my case in point.

Second, he told me that from a psychopathology perspective, some of our patients have cancer. He was speaking metaphorically, of course, but I still recalled his caution on those days that my clinical skills seemed hopelessly inadequate to contain the sometimes incorrigible forces of my patients' mental illnesses.

I was tempted to share those pearls of wisdom with Bill Miller the day that he brought his wife into my office for evalua-

tion. But I didn't. His hope was too inspiring to behold. His desire to lift his wife up was too gratifying to witness. He didn't want to believe that his wife had the mental health equivalent of cancer. I feared that indeed she might, but I wasn't ready to believe it either. That's how powerful his hope was.

Despite the fact that I thought I'd pulled just enough of my punches to allow Mr. Miller's hope to stay afloat, my ultimate assessment that day, and my verbalized prescription for further care, sucked all the oxygen out of the room.

Every last molecule.

In contrast to bipolar disease, which at its heart is a disorder of mood, schizophrenia is a disorder of thought, of perception. Schizophrenic thinking results in a myriad of cognitive symptoms. Hallucinations, delusions, and paranoia are the most common. In a schizophrenic's world, what most of us consider orderly thought begins to deteriorate, and cognition becomes subject to interferences from beyond the confines of usual perception. The process that results appears to an outsider to be bizarre, tangential, repetitive, or oddly referential.

An extreme example was my Samoan's

baffling chorus of hohos. But in a schizophrenic's brain the variety of ways that faulty neurochemistry can cause thinking to deteriorate is large. In severe cases the outcomes are almost universally tragic.

The problem that was most apparent to me during my brief appraisal of Mrs. Miller was the extent of her delusional thinking — specifically her irrational belief that she had been a special invitee to all those weddings. Although the nature of the invitations remained her secret during our interview, that was where I focused my attention as I presented my suggestions to the Millers.

Mr. Miller seemed somewhat relieved by my prescription for additional help. For him, it represented an injection of helium that might provide enough lift to keep his airship of hope afloat. But Mrs. Miller resisted my recommendation and argued and bargained and then bargained some more. I couldn't follow her train of thought as she tried to explain the imperative she felt about attending the weddings. The truth was that her thinking more closely resembled a corral of bumper cars driven by preadolescents than anything like a metaphorical train.

She wept for a good five minutes before

she ultimately relented to my suggestion and to her husband's gentle prodding. She only relented, I was certain, because of her husband's insistent kindness and his repeated promises that he'd be beside her no matter what, and because I'd managed to make it clear on that day that my resolve was a more than decent match for her thought disorder.

The fear in her eyes when she realized what was about to happen next was as poignant a thing as I had witnessed in my office in a long, long time. She rested her head on her husband's shoulder and with eyes full of fat tears she said, "Okay, okay. Okay, okay. Okay, okay. Okay, okay."

He said, "I'm here. I'm here. I'm here."

I'd been doing clinical work for too long to consider entertaining the clinical delusion that the fact that Mrs. Miller had relented for that moment meant that the road ahead would be smooth.

"No more weddings?" she'd asked me incredulously only a moment after her four pairs of *okay*s had trumped her husband's three-of-a-kind of *I'm here*. "Oh Willy, does this mean no more weddings?"

Bill — Willy — looked at me for direction.

I said, "Yes, I'm afraid it does."

With a despair that I could feel all the way to my toes, she lamented, "What will they do? Oh, what will they do?"

What I saw in her eyes wasn't concern, it was fear. She hadn't said, "What will *I* do?" She had said, "What will *they* do?" She was worried about "them."

I wondered, of course, who "they" were. The brides and grooms with whom she hadn't yet celebrated? Or perhaps — and I knew this was more likely — the speakers of the voices that I suspected were whispering or shouting wicked nuptial imperatives into her ears.

I didn't know. Nor did I suspect that she would tell me. Not that day.

While the Millers were sitting in my office I'd already acknowledged to myself that I wasn't the best-equipped mental health professional in town to help Mrs. Miller with her individual treatment. I explained my rationale to the Millers, and with their consent I picked up the phone and called Mary Black — the same psychiatrist who was sharing offices with Hannah Grant before Hannah's death — and asked if she could do an urgent emergency assessment.

I'd chosen a psychiatrist to assist Mrs. Miller because I knew that the initial

104

phases of Mrs. Miller's treatment, and likely the long-term progression of her care as well, would involve the shuffling and management of antipsychotic medications, and in Colorado the provision of those pharmaceuticals was the domain of the medical profession. I'd chosen Mary Black as a psychiatrist for Mrs. Miller not only because Mary was good, but also because she was relatively new in town and she was still hungry for fresh patients. I didn't think it was advisable for the Millers to wait weeks to see a psychiatrist and begin treatment.

Mary graciously agreed to evaluate Mrs. Miller later that afternoon. Mr. Miller had driven his wife the few blocks over to Mary's office directly from mine, and I'd never seen the Millers together again.

Months later, at a summer party at a mutual friend's house, Mary Black had suggested to me — "You know that woman you referred to me? The wedding woman?" — that Mrs. Miller's care had quickly degenerated into a carousel of poor treatment compliance, failed trials of conventional drugs and the newer atypical antipsychotic compounds, and repeated short-term, stabilizing, acute hospitalizations.

The wedding planners and pastors and ministers and rabbis in town knew all about Mrs. Miller by then. Ushers at virtually every wedding ceremony in the county carried an eight-by-ten glossy of her in full nuptial regalia, and after six months of futile mental health treatment she was being turned away at some church or synagogue door almost every Saturday.

It was precisely the kind of outcome that I had feared.

When she was done telling me the story of what had happened to Mrs. Miller, Mary Black told me one other thing. She said, "I don't think my husband would stand by me the way her husband has. It's inspiring. Truly inspiring. The things he's done for her . . ."

Mary's eyes told me something else: that she knew that I knew that I owed her one.

Bill Miller came back to see me a little over a year later. It was the January right after the horrid Christmas when Boulder's little blond beauty queen had been discovered dead in the basement of her home. Bill and I met for only a few minutes, maybe fifteen. He'd asked for the time so that he could thank me for my help with Rachel. I'd told him, honestly, that I didn't

11

"The girl was anxious about the holidays? And she misses her mother? That's what the session she had with Hannah was about? That's it?" I said to Diane.

"No. No, that's not all of it," Diane said. "Come on, I'm doing this from memory. It was no big deal at the time. I didn't take any notes. The whole consultation lasted five minutes, maybe. God, I should write things down. I just should."

"What do you remember?"

"The girl told Hannah that her mother has a severe mental illness and had left Boulder years ago. The girl doesn't talk to her much, misses her. Hannah was speculating about the mother having bipolar disorder or schizophrenia, but she didn't really have enough information. She was worried about the girl developing symptoms."

I wanted to tell Diane that I already knew the details. I wanted to tell her about

all the weddings that Mrs. Miller attended, about the lovely bonnets and the QVC gifts, and about the delusions, and the voices. I wanted to tell her that at the time I did my eval that I thought Hannah was right about the schizophrenia, wrong about the bipolar disorder.

Instead I said, "You can't tell anybody, Diane. You can only divulge the fact that this girl saw Hannah for psychotherapy if you have reason to suspect that there has been, or is likely to be, child abuse. Otherwise the privilege holds."

"But she can't seek care without a parent's permission until she's fifteen."

"You're sure about that?" I asked.

"Yes."

Diane was often sure about things that turned out not to be true, but I suspected she was right about that one. "Even if it's true, I don't know whether that would abrogate her privilege."

"But it might."

"You're not even sure it was really Mallory. You'd have to violate privilege even to be certain. God knows there would be lawyers involved, and once there are lawyers involved, anything can happen. Either way, the privilege won't evaporate today. If they started litigating this to-

morrow you wouldn't have an answer before next year's aspen season. You know
lawyers better than I do."

"What do you mean? You're married to
one, while I" — she paused for effect —
"am married to a Mediterranean god."

I decided not to take that detour with
her.

"What if she's dead?" Diane asked.

Shit. "Diane, do you know that she's —"

"No, no, I don't. I don't. But if she were,
if that was determined, I was wondering if
I could —"

"No, you couldn't — confidentiality survives death. Well, actually you'd have to tell
her parents if they asked, because they
would probably have control of her estate,
which includes all her medical records,
but —"

"Why would they ask? If they didn't
know she'd been in treatment, why would
they ask?"

"Exactly."

Diane and I had been partners longer
than Lauren and I had been married. I
wasn't surprised that we were finishing
each other's thoughts. But the ping-pong
nature of the conversation we were having
felt awkward to me. Why? I suspected that
each of us was in possession of some infor-

111

mation that we weren't sure how to handle, information we didn't want to keep to ourselves, but information we weren't at all sure we were permitted to share.

"The girl also told Hannah —"

"Wait, I want to do this face-to-face. I have a patient late this afternoon at the office. I'll come downtown. You available?"

She sighed. "I was just about to head out to the after-Christmas sales on the Mall. Things are going to get really picked over if I don't get down there soon."

After-Christmas shopping on the Pearl Street Mall? I would have preferred to be strapped into a chair and serenaded by The Captain and Tennille.

"With Raoul?" That was wishful thinking on my part. The worse the party, the more grateful I was for Raoul's company. After-Christmas shopping on the Mall sounded like a very bad party.

"Shopping? With me? Are you kidding? He won't shop with me."

There was a caution there I knew; Raoul was a wise man. I swallowed a sigh. "Okay, where do think you're going to be? I'll meet you someplace."

The little office building that Diane and I owned together was an architecturally pe-

destrian — certainly not a painted-lady — early-1900s Victorian house on the west end of Walnut, a couple of blocks from the Pearl Street Mall. The odds of finding street parking in downtown Boulder during the closeout-sale-frenzied week between Christmas and New Year's were about the same as the odds of being eaten by a great white shark, so Diane was planning to stash her Saab behind our building and start her quest for bargains near Ninth and Pearl on the west end of downtown. Since I had a patient to see, I told her I'd park at our offices, too, and suggested we rendezvous outside Peppercorn at three.

Dirty snow from the Christmas-night snowstorm lingered in shady places along the herringbone brick pathways of the Mall, but despite what the calendar said, the day was pleasant in the sun. That's where I was sitting enjoying an afternoon interlude when Diane sauntered up to me at about ten after. She was carrying two huge shopping bags. I gave her a hug and a kiss on one cheek. She gave me one of the bags to carry. In many ways — mostly but not entirely good — Diane and I were like an old married couple.

We began walking, the sun low against our backs. From the heft of the bag in my

hand, I surmised that she had been scouring the sales for either bricks or bullion.

"This doesn't happen to me, you know," she said. "This is the sort of thing that happens to you. This stuff with this mystery girl and Hannah. This murder and kidnapping and cops and criminals crap I seem to be mixed up with. It's your specialty, not mine."

I was tempted to argue that it was debatable that Hannah had been murdered, and that it seemed more likely that Mallory was indeed a runaway and not a kidnap victim. But Diane's bigger point was close to the truth. Karma did seem to deliver mayhem to my door with disturbing regularity.

"If it's what you think it is, I'm mixed up in it, too, Diane."

For a moment she was quiet. She either didn't quite hear me, she didn't quite believe me, or she was busy discounting my words as an unwelcome empathic gesture.

Finally, she replied, "Sure, you were part of the Hannah thing. I know, I know. I know you were there. And well, now you're part of this other thing, but that's only because I've dragged you into it. Listen, if you'd rather I talk to someone else about this, I understand. But I really felt I

needed a second opinion about what to do next, and I don't know anyone else who has as much experience with crazy therapy crap as you do."

Crazy therapy crap? Once again I was tempted to argue her premise, but recognizing the futility, I said, "The truth is that I was a little bit mixed up in the Mallory thing already, even before we talked."

She heard me that time. Her voice grew conspiratorial. "What?"

I shook my head and kept walking. "I need to make this a consultation, too. My knowledge is clinical, just like yours."

She'd grown tired of the forced-infantry-march nature of our pace and abruptly stopped walking. Once I realized she had stopped I did, too, and turned back to face her. Over the top of her head the sun was looming just above the highest peaks of the Front Range in the southwest sky. The light was sharp but gentle. It felt only faintly warm on my face.

"Tell me," she said.

It was a shrink phrase, psychotherapy shorthand for "go on" or "don't stop there" or "damn your resistance, spill the beans."

"This is for real — a professional consultation — you can't tell anyone."

"Holy moly," she said.

I wished I had my sunglasses on my eyes instead of in my jacket pocket. I was squinting into the sun. *Holy moly?* "Is that a yes?"

"I'm thinking. You get into the weirdest things, Alan. I'm not sure I want any part of whatever it is."

She was playing with me. "Sure you do," I said.

"You're right, I do. I'm a glutton for punishment. Okay, go ahead and consult with me." She raised her chin an inch and tilted it up to the side as though she were opening herself for a right cross. I opened my mouth to reply just as she changed her strategy. "No, no, let me guess." She made a face that a bad acting student might make to try to portray someone cogitating, contorted it a few times for dramatic effect, and finally said, "Nope, I give up."

"Years ago, I saw the Millers, Mallory's parents — those Millers — for an assessment. One session only. Turned out to be a long eval, over two hours. I saw them as a couple, immediately recognized that Mrs. Miller's individual problems were . . . significant, and referred her on to Mary Black for ongoing treatment and some serious pharmacological intervention. I never saw them again. Mary took over from there.

Mr. Miller came back sometime later to thank me for my help. But I never laid eyes on the kids, don't even remember if I knew their names."

Diane was a smart lady. She made all the appropriate connections instantly. "That must be how Mallory knew about Hannah, right? Right? I bet the crazy mother parked Mallory in the waiting room while she had her psychotherapy sessions and her med consultations with Mary. Don't you think? If Hannah had seen a little girl alone in the waiting room she would have chatted her up. You know she would have. She would have made friends with her. Especially if she saw her sitting out there alone on a regular basis. That's the connection. That's it."

"Yes," I agreed. "That's probably it." Hannah's kindness was almost as legendary as her obsessiveness. I had no trouble manufacturing a vision of Hannah on her knees in the waiting room connecting with a lonely or frightened little girl who was waiting for her mother to finish an appointment with her psychiatrist.

Hi, sweetheart, what's your name?
I'm Mallory.
I'm Hannah. You waiting for your mom to

117

finish her meeting?

"Holy moly," Diane repeated.

Diane started walking down the Mall again. I tagged along behind. "Holy moly" was a new phrase for Diane. I was already beginning to hope that — like most everything designed by Microsoft — it came equipped with built-in obsolescence.

I said, "I'd bet mortgage money that her disease isn't stable. Rachel Miller sabotaged every last treatment that Mary Black tried years ago."

Diane added an edge to her tone and said, "Why do you say 'disease'? Almost everyone else says 'illness.'"

"A lot of other people say 'clients.' I say 'patients.' Do you know why? 'Patient' is from the Latin. It means 'one who suffers.' It fits what we do."

She smiled, and shifted her voice into sarcasm mode. "I bet if a new client walked into your office and had to listen to you parsing Latin all day long, she'd become one-who-suffers in no time at all. You didn't answer my question."

"Other people say 'illness'?"

"They do."

It probably wasn't true. Diane's penchant for assuredness about this kind of thing often had scant correlation to reality.

118

Regardless, it took me only about three steps to arrive at an answer to her question. "Think about it. The word is *dis-ease*. *Dis. Ease.* It's apropos, don't you think, to what we deal with every day?"

In my peripheral vision I could tell that Diane had shaken off my explanation with the same ease with which she'd just ridiculed the tiny bit of Latin I recalled from high school. I consoled myself with the fact that she was equally dismissive as she discounted her husband Raoul's opinions about just about everything political.

Thankfully, she moved on to a fresh thought, and said, "In case you didn't know it, she's in Las Vegas. The girl told Hannah that her mother is living in Las Vegas. She gets phone calls from her every once in a while. Her father doesn't know that they're in touch as much as they are. It's a source of conflict. The girl wasn't sure what to do."

"Vegas?" I asked, but it was more of an "ah-ha!" exclamation than a question. I was thinking, *Of course Rachel Miller is in Las Vegas. Where else would someone go who is addicted to weddings?*

"You don't sound that surprised, Alan. Does she gamble? Is that part of her pathology, her dis-ease?"

119

"No," I said, refusing to bite. "She goes to weddings. That's what the presenting complaint was for the couple's therapy: Rachel Miller went to lots and lots of weddings. She thought she was a special guest at all of them. It was the center of her delusional world. I suspected that she had command hallucinations but she didn't admit to hearing voices during our one interview. Her husband told me she did, that she heard voices."

"Paranoid schizophrenia?"

"That's what I thought at the time, but a lot has changed in how we all view psychotic process, you know? I'm not sure how I'd diagnose her today."

"Mixed thought and mood disorder? That's what you're thinking?" Diane asked.

"Something like that, yes."

By that time Diane and I had covered all four blocks and were at the east end of the Mall. We were waiting at the light to cross Fifteenth onto the sidewalk on the still-sunny side of Pearl Street. I said, "You want to keep going or head back?"

"I don't care. We can walk to Denver if you want, but I want to hear more about Mallory's mother and all the weddings."

It took me a while but I explained Mrs. Miller's odd nuptial delusions to Diane,

120

who had many questions, some psychological in nature, more having to do with wedding logistics, owning all those outfits, and buying all those gifts.

I had answers for a paltry few of the questions in any of the categories, psychological or matrimonial. After multiple prods on her part I tried to refocus her by saying, "I only saw the Millers for that one session. That's all. Most of my energy went into trying to understand her history and then trying to prepare the two of them for a whole different kind of treatment than they'd come in the door thinking they'd get."

"Receptions, too?" Diane asked, ignoring my pleas of ignorance.

I told her, yes, that Rachel had also attended the receptions. I shared the story about the one at the Boulderado where she'd been busted by the sheriff's deputy.

Diane had more questions. While I protested my continued ignorance about most things matrimonial, Diane chided me that it had been a very long session I'd had with the Millers, and I should know more than I was letting on.

Once Diane had — finally — exhausted her queries about Mrs. Miller and her serial wedding attendance, I had a question of my own. It was the question that I had

wanted to ask Diane since the moment she told me that Hannah had done an intake with the girl who was probably Mallory. "Do you think it's possible that Mallory went to Vegas to see her mother? Based on what Hannah told you, would she have done that? Could that be what this is all about?"

"It's possible. Hannah stressed that the girl missed her mother. May even have said it a couple of times, so you have to wonder. Hannah focused on the mother/daughter relationship and the conflicts between the girl and her dad."

"Might explain the Christmas Day stomachache," I said. "Her holiday anxiety, missing her mom."

"Psychosomatic?"

"Why not? If she was worried enough to seek a therapist on her own, she could certainly be worried enough to develop symptoms."

She paused after a couple more steps. We had walked all the way down to Eighteenth Street by then, almost a full ten blocks from our cars. I stopped and turned back to the west. The late December sun was just a slash of brilliance above the Divide and pedestrian traffic was thinning out on the Mall.

"What was the mother like, Alan? Could she have come and taken Mallory?" Diane asked.

"I suppose that's possible. Anything is, but —"

"The cops would check that first, right? They would have gone to Vegas and checked with Mallory's mother to see if her kid was there, to see if the mom had been in Boulder?"

"Yes," I said. I was also thinking that the Boulder cops who went to Vegas would probably have found a truly disturbed woman.

Diane casually tapped me on the shoulder and handed me the second shopping bag. Like a fool, I took it.

We started walking back in the direction of the mountains. The western sky was much brighter than the eastern sky had been. She asked, "So are you ready now?"

Segue or no segue, I knew exactly what she was talking about. We really had been friends a long, long time. "Sure, as ready as I'll be. So what else did the girl tell Hannah?"

12

The moment the sun completed its descent behind the Rockies the day turned from pleasantly brisk to downright cold. What I had been considering a light breeze felt decidedly like an icy wind. Diane had seen it coming — now that I was schlepping both of her shopping bags she was able to shove her mittened hands deep into her jacket pockets for additional warmth.

My gloves were in my car and the flesh on my hands was the color of the fat on a slab of uncooked bacon.

"The kid was concerned that her dad was 'up to something' or 'into something.' She'd left Hannah with the impression that she didn't like it, whatever it was. The girl was feeling like she had to do something about it, or else. That kind of thing."

" 'Up to something'? That's a quote?"

"Close as I can remember. It was a casual consultation — I didn't exactly mem-

orize it. I didn't know what was about to happen."

" 'Or else'? What did that mean?"

Diane shrugged. "I should have asked. I didn't ask. She also had some friend trouble, too, was conflicted about some guy she was seeing."

"Boyfriend?"

"I guess."

"It felt like typical adolescent stuff to you?"

"At the time it did."

"And the nature of what the girl's father was up to?"

"Hannah didn't know."

"Precipitant?"

"See, that's the thing. I asked Hannah that, too. Hannah felt there was some urgency for the girl, but couldn't get the kid to admit to anything."

"A secret?"

"I wish I knew."

"The holidays?"

"Hannah didn't stress that part. I suppose it's possible."

"The police should know all this," I said. "Boulder's two most high-profile recent . . ."

I didn't know what to call Hannah's death and Mallory's disappearance. Diane did. "Crimes. The word you're looking for

is 'crimes.' 'Felonies' would work fine, too."

"Whatever. The police would want to know that there's a possible connection — a big connection — between Hannah's death and Mallory's disappearance. But nobody knows about it but you," I said.

"And you," she reminded me.

"Mostly you. It's too bad you can't tell the police."

She skipped for one step. I think that's what she did, anyway — just one little schoolgirl skip. Why? Who knew? "I bet that twerp Slocum would love to know what the two of us know, wouldn't he? He'd probably cuff me again and throw me in the slammer if he knew what I was keeping from him."

I was thinking that not only would Detective Slocum like to know, but so would Diane Sawyer, Katie Couric, Geraldo Rivera, and Oprah. Not to mention the *Enquirer* and the *Sun* and the *Star*.

And Bill Miller.

I was also thinking that Diane's continuing animosity toward Detective Jaris Slocum, though completely understandable, was one of the ways that she was postponing her grief about Hannah's death. That moment, however, wasn't the time to

confront her with that particular reality. Years of experience with her had taught me that with Diane I had to pick my spots.

"Raoul wants me to sue Slocum. Did I tell you that?"

"For what?"

"He doesn't care. He calls him 'that little fascist.' 'Let's sue that little fascist, baby,' he tells me. He hates it when I say it, but sometimes he's such an American."

I said, "Raoul has too much time on his hands. He needs to go start a new company or something." Diane's husband was a legendary Boulder entrepreneur. When he wasn't nurturing somebody else's start-up tech company, he was busy casting the bricks to create a new one of his own.

As we crossed back over Fifteenth to the herringbone pathways of the Mall, Diane asked the money question: "So what do I do about all this?"

"Did Hannah leave any notes?"

"She named me in her will to handle the details of closing up her practice should anything happen to her. But I haven't found any notes about that session. Zip, *nada*."

Few therapists show the foresight to make death stipulations in their wills. But Hannah had. I said, "She knew Paul

127

Weinman back when, didn't she?"

"Yes, she knew Paul." Paul had been another friend of Diane's, a psychologist who'd skied into a tree at Breckenridge years before. His sudden death, and the subsequent uncertainty about what to do with his current cases and his practice records, had caused a lot of procrastinating Boulder therapists to make plans for what would happen to their practices in case of their own death.

"Do the police have her appointment calendar?" I asked.

"Hannah just used initials, same as us. They would have to cross-reference the calendar with her billing records or her clinical files to find out who she was seeing. Cozy is handling the cops for me, and he's not going to let them see anything confidential."

"Anything else important in Hannah's records?"

"Not really. Closing her practice has been routine. I've done a few one-time visits with her patients to check for decompensation or acute reactive problems to her . . . death. I decided to pick up a couple of her cases. Oh, and did I tell you I'm going to see the woman who was at her office that day, the day that Hannah died?"

"The woman with the hair?" *And the Cheetos.* "You're seeing her for treatment?"

"I am. She's having a lot of trouble. I guess it's not too surprising, considering. She's coping by becoming a little Nancy Drew, trying to solve the mystery of what happened to her therapist."

"Isn't it kind of odd seeing her? Given what happened."

"You don't think it's a problem, do you?"

I wasn't sure. Psychologists are prohibited from treating people with whom they have another existing relationship. It means, for instance, that I couldn't treat Grace's preschool teacher, when Grace gets around to having one. But I didn't know if the fact that both parties had been present when a possible murder victim's body was discovered really constituted a preexisting relationship. The issue had never come up before in any of the ethics discussions I'd had.

I didn't want to make Diane crazy, so I immediately resolved my ambivalence by saying, "No, I don't think so."

"Good. Anyway, I've referred a few of Hannah's other patients to other therapists in town. Don't be hurt. I'm not ignoring your talents — they all wanted female therapists, baby. But most of them decided not

to continue for now. I'm still having her office phone lines forwarded to my number. The hardest part of the whole thing has been letting people who hadn't heard what happened to her know that she is dead. And, you know, how she died."

"I can imagine." We took two more steps. "Is it possible you spoke with her?"

"With whom?"

"Mallory."

"What do you mean?"

"Is it possible she was one of the people who called who hadn't heard about Hannah's death?"

"Oh my God."

"Well?"

"It's possible. I had a couple of difficult calls . . . a woman asked . . . she was young — I guessed a CU student — wanted 'Dr. Grant.' I'm not sure I ever got a name. I told her what had happened and she . . . hung up. Oh my God."

"When was that call?" I asked.

"Last week. Maybe Monday. Oh my God, I may have talked with her."

"Do you remember what you said?"

"I've been upset," Diane said, her voice suddenly hollow. "I might not have handled it well. When Hannah's patients asked me how she died, I . . ."

"Suggested the possibility she'd been murdered?"

"It's not just me, Alan. Everybody — the papers — I'm not the only one . . ."

I touched her. "It's okay."

"The kid was really upset. I offered to meet with her, but she hung up."

What did it mean that Diane might have talked with Mallory a few days before she disappeared? Maybe nothing. But it was possible that Mallory walked away from the conversation believing that her therapist had been murdered.

"What about the other call? You said there were two difficult calls."

"The other one was from a man. Wanted to know what would happen to his therapy records. I assured him I had custody of them and that they'd stay confidential. He wouldn't give me his name, either. He asked how he could get the records. I told him. He didn't want a referral. He was almost . . . belligerent."

I didn't reply right away. Diane wanted to move on. "Speaking of records, Hannah's attorney — the guy who drew up her will — called me a couple of days before Christmas and asked if she had left any records that would allow final bills to be prepared."

"For her patients?"

"Yes."

"That's rude. Who's the attorney?"

"Guy named Jerry Crandall. I don't know him. He's a general-practice guy, doesn't do much divorce work." Diane did do a lot of divorce and custody work; she knew all the family-law attorneys in town. "But that's what I told him, too, that it was kind of cold. He said he had a fiduciary responsibility and that Hannah's accounts receivable are an asset of her estate."

"Fiduciary responsibility aside, I'm not sure I'd like to get a bill from my dead therapist."

"He's a lawyer. Can I finish?" Diane didn't wait for me to say yes. "I told him I'd take a look and get back to him. While you guys were up skiing I checked through Hannah's practice calendar and matched things up with her recent process notes, gave him a list of unbilled sessions. When I compared all her records I realized that the session with this kid wasn't in her calendar, didn't have any notes, and had never been billed. It was the only one not in her calendar."

"No other sessions without notes?"

"None that I found. Hannah was Hannah." Loud exhale. "What do I do, Alan?"

"In a word, nothing. Hell, Diane, you're not even sure it was Mallory. I think the kid is entitled to confidentiality, so you can't reveal what you know from the session."

"It was her," Diane said.

I ignored that. "Any hint of abuse during the consultation?"

"No."

"You can't tell anyone then, including the police."

"What if the police knew Mallory had been kidnapped? If the parents got a note, or a ransom demand. Would that change things?"

I thought about it for the length of time it took to try, and fail, to pass three young mothers pushing strollers wheel hub to wheel hub on the bricks of the Mall. It was the pedestrian equivalent of trying to drive past some recalcitrant semis that were rolling side-by-side on the highway.

"Sure. Then it would be a whole different ball game. By definition a kidnapped kid is a kid who's being abused, and abuse changes all the privilege rules. If you thought you knew something that could aid the investigation into her kidnapping — once the authorities decided it was a kidnapping — you would have an ethical

and legal responsibility to divulge it to the police because of the child-abuse exception."

Diane said, "But the police say she ran. As long as that's the current theory, I can't play the I-think-she's-been-kidnapped card."

The holiday lights that were strung on the trees on the Mall began snapping on block by block, and within seconds snakes of twinkling dots wrapped the skeletal forms that stretched out in front of us. Diane and I both watched the spectacle develop for a moment.

"That was pretty," I said. "Sorry, your hands are tied."

Hers may have been figuratively tied; mine were literally going numb from the cold and the weight of the shopping bags I was carrying.

"I suppose this means that I probably shouldn't prepare a bill for the intake and send it to Mallory's father."

Diane's last comment was intended sardonically, but I recognized some fuzzy edges at the margins; the ramifications weren't as clear as she might have expected. "It's an interesting point, Diane."

"What do you mean?"

"If you were looking for a way to tell her father that you know something, sending

him a bill would probably be an ethically acceptable excuse for letting him get a toe inside the consultation room door."

"And why would I want to do that?"

"I'm not sure you would. But just for the sake of argument, let's say you believed that what you learned from Hannah's consultation might help track down Mallory."

"And if I did believe that . . ."

"The fact that no bill has gone out yet might give you an avenue to breach confidence with her father. If you were sure the kid was Mallory. Did Hannah say anything about billing arrangements for her session with the girl?"

"Not a word. But I have to work under the assumption that the kid didn't want her parents to know about the therapy, don't I? Knowing Hannah, I bet she did the session pro bono, anyway."

"Why? Why would you assume that the girl wouldn't want her father to know about the therapy?"

"Why? Because the kid just showed up without an appointment, and she told Hannah that he was up to something and she wasn't happy about it."

I played devil's advocate. "But what if he's the one who sent her to see Hannah? What if her father already knows all about

whatever it was that caused her to go? Ninety-nine out of a hundred kids are in psychotherapy because somebody sends them, and the someone is usually one of the kid's parents. A kid doesn't often go on her own."

Diane's tone grew dismissive. "If Mallory's father sent her into treatment he'd have told the police that his daughter had seen a therapist recently, right? That would be important information to consider after her disappearance."

"You would think."

"And the police would have contacted that therapist, right? To try and find out what the kid was troubled about."

I knew where she was going. "Unless the police already knew that the therapist was dead."

"But if they knew that Mallory was seeing Hannah and that Hannah was dead, they would have sent whoever had legal custody of her practice records — *c'est moi* — a subpoena in order to get access to the treatment notes."

"Agreed. If the cops were thinking."

"Well, none of that happened. None of it. Nobody from the police department has contacted me about Mallory. And I certainly haven't been subpoenaed." As she

began to connect more of the dots Diane's foot speed kept pace with her mouth speed, and I had to hustle to keep up with her. "So I'm left thinking that Mallory sought out Hannah for treatment on her own, which would tell me that she didn't want her father to know what she was up to. Or . . . her father had sent Mallory to Hannah, which — given his subsequent silence on the matter — would tell me that for some reason he doesn't want the police to know what his daughter was up to."

I said, "That about covers the possibilities."

"As a therapist, I don't especially like either theory. But I'd put my money on Mallory as the one who was trying to keep the secret."

We arrived at the intersection with Broadway. The pedestrian signal was red and enough traffic was humming past us to rule out jaywalking. I lowered Diane's shopping bags to the bricks and lifted my hands so I could show her that my fingers were curled into hooks. I asked, "Do you mind taking these bags back? My hands are frozen."

She looked imposed upon.

And I realized, belatedly, why her husband refused to shop with her.

13

I had an additional tie to the Miller family, one that certainly fit any definition of tangential anyone might wish to apply, one that was marked by the requisite degree or two of separation. The link didn't come into focus for me until my solitary psychotherapy appointment late on the afternoon of the day that I played reluctant Sherpa for Diane as she trolled the Mall for Christmas bargains. The source of the connection was someone I never would have anticipated.

Bob Brandt.

Bob had been coming to me for individual psychotherapy for almost two years, and progress had been glacial. Pre–global-warming glacial. The meager speed of the treatment neither surprised nor particularly disappointed me. Diagnostically, Bob's underlying character was a caustic blend of toxic pathologies. Had he been using health insurance to pay for his treatment — he wasn't — the DSM-IV code his

insurer would have required would have had as many digits as a Visa card.

The first five of those digits would have spelled out the cipher for schizoid personality disorder. In addition to having a serious schizoid character, Bob was also a chronically depressed, mildly paranoid guy. Forty-three years old, he'd been ensconced in the same dead-end clerical position in the physics department at the University of Colorado for almost two decades.

His mother and an older brother were his only living relatives. Bob had maintained contact with his mom for most of his adult life. A few years before, however, his brother had written him a letter notifying him that their mother was moving to an assisted-living facility near his house in southern Colorado. Bob had interpreted the missive as his brother's order to "butt out," and he hadn't spoken with either his mother or his brother since.

Where did reality lie? Sadly, I didn't know. Nor was it clear to me exactly how Bob felt about the artificial estrangement. He deflected all my inquiries about it, and resisted my occasional attempts to question his harsh appraisal of his brother's letter.

Bob had no current friends or romantic

relationships and no history that I could uncover of any significant friendships since childhood, or of romantic relationships, ever. His sole social outlet was occasional attendance at local Scrabble clubs and tournaments. Mostly, though, he preferred to play his games online.

The Internet, for all its interpersonal anonymity, is a schizoid's dream.

Schizoid.

The dictionary, nonpsychological meaning of the word is the "coexistence of disparates." Something that is part this, part that. In mental health terms, schizoid has surprisingly little in common with either its *Webster's* definition or its similar-sounding, polysyllabic psychopathology cousin, schizophrenia. Unlike schizophrenia, schizoid personality disorder isn't a disorder of thought or perception.

Not at all. Schizoid personality disorder is a disorder of relating.

People with the malady have a history, often since early adolescence, sometimes even before that, of aloofness from relationships, emotional coldness, immunity from praise or criticism, generalized anhedonia — the inability to experience pleasure — and limited affective range.

The portrayal fit Bob like a custom-made wet suit.

Bob was, by his own description, "a dork, a geek, a nerd, a snarf — you pick the synonym for loser, that's me." He had a head shaped like the bow of a boat, and I surmised that his hair had been receding from his temples since the second or third grade. Exploratory surgery would be necessary to determine if he actually possessed a chin. His eyes were tiny and at times they seemed to shake in their sockets. The effect was so disconcerting to me that early in the treatment I'd actually referred him for a neurological evaluation to have those vibrating orbs assessed.

The neurologist had a name for the condition, which he assured me was benign. As was my style, I'd managed to forget the specific medical terminology by the time I was reading that night's bedtime story to my daughter.

Bob liked cars, or, more accurately, was enamored of his own car. He had a thirty-something-year-old Camaro with a big motor that he'd bought from a guy in Longmont who'd lovingly restored it to its original ebony luster. Every time Bob mentioned the old muscle car, which seemed like at least once a session, he reminded

me that its condition was "cherry," and every month or two he assured me that it was a "matching numbers car."

After two years of reminders I still didn't know what that meant.

Bob lived in a couple of rooms he rented above the detached garage of a modest house near Nineteenth and Pine. He described his landlords as "old people," and maintained that he never spoke with them at all. Despite the fact that they lived less than fifty feet from his rented rooms, he mailed his rent check to them every month.

He could walk to work at the university from his flat and used the classic Camaro primarily to cruise around downtown or the Hill or other student haunts on weekend nights. In a rare flash of insight he'd once acknowledged that he drove his prize around town on pleasant evenings hoping that someone would find his ride cool, though the few times that he and his car had generated attention out in public he'd been pretty certain that the students had been taunting him.

After a lifetime feeling that he'd been born with the birthmark of a bull's-eye on his chest, Bob was familiar with being taunted and appeared immune to it.

Frankly, the incidents with the university students hadn't seemed to trouble him. He was perplexed, however, that the kids didn't find his car cool.

To Bob, that was crazy.

Over the last year he had begun to visit Boulder's clubs and bars with some regularity, at least a couple of times a month. His pub-crawling wasn't designed to accommodate a drinking habit — a period of severe bingeing in his early twenties had actually caused him to swear off alcohol. Regardless, he was way too cheap to splurge on nightclub-priced drinks. And he didn't go out to the clubs to hang out in the glow of the pretty people. After a firm confrontation from me one day — "Come on, Bob, why do you go?" — he admitted that he went out to nightspots to "watch them."

I guessed that he meant the girls, but I couldn't get him to admit it. So I reserved judgment, aware that Bob could just as well have been spying on the boys. In my presence, he'd never admitted to any feeling that I would categorize as either romantic or sexual toward people of either gender.

That's all he would say about his clubbing predilection, that he went to "watch

them." I was left to wonder: If the watching wasn't some once-removed sexual thing, was it voyeuristic? Anthropological? Maybe part of some arcane sociological experiment? After almost two years of trying to understand such things about Bob I still wasn't sure, and on those Tuesday nights when I was driving home after I'd completed a session with him and found myself still musing about Bob's narrow life, the fact that there was so much I didn't know troubled me.

I suspected that the pretty objects of Bob's fascination were at least equally troubled when they looked up to discover Bob's shimmying eyes locked on to their own as they downed designer cocktails in Boulder's latest trendy nightspot.

I also had little doubt that Bob would avert his eyes the moment his prey noticed that he was staring. I knew it because in two years of sessions Bob had never held eye contact with me for more than a split second.

Other than the regular interaction he had with his boss in the physics department at the university — it was at her insistence that he'd sought therapy — the psychotherapy with me was, to my knowledge, Bob's primary ongoing human rela-

tionship that didn't include at least one cyber-buffer. Although I suspected that he trusted me more than he trusted his boss, I reminded myself that he didn't even trust her enough to allow her the responsibility of keeping the begonia on his desk watered during his infrequent holidays from work.

He certainly didn't trust me enough to accept my oft-repeated suggestions about the potential benefits of psychopharmacology. I raised the issue occasionally, but never pressed it. Although I held out hopes that the right antidepressant might dent his veneer of despair, the odds of medication impacting Bob's underlying character disorder were slim. But then — I had to admit — so were the odds that psychotherapy would ever make any profound difference in his functioning.

That didn't mean I wasn't going to try.

Bob did trust me just enough to come back to see me every Tuesday afternoon at 4:45. That was the foundation of our relationship. In two years of treatment, he'd missed only one session, and had canceled that appointment four weeks in advance. Forty-five minutes, once a week, that was our deal. Bob knew what time our appointment started. He knew when it ended. After a hundred tries, though, he still had

only the most vague concept of what should happen in between.

I saw him on a sliding scale, discounting my usual fee by well more than half so that he could afford to come in. Bob would always pay me at the beginning of the last session of each month, just before I handed out my bills. His personal check to me was always placed in the same type of security envelope, was always folded the same way, and was always double sealed, once by licking the flap, and once by the addition of two long strips of Scotch tape.

Bob's handwriting was tiny and precise and rounded. The first time he gave me a check I had to use a magnifying glass to read the amount. I didn't know how the university credit union managed to clear his checks. But it did.

On occasional Tuesdays during our time together we did something that loosely resembled traditional psychotherapy. More often the sessions were an odd interchange that to an outsider probably would look more like social skills training than anything psychotherapeutic. Not unlike someone afflicted with Asperger's syndrome, Bob had no innate sense of how human interaction should work. He would end up being insulting when his intent was to be

impersonally cordial. He would often be cruel while he was merely trying to create some protective psychological space. During the first year of treatment we'd spent a half dozen autumn Tuesdays troubleshooting how Bob might respond differently when a student walked up to his desk in the physics department and said, "Good morning," or "Hi."

His previous stock reply — "What difference does it make?" — hadn't been working too well for him.

The most surprising thing about psychotherapy with Bob? As the months passed I'd grown fond of this man who was about as easy to get close to as a porcupine. In the lingo, I had developed a positive countertransference for him. And maybe because I'd developed affection for Bob my empathy for his plight was sometimes swollen out of proportion.

I vowed to keep an eye on it.

14

Bob's connection to the Millers didn't appear to be particularly unique or interesting. He hadn't babysat Mallory, nor had he gone to high school with Mrs. Miller. He wasn't a family friend, hadn't played Santa at any Miller family holiday gatherings. In fact, his particular connection to the girl's disappearance seemed to be a relatively common affliction that he shared with many viewers of cable news TV stations. Bob, it turned out, had quickly grown obsessed by Mallory's disappearance, which, I feared, meant that for at least forty-five minutes a week I was likely to be forced to be vicariously obsessed by Mallory's disappearance, too.

I was less than thrilled by the revelation that Bob was transfixed by Mallory's plight. As he described his fascination my silent protest was a pathetic *No, please no.* At a clinical level Bob didn't need the obsession; his pathological casserole was certainly not wanting for the addition of an

obsessive crust of any description. At a more selfish level, I'd already begun hoping — like the great majority of Boulderites — that the case of the disappearing girl was going to go away gently, that Sam and his like-minded police colleagues were right and that this time the case of the disappearing girl wasn't really a case of a disappearing girl at all. Like ninety-nine percent of Boulder's residents, I was hoping that Mallory Miller — despite what I'd learned about her recent history from Diane — was just a girl who'd left home for one of the many bad reasons that young teenage girls choose to leave home.

But I wasn't to be so lucky. From the first time Bob mentioned her name — "Do you think she ran? Or do you think she was kidnapped? Mallory?" — I became concerned that Bob and I would begin to spend some unknown number of Tuesday sessions rehashing the latest news and gossip about her. Since Bob devoured the *Enquirer* and the *Star* — he didn't buy them; he scoured the student union looking for discarded copies — I was even going to be force-fed tidbits about Mallory that I wouldn't have been exposed to in the more reputable news sources.

How did I know all this?

Because Bob had been transfixed by the Kobe thing, too. And the Michael Jackson thing. Not to mention the Scott Peterson thing. That's how I knew.

I was realizing, almost even begrudgingly accepting, that it was beginning to look like I couldn't get away from Mallory Miller no matter how hard I tried.

The Tuesday session with Bob during the week between Christmas and New Year's was like dozens before it. Bob was distracted and distant, and we spent a chunk of the allotted time in silence. He surprised me by ending the appointment with a request he'd never made before: He asked if we could meet again later that week.

Could I actually be witnessing nascent signs of attachment, the therapeutic Holy Grail in the treatment of a schizoid personality? Highly unlikely, but I gladly offered him an additional session on Thursday, the penultimate day of the year.

15

The phone rang later that evening while I was giving Grace her bath. Lauren spoke for a few minutes before she joined me in the bathroom and handed me the portable and a towel for my hands. "It's Diane," she said, and I exchanged the delights of playtime in the bathtub for the dubious pleasures of the telephone.

It struck me as not a great deal.

"Hi," I said as I moved out of the bathroom and walked across the master bedroom to the big windows facing the mountains. The still-snowy spots on the winter landscape seemed fluorescent in the moonlight.

"I've been thinking," Diane said.

"Yeah."

"About Hannah."

I wasn't at all surprised. Diane and I had talked about Hannah a dozen or more times since her death. We'd do it a dozen more, and maybe a dozen more after that.

My friend liked to process out loud, and Hannah's death continued to haunt her.

"These things take time, Diane. They just do. This time of year especially, you know. The holidays make it harder."

She sighed. "That's not what I mean."

I stuffed my repertoire of grief platitudes back into storage and said, "Okay."

"What if this is why she died? Because she met with Mallory Miller. What if somebody killed Hannah because she met with the kid that one time?"

"I'm . . . listening."

"Don't use that voice. I hate that voice. You think I'm crazy? Tell me this didn't cross your mind."

"I can honestly say it didn't cross my mind." It had — briefly — but I wasn't about to admit it and inadvertently provide monster chow for the dragons inhabiting Diane's cave of paranoia.

"Hannah might have been murdered, right? That's a possibility?" Diane's tone was hoarse, slightly conspiratorial. I couldn't figure out why.

"Are you at home?"

"Yes."

"Why are you whispering?"

"I don't know. This is the sort of thing people whisper about, isn't it?"

152

"Okay, just wondering."

"Now answer me." She was still almost whispering. "It's a possibility that Hannah was murdered, right?"

"Yeah." The coroner's finding on manner of death was "undetermined." That conclusion didn't mean Hannah had been murdered, nor did it mean that she hadn't been murdered. We both knew Diane had her own hypothesis on the matter.

She spelled out her theory for me anyway. "Slocum hasn't been able to identify a motive to support a conclusion of homicide, right?"

"Yeah." I could graciously grant Diane the motive argument, fully cognizant that Slocum hadn't been able to identify means or opportunity, either. He was 0-for-3.

"Well, what if this was the motive? Something Mallory told Hannah. Something that needed to stay secret."

I tried to imagine some possibilities. Couldn't. The time frame seemed wrong. Hannah had died over a week before Mallory disappeared.

"Like?" I asked.

"I don't know. I thought you would have . . . an idea. This is your bailiwick, not mine."

Bailiwick? I was hoping it wasn't a new

companion word to *holy moly*. Regardless, Diane was doomed to be disappointed by the sparse contents of my bailiwick. I didn't have any theory about the secret that Mallory might have shared with Hannah.

From the bathroom Lauren called out, "Check the stove for me, sweetie. I have something cooking."

I inhaled, and followed the tantalizing aroma of spicy hot cider all the way to the kitchen. A cinnamon stick and some cloves were floating in a steaming apple brew. Lauren had been preparing a treat for us when the phone rang. I shut off the gas to the burner but stayed close by so the steam would rise toward my face.

Diane wasn't patient about the delay. "You still there?" she asked.

"I'm thinking." What I was thinking about was whether I should add some good whiskey or a dollop of rum to my cup of hot cider.

"You done yet?"

I said, "Maybe if Hannah had died after Mallory disappeared, it might make some sense to wander down this road. But Hannah died first. And that was over a week before Mallory disappeared."

"You think I'm crazy."

It wasn't a question. "No crazier than I thought you were before you called."

"Funny."

"Based on what you told me there was nothing incendiary about the session. Nothing worth killing Hannah over."

"She said her father was 'up to something.' Remember?"

"But the question is what? She may have meant that he wanted her to take up the viola, or change schools, or get braces. Who knows? Hannah didn't spell it out."

"I expected you to be more helpful, Alan."

No doubt because this is my bailiwick. I said, "Sorry."

"You don't want to do this, do you?" she asked.

Her question wasn't an accusation. Diane was belatedly recognizing my resistance to be involved with anything that had to do with Boulder's latest missing girl.

"No, I don't. But I will."

"Is it because of Grace?"

"I'm sure that's part of it."

"What then?"

"I'm working on that. I don't like the parallels to eight years ago. The whole thing is creepy. I'm a father now, it's . . ." I could have just admitted that I wasn't

155

working on it very hard, but Diane wouldn't have let me off the hook. The truth was that I wanted the whole Mallory Miller thing to go away.

She softened. "Think about it, please. See if anything jumps out at you. Can you at least do that?"

"Sure," I said. "I can do that."

Grace was in fresh jammies, Lauren was swathed in soft flannel, her slender feet cushioned in sheepskin Uggs, and the mug of hot cider, with a little bourbon, was warming my hands. The three of us sat together on the couch in the living room and read bedtime stories about little girls and flowers, and dogs and friends.

Grace cackled and giggled and was delighted at the pages.

I held my daughter a little tighter than usual as Lauren's late-day gravelly voice soothed us all.

I waited until Grace was in bed and Lauren was settled into the soothing rhythms of a game of pool in what — had we possessed a table and chairs instead of a tournament-quality pool table — should have been the dining room, before I went downstairs and climbed on the road bike

that I'd set up for indoor workouts in the basement. I warmed up quickly, maybe too quickly, and soon had my spin up where I wanted.

If a girl, I wondered, a fourteen-year-old girl, had shown up in my waiting room wanting an emergency appointment, what would I have done?

Mallory had probably told Hannah it was "important," or something similar. I didn't know a therapist, myself included, who wouldn't have listened to what she had to say. Why? "Important" could have meant she wanted to report abuse. And if a kid wants to report abuse, it's the responsibility of adults, especially mental health professionals, to bend over backward to listen.

I also wondered whether Hannah had made the connection between the teenager in her office and the little girl she might have seen in her waiting room ten years or so before. Had Mallory said anything to remind her?

Remember me? I'm Mallory.

I tried to put myself in the same circumstances. Would I remember a kid so many years later? Would I even recognize that it was the same kid?

I didn't think I would. Miller is a

common name. Sometimes my friends' kids changed so much in only a couple of years that I hardly recognized them. Adrienne's son Jonas had grown so much in the past year that he looked like a completely different child. Sam's son Simon had gone from little boy to man-child, it seemed, in weeks.

Even if Hannah had remembered the small child she had befriended in the waiting room, the memory wouldn't have given her many clues. Hannah would have no reason to know anything about the details of Mary Black's care of Rachel Miller.

But why was Mallory so vague about her concerns about her father?

That was my most troubling question: Why would a girl insist on a session with a therapist and then be vague about what was happening at home?

I made some assumptions about the session that I thought were safe.

Hannah would have asked Mallory directly about drug use, specifically about alcohol. Hannah hadn't told Diane about any concerns with substance abuse, so apparently she felt satisfied with whatever answer she'd received from Mallory.

Given that Mallory had revealed her mother's history of mental illness, I sus-

pected that Hannah had directly or indirectly done some version of a mental status exam during the interview to see if what afflicted mother might also be afflicting her progeny. Had Mallory passed?

I didn't know that. Probably. But there were plenty of unknowns.

I listened for a moment to the sharp cracks and gentle taps that punctuated Lauren's pool playing. Returning my attention to the bike, I reminded myself that I was doing a lot of speculating.

Mallory had said her father was "up to something."

But what had he been up to?

Was it related to Mallory's anxiety about the holidays?

And why had Mallory chosen that day to sit in the waiting room to see Hannah? A great question.

I didn't have a great answer, or even a good one.

16

Coloradans don't tolerate gray skies with any equanimity.

Other weather we endure. Gray skies, no.

On the high desert landscape where the Great Plains rise into the Front Range of the Rockies, we live through the often relentless heat of June and July with little complaint, reassuring each other that even though it's 103 degrees outside, at least it's a dry heat.

Our once-a-decade oh-my-God blizzards, or our annual winter cold snaps of day-after-day temperatures below zero and wind chills that feel arctic? Most of us write them off as the price of living in close proximity to the best skiing on the planet.

The hundred-mile-an-hour winter Chinooks blowing out of the mountains in January and February? *Hey, lean into it, it's only a little wind.*

Golf-ball-size hail? Fierce summer thun-

derstorms? *We live in a desert. We need the moisture.*

But the absence of sunshine?

After two consecutive overcast days the grumbling begins, everyone's temper shortens, traffic cops stop giving warnings, and people aren't quite as nice to their dogs. Add a third or, God forbid, a fourth day of concrete-colored skies, and most of the state's residents, especially the natives, begin to wonder for what it is they're being punished. A few furtively check their IDs to see if they've been magically relocated to Seattle or Cleveland or Buffalo or some other sunshine-deprived location as penance for an obviously serious transgression against humanity.

It's not that it's always sunny here. But I have to admit that it feels like it's always sunny here. The tourist board throws around statistics: We have 300-plus days of sunshine each year, we're sunnier than San Diego, much sunnier than Miami. I don't know if any of it's true. But I do know that the reality is that in Colorado I awaken every morning expecting to see the sun for a healthy chunk of the day.

One day of gray is disappointing. Two days in a row becomes a mini-crisis.

Anything more is cause for alarm.

★ ★ ★

Once the sun had set on Diane and me as we walked the Mall sharing our secrets about the Miller family, the rest of that week between Christmas and New Year's — the week after Mallory disappeared — was meteorologically bleak. Thursday brought constant flurries under steely skies. Friday taunted — the sun's silhouette was occasionally visible behind quickly passing clouds, but warming rays never reached the ground in a way that left behind even a hint of a shadow. Saturday, snow flurries fell intermittently all day long, icy winds howled from Wyoming, and by nightfall downy drifts began to cushion the bases of fences and the low sections of walls that dared to face north.

The sun had disappeared from our state — probably forever — it seemed.

A googol of reporters was camped out in Boulder, still expecting — or, God forbid, hoping for — a garroted body to emerge from a Boulder basement.

But Mallory Miller stayed stubbornly missing.

I was getting dragged into the riddle of her absence further and further.

Everybody was cranky.

★ ★ ★

Everybody, that is, except Sam Purdy.

And Sam probably should have been cranky. He had been for all of the many years we'd been friends. A lot was going on in his life. He was on the cusp of completing his first holiday season as an unmarried man. He had just celebrated the anniversary of surviving for a year after a heart attack — he'd reminded me that it beat the alternative, hands-down — and he had just managed to complete twelve-plus months without developing a fresh gallstone.

He was still learning the ropes of single-parenting his son, Simon.

And because of Mallory Miller, he was being forced to work overtime on a high-profile holiday crime, not exactly his thing, as part of a team of many detectives, most definitely not his thing.

But Sam's mood was good. Boulder's streak of gray days was nothing compared to the winter stretches he'd endured in his family home on Minnesota's Iron Range. His health problems? He had grown philosophical about them, felt he was doing all he could — with diet and exercise — to manage them. His divorce? Despite some stumbles he thought that he and Sherry had handled it all like grown-ups. Was

there enough money to go around? Of course not — as Sam had indelicately put it, "I live in fucking Boulder. How could there be enough money?" Sam's son Simon? He was a good kid. He had some emotional bruises from what his parents' marital disruption had forced him to endure, but Sam was confident that his son would do okay.

I didn't disagree.

The Mallory Miller case? Right from the start, Sam had pitched his tent in the don't-get-too-worked-up-about-this, she's-a-runaway camp. But he was a professional cop, and until his captain told him otherwise he planned to continue to investigate the details of her disappearance as though she might have been kidnapped by some mysterious intruder.

I knew the truth about Sam's personal life. I knew that Sam's pleasant demeanor wasn't due to his positive outlook, but rather that his positive outlook was due to a girl.

Okay, a woman. Her name was Carmen Reynoso. She was a cop, another detective, a class act who lived somewhere within commuting distance of the police department in Laguna Beach, California, and she and Sam were in love. They had met a little more than a year before while on the

track of a serial killer.

It was a long story in which I'd had a part, and I liked to think I'd introduced them.

Sam and Simon had tickets, or some airline's digital equivalent, to fly to John Wayne International Airport to spend the New Year's holiday with Carmen and her daughter, Jessie. Jessie, a student at UC Santa Cruz, had promised Simon a trip to Disneyland during the visit.

In Sam's world, gray skies or blue skies, all was cool.

I met Sam at the new ice rink off the Boulder Turnpike in Superior, where Simon's peewee team was playing on the Wednesday night that fell within our streak of end-of-the-year bleak weather. Simon — who, unlike his father, played offense — was doing a sleep-over at a teammate's house after the game and Sam and I were going to go someplace for a beer. It had been a while since we'd had time to get together socially.

Perhaps the flyers that were posted all over the ice rink doors should have been a caution for me about how the evening might progress, but, like most people in Boulder County, I was already growing somewhat immune to them. Two types

predominated. Each version was on a standard eight-and-a-half-by-eleven sheet of paper. One was on brilliant yellow stock, screamed "MISSING!" and had a black-and-white photograph of Mallory — she was airborne, just launched from a trampoline — above a brief physical description. The other flyer was on white copy paper and was adorned with a color photograph that had been taken by a school photographer who had already taken too many pictures that particular day. Large block letters asked, "HAVE YOU SEEN HER?"

No, was the short answer.

I hadn't seen her. But in the few days since Mallory's disappearance I'd seen, literally, thousands of the flyers. Volunteers had papered almost every vertical surface Boulder had to offer, and some horizontal ones as well, with a yellow flyer or a white one, or more often, with multiple copies of each.

Towers of Mallory.

White and yellow checkerboards of Mallory.

Although I was growing inured to the posters themselves, the messages weren't lost on me. MISSING! and HAVE YOU SEEN HER? ran through my mind like an ever-repeating crawl at the bottom of some

cosmic TV, the messages as insistent as the lyrics of an annoying jingle.

The two photographs of Mallory — one smiling and content, the other mischievous and teasing — had a much more subtle effect on me than did the banner headlines. The photos of the young girl lingered in my preconscious and provided fodder for unsettling dreams of the things that fathers dread. More than once I woke with a startling sense of vulnerability, a visceral awareness that I had a daughter and that it could have been she.

Sam had lost a lot of weight — I was guessing thirty-odd pounds — in the last year, but none of it in his face. He still had the face of a big, round guy. Much of the motivation for the weight loss had been medical. The past few years had confronted my friend with a minor heart attack, kidney stones, and gallstones. A new, healthy diet was one of his ways of fighting back.

He'd sworn off doughnuts and bacon and brats, and hadn't had a burger and fries in most of a year. He was learning to cook and he'd already warned me that he was going to count on me to be his running buddy while he trained to run his first

10K, the late-spring Bolder Boulder.

Health aside, most of the motivation for his self-improvement program, though he'd never admit it to me, was his recent separation and divorce, and that new girlfriend in California. Sam was a mature guy, a serious cop, and a devoted father. Still, he wanted to be buff so he could get the girls.

Prior to that night, I'd never observed Sam watching his son play in a competitive game in any sport, and anticipated that it wasn't going to be an inspiring sight, especially given the fact that the sport was hockey. Sam had a little bully in him — ask me, all effective cops do, they have to. In addition, Sam had the natural-born arrogance of Minnesotans who believe that they know more about hockey than any native — read: citizen of the United States of America — referee who might tie on skates and pull on a striped blouse in some Colorado barn. Sam granted Canadians special hockey dispensation.

I feared that it was a combustible combination of traits, and that I was about to discover that Sam was going to be one of those parents who give youth sports a rotten name. If, or when, he got too embarrassing to be with, I was more than pre-

pared to move to a seat in the arena as far from him as possible.

Sam, as he often did, proved me wrong. Every word he screamed at the game was a word of encouragement. He knew the names of every one of Simon's teammates and lavished praise on the kids for their shots and their passing, but especially for their positioning and their defense. He even screamed out some kind words for the opposing players.

The two times he yelled out to the referees it was with a hearty, "Hey, good call, guy. Let's keep 'em safe out there."

Between periods I asked, "Case driving you nuts?"

"Nah," he said. But he knew what case I was talking about. "If cases like that drove me nuts, I'd have been hanging out in your office a long time ago." That thought caused him to chuckle to himself; Sam's opinion of psychotherapy wasn't particularly benevolent. Then he lowered his voice and tilted his big head toward me. "There're still some guys who think somebody took her, a few. But it didn't come down that way. She was a kid with issues, Alan. The girl ran, plain and simple. Because of all the media and, you know — that other girl, back when, and what hap-

pened to her — the bosses have to go over-board on this, look for intruders under rugs, dot all the *t*'s and cross all the *i*'s, but everything or damn near everything says that she ran.

"Hey, a fourteen-year-old girl gone from home? It's a sad thing. Worse around Christmastime. But it happens. This time it happened at the wrong time in the wrong town in the wrong neighborhood under the wrong circumstances, so now the whole world is watching one family's tragedy unfold. But that's all it is: one family's tragedy. I'm afraid that the real tragedy is what happened to her after she ran; that's what keeps me awake at night. Is she in a ditch somewhere? Discarded by the side of some highway? In some asshole pimp's hands? When I hear what happened to her I think it's going to break my heart. My advice? Leave it alone."

He was probably right. But Diane's story about Hannah Grant's intake interview with Mallory was still haunting me. I wasn't able to leave it alone.

"What about the guy that the Crandalls saw, the neighbors? The one they thought was loitering on the block before the snow started?"

Sam grimaced. "If those people were re-

ally so concerned, why didn't they call us when they saw him? He was probably just some guy out for a stroll, trying to walk off his Christmas dinner. Maybe his kids were out caroling and he was keeping an eye on them. You know what it's like after something like this. People think they've seen all kinds of things."

"What about the blood?" I asked.

Sam looked at me sideways, as though that question had surprised him. "Simon cut his heel on the back door last summer, on the screen. My God, did it bleed. He hopped all over the house looking for me to get him a bandage and by the time he found me, there was blood everywhere. I still don't think I got it all cleaned up. I'm not the world's best housekeeper, and I promise you that I wouldn't want the crime-scene guys checking my house for splatter. The fact that there's some blood in the Millers' house doesn't mean any felonies came down. Hey, I bet if I walked in with some Luminol I could get your house to light up, too."

"Well, then what about the snow thing?"

17

The snow thing.

Christmas had been on the previous Saturday. The day had been clear and cold with a high temperature in the mid-twenties. An upslope developed and snow started falling in earnest in Boulder some time around seven o'clock in the evening. At first, it had been a steady snow; three quick inches fell before the wind shifted directions around 9:30 and the snow paused for an hour. When the upslope resumed so did the snow, which fell insistently until early morning.

"All these questions? It isn't like you," Sam said. "You working as a stringer for the *Enquirer* in your spare time?"

"Actually, I've been trying my hardest to keep my head in the sand about this whole thing."

"You're failing miserably."

"I don't get the snow thing. Humor me."

"I don't either," Sam admitted.

Bill and Reese Miller left Mallory at home alone with her stomachache around 6:30, just before the snow started. Her cell-phone records show that Mallory made a few phone calls — all to girlfriends — in the next couple of hours, and received a few others. The first call out was at 6:39. The last call in came at 8:47. It was from her father, checking in on her from the Christmas gathering, and letting her know they'd be home soon.

Bill Miller said that his daughter answered the phone, and reported to the police that Mallory told him she was doing okay. She was all packed up for the next day's ski trip, had a heating pad on her belly, and was watching a DVD she got that morning for Christmas.

"The snow thing isn't important?" I asked Sam.

"I didn't say that. I said I don't get it. There's always something in every case that I don't get. Always."

"Where are her footprints?"

"I said I don't know. I wasn't kidding — I really don't know." He popped a peanut into his mouth and pointed toward the ice. "So where do you think a place like this gets money for a Zamboni like that?"

173

The Zamboni that was scooting around the rink between periods grooming the ice surface looked brand-new. All shiny and painted a shade of green that was much too close to chartreuse for my comfort. It was covered with more commercial messages than the NASCAR champion stock car.

"I don't know," I admitted.

"When I retire, I think I'd like to drive a Zamboni in a place just like this. I'd do it for free, just for the fun of it. For the kids. You know about Zambonis? How they got started?"

I admitted I didn't.

Sam did. He explained the whole history of the Zamboni as though he'd grown up with Mr. Zamboni's daughter and lived through the experience himself. I listened with some wonder, not because of any particular fascination with Zambonis but because of the extent of Sam's knowledge base. The truth was that Sam knew a lot of crap. He was the kind of guy with whom you did not want to play Trivial Pursuit.

"How come you know so much trivia?" I asked him when he'd exhausted the Zamboni tale.

"I just remember stuff. It's one of the things that makes me a good cop. And I

don't consider it trivia."

"No?"

"No. I like to think of it as information of infrequent utility."

"It's occasionally important to know that the first Zamboni was made from an old army Jeep?"

"That's the thing. You never know what might be important. It's all just information and then, out of nowhere, something becomes useful. I just store it so it's there when I need it."

Like the snow thing, I thought.

The Millers' home was on the eastern side of Twelfth Street, facing the mountains that rise dramatically only a dozen blocks away. How dramatically do the Rockies jut out of west Boulder? On one side of a street you're on a gentle hill. On the other side, you're on the slope of a mountain.

But that's to the west. A block to the east — in that part of the Boulder Valley "east" means downhill — and a few doors north of their home, the Millers had a new neighbor. A neighbor they had probably never met. The new family, the Harts, had moved into their brick Tudor the previous spring and within two months of un-

packing their moving vans had begun diligent work on the family passion — which involved turning the facade and entire front yard of their house into a garish, illuminated, motorized tribute to the Christmas holiday.

The number of lights involved — all of the family members seemed to prefer to call them "points" when they spoke to the media, which they did frequently — ran well into five figures. Six major illuminated displays — exactly half were loosely biblical in theme — ranged from three feet to nine feet in height, and eleven different motorized extravaganzas kept elves bowing, stars shooting, donkeys walking, and reindeer flying all over the front of the house and far up into the trees. An enterprising reporter with an incipient personality disorder found 116 distinct representations of Santa Claus secreted in various locations. On the wide expanse of roof beside the center gable of the house a huge arched sign of shimmering red neon announced to all that this home was indeed "The Very HART of Christmas."

It was something.

Families who like to make an annual trek through other people's neighborhoods in search of the best and brightest Christmas

decorations seemed to adore what the Harts had done to their home. The Harts' neighbors, and the neighbors of the Harts' neighbors, all of whom had to endure the endless crawl of traffic down Thirteenth Street, were probably not quite so enamored of the family's efforts.

Boulder being Boulder, the controversy became sport, and arguments flourished about light pollution and the environmental consequences of all that electricity being used on something so, well, garish and transient. The local paper, the *Camera*, actually published a series of letters about the brouhaha, the first of which compared the Harts' extravaganza to one of Christo's installations. Follow-up missives predictably belittled the aesthetic sensibilities of anyone who could possibly think that way.

"But," I asked Sam, "do you think the news footage shows what everybody thinks it shows?"

"Pretty much," Sam said. "It shows what it shows, I guess. I don't have much argument with Fox News. Well, that's not exactly true. Let's just say I don't have much argument with what Fox News has to say about those few minutes in the Millers' neighborhood on Christmas night."

"So?" I said. "Explain it to me."

"What?"

"The snow thing."

"I can't."

"You can't?"

He smiled. Not at me, exactly. He smiled as though he were enjoying my consternation. "So that's it? You can't explain it?"

What he couldn't explain was the footage that had been shot by the Fox News helicopter on Christmas night. The shot was live for their 9 p.m. newscast — which had included an announcement of the three winners of Fox's best-holiday-decorated-house-in-the-metro-area contest. The Harts' home had been awarded a disappointing, to them, third place, which earned the earliest appearance of any of the winners on that night's evening news. Records revealed that the live chopper footage from Boulder was aired beginning precisely at 9:16. Viewers eager to see the ultimate champion would have to stick with the newscast until the bitter end because the helicopter would have to make a trek across the entire metro area to Aurora for a shot of the grand-prize winner.

"Snow started sticking right away, yes? Around seven?" I asked.

"At my house it did."

"And phone records show that Mallory was still home at eight forty-seven?" That tidbit of information had been leaked to the media earlier in the week. Locally, it had been played up by one of the TV affiliates as though the scoop was as important as a cure for cancer.

Before Sam had a chance to reply the kids skated back onto the ice to warm up for the next period. "For the sake of argument, yes, let's say there was phone activity at eight forty-seven," Sam said. "I don't want to talk about this during the game, so make it quick. I'm getting bored."

After the news helicopter completed its shot of the Harts' home, it had banked away for a wide shot of the neighborhood, which included, for about three seconds — Fox timed it at 2.8614, and who was I to argue with that — the Millers' totally undecorated house on Twelfth Street. Two days after Mallory's disappearance, an astute Fox producer realized what the station might possess in the additional neighborhood footage that had been shot on Christmas night, and Fox launched a huge advertising blitz to promote its "crucial new information in the Mallory Miller case. Tune in Tuesday. Exclusively on Fox News at Nine."

"Mr. Miller and Reese got home around nine-twenty, right?"

"Give or take."

"But close."

"Close."

"Mallory was gone by then."

"Correct-o. We think. Nobody actually looked for her until the next morning. People forget that little detail. She had a big head start."

"You think she was home at nine-twenty, Sam?"

"No, I think she'd already split. But I do like arguing with you. That part's kind of fun."

Fox had done digital magic to the Christmas night footage. The resulting images of the Miller home were grainy, and the shadows were darker in a few places than was ideal, but the video was clear enough that the conclusions Fox reached really weren't controversial.

"The helicopter footage from Fox shows no footprints in the snow around the Millers' house. Not on the walk, not on the driveway, not through the yard. And no tire tracks up the driveway into the garage." I waited for him to disagree, but he seemed to be ignoring me. Finally, I added, "And lights were on in the house,

right? Both floors."

"So what? You know any kid who remembers to turn off lights?"

"All that's at nine-sixteen?"

The buzzer sounded. Sam said, "It was actually nine-eighteen by then. But why quibble? We're friends." He pointed at the fresh sheet of ice down below. "Game's starting."

"So are you saying you think that Mallory just happened to hustle out the door between like nine-eighteen and nine-twenty?"

Sam smiled at me pleasantly and said, "Maybe she was watching the Christmas thing on Fox News and timed her exit perfectly to confound the helicopter. We hear she's a bright kid."

I made a face that expressed my displeasure at his condescension.

He kneed me gently. "Hey, Alan, so far I've just been agreeing with you about stuff you learned from somebody else. Maybe some of it's right. Maybe it isn't. But I can't tell you what I think, you know that, not if it involves what I know as a cop. But you know what else? Intruder theory, runaway theory — it doesn't make any difference. None. The lack of footprints in the snow on Christmas night is an anomaly no

matter what theory you like. The kid got out of the house without leaving a trace. How? Microclimate? I don't know. Come on, it looks like Simon's on the ice for the start of the second period. Let's give the kids some support."

Simon was indeed on the ice, at left wing. Both teams were sloppier with the puck at the start of the second period than they had been in the first. I was about to ask Sam whether the kids might be having trouble with the fresh ice laid down by the Zamboni when he spoke first.

"Reese Miller's a hockey player. Did you know that? I've seen him play a few times. He's good."

I hadn't seen any mention of Mallory's little brother's hobbies in the paper. But then I'd been making a concerted effort not to read about the more gossipy aspects of the case. "No, I didn't know that."

"He's had some trouble."

I leaned forward so that Sam would know that I was looking at him. "And you know this as a cop or as a parent?"

"The latter."

"What kind of trouble?"

"God, you're nosy tonight. You heard that his dad sent him out of town for a while until the commotion dies down?"

"To visit family?" I asked. I hadn't heard.

"I shouldn't say, but yeah," Sam said. "I'm not sure I would have done that. Seems like a time when you'd want your kid close by." I opened my mouth to agree, but Sam was done with the conversation. "Let's watch the game."

18

Bob entered my office for his additional, day before New Year's Eve appointment carrying a boom box.

Mallory Miller had been missing for five days.

He and I had met almost a hundred times by then and he had never walked in the door with a boom box, or any other prop, for that matter. Without preamble, but with an almost sinister smile that underscored the fact that he seemed to lack a chin, Bob set the stereo on the table between us and pressed the "play" button. I didn't recognize the tune at first — maybe because I'd managed to make it through the years on both sides of the recent cusp of centuries deprived of any familiarity at all with boy bands — but I realized soon enough that I was listening to a disappointing cover of Del Shannon's glorious "Runaway."

A run run run run runaway.

Bob's preferred, but dubious, choice of versions was a seriously overproduced adaptation of the classic featuring a harmony of voices obviously lacking in testosterone. I patiently adopted the role of audience, unsure why that day's psychotherapy required musical accompaniment, and unsure why — if we required music at all, and that song in particular — we couldn't be listening to the almost flawless original. At what appeared to be a predetermined moment Bob decided to turn the session from surreal soundtrack to painful karaoke. His voice, a strange mix of soprano and something else, added a decidedly creepy new layer to the sugary harmonies that were filling my office.

Bob had chimed into the song at the precise point that the lyrical progression had reached *And I wonder/I wa wa wa wa wonder.* But he didn't stop there. He sang, *"Why/why why why why she ran away/And I wonder where she will stay."*

He reached forward and hit the "stop" button.

I wondered if I was supposed to clap.

Bob could carry a tune. I had to give him that.

Once I was certain he was finished, at least for the moment, I tried to think of

something intelligent to say. I failed.

Sitting back, Bob was quiet for most of a minute before he said, "I'm writing about it."

"You are?" I asked, trying not to reveal the true level of stupefaction I was feeling at what was happening in my office. Was Bob writing songs?

"Yes."

Bob played board games. His favorite was Scrabble, but he'd always maintained that he was a pretty decent chess player, too, and I had no reason to doubt him. And I knew that he'd once driven all the way to Laughlin, Nevada, in his Camaro for a big Monopoly tournament at one of the casinos. Ideally, Bob's vision of ideal human interaction was that everyone should follow game protocols, that people should take turns, that everyone should know the rules, and that any and all disputes should be handled via consultation with a reference manual.

Needless to say, since most people acted as though life had no rules and as though there were no manual to consult, in real life Bob was frustrated more often than not by the manner that people behaved.

In Bob's game-centered worldview — a perspective that he definitely applied to

conversations — it was my turn to speak. His hollow yes had constituted the totality of his turn and started the clock on mine. Given the presence of the boom box on the table between us, and the revelation about the writing he was doing, that probably wasn't a good time to reiterate a salient point I'd been trying to make for most of a year about the actual parameters of human communication. I took what I hoped was a safer road. I asked, "What kind of writing are you doing?"

"A story. I think it'll be a novel. I don't know."

My turn again. "What . . . are you writing about?"

I knew, of course. I was hoping that I was wrong, but I knew.

"I know some things about what happened to the girl. That's what started it but it's mostly stuff I'm making up."

"You know some things?" I said, trying to smother the skepticism that had crept into my question.

"Things that aren't in the news. I'm thinking I might call it *My Little Runaway*."

And thus the song.

"The girl" had to be Mallory, right? She was Bob's current obsession, wasn't she? Had to be her.

Maybe, maybe not. In psychotherapy, assumptions are termites. Let them survive unchallenged and they'll eat away at the foundation. In an effort to exterminate at least one termite, I said, "Mallory Miller? You know some things about what happened to her?"

"Yes." He leaned forward, his elbows on his knees, his hands clasped in front of him.

Bob leaning forward startled me. Why? Simply because it brought him closer to me, and "closer" wasn't one of Bob's things. "Closer" is what schizoid personalities try to avoid the way arachnophobes try to steer clear of spiders. For a moment I considered the possibility that Bob had only leaned forward to once again turn on the boom box so that he could sing along to another song.

But he didn't touch the stereo. He had leaned closer for some other reason.

Belatedly, I realized that it was again my turn. All I could think of to say was "Wow."

Bob nodded an acknowledgment that I'd caught up with the conversational progression. "What she was thinking. You know, like that. Nobody else knows it."

With those words I decided that Bob had indeed leaned forward to share a secret

with me. From a therapeutic perspective, it was a sign of true progress. I began entertaining the possibility that he might, against all odds, be getting better, but that fantasy was short-circuited by my wish that Bob had shared a different kind of secret with me — something about sex, or petty theft, or self-medication, or violent dreams. Just about anything else.

Anything other than something about Mallory.

Bob had many personal faults. Some were born of his underlying pathology; some were more difficult to explain. He was cold. He was irritable. He was intolerant. I suspected he was a bigot. He was mistrustful. Organic vegetables were more compassionate than he was. The list could go on. And on. But as far as I knew — and after two years of Tuesdays I knew as much about him as anyone — Bob wasn't a liar.

Which meant one of two things. The first possibility was that Bob somehow did know some details about Mallory's disappearance, or at least about her state of mind prior to her disappearance.

The other option that I was considering? That Bob just thought he knew those things.

But was it likely that he could be so

wrong? The natural history of schizoid personality is not that it's a precursor to schizophrenia. Although schizoids may display idiosyncratic thinking, failure in relating typically doesn't lead to psychotic failures in thinking. But, I reminded myself, the natural history of schizoid personality doesn't rule out progression to serious thought disorder either.

I forced myself to entertain the possibility that I was witnessing initial signs that Bob might be showing signs of decompensation. Usually the resolution to such therapeutic quandaries mattered little, if at all, outside the confines of the consultation room. That time? That time it might make a hell of a lot of difference. The girl in question, Mallory, was still missing, and . . . I realized that I didn't know how to finish that sentence, but also realized, belatedly, that it was my turn to finish some sentence. I said, "You know things that the police don't know?"

He replied to my question with an apparent non sequitur. "I rent a garage for my Camaro. I've told you that. It's why it's still so cherry."

"Yes, we've talked about the garage." I had to try not to sound exasperated.

"Well, the garage is right next door to

Mallory Miller's house."

He paused a long time, long enough so that I considered that it might, again, be my turn to speak. Although his news was interesting, I was getting ready to squander my move intentionally by saying something innocuous, like, "It is? Right next door?" But Bob wasn't really done with his turn — he was the hesitant chess player who hadn't quite lifted his fingertips from the piece he'd just slid across the board.

He said, "See, I know things. They say 'write what you know.' Well, I know about . . . this. At least a little." He grimaced. Before I had a chance to respond and ask him about the reason for the grimace, he explained on his own by saying, "But I don't want to be on TV."

Although I'd not heard a direct answer to my earlier question — "You know things that the police don't know?" — I was left with the impression that the answer was yes. Still, despite some concerted effort, I couldn't get Bob to say another word about Mallory that day. My intuition told me that his provocative tease about the missing girl would lose its energy if a long weekend intervened. I said, "Let's continue this tomorrow."

"What?"

191

"This seems important. Can you come back tomorrow for another session?"

"Because of her?"

"Because it seems like a good idea. To me." What I didn't say was that scheduling three appointments with a schizoid personality in the same week was a clinical strategy that bordered on the absurd.

"I can't afford it."

"I'll work with you on that."

He didn't agree; he acquiesced.

His departure at the end of his session was much less dramatic than his boom box entry had been. As he did sometimes, he asked for permission to leave using the French door that led directly outside from the back of my office. The alternative route — returning down the hallway that my office shared with Diane's and then out through the waiting room — brought with it the risk for Bob of confronting another human being, an option that, on most days, he was unlikely to choose. I assented to his request, of course, and he grabbed his things and walked into the cold without a thank-you or a good-bye or a see-you-tomorrow.

I kept my eyes on him until he'd traversed the small backyard of the old house, scissored his way over the poor excuse for

a fence on the south side of the property, and begun to close in on the distant sidewalk along Canyon Boulevard.

As I watched him trail away, I belatedly wondered whether I should have pressed him harder about Mallory and what he knew. But the truth was that at that moment, were I a betting man, I would have wagered that Bob's knowledge of Mallory was something that approached delusion.

The conclusion saddened me. Regardless, I'd know more soon enough.

My last clinical appointment of the year was going to be the next day, with Bob Brandt.

19

Diane didn't miss much.

"Did your schizoid man bring that boom box with him into therapy?" she asked me as we both rushed toward our office suite's only bathroom in the few moments that we were stealing between sessions.

I'd never told Diane that Bob suffered from schizoid disorder. But she was an astute diagnostician and had probably come to her own DSM conclusion about him after one or two awkward encounters while she was retrieving a patient in the waiting room.

For appearance' sake, I played coy. "My last appointment brought a boom box with him, yeah. Actually played me a song on it. Could you hear it through the wall?"

I slowed so that Diane could make it through the door into our tiny kitchen before I did. As she crossed the space and spun into the adjacent bathroom she didn't pause to thank me for my gesture.

"What song?" she called through the closed door.

Diane was just making conversation. She didn't really care what song. I was pleased that her mood seemed improved. She hadn't enjoyed too many good days since Hannah's death.

" 'Runaway.' "

"Del Shannon?"

"No, some boy band."

"Holy moly. Which one?"

To my dismay, "Holy moly" had apparently survived the cut. "How the hell would I know? All I listen to anymore is Raffi and The Wiggles."

"Your boy-band days will come sooner than you'd like and you'll look back wistfully on the Raffi period. Was it about Mallory? Is that why he played the song?"

The toilet flushed loudly as I pondered the eerie accuracy of Diane's associative intuitiveness. "Why would you guess that?"

Efficient sink sounds. The door opened. Finally.

"Because I am the psycholog-ess," she offered, as though it somehow explained her rare perceptive skills.

"What?"

"Never mind. Could he be an Asperger? Your guy? Mr. Boom Box."

Diane's question knocked me off balance just a little. Fortunately, I'd already given the issue some thought. I said, "From a pure social-skills point of view, maybe. But the criteria for schizoid fit him like a glove."

"It's trendy, you know. Diagnosing Aspies. Schizoid is so . . . sixties."

"Yeah." I squeezed past her into the bathroom. I didn't feel comfortable discussing Bob's diagnosis and, anyway, my bladder was screaming.

"You want coffee?" she asked.

"No thanks," I called through the door as I fumbled with my zipper. At that moment, the thought of adding another liquid, especially a diuretic, to my system seemed masochistic.

Diane said, "I still haven't heard from the cops about Hannah's session with Mallory. I kind of thought I would."

"After this much time I don't think you're going to." The relief I'd begun to experience in the privacy of the bathroom was exquisite. Talking out loud felt like a particularly intrusive chore.

"Do you think she ran?" Diane asked.

"I do."

"Someone should know what I learned from Hannah."

I moved to wash my hands, but didn't reply. Wasn't sure how to reply. Eventually I said, "It'd be great if you could say something, but you can't."

"Too many people think they know what was going on in that family. The media does, the cops do, Mallory's father probably does, too. Truth is that it seems like a lot of people all know a little bit but nobody is talking to each other. Nobody has the whole picture."

I dried my hands while I considered her point. I had to admit she had one. Although I could have argued that the same thing was true about almost any family anywhere, the Miller family was a special case. It seemed likely that despite the intense law enforcement and media assault on their privacy, no one had developed a complete picture of what had been going on in the Miller household prior to Christmas night.

"I've been wondering," Diane said. "Do you think Mary Black would talk to me?"

I opened the door. "About what?"

Diane had one hip against the kitchen counter. She was sipping from a big pink mug of coffee. "Mrs. Miller, Mallory's mom."

"No, of course not. Why would she?"

She ignored my question. "Would she talk to you, then? You referred Mrs. Miller to her."

"Last time I checked it didn't give me lifetime access to the woman's mental health records." I squeezed past Diane, and began to snoop around in our little refrigerator for something with caffeine. "What do you hope to find by talking to Mary, anyway?"

"I can't talk to her father. There has to be some way to pull all this together."

" 'All this' being the Millers' family situation?"

"Yes . . ."

She'd spoken the simple affirmation as though it constituted an incomplete sentence. I suspected that the other part of the sentence — the part she'd kept to herself — would be something about Hannah's death and Diane's ongoing lament that the cops — specifically the evil asshole, Jaris Slocum — weren't doing much to find Hannah's killer.

Diane remained certain that out there — somewhere — was Hannah's killer.

For whatever reason, she decided that it wasn't judicious to go there with me right then. I couldn't see a reason to quibble with that judgment so I spent a silent mo-

ment reflecting on some of the crazy cases I'd been involved with over the past few years, looking for lessons on how to "pull all this together."

All I saw were ways to repeat mistakes I'd already made; I couldn't see a single advisable choice. I said, "Sometimes there isn't, Diane. Sometimes we end up knowing things that other people should probably know. But that's just the way it is."

Her reply? "This coffee's old. When did you make it?"

"Before lunch."

She poured the contents of her mug into the sink. "I know somebody who might talk to me. Fill in some pieces."

"Yeah, who?" I expected a punch line.

She fumbled around in a cupboard and came out with a mint Milano. "I never got my trip to Vegas."

I wondered where the cookie stash was hidden; I hadn't spotted them earlier in the day. A millisecond after I absorbed her taunt I realized that she might not be joking. "Diane, you wouldn't."

"I wouldn't? Watch me. It's winter and it's cold here, if you haven't noticed. It's warm there. The craps tables are open twenty-four seven. Want to come?"

She'd stepped out of the kitchen and

started back down the hallway to her office.

I stuck my head out the door. "You're kidding, right? Tell me you're kidding."

As she turned the corner toward the waiting room to retrieve her next patient she wiggled her ass in reply. Over her shoulder she called out, "For the record, I think he's schizoid, too. Asperger, my . . ." She gave her ass one final shake to finish the sentence.

20

No boom box on New Year's Eve afternoon during Bob's additional, additional therapy time. I wasn't surprised; I actually half expected that he would behave as though our conversation about Mallory had never taken place.

Bob slipped his ancient leather-bottomed North Face backpack from his shoulder onto the floor and sat heavily across from me. He didn't bother to remove the well-worn fleece-lined denim jacket that covered one of the button-down blue oxford dress shirts he wore year round. Bob had two denim jackets. This one, with the fleece, was the winter version. The other one, unlined, was reserved for spring and fall.

He didn't say hello to me. He hadn't looked in my direction since I'd retrieved him from the waiting room and led him to my office. I thought he looked particularly tired and distant, which left me again

questioning the wisdom of scheduling a third session with a man who used so much of his energy to maintain interpersonal distance.

I said, "Hello, Bob."

His gaze was locked on a particular spot on the wall behind me, over my left shoulder. I was tempted to turn and see what was so interesting to him, but I didn't. I knew I'd discover nothing there but paint.

If you were to examine the family histories of the last hundred patients who had sought my help, you would find quite a few who had, arguably, suffered worse childhood trauma than Bob. I don't say that to minimize what he endured when he was young, but rather to create some perspective.

As adults, none of those other patients was as psychologically damaged as Bob. To me, that meant that Bob's unfortunate childhood wasn't sufficient to explain his psychopathology.

Bob's father — the man had been emotionally abusive, and I wouldn't have been at all surprised to learn someday that he had been physically abusive as well — had abandoned the family when Bob was only four. Bob's older brother — the one who

lived near his mother — was a high school football star who'd become a college football star who'd become a successful tax attorney. Bob had more than enough insight to know that despite the fact that they had shared a house growing up, he and his brother had never really lived on the same planet.

His sister, five years older — Bob's memory of her is innocent, and his worship of her saintlike — died of leukemia a year after their father deserted them, on the very day that Bob entered kindergarten.

She'd died at home before breakfast and Bob's mother didn't permit him to miss his first day of school.

His mother was, by Bob's description, a hot-and-cold, smother-and-reject kind of caretaker whom I surmised, had she made her way into a clinician's office for a diagnostic sit-down, would probably have walked out with the dreaded 301.83 label of borderline personality disorder.

As a childhood tableau, it was an awful set piece. But sadly, I saw worse all the time.

All the time.

If a traumatic upbringing wasn't responsible for Bob's seemingly intractable char-

acter pathology, was nature to blame? Did the shuffle and deal of genetic bounty leave Bob with a particularly bad hand? Possibly.

Most likely, though, it was some combination of two powerful forces, some unpredictable interaction between Bob's genetic fabric and the bedeviled caprice of his human family.

But I didn't know for sure. The only solace I could find was that a lot of work was being done on the spectrum of disorders that covers the broad territory from autism to schizoid personality. Someday soon, maybe, we'd learn something that would allow me to be a more effective therapist for people like Bob.

Bob said, "When Doyle sells it, I'm going to have to find a new place to garage the Camaro."

Something I'd learned about Bob over our years of Tuesdays together was that he often started our conversations midstream, as though an important dialogue had been going on in his head and at some point in my presence — a random point possibly, but more likely not — he decided to put voice to one of the thoughts. I was left to wonder why segue, context, and transition were absent from those rhetorical equa-

tions. For the time being, until the long list of goals that comprised my treatment plan for Bob was completed, keeping up with the nature of the progression of his thinking was part of my responsibility.

That day, though, what I was most aware of was that Bob hadn't started the session talking about Mallory.

"Doyle is . . . ?" I asked.

"The guy I rent the garage from. For my Camaro."

Bob explained the simple fact as though he was annoyed that he was being forced to repeat it for my benefit. Although Bob had mentioned the garage arrangement already that week, the truth was that I'd never heard him mention anyone named Doyle before. I was certain.

"And he's selling . . . ?" I guessed that Doyle was selling the garage.

"The house. It's been on the market for a while, since fall. When he sells it, I'm going to have to move my car, obviously."

Bob garages his car next door to the home where Mallory Miller lives with her father and brother. And a guy named Doyle owns the house.

Interesting. Lauren hadn't mentioned that last fact to me. Nor did I think I had seen that tidbit in the paper. Not in the Boulder

205

Daily Camera. Not in the Denver papers.

The house had been on the market for a while before Mallory disappeared. Had I seen that detail in the paper? I wasn't sure about that either. Maybe. I reminded myself that I wasn't exactly a student of the case.

Bob is concerned about losing the garage for his Camaro.

Check.

"Have you spoken with this guy Doyle, Bob? Do you know his plans for the . . . garage?"

With Bob, where interpersonal relationships were involved, the obvious step often wasn't obvious at all.

"He's selling the house. There's a sign up outside. What's to ask? He moved out a couple of months ago. It's a nice place. I can't afford to buy anything like that."

Bob's reply was edgier than usual. I noticed that I was tiptoeing with him. I wasn't sure why I was doing it, but I could feel the care I was forcing into my words as I said, "When he sells the house you'll have to look for a new place for your car?"

Bob was pulling his lower lip across the sharp surface of his front teeth. He did it three or four times before he said, "I don't actually pay him."

It was my turn. "You don't pay Doyle? For the garage?"

"He, um . . . builds fountains and ponds and streams and waterfalls, you know, crap like that for rich people. That's his . . . his business. He does pretty well. I mean, to buy that house, right? It has a theater — a real theater — in the basement. It's like . . . a great place to watch movies. So cool. He has to be doing okay. I help him sometimes, on weekends mostly. He lets me use the garage for the Camaro, and lets me watch movies sometimes. The Trilogy down there? Oh, that's the deal. That is the deal. It may turn out I've been getting screwed. I don't know. I really should have done the math."

For two years I'd known Bob and I didn't know anything about Doyle, nor did I know anything about his weekends spent building fancy water features for people self-indulgent enough to expect to have large quantities of scarce water decorating their high desert properties. What else didn't I know about this man across from me?

Experience had taught me that with someone like Bob, the scope of my ignorance could be breathtaking.

"The Trilogy?" I asked, trying to fill in

at least one blank.

"*The Lord of the Rings*?" he explained as though I were a dunce.

"Of course," I said, feeling appropriately chastised. *Of course.* For Bob, what other trilogy could there have been? "I didn't know you worked for anyone else, Bob."

"It's just moving dirt."

"And that means it's not important?"

"What's the big deal? We put down liners. Move rocks. Lay down some pipes, attach pumps. It's pretty easy. But people pay him a mint for this stuff. You should see his yard. Surrounded by berms and rocks. A big pond, a stream, a bridge, two waterfalls. Those fish — koi. It's pretty cool. We moved a lot of dirt for all that. I like driving the little tractor, the Bobcat? That's a trip."

"But no more?"

"I told you, he moved. I'm watching his house now until it sells. Keeping the walks shoveled, sweeping up, checking on stuff. Timers, lights. Like that. I think I will go back and do the math. I probably got screwed in the deal."

If he had been screwed, he didn't sound too upset about it.

Assuming that he had one, I wasn't certain precisely what emotional point Bob

was trying to make. Was he aggravated at losing his garage space? Was he sad that he would no longer have a part-time job building water features? Was he going to miss whatever relationship he had with Doyle?

All of the above? I had no idea.

"Will you miss it?" I asked. The "it" was deliberate on my part. Bob could select an object himself. Garage, job, friend. His choice.

"Miss what?" he asked, instantly abrogating the intent of my clever quiz.

Forcing myself to remain placid, I asked an obvious shrink question. I said, "I don't know. What do you think you will miss?"

Bob sometimes did this thing with his head that was exactly half of a shake. He'd turn his head to one side — I thought exclusively toward the right, but I wasn't done testing that hypothesis — and begin a head-shaking motion, but he would interrupt the arc of the shake precisely at the moment his nose was back at the neutral position. The movement wasn't graceful; it was abrupt. His face would jerk to a stop as though it had smacked into an invisible obstacle. Typically he accompanied the motion with a verbalized, "Sheeesh."

Years before, I'd had another patient

who possessed the same bizarre affectation. I found that curious; it was like knowing two people who each had a sixth finger growing out of his elbow.

Bob chose that moment — after I pressed him a second time on what he would miss were Doyle to sell the house — to do the half head-shake thing, and he included the exasperated "sheeesh" for emphasis.

As I always did, I interpreted the little choreography as a sign of his impatience. With many patients I would probably have kept my interpretation to myself, but with Bob I tried to do as much as possible out in front of the curtain. Human behavior was already enough of a mystery to him.

"You didn't like my question?" I said to reveal the progression of my thoughts.

"I don't like anybody's inane questions."

The "anybody's" was Bob's way of cushioning the blow, of telling me not to take his "inane" rebuke personally. I considered the fact that he was depersonalizing the insult as another sign of clinical progress. On another day I would have been patting myself on the back at the emergence of even that paltry evidence of Bob's growth in compassion.

Not that day, though. I knew it was my

turn to speak, but I decided to pass. Where Bob chose to go next would tell me something.

I figured that Bob was waiting for me to take my turn in this real-life board game of ours. After a long pause, he shifted his gaze from the fascinating blankness on the wall behind me, chanced the briefest of glances at me, and then began looking at his hands. His eyeballs began to shimmy.

As always, it gave me the creeps.

Finally, resigned that I was upsetting the world order by skipping my turn, he said, "It's not safe yet. I'm not sure what I've gotten into. It's just too soon."

Huh? "What's too soon? I don't think I understand."

"There's a lot I don't get," Bob said.

What the hell are we talking about? "For Doyle to sell his house?"

"I'm not sure everything is turning out, you know, the way . . . It might have been a mistake. I stumble into stuff, I do. Not very often, but, boy, when I do . . ."

"Are you talking about Mallory again, Bob?"

He did the half head-shake thing one more time and exclaimed, "Sheeesh."

21

I am — almost without fail — thoughtful during psychotherapy sessions. My words are measured. My mannerisms are controlled. It is unusual that I say or do anything while in a treatment session that is not considered and deliberate. That is not to say that I don't often say things that are, in retrospect, ill advised or outright stupid. Rather it is an acknowledgment that when I do, it turns out that I have made the ultimately questionable move with conscious intent.

But the next question that I asked was actually no more deliberate than had been my decision to reach across the hall and try the knob on Mary Black's office door on the day that Hannah Grant died. What I said was, "Why don't you tell me about Doyle?"

Doyle *had* to be important. Bob, who lived his life devoid of relationships, apparently had one — however loosely defined — with this guy Doyle. In this psycho-

therapy, with this patient, with his problems, that was monumental news.

Was the presence of Doyle in Bob's life a sign of some drift in the continental plates of Bob's pathology? I had to suppose that it was. Could Bob really have a friend? But if Doyle was important, why hadn't Bob mentioned him to me before that day?

Did Doyle's sudden appearance say something I couldn't afford to miss about my relationship with Bob? Or perhaps, more importantly, about Bob's perception of his relationship with me?

The context of Doyle's emergence in Bob's psychotherapy was significant, too. Bob had decided to talk about Doyle while he was discussing loss. The "loss" in question was, at the surface, the loss of a garage for his cherished Camaro, but the fact that he raised the issue of Doyle in the context of any attachment had to be significant. Right?

Maybe. I admit that I wasn't totally certain. Part of me thought I might be making a classic psychotherapy reach.

This work I did was much more art than science.

"Doyle's just a guy," Bob said in reply to my question.

With as much nonchalance as I could muster I said, "But you've known him a while? I don't think you've mentioned him before."

"I don't *know* him. I park my car at his house. And I'm *sure* I mentioned him."

"And you work for him sometimes."

He pondered my words for five seconds before he said, "I work for the state of Colorado, too, but I don't know the governor."

It was a good retort; I reminded myself that Bob was a smart guy. As an employee of a university that was suffering through an era of eroding state support, Bob wasn't terribly fond of Colorado governor Bill Owens's style of leadership. When Bob mentioned the gov during one of his not-infrequent political rants, he typically called him "Invisi-Bill," not "Governor Owens."

I chose to avoid the partisan detour. "Before last week you hadn't mentioned Doyle."

He backed off his earlier position. "So you say. Unless I've been misunderstanding something, I'm here to talk about problems. Doyle hasn't been a problem. He's a guy. I do some work for him; he lets me use his garage. That's all, folks."

The Looney Tunes allusion was an inter-

esting addition to Bob's repertoire. I hadn't heard it before; with him, comical touches were as rare as zits on starlets. But I convinced myself to ignore it, confident it would come back around if it was important. I could've let the Doyle thing drop, too, maybe should have. But instead I chose to push a little harder. "I find it interesting that you've never mentioned him before."

His frustration blossomed. "Really? You find that interesting? I haven't talked about the teller I use at the bank either. But I see her every week, too."

Did he say "use"? He "uses" a teller? And who, in the age of ATMs, lays eyes on a bank teller every week? Wouldn't a schizoid guy love the age of ATMs?

I had a few choices as to where to go next, one of which was the tempting bank teller/ATM question, but I suspected that it — like Invisi-Bill and Looney Tunes — was a blind alley. I went with what looked like the no-brainer: "By talking about him now are you suggesting that Doyle has become a problem?"

"Only if I need to find a new place to park the Camaro. When that happens, then, well . . . then I have a problem, don't I?"

"If Doyle sells the house?"

"When. Yes."

"And your current landlord doesn't have any garage space you can rent?" I wouldn't have asked most patients that question. But Bob often missed the forest for the trees, or vice versa, and part of my job was to help him understand how the world works, especially those parts of the world that are inhabited by other people.

"He owns some big stupid supercab macho truck. There's no room in the garage."

I leaned forward slowly, resting my elbows on my knees, slightly closing the space between us. I was almost certain that Bob felt my postural readjustment as an unwelcome intrusion. That was okay; it was my intent. "You said it wasn't safe yet. What did you mean? Was that about Doyle?"

I was challenging Bob much more than I usually did. For many patients, perhaps most, my insistence on talking more about Doyle and the garage would not have been perceived as much of a confrontation. But Bob was feeling pressured by my persistence and he was figuratively reaching out behind him, searching for the perimeter of the corner I was edging him toward. His breathing grew more rapid and his normally pale cheeks

drained even further of color.

"Yes," he said, but it was tentative. His defenses were much more nimble than I would have predicted.

As I swallowed a silent question to myself about whether my persistence was really therapeutically indicated, I made the point I'd been leading up to for minutes, "And I thought you were implying that you're concerned about Mallory."

He snapped back, "Isn't everyone?"

Another good reply. I was impressed, but perhaps I shouldn't have been. The one thing that schizoid personalities usually have mastered is distancing behavior.

Two years and counting and I was still learning things about Bob.

The banter was therapeutically enlightening, but I wasn't about to be deterred from my quest to understand more about his surprising revelations about Doyle, and his intimations about Mallory. "Earlier in the week — when you played the song? — shortly after you mentioned the guy you rent the garage from, you specifically expressed concern about Mallory, and talked about the writing you're doing. And today you said, 'It's not safe yet.' "

"So?"

"What connects Doyle's garage, your

writing, and Mallory?"

Bob's mouth was open about half an inch and he'd thrust his jaw so far forward that it momentarily appeared as though he had a chin. He said, "She's been gone a . . . while. Everyone's concerned. I bet even you are. Aren't you?"

Even me? "Bob, this is important. Do you know if Doyle has anything to do with Mallory's disappearance?"

He shook his head. "You never really know about people, do you? You think you know . . . but then," he said, his voice unsteady. "I think . . . things always turn out to be different."

Bob's platitude was true, of course. And Bob's psychopathology probably left him more vulnerable to doubt about other people's motives than most of us. But I also knew that Bob's statement hadn't been an invitation to parse psychological principles. I asked, "What are you thinking specifically?"

"Nothing," he said. Then he added, with a side of sarcasm, "My mother."

I went back to the beginning. "Why don't you tell me about Doyle?"

Bob stuck his tongue between his teeth. When he released it, he said, "I know her. Mallory. I didn't think you'd . . ."

What? You didn't think I'd what?

218

22

I know her. Mallory.

Interesting non sequitur. Or apparent non sequitur. He hadn't answered my question about Doyle. Instead, he'd turned my attention back to Mallory. Or . . . perhaps talking about Mallory was his way of talking about Doyle.

Patience, Alan.

"You do?" I asked. "You know her?" Despite what I'd learned about the location of the garage, and about Doyle, I wouldn't have guessed that Bob knew Mallory. Why?

Because Bob was Bob.

"We talked. While I was working at Doyle's. She'd come by sometimes. She was curious what we were doing. She liked the fish. And the waterfall. She said she could hear the water running from her bedroom window. I saw her up there sometimes. At her window. When Doyle wasn't home she'd go down and sit by the pond

219

and watch the fish."

Bob was having trouble stringing the short sentences together. Something was aggravating his natural wariness. Was it thoughts of Mallory?

Had to be. Or maybe Bob's admission about Mallory was diversion? Was he uncomfortable talking about Doyle and was he taking me someplace he figured I'd willingly go instead? Was Bob that cunning? I didn't think so, but I couldn't rule it out.

"We talked through the fence," he added, not waiting his turn. "A few different times."

Not waiting his turn was another sign of his discomfort. The fact that he and Mallory talked through the fence? I suspected that the physical separation of the barrier made the conversation more palatable for Bob, maybe even made the conversation *possible* for Bob. Metaphorically, it was elegant.

But still . . . "Go on," I said.

"She's a nice girl."

"And you spoke with her?"

"I have, yeah. A lot of times."

Well, Bob, was it a "few times" or "a lot of times"?

He squinted his eyes and tightened his jaw. The grimace caused his chin to re-

treat. It looked for a moment as though his face just melted away half an inch below his lower lip. "She's my . . . friend."

As surprising as it might sound, the fact that Bob had personally met Mallory was merely a curiosity to me, another one of those "I know someone who" anecdotes that were still swirling around Boulder about the Millers. But the fact that he'd conversed with Mallory on a personal level? And multiple times? And that he considered her a friend? That was epiphany-quality news where Bob was concerned.

From what I knew about him socially — and before that day's session had started, I thought I knew most of what there was to know — Bob didn't have repeated personal conversations with people with whom he wasn't somehow compelled to relate.

He just didn't.

"She's your friend? You talked about . . . ?"

"I told you. The waterfall, the pond. The fish. She loved the waterfall. Other things. She likes my car."

"Other things?" I was reaching. I knew I was reaching.

"Yeah."

"Such as . . . ?"

Another grimace. Then, again, "My mother."

I went to safer ground. I didn't want to. But I felt I would push him farther away if I came any closer. "And you thought she was nice?"

Shortly after the words exited my mouth, I realized that my caution had come too late and that our rat-a-tat conversation was over. Silence descended on the room the way darkness follows a closing curtain. I waited. Bob had started breathing through his mouth. Each exhale was accompanied by a faint whistle.

Finally he spoke. He said, "She doesn't look fourteen."

My spleen spasmed. At least I think it was my spleen — something in there suddenly got twisted into a big, fat knot. I hadn't been aware that I didn't want to hear those specific words from Bob, but now that he'd said them I knew that I hadn't wanted to hear them.

"Time's up," he said.

I looked at the clock.

He was right. Time was up.

Didn't matter to me. I needed some magic that would encourage Bob to stay and tell me what was haunting him. Because something was haunting him. I couldn't find any magic, so I focused on what I feared: "You don't think she looks fourteen?"

"Do you?" he asked.

Frankly, no. In Boulder, most eleven- and twelve-year-old girls look fourteen. Fourteen-year-old girls look, well, older — sometimes a lot older. Sometimes way too much older. But I wasn't about to tell Bob that. I suspected his comment about Mallory's age had little to do with musings about the sociological implications of the increasingly early psychosexual maturity of adolescent girls.

I said, "Bob, look at me. Please."

He did, holding the connection for almost two entire seconds. I asked, "Do you know something about Mallory? Where she is? How she's doing? Had she said something to you? Has Doyle?"

Way too many questions on my part. Way too many. A rational observer would have had a hard time determining who was more flustered at that moment, doctor or patient.

"Maybe you know something you should tell the police," I added — my way of adjusting the seasoning on a therapeutic dish I was already responsible for overcooking.

Bob did the half head-shake thing again, this time minus the "sheeesh," before he said, "I have to go."

I barely heard his words. The echoes of

his earlier pronouncement — *"She doesn't look fourteen"* — were gaining volume in my head. Silently quoting Diane, I thought, *Holy moly.*

"Did you talk to Mallory just before Christmas, Bob? Did you know what was going to happen?"

"I have to go."

"I have a few extra minutes. We can go on."

Bob didn't acknowledge my offer. He stood, grabbed his daypack, and stepped toward the French door that led outside toward the backyard, but he didn't ask me for permission to use it as he had on previous occasions. As he pulled the door open, air that was much colder than I expected flooded into the room, chilling my feet. He paused in the open doorway and turned his head back in my direction.

Our gazes failed to connect by about ten degrees. It was as though he were blind, wanted to find my gaze, but couldn't quite manage to make eye contact.

He said, "Is something a secret if nobody knows you know it?"

My gut was still in knots. "I don't know what you mean."

"For something to be a secret, somebody else has to know it, right? Or . . . do they? I

tell you things and you have to keep them secret. But I've never been . . ."

Been what?

I suspected that Bob's naiveté was talking, or that he was posing a trick question — a-tree-falling-in-the-forest clone — but I couldn't find the trap. Reluctantly I said, "A secret is a secret, I guess."

He suddenly shifted his gaze and we locked eyes for a period of time that was about the duration of a solitary flap of a hummingbird's wings. There, and then gone. He persisted. "If nobody knows something but the person who knows it, is it really a secret? Or is it something else? What would that be?"

"What are we talking about, Bob? Is this . . . something about Mallory? Is she okay? Do you know something about where she is?"

"Other people have secrets. I didn't really know that. I mean I knew it, but I didn't . . . I don't know everything yet, but it's not as simple as I thought at first. I'm not even sure about what I know. Does that make sense?"

No, it doesn't.

I could feel him pulling away. He hadn't moved an inch farther away from me, but this prolonged connection between him

225

and me had existed at a level of intimacy that I knew Bob couldn't tolerate for long. Now he was floating away like a helium balloon in a stiff breeze.

I tried to grab for the string that would bring him back. I said, "But you know something? You know a secret?"

I kept thinking, *You know that she doesn't look fourteen.*

"You know secrets, too," he replied. "People tell you things. I do. Therapists."

What did that mean? Was he speaking generally or was he referring to something specific that he thought I knew?

I didn't know.

He pursed his thin lips and shook his head, just a little, as though he was mildly disappointed with me. "The story's not over. I have to figure stuff out, who to trust. I think I've already been wrong once. Doyle's not . . . the guy I thought he was."

Trust me. Please.

"Doyle's not what? What do you mean?"

"Maybe you should read it. What I wrote."

I opened my mouth to reply, but Bob closed the door behind him.

I was about to say, "I'd love to." The cold air that had rushed in wasn't the only cause of chill in the room.

I stepped outside into the frigid air. "Bob," I called. After two more steps across the yard he stopped and turned to face me. He didn't bother to look at me, but he faced me. I said, "Tuesday, our regular time, okay?"

"Yeah."

"If you'd like to meet before then I can do that. Don't worry about the money."

He said, "Okay," hunched his shoulders forward, dropped his poor excuse for a chin, and paced off into the night.

23

Sam had blown some serious bucks at Runners Roost.

A year before if you had asked me what was more likely, a giant meteor destroying our planet, or Sam Purdy adorned in head-to-toe burgundy running Lycra, I would have been warning everyone to duck. But there Sam stood, right at my front door, jogging in place, his breath puffing out in little frosty clouds that stood out like flares against a sky the color of deep water.

It was 5:10 in the frigging morning on the first Monday of the year. My initial thoughts upon waking had been about my disconcerting session with Bob a few days before.

"You ready?" Sam asked. "I say we do a couple of slow miles, then we try to bring one in around nine. What do you think? We'll work up from there."

I tied both of my shoes before I replied. "I think it's January, Sam, and this could

really wait until March or April. The race isn't until May, for God's sake."

The race on Sam's radar was the Bolder Boulder, the Memorial Day Weekend 10K classic, and for some reason Sam had decided that his training regimen couldn't be put off until spring. I'd volunteered to be his workout partner, and unfortunately for me his ardor for physical fitness was that of the newly converted.

"Emily coming with?"

Sam was asking about our Bouvier des Flandres. Emily was a big bear of a dog and her natural instincts spurred her more toward herding livestock than jogging on a lead alongside human beings. "Maybe next time. Running in straight lines isn't one of her best things. She likes to roam. Let's see how it goes without her this time."

"What about the little one? Anvil?"

"Hardly. Three miles is a marathon for a miniature poodle. At least it is for him. I'm afraid it's just you and me." I stared out into the darkness. "I don't even think we'll see the milkman or the paperboy at this hour."

"Cool, let's go."

Although it was contrary to his character to yield control, Sam wanted me to set the pace. Two reasons: From a thousand dog

walks I knew the trails in the nearby hills, and since I'd run a couple of Bolder Boulders when I was younger he was granting me the status of running guru.

I knew the status assignment wouldn't endure for long. Near the end of mile one, I asked, "What kind of trouble has Reese Miller been in?"

Sam didn't move lightly. I don't know whether it was inexperience, poor technique, just the fact that he was a big guy, or what, but the pounding beside me on the dirt trails of Spanish Hills sounded more like the *clop, clop* of a Clydesdale than the heel-toe patter of a jogger. I'm not much of a runner. Bicycling is my thing. But running beside Sam and his plodding strides I felt like I was floating.

"Fights."

I didn't expect that he'd answer me at all, but his reply was too parsimonious for my taste. I considered the possibility that Sam was too winded to be more expansive, but he was in better shape than at any time since we'd met and I decided that the brevity was an indication of caution while he figured out where the hell I was coming from.

"Hockey fights?" I asked.

"Some."

"But some not?"

"I think you're watching too much cable. It's bad for your health."

I probably had been watching too much cable news, but I wasn't about to admit it to Sam. Blame it on Bob, and Diane. "I don't know. I'm curious, I guess."

"Ask me, there's already way too much curiosity about that case."

"You brought up Reese, Sam. Not me."

"First time, I did. And I regret it. This time you did. You still pissed at Jaris Slocum?"

I wasn't surprised that he'd changed the subject; I was surprised where he'd gone. "What he did to Diane? Of course. He was an asshole."

"There're reasons. Not excuses. Reasons. Cops feel pressure, too. Just like everybody else."

"Reasons to rough up a witness who's grieving about finding her friend dead? Yeah? Like what?"

"Maybe you could cut him some slack, get over your hurt feelings. In the end it's not about what he did, it's about whatever happened to that woman."

"That woman" was Hannah. "I'll think about it," I said, curious as to why Sam

was suddenly so concerned about Jaris Slocum's welfare.

"You have other reasons, don't you?" he said.

"What?"

"For asking about Reese."

The boomerang of subjects threw me. All I managed was a solitary, "What?"

"Thought so."

I had been trying not to sound defensive; apparently I wasn't succeeding. The truth was I wasn't that interested in Reese. Reese was a foot in the door. I wanted to hear Sam's thoughts on anything to do with the Millers, hoping to hear something that would ease my mind about my last meeting with Bob.

I said, "No, no. What you said at Simon's hockey game got me thinking, and I've been wanting to hear what you know about Reese. Not as a cop, just as a parent."

"Yeah? That's all you're wanting to know, what I know as a parent?"

"Exactly."

"Pardon me if I don't believe you." Sam's thunderous strides punctuated the silence that followed. *Boom, boom. Boom, boom.* He broke the tension by asking, "What do you know about the Pearl Street

Mile? I'm thinking it's more my distance than 10K."

The Pearl Street Mile is a summer evening race run around the Downtown Boulder Mall. Compared to the carnival spectacle of the massive holiday weekend Bolder Boulder, the Pearl Street Mile is a relatively sedate event.

"Not much." I told him what I knew, adding, "You're going to pass on the Bolder Boulder?"

"No. Just trying to find the right distance for my running style."

"And you're thinking you're built for speed, not endurance?"

My sarcasm was rarely wasted on Sam.

"You take what God gives you, you know."

Nor his on me.

"I know."

Sam pulled up short and put his hands on his ample hips. I stopped a couple of strides later and turned back to face him. He wasn't breathing hard but each exhale temporarily hid his round face behind a miasma of fog.

My neighborhood, Spanish Hills, is a rural enclave of mostly elegant homes — ours was one of the few exceptions — on the hillsides that comprise the eastern rise

of the Boulder Valley, not far from the scenic overlook on the Boulder Turnpike. The western rim of the valley is formed by the Front Range of the Rocky Mountains, and by comparison the vanilla hills of the eastern rim are, well, wimpy.

The spot where Sam paused on our run was on the top of a rounded ridge just north and east of my house. From where I stood, Sam's right ear was totally obscuring the rock formation known as Devil's Thumb. I'd always thought that the huge natural sculpture more closely resembled an altogether different part of the devil's anatomy, but maybe that was just me.

"What?" I asked for about the tenth time that morning.

"You got something. So tell me what it is, get it off your chest. No secrets, just get it off your chest."

Sam wasn't being a bully. He was perfectly capable of it, but at that moment he was merely making me an offer. The features on his face suddenly lit up just a little. The phenomenon was illumination, not insight. Far behind me the morning sun was breasting the almost imperceptible arc of the wide horizon of the Great Plains.

Sam and I had been here before. I knew something I'd learned in therapy that I

thought he should know, but I couldn't tell him about it. With a few exceptions, the rules said I couldn't tell Sam anything a patient had told me. Life had taught me over the past few years that assiduously adhering to those rules was sometimes as dangerous as breaking them. I was confident that I would ultimately decide what to reveal based on that reality, and that with enough creativity I could find a way to tell Sam what I wanted to tell him without the rules ever knowing they'd been sullied.

Below us, the headlights of a car snaked down the dirt and gravel lane that led to my house. In the predawn shadows I couldn't identify any features of the car. The guy who delivered the morning paper? No, it wasn't him; he had a rusty, old post–World War II Dodge Power Wagon that sent its bass rumble bouncing through the hills. In its own way, the sound was as distinctive an announcement siren as the syrupy melody of the ice cream man.

I watched the car's progress until it disappeared behind the contour of an intervening hill. It was probably the nanny that Adrienne, our urologist neighbor, sometimes brought in to watch Jonas at an ungodly hour so she could keep her morning surgical schedule.

To Sam, I said, "Do you guys know much about the house next door to the Millers? The one that's for sale?"

"Us guys?"

"The cops."

Sam started jogging in place. The sight of the ruby fabric stretching across his thick thighs made me think of a matched pair of prosciutto di Parma.

He took off down the trail. I did, too. Over his shoulder, he said, "There something you think we — us cops — should know about the guy next door?"

After a few strides I replied, "Not really."

"Not really? Or not at all?"

I didn't know enough about the Millers' neighbor to answer Sam's question, and I wasn't totally comfortable with the territory I was taking him, so I asked, "What kind of fighting did Reese have trouble with?"

"If you've been watching all that cable then you know what those kids have been through. He's a good kid."

He hadn't answered my question. I was forced to hustle to keep up with him; the pace he was setting for the second mile was way too fast. "You mean been through with his mom?"

Without any hesitation, Sam said, "What

do you know about the trouble with the kids' mom?"

Startled, I realized three things. The first two? The eastern sky was brightening, and the day had begun. Number three? Maybe there hadn't been anything in the news about the difficulty that the Miller children might have had with their mom, and I'd just told Sam Purdy that I knew something he didn't think I should know.

Oops. The information wasn't particularly important. The fact that I had an avenue to know it? Sam would find that important.

24

The pace that Sam set for the last mile and a half of our run precluded chatting. Despite my usually rigorous bicycling regimen I was seriously winded by the conclusion of our morning jaunt. To my relief Sam was, too.

As soon as we'd come within sight of my house I'd started looking around for the car that had come down the lane a little earlier. It wasn't there. It wasn't in front of our house. It wasn't in front of Adrienne's either.

The hue of the sky told me that we'd arrived back where we'd started shortly before six. I invited Sam in for coffee. He declined. "Sherry has Simon. She's bringing him back over early so she can get to class. I need to be home to feed him and get him off to school."

Sherry was Sam's ex. She was living in Northglenn, a suburb north of Denver, and attending school at Auraria. She'd sold

her flower business and was studying to be an EMT. The custody arrangement that she and Sam had negotiated was so complicated that I thought it would require single-variable calculus equations to put it on paper. But the plan worked; I'd not once heard Sam complain about the convoluted logistics.

He opened the door to his old navy Cherokee. In the thin light the dried muck on the lower third of the squat body made the car appear to have a custom paint job. Almost. "How many miles you have on this thing?" I asked.

"Odometer broke at one-forty-seven-something. That was on the day that the Supreme Court decided who our president was going to be. So more than one-forty-seven. Plenty more than one-forty-seven."

"How old is it?"

"It's a '90." He climbed in. The concave driver's seat accepted his rear end the way Lauren's out-thrust hip supported our daughter's cute butt. Naturally. With just the slightest trace of a smile in his eyes — it was impish, almost ironic — he said, "You know what? That makes this car the same exact age as Mallory Miller."

I didn't know what to say to that.

He wasn't done. "And the other girl, too.

I'm sure you remember her. She was a 1990, too."

The one who had been murdered in the dark hours overnight on another Christmas Day. The pretty little blonde whose one-time beauty-queen momma wanted her daughter to be a beauty queen, too. The one whose pathetic father had carried her lifeless body up the stairs from the basement like a spray of damaged flowers. Yes, I remembered that other girl. Too well.

"See you," Sam said. "Thanks for the run."

The Cherokee chugged north down the lane. Before it was out of sight the rumble of the old Dodge Power Wagon signaled that the newspaper delivery guy was heading in our direction. I watched his headlights dance in the grasses before I stepped inside and started a pot of coffee. A few minutes later I was still wet from the shower when Grace announced the beginning of her day. My sleepy wife crashed into me in the doorway as we rushed toward our daughter's room.

I cherish morning in our home. I love the soft carelessness of my wife after she's slept, her flesh exposed near the unbuttoned top button or two of her pajamas. I

240

love the fragrance at the nape of my daughter's neck after a night of sweet dreams. I love the frantic energy that the dogs bring to each and every dawn.

I adore the tang of fresh juice and the texture of bananas and the yeasty smell of toasted Great Harvest bread. I adore the first sip of hot coffee almost as much as I adore the aroma, and I relish the light that pours over the infinite plains and fills our little kitchen seconds before it jumps up and causes the crystalline formations on the Flatirons to sparkle like the facets of diamonds.

No, that day I wasn't necessarily thrilled about running around like a madman in order to make it to my office for my 7:15 appointment downtown, but it was, I figured, all part of the package.

And all in all, it was a damn good package. I felt that way almost every morning and felt great fortune that almost every day in my home started with the unspoiled promise of fresh bliss.

A year and a half earlier, Lauren had bought me a new BMW Mini as a gift. The generous gesture was intended to snap me out of a professional funk that I'd been sliding into, and her choice of cars paid

homage to an old love of mine, a classic Mini Cooper named Sadie that I'd adopted in my youth. I drove the gift Mini on nice days for over a year before I sold it. I didn't sell it because I didn't like it. I sold it because every time I drove it I felt as though I was taking a holiday from responsible parenting. All the data said it was a safe car for its size. The problem, though, was its size. Compared to an elephantine Ford Expedition — and way too often on Boulder's roads that was exactly the comparison I was forced to consider — my little Mini felt like a dainty ladybug.

I'd put an ad in the paper after the previous autumn's aspen season had peaked and ended up selling the Mini to a sophomore volleyball player from CU who had apparently convinced her parents that the little car was safe enough for her.

When I pressed the button that opened the garage door the car that was waiting to take me downtown to my office was a three-year-old, four-wheel-drive Audi wagon with 27,000 miles on it. I'd bought it from Diane's next-door neighbor when she moved to Phoenix to trade the cold of Colorado's winters for the heat of Arizona's summers. The Audi was a fun car. Not as much fun as the Mini. But fun enough. It

could handle all but the deepest snow, there was room in the back for both dogs, and — most important — it had more airbags than cylinders, much more sheet metal than the Mini, and, rational or not, I didn't feel like a lunatic when I strapped Grace into the backseat.

I was only two steps away from the open garage door when I spotted a fresh set of headlights snaking down our lane.

I stopped. Four cars at my house before 7 a.m.? For us, that constituted a parade.

The approaching car had a throaty rumble, not as *thumpy-thumpy* as the newspaper guy's Power Wagon, but certainly not that of a lightweight, well-mufflered, catalytic-converted Honda or Subaru either.

Despite the incipient dawn the headlights were aimed right at my eyes and they blinded me until the car was about twenty feet away. I stood still, waiting for the reveal. Finally, the driver turned the car abruptly to the left and pulled it to a stop that was short enough to cause the vehicle to slide a foot or so on the dirt and gravel.

The car was a shiny black Camaro that was much, much older than Sam's Cherokee, but still a modern automotive won-

der compared to the paper guy's ancient Dodge truck.

Bob Brandt climbed out from behind the wheel. He didn't kill the engine, however, and the growl of the big motor in the Camaro continued to thunder off the hillsides. Bob didn't say "Hi," or "Good morning," or "Sorry to intrude," or anything else that most people might say in similar circumstances.

I didn't say some things, too. I didn't say, "What are you doing here at this hour?" or, "How the hell do you know where I live?"

My home phone number wasn't listed. My home address was a carefully guarded secret. I didn't encourage patients to call me after hours. I certainly didn't encourage them to drop by whenever the hell they felt like it. Whatever early-morning calm the serenity of my family in my home had afforded me evaporated like the steam from pancakes on a hot griddle.

I was feeling violated by Bob's presence in front of my garage. But at some level I also felt grateful for another opportunity to connect with Bob about Mallory Miller.

Bob spoke first. That was fine; it was definitely his turn. "What do you think about my car?" he asked. The Camaro's

motor — had he told me once, or twice, or ten times that it was a 396? — provided a percussive accompaniment that sounded like a big sub-woofer with an electrical short.

I had no intention of chatting about cars with Bob at seven o'clock in the morning only steps from my front door and my darling daughter. "Good morning," I said, while I told myself that Bob must have a reason — a good reason — for mounting this kind of intrusion.

Bob was dressed in his ubiquitous outfit. Chinos, long-sleeve blue dress shirt, denim jacket — the fleece-lined one. Trail runners. He appeared nervous. I'd never before seen him outside the confines of my office, though, and was more than prepared to believe that he spent much of his life appearing nervous.

"I have something . . ." He was looking at my Audi. "That yours?"

He sounded surprised, as though he expected someone else's car to be in my garage. "Why did you get rid of the Mini?"

He asked as though he been wondering about it for a while and thought that he deserved an explanation. I wasn't going to go there with him, either.

"You like this better?" he asked, per-

severating on the car.

I counted to three. "Bob, you said you have something . . . What? Something you wanted to tell me —"

"Something to give you. Is it the turbo? That's the turbo, isn't it?" He was still focused on the wagon. "Fixated" might be a better word.

"I assume you came to my house because something feels urgent, Bob." I could have just said, *"Why are you here?"*

Bob didn't get my drift. He thought about my question for a few seconds before he said, "Should it?"

Seriously schizoid people relate the way people with sleep apnea breathe at night: in fits and starts. No organic rhythm. Just enough to maintain life. Sometimes not even that much. Nothing that should be natural and predictable about interacting with another human being is natural and predictable for them.

Allowing the realization to settle that Bob's appearance at my home at dawn was undoubtedly meaningful, I forced my discomfort that he knew where I lived away from center stage and stuffed some composure into my voice. I asked, "What brings you to my home so early in the morning, Bob?"

What was I thinking? I was thinking *"Mallory."*

"I have to . . ." he said. I thought he'd stopped himself before he completed the sentence. "I wanted to give you . . . what I've been writing. We talked about it. Remember?"

You bet I remember.

He leaned into the Camaro and came back out with an old, beat-up, dark-blue box imprinted with the logo of Kinko's, the copy palace.

"Here it is. It's not done," he said.

He held it out for me. I took it. The ream-sized carton was far from full. I guessed it held fewer than a hundred pages. I was already wondering: *Is this it? Is this really the reason he's come to my home shortly after dawn? To give me part of a novel?*

"Don't read it, yet. I'll tell you when."

"You want me to have it, but not to read it?"

"Yes."

I thought my question warranted a better explanation. Bob, apparently, didn't agree. "That's it?" I said.

"I have a long way to go. I'm still trying to get it . . . I want it to be right before you read it."

"Couldn't you have just held on to it until you decide that you would like me to read it?" *Or until you see me tomorrow?*

He chanced a glance at me. The tenor of his look was questioning whether I had suddenly become mentally challenged. As though it would explain everything, he said, "This is a copy. It's not the original. I have one, too."

He'd totally missed the point of my question. With Bob, that happened with some frequency.

"Okay," I said. I was already putting together a list of things we'd have to discuss during the next day's session.

"You'll understand," he assured me. "When I tell you it's okay to read it, you'll understand."

"You'll explain?"

"Yes. You like it?"

I raised the box up a couple of inches. "I'll let you know. After you tell me when I should read it."

"I meant the Camaro. It's cherry, don't you think?"

I gazed at the glossy black car, its pristine paint marred only by the faintest hint of Spanish Hills dust. "Sure is," I said. "It sure is."

"Yep," he agreed.

I took a deep breath and asked, "Bob, have you thought more about the question I asked you last week? Whether you know something about Mallory Miller that you should share with the police?"

He kicked at the dirt. "You know the . . . that woman who was killed? Who died? On Broadway? The therapist, like you?"

Like me? I felt gooseflesh on my back. "Hannah Grant? A few weeks ago?"

"Her. She was Mallory's . . . therapist. Mallory was afraid after she died. Really afraid. She thought . . . Mallory has this thing about Christmas. The guy that the neighbors saw? You know about that?"

Oh shit. "Which guy? On Christmas night? Outside? That guy?"

If Bob knew anything new about Mallory and the Christmas guy it meant that he'd seen Mallory since she disappeared.

"I was watching a movie."

"At Doyle's house? You were there?"

"Before Christmas she thought someone may have found out about . . . oh boy. And because of . . . that's why . . . she wasn't comfortable. No, not at all."

"That's why what?" There was enough pressure in my questions to launch a rocket.

Smooth, Alan. Real smooth.

"She doesn't really like Christmas. I don't either. She was scared that she might be — Sheesh. I can't, I shouldn't . . . It happened once, it could happen . . . I have to go. I don't want you to . . . ," he said. "Anyway, I don't like to be late."

You don't want me to what? "I'm very interested in hearing more, Bob. It will just take another moment. You came all the way out here."

I'm sure I sounded pathetic.

"I have to go." He opened the door and climbed into his car. The vinyl seats were so cold that they squeaked with his weight.

"Are you scared about something, too, Bob?" I asked through the glass.

He shook his head.

"Do you know anything about where Mallory is? Anything? Please tell me."

"I'm late."

"I'll see you tomorrow then," I said.

"Sure," he said, barely loudly enough so that I could hear.

He fishtailed a little as he spun around to head out the lane. The rumble of his motor was almost enough to stifle the pounding in my ears.

She was scared. He'd said she was scared.

★ ★ ★

Was I tempted to read what Bob had written? Of course I was, right that minute. I was also certain that my temptation was part of the challenge that Bob was positing.

Why was he setting things up to tantalize me that he might know something about Mallory Miller's fate and then keep the evidence of what he might know just out of my reach? He had taunted me already with the proposition that he knew her, was friends with her. He had just added the proposition that he knew that Mallory had seen Hannah for psychotherapy. And he'd added the tantalizing possibility that he'd been right next door in Doyle's house on Christmas night. He'd said that Mallory was scared.

I didn't know what Bob was up to with Mallory. Far from it. But trust — therapeutic trust between Bob and me — was on the table in the form of the manuscript in the Kinko's box. That much was perfectly clear.

What were the odds that Bob actually knew something crucial about Mallory?

Low, really low.

Bob's life was smoke, not fire. Heat, not light. Bob hadn't told me anything that

was really new to me. I was already aware that Mallory had seen Hannah for psychotherapy. I already knew about the man who had been loitering outside, everybody did. All Bob had really added to the equation was that Mallory was scared.

And that he'd been next door watching a movie.

Hopefully, the next day I'd learn what Bob thought Mallory was frightened about. I could wait until then.

Long before the dust had settled on the lane from the Camaro's too-rapid departure, I'd flicked off the lid of the Kinko's box and looked inside. The flimsy cardboard box was less than a quarter full of 8½ X 11 sheets. The title page was simple, the typeface minuscule.

My Little Runaway
By R. C. Brandt

In the lower right-hand corner Bob had carefully sketched the encircled *c* of the copyright symbol and beside it had typed out the word "copyright" and beside that, the year.

I closed the box.

25

I didn't see patients most Fridays. Diane skipped most Mondays. So I wasn't at all surprised that her Saab wasn't in its usual spot in front of our wreck of a garage all day Monday while I was at the office. Anyway, she'd asked me if I would cover her practice in case she and Raoul went away for the weekend, and weekends for Diane almost always included Mondays.

But the phone call she made to me that evening caught me off guard. Dinner was done, the kitchen was clean, Lauren had Grace in the tub for a mother-daughter bubble soak. Their giggles and laughter filled the house and buoyed my spirits like a healthy dose of rock and roll.

I had the dogs at my feet. Life was good.

"Can you hear that?" Diane asked.

I heard noise but it sounded like nothing more than routine mobile-phone clutter crap. I figured Diane was in her Saab, driving behind the spine of a hogback

someplace, or in the deep recesses of one of the many canyons that snake west out of Boulder into the heart of the Rockies.

"No, I don't think so. You're breaking up."

Then I heard it — the frenetic calliope melody of a slot-machine jackpot followed by an orgasmic scream of "I won! I won! Yes! Yes! I told you about this machine. Didn't I?" I could almost hear the cascade of dollar coins tumbling into the stainless-steel tray.

"You up in Blackhawk?"

"Nope."

"Central City?"

"One more try."

I could have wasted my third guess on Cripple Creek, the final member of the triad of Colorado pioneer mountain towns that the electorate had burdened with legalized gambling. Instead I went for the jackpot.

"You're in Vegas. You really went."

"Told you."

"How much of Raoul's money have you lost?"

"I make plenty of my own money."

"Yeah, but you told me once that you only gamble with his."

"I forgot I told you that. I can't believe I

told you that. I'm down a grand or so."

"Or so?"

"Maybe a little more. Single digits."

"Single digits plus, what, three zeros?"

"My luck will change. I rescheduled my patients until Thursday. That's a lifetime in craps. Can we talk about something else? How about matrimony? You want to talk about matrimony?"

Part of me didn't want to know. But I said, "Sure."

"I found her. Mrs. Miller. She was hanging out at a place called the Love In Las Vegas Wedding Chapel." Diane made sure that her pronunciation of "love" had two syllables. "Everybody knows her in the Vegas wedding racket; she's kind of a local legend. I only had to go to three chapels and ask a few questions."

I had a picture in my mind.

A woman who had once been pretty dressed in an outfit that had once been fashionable topped by a hat that had once been fresh was sitting by herself on the bride's side of a chapel that had never, ever really been pretty or lovely or fresh, and she was celebrating the nuptials of two people who had known each other for hours or days or months or years.

Elvis was there, too, or he wasn't.

The woman heard voices in her ears saying cruel, frightening things and one glance at her made clear that she spent many more of her waking hours tormented than she did at peace. Her face was sometimes molded into odd grimaces with tight, scared eyes, a cockeyed mouth, pursed lips, and a protruding tongue. She mumbled replies to the voices at inopportune moments and strangers in all walks of life kept their distance.

Her hygiene was lacking, her makeup was abundant and applied with idiosyncratic whimsy, and she'd resorted to wearing bad wigs to cover a tangle of hair that, during moments that approached sanity, she realized she could no longer manage.

Her teeth had begun to rot and her breath smelled like roadkill.

She lived in a homeless shelter, or worse.

She had a paper bag full of medicines but most days she hated the side effects more than she hated the voices. Although she would occasionally take a pill or two or three to quiet the rageful ranting, or to still the incipient panic, or to dull the despair that urged her closer and closer to the futility of suicide, she lugged the stained brown bag of pharmaceuticals around

more as a totem than anything else.

She was a lost life who was ordered by unseen powers to celebrate the marriages of pairs of strange people eager to believe that their own lives were full of nothing but promise. As each newlywed couple walked out the door of some tacky wedding chapel, whatever future the woman saw in them would disappear like a convention-eer's promise to his wife to behave himself in Vegas.

That was the picture I had in my mind.

"Is this going to make me sad?" I asked Diane. "Is it going to do me any good to know?"

Lauren sometimes asked that exact question of me late in the evening when we were in bed and the late news was on TV. A story would start to air — something about murder or rape or previously un-imaginable despair or desperation in a part of the world that seemed always to bring unimaginable despair and desperation. The anchorperson's eyes would be stern, his voice would be grave, and Lauren would hit the mute button and ask, "Is it going to do me any good to know this?"

The carnival midway refrain of another jackpot, this one at a more distant location

in the casino, filled my ear. Almost as if prompted by the loud celebration that followed the slot machine victory, Diane said, "This is Vegas. You can't stay sad here long."

She said it, I was sure, for her own benefit as much as for mine.

"Something tells me that she's managed to stay sad."

"Mallory's mom? Yeah," Diane admitted. "I think she has."

I was thinking *Reese's mom, too,* but I didn't throw his name into the mix. The refrain from the previous week's morning run with Sam was still part of the soundtrack spinning in my head.

"She's still crazy?" I asked. My question was irreverent and my choice of descriptors pejorative, but Diane knew that I was asking with a heart laden with pathos.

"You know," she said.

I did know. It was because I knew that I was so certain that it was going to make me sad. "Did you learn anything?" I said, but I was thinking: What could she have learned? What could Mrs. Miller know? I didn't think that Mallory had gone to Vegas to see her mom. I didn't think that Mrs. Miller would know anything that would help Diane understand the connec-

tion between Mallory and Hannah.

"It's not what you think, not what I thought. Coming here to see her? It's like poking at a hornet's nest, for some reason it gets a lot of people stirred up. It's . . . just a sec. I can't talk here — I'm going to go outside, or at least to a quieter part of the . . . It's such a trek to get out of the casino from here; if the call gets dropped I'll phone you right back. You really need to hear this." Her next words were a simple, pleasant version of "Yes, I'm out." I suspected the message was intended for the croupier or whatever you call the person who handles the dice and the chips at a craps table.

Diane dropped the phone on the floor — at least that's the way it sounded — cursed, kicked it, picked it up again, and asked, "You still there?" She laughed. "The phone slipped out of my hand while I was trying to pick up all my chips."

"I'm still here."

"Good. I won five hundred or so. That's pretty good. This place is so huge." A moment of silence. Then, "Hi. Do you know which way's the door?"

Hi? Was she talking to me?

"Which means you're only down . . . what?" I asked.

Thud. I thought the phone must have fallen out of her hand again.

"Diane? You there?"

That's when the call died.

Diane didn't call right back.

I gave her five minutes before I tried to reach her. Her cell phone rang and rang and rang before it clicked into voice mail.

I waited half an hour, hitting redial again every ten minutes or so with the same result. I was chewing on the possibility that technology had failed somewhere, that her phone had died or that the network had burped.

Soon I started thinking that she'd simply changed her mind about talking to me right then. Maybe she'd passed an open seat at a twenty-dollar blackjack table that she was sure had her name on it in raised gilded letters, or she'd eyed a spot at a new table and thought she'd seen steam rising from those dice.

I also considered the possibility that she'd run into someone she knew — Diane knew more people than anyone I'd ever met — while making her way out of the cavernous casino, and that they had headed somewhere for a drink or a meal or . . . what?

Diane, I guessed, was staying at the Venetian, the mid-Strip gambling palace that was decked out to look like Venice, Italy; that's the hotel where she'd booked us to stay the weekend after Hannah's death. I'd never been, but she'd told me that the canals in the hotel were lined with shops and I knew from long experience with Diane that a garish SALE sign in a store window could have distracted her. Easily.

All were reasonable explanations. But none, I thought, were likely.

Had her plans changed, Diane would have called me back and told me she'd talk to me later. She certainly would have picked up my call to her cell. Were her cell not working properly she would have gone to a pay phone and called me the old-fashioned way. After tracking down the mother of a missing girl — a girl who was the patient of Diane's dead friend — and after telling me she had news I needed to hear, Diane would have done something to reach me. She wouldn't have left me hanging, waiting, wondering.

She wouldn't.

I called Raoul at home to see if he'd heard from her. He wasn't there.

I followed happy voices down the hall and found Lauren and Grace on the bed in

the master bedroom, where I interrupted Lauren's dramatic rendition of *Alice in Wonderland*. She told me she thought she had Raoul's mobile number in her Palm. With monumental inefficiency, and only after pecking enough tiny faux buttons to book an entire round-trip flight to Kathmandu — including arranging for Sherpas — I tracked down Raoul's mobile number and dialed the ten digits.

"Raoul," he answered almost immediately.

He sounded tired. The usual gorgeous timbre of his voice was disguised by the wireless ether.

"Hey, Raoul. It's Alan. Where are you?"

"San Francisco, consulting at a clueless incubator. How these people expect to make any money is beyond me. What's wrong?"

His question made perfect sense. I don't think I'd ever before called Raoul on his mobile phone. Instinctively, he knew I wasn't calling him in San Francisco to recommend a restaurant.

"It's probably nothing," I said.

He replied, *"Mierda."*

26

Raoul's voice, when he wanted it to, carried no echoes of his childhood in Catalonia. I'd never given much thought to whether or not the tonal charade required much of his energy or attention. I'd always assumed that he could move back and forth between the American and Catalonian accents effortlessly, the way that a skilled actor does Kerry one minute and New Jersey the next.

Raoul said, "Back up. When did all this start? When did she call you?"

I heard echoes of Barcelona, and of worry, in his perfect English. I supposed that I was hearing the Barcelona only because I was hearing the worry. The caller ID unit by the phone told me that Diane's call to me from the craps table had come in exactly forty-seven minutes earlier.

"Forty-five minutes ago," I told Raoul.

"So she's been out of touch less than an hour?"

"Right."

"That's not a big deal."

I'd been doing the same comfort calisthenics. But I clearly remembered the intensity of Raoul's barely contained outrage while Jaris Slocum was holding Diane hostage in the backseat of the patrol car after Hannah Grant's death, and I remembered how resistant he'd been to any reassurance at that time. I knew that all the fret-yoga he was doing to convince himself that the current circumstances were some version of ordinary wouldn't, ultimately, do him a bit of good. Diane being out of touch for forty-seven minutes in the current circumstances required explanation.

And when I told him what I knew, I knew he'd agree with me.

"Raoul? Do you know why Diane went to Las Vegas?"

He spent a couple of heartbeats mining the apparent innocuousness of my question for innuendo before he replied, "She likes it there. She missed her chance last month when . . . you know."

"Do you know why she went now?"

There it was again. The shrink's "precipitating event" question. *Why now?*

Raoul was one of the brightest people I'd ever met. I could almost hear the gears turning in his head as he tried to make

sense of the bare glimpse he was getting as he strained to see where it was that I was leading him.

"She told me that a patient's mother was there. In Vegas. Somebody she wanted to talk to about a case. That was her excuse, but she really wanted to play craps and the mountain casinos have a five-buck limit. Small bets bore her."

"It wasn't one of *her* patients' mother she was planning to talk to, Raoul."

"I don't follow."

"The patient whose mother is living in Las Vegas? That patient wasn't Diane's; it was Hannah Grant's."

I could hear his breath blow hard against the microphone. "And you knew this? You knew that was why she was going?"

It was an accusation. His unspoken words were *"And you let her?"* I felt his finger pointing at me physically, felt it mostly in my gut. I could no more have stopped Diane from going to Las Vegas than I could prevent January from being colder than July. But that didn't matter to Raoul, not then.

"She told me she was thinking about it, about going to Vegas to talk with this woman. But I thought she was just being provocative with me. You know how she is.

I didn't think she'd really go."

"Diane always does things that other people don't think she'll do. It's who she is."

It was another accusation. And it was right on target. "I wish I'd listened to her. I'm sorry."

Raoul had no time for my *mea culpas*. "Had she talked to this person, yet? This mother?" he asked.

Before I replied I used a moment to recall the specifics of my last conversation with Diane. "When we talked, she told me that she'd found her, tracked her down. I don't know whether or not she actually spoke with her. I think that's what she was going to tell me when she got outside. She said it was important."

"You know what patient it is, don't you, Alan?"

My impulse was to hesitate, to cover my ass. To my credit, I didn't. I mouthed a simple "Yes."

"You know who the mother is, too?"

"Yes."

"You're going to tell me."

"You know how this works."

Raoul was the husband of a psychotherapist. Spouses of mental health professionals know the rules. He said, "This is

Diane we're talking about. You are the one who had better know how this works."

I tried to deflect him, to steer him back to the current crisis. I said, "I don't even know where's she staying. Where do you stay when you're there?"

He took a deep breath. "I try not to go at all if I can help it, but where faux Italian is concerned I prefer the Bellagio. The fountains are . . . something. She's at the Venetian," he said, confirming my suspicion. "She likes the canals. I take her to Venice, I take her to St. Petersburg, I take her to Amsterdam; it turns out the canals she likes best are inside some vapid casino in Las Vegas."

"I'll try her room and call you back."

"You've tried her mobile?" he asked.

"A few times."

"*Merde.*" I recognized the move from Catalonian to French. The man could curse in more languages than anyone I knew. He never cursed in English, however. Not in my presence.

"It's probably nothing." I didn't believe my own words. I said it because it was just one of those things that people say in circumstances like those.

While Raoul was still on the line, I pulled Lauren's cell from her purse and

punched in Diane's mobile number. After three rings someone answered.

A female voice, not Diane's, said, "Yeah? Who is this?"

Speaking into both phones simultaneously, I said, "Hold on a second, Raoul. Someone's on her cell."

"Go on," he said. *"Allez!"*

The voice on Diane's phone demanded, "Who's Rule?"

The lilt of the woman's voice triggered some clinical trigger in my brain. Instinctively I went into therapist mode, specifically I went into psychiatric-emergency-room therapist mode. My voice calmed, my hearing sensitized for the unexpected. Psychologically speaking, my weight was on my toes; I was prepared to change directions in a heartbeat.

"This is Dr. Gregory, may I speak to Dr. Diane Estevez, please? You answered her phone."

"Well, she's not home." The woman laughed. "No one's home. That's the whole point, isn't it? Not being home? This is about as far from home as I get. So there."

I considered the possibility that I'd dialed Diane's number incorrectly and that I was simply being confused by the lottery of errant connection. Then I heard the fa-

miliar frantic calliope riff of a slot machine jackpot and I knew that what had happened wasn't a simple wrong number. This woman was in a Las Vegas casino and she was holding Diane's phone in her hand. Why?

"The phone you're holding belongs to a friend of mine. Do you mind if I ask how you got it? Did you find it?"

"The doctor? It belongs to the doctor? Rule? Dr. Rule?"

"Yes." I let it go. I didn't want to try to explain to this woman who Rule, or Raoul, was, or wasn't.

"Well," she said. "I would guess he's out playing golf." She laughed again. Her cackle was sharp and high-pitched — the yelp of a distressed tropical bird. You wouldn't want to be sitting in the vicinity of this woman in a movie theater during the screening of a half-decent comedy.

"That's pretty funny," I said in a voice intended to convey that, against all odds, I found her act cute. "But I'm actually being serious. Where exactly did you find my friend's cell phone? It's important. She'll want to know when she . . . thanks you."

"I'm playing slots. Two machines — I always play two machines. It was in the tray on the left when I sat down. Or is that the

right? I get my lefts and my rights mixed up, especially when I've been drinking, and I've been drinking. Who the heck are you?"

I played the doctor card. "I'm Dr. Gregory."

"You out playing golf, too?" She laughed again. I had to hold the phone six inches from my ear to provide a cushion from the intensity of the din.

Diane had dropped her phone on the way out of the casino. That was the explanation for everything. That was why she hadn't kept her promise to call me back as soon as she was outside the casino. That was why she hadn't been answering my repeated calls to her cell phone.

Simple. "You're in the casino at the Venetian?"

"You wanna bet?" She laughed. "Or, I . . . wanna bet. I guess I'm the one who's betting."

"What's your name?"

"Michelle. You know about Harvey Wallbangers?"

"A cocktail, right?" I reminded myself to be patient. *Corral her,* I thought, *don't lasso her.*

"Ver-y good. Nobody here knows how to make 'em. Nobody. I order one and I keep

getting Tequila Sunrises. Can you imagine? I don't like the red stuff, I like the yellow stuff. In the tall bottle? You know what I'm talking about?"

"How many have you had?"

"Three, or . . . not — no, four." She paused. "Four. Not counting this one. Oops, this one's almost gone, too. Do you know how hard it is to make any money playing nickel slots? Well, it is. Even if you max your bets, and I do sometimes, I really, really do, it's like . . . when you win you still just get . . . well, nickels. Is that fair?"

"So you're playing nickel slots at the Venetian?"

"I am."

"Are there any casino employees around, Michelle? Maybe right behind you? Somebody in a uniform, someone making change or . . . serving cocktails, or something? An attendant?"

"Yep, there's one right there — how'd you know? Is there a camera on me? Am I like on one of those TV shows or something?"

"Could you please give my friend's phone to the person who works for the casino? Tell him I would like to speak with him?"

"Her."

"Her. Fine."

"Here," she said to somebody, possibly the casino employee, but certainly not to me. "Some doctor named Rule or . . . Gregory or something lost his phone while he was playing golf. Here, you take it, go on. I don't want it anymore. I need more nickels."

A heavily accented voice — Caribbean? Jamaican? — said, "What you need, ma'am? Change?"

And that was the end of that call.

"Raoul, you still there?"

"Of course."

"Diane doesn't have her phone with her. Some drunk woman in the casino found it, just turned it over to a casino employee. The call died. I'll try calling back again in a minute. Diane must have lost her phone."

"At the Venetian?"

"That's what the woman said."

Raoul said, "I'll call her room. Keep your line open in case she calls you."

"Of course. Raoul, I'm sure it's okay. There will be a simple explanation for this."

He'd already hung up.

Diane had lost her phone. Raoul would call her hotel room and find her sitting on

her king-sized bed lambasting somebody from hotel security about the casino's inefficient lost-and-found procedures. That's what I was telling myself. No big thing.

In my heart that's what I didn't believe. As innocuous as the events sounded — a friend failed to keep a promise to call another friend for less than an hour — my heart told me that something sinister had occurred.

You really need to hear this, she'd said. Diane would have found a way to call.

I tried Diane's cell one more time. Without even a single ring, my call was routed to voice mail. I left a simple message, "Hey Diane, it's Alan. Still trying to reach you in Vegas. Give me a call. I'm getting a little worried. Raoul is concerned, too. Call him."

I surmised that the casino employee who possessed Diane's phone had killed the power and that Diane's phone was programmed to send power-off calls to voice mail.

I walked down the hall to find Grace and Lauren asleep together on our big bed. One big spoon nestled protectively around one little spoon. I adjusted the comforter so that it covered both of them, flicked off the lights, took the bedtime volumes away

from the pillows, and kissed them each on the head before I retraced my steps back to the kitchen counter. I'd carry Grace from our bed into her room later on.

The phone chirped in my hand. I caught it after half a ring.

Raoul. He said, "She's not answering. *Quin merder.*"

It was my turn to curse. I'm not multilingual; I said simply, "Shit."

27

"I tried her cell again," I said. "I think someone turned it off. The call went straight to voice mail."

"That's enough for me. I'm going to call hotel security," Raoul said. "Get them on this."

"Get them on what?" I asked, gently. "You'll tell them you've been unable to reach your wife for an hour? So what? In Vegas terms that's an eye-blink. You know what the security people will say: She met somebody she knew, got distracted. She met somebody she didn't know, got distracted. She went to a show, went to a club, went for a walk, found a hot slot machine or a hotter craps table, went out for a meal, went out for a drink. So she's been gone for an hour? Nobody's going to care. Not for an hour, not for a day. Maybe not even for a week. Not in Las Vegas."

"They don't know Diane. I do. You do,

too. This isn't like her. If she said she was going to call, she would've found a phone. She would've called."

"But that's the point. They don't know Diane. To them, she's just a tourist who lost her cell phone. Big deal."

Stubbornly, Raoul said, "I'm going to call hotel security."

"Okay," I said. I knew that were I in his shoes I would want to do something, too, no matter how futile.

"Write down my hotel number here." He dictated it. "Call it if you hear from her. I'll be on my mobile."

I curled my tongue against the roof of my mouth and forced just enough air through the gap to cause a high-pitched, low-volume whistle to emerge. Emily, the big Bouvier, responded immediately. I could hear her lumbering in my direction from the other side of the house. The sharp tips of her nails *click-clacked* as she made the transition from carpet to hardwood. I knew that Anvil, the miniature poodle, would follow her. He'd follow not because he found my whistle alluring. He'd follow because whatever Emily found alluring, he found alluring.

In our tiny neutered dog pack, Emily

was the alpha-Amazon and Anvil was the eunuch slave.

The dogs waited impatiently while I pulled on a jacket and stuffed the cordless phone from the kitchen into one pocket and Lauren's cell into the other. We all crashed together heading out the front door.

Emily ran immediately across the lane toward Adrienne's house. For her it was like visiting extended family. I stage-whispered to her that everybody was in bed; she apparently didn't care. Anvil peed copiously in the dust before he loped off in the same general direction.

Raoul's version of my predicament was simple. In his view I possessed information that might help him find his wife. Sure, he'd been married to a psychologist long enough to know that the information he wanted was privileged. Realistically, of course, he didn't care. Who in his position would?

The fact that I'd already revealed that the information had at least a tangential tie to Hannah Grant's unfortunate demise would only aggravate his insistence that I breach confidence and tell him what he wanted to know. But what he also didn't know was that the patient of Hannah

Grant's whose mother was in Las Vegas was Mallory Miller and that the reason for my anxiety over Diane's sudden vanishing wasn't only because I was concerned that it might have something to do with Hannah's death, but also because I feared it might have something to do with Mallory's disappearance.

I'd already decided that, ethical or not, as soon as I felt that Diane had been sucked into that vortex I'd tell Raoul whatever I knew.

It wasn't the way the rules were written. But so be it.

Ten minutes outside with the dogs and I was getting cold. It was apparent that Emily — she didn't get cold until windchill numbers were in double-digit negatives — was eager to head down the lane on her usual evening jaunt, but I feared that kind of walk would yank us out of range of the cordless phone so I forced both dogs to roam the area between our house and Adrienne's. Emily found some smells that were compelling and she adapted. Anvil hung around close by. Raoul called back just as I was coaxing the reluctant dogs back inside the front door.

"Hi, Raoul?" I answered. "You hear anything?"

"Not from Diane. Security's not going to help. I'm in a cab on the way to the airport. I'll be in Vegas in a couple of hours."

"You're sure that's a —"

"Yes, I am. You didn't hear from her?"

Raoul's interruption shouted at me that his usual unflappable civility was developing fissures. "No," I said.

"Sometime tomorrow morning, if I'm not waking up next to my wife, I'm going to want to talk to this patient's mother, Alan. Be prepared to help me find her."

"Raoul, I —"

He hung up.

"— will do whatever's necessary."

28

Diane's husband was wealthy. She didn't work the long hours I did. She didn't have to.

On a typical weekday before eight in the morning my car would've been the first to slide into the parking spaces beside our office building. That Tuesday should have been no different. On a typical Tuesday morning, Diane would show up at around 9:00, or 9:30. That Tuesday should have been no different.

She'd told me on the phone the evening before that she'd already canceled her appointments until Thursday. Still, given the events at the Venetian, the driveway felt empty without her Saab, the waiting room felt empty without her patients, and the offices felt empty without her laugh.

Raoul had called me near midnight the night before from the room he'd checked into at the Venetian after flying to Vegas from San Francisco. He had a suite fit for

the doges overlooking the Rialto Bridge, but he didn't have any good news to report. Diane hadn't phoned him. The fact that she hadn't at least left a message on Raoul's cell was unprecedented between them. When one of them was traveling they always talked at the end of the day — always. When they were traveling separately they always talked at the end of the day.

After a lot of cajoling, and a five-hundred-dollar incentive, Raoul had finally persuaded a housekeeping manager to agree to check Diane's room for him. The manager wouldn't give Raoul the location of her room, but reported back that there was no sign of anything out of the ordinary, nor was there any indication that she'd been there since late that afternoon. No phone calls had been placed on the hotel room phone since midafternoon. The minibar was untouched after it had been replenished midday. The housekeeper who cleaned the room reported that she'd finished the evening turndown service around 6:30. From all appearances, no one had disturbed the bed or bath linens since that time.

The casino attendant who'd been given Diane's cell phone by the drunk woman

who played nickel slots and inhaled Harvey Wallbangers had promptly turned it in to the casino's lost-and-found department.

Diane had not inquired about it.

Raoul had also begun what he anticipated would be a long, difficult process of badgering the hotel security officers to review the casino security videotapes for the time that Diane was walking across the gaming floor talking with me on her cell phone. He assumed that hotel security cameras videotaped every square inch of the casino twenty-four hours a day. Security was resisting his pleas to review that section of the tapes.

Their argument? What his wife did when she was in Las Vegas was her business, right? Not her husband's, right?

He was European, he understood. Right? They can't very well start showing videotapes of what one spouse does in their casino to another spouse, can they? Would that be fair? What happens in Vegas stays in Vegas, right?

Raoul knew that it was hard to disagree, unless you knew her.

Raoul knew her. I knew her.

Venetian security didn't know her. The identity of the person she'd run into as she walked across the casino floor? Venetian

security thought that was her business.

How had she lost her cell phone? Venetian security thought that was her business.

Had she left the casino at all? Her business.

What else had Raoul accomplished by midnight Colorado time?

He'd called all the hospitals in a ten-mile radius of the Strip, searching for even the barest hint that his wife might have been treated or admitted that evening. He'd learned nothing that helped.

He'd called the Las Vegas police, seeking any indication that the local authorities had crossed paths with someone who even vaguely resembled his description of Diane. He'd learned nothing. He'd called American Express to see if he could get a list of charges she'd put on her card in the previous twenty-four hours. A supervisor would speak with him in the morning.

He'd tipped the concierge at the Venetian a hundred bucks to find a twenty-four-hour copy shop that could blow up and print a hundred copies of the photograph of Diane that he kept in his wallet.

She promised him that the prints would be waiting for him before breakfast.

"I eat early," he'd told her, suspicious of her promise.

"I stay up late," she'd replied with a smile.

"It's the suite," he explained to me. "They must have run my credit report. I think she's hoping I'm a newly calved whale."

The midnight call from Raoul had awakened Lauren. I didn't see any advantage to be gained by alarming her into having a fitful night's sleep, so I'd explained, benignly, that Diane was in Vegas and that Raoul hadn't heard from her, that he was worried, and he'd called to see if I'd talked to her since early that evening.

Had I? My wife wanted to know. I had not, I told her, not since early evening. I kissed her, and murmured that she should go back to sleep.

Over coffee in the morning, I explained the rest of the mess to Lauren, obliquely highlighting the slippery ice of the confidentiality hazards that were out in front of me, and specifically including the fact that before we'd hung up the night before, Raoul had reminded me that he wanted to know which patient's mother Diane had spoken with the previous day. Lauren, of course, knew nothing about my patient Bob and his odd connection to the Millers' neighbor, Doyle. And she certainly didn't

know that the patient's mother that Diane wanted to see in Vegas was Mallory's mother, Rachel.

"What do you think about Diane not calling?" Lauren asked me as I was kissing her and Grace good-bye before leaving for my office.

"I'm worried. It's not like her."

"There's probably an explanation," she offered.

"I hope you're right. But I can't think of what it might be. Diane's a stay-in-touch kind of person."

"She's always been unpredictable."

"About some things, yeah. Not about staying in touch. About that she's as reliable as sunrise."

She kissed me again. "If Raoul doesn't hear from her by midday, let me know, and I'll see if there's anything I can do. Maybe somebody knows somebody in the DA's office in Las Vegas. Okay?"

"Thanks."

"Sam might be able to reach out, too," she added. "He might have cop contacts out there."

And what, I thought, was I going to tell Sam about the Millers and Bob and Doyle and Hannah Grant that might entice him to reach out to cop colleagues in Las

Vegas? "Maybe she'll call," I said, not quite believing that she would.

I unlocked the front door of the building, flicked on the lights in the waiting room, and started a small pot of coffee in the tiny kitchen. At 7:43 the red light that indicated that my first patient had arrived for her 7:45 appointment flashed on in my office.

It was time to go to work.

29

Raoul had my pager number. I'd told him to use it as soon as he knew anything about Diane and that I'd call him back as soon as I could.

Lunchtime came and I didn't hear from him. I tried his cell phone. My call was routed to voice mail; I left a message asking him to phone me with news immediately.

Nothing.

Midafternoon I went through the same routine with the same result. Just to be certain that my bases were covered, I left an additional message on Raoul's hotel room voice mail at the Venetian.

Nothing.

When 4:45 came around and the red light on the wall in my office flared on, I found myself becoming alarmed that almost an entire workday had passed with no news about Diane. My level of concern for her was approaching ten on a ten-scale.

I walked down the hall to get Bob. My apprehension about the session was high. I had almost convinced myself that Bob really did know something important about Mallory.

Bob wasn't sitting in the waiting room. No one was.

My first reaction? *Who flicked the switch that had turned on the red light?*

I checked my watch. Four forty-four.

I waited a minute. Four forty-five. Had Bob ever before been late for therapy? Maybe once or twice, but his absence from the waiting room was certainly an anomaly. Had he forgotten that we'd made this appointment the day before? How could he have? Given the drama in front of my house at dawn, I was sure Bob would have remembered his usual appointment time.

I flicked off the switch that illuminated the red light and returned down the hall to check my calendar and my voice mail. I was still thinking that Bob would show up any minute.

I was wrong.

Five o'clock came and went, then five-fifteen, and finally five-thirty, the time that Bob and I would usually be finished with his session.

The reality was that patients missed

scheduled appointments all the time. If I had a busy week I could usually count on at least one no-show among my patients. Sometimes patients forgot their appointments and that was that; other times patients spaced out their appointments and the fact that they'd forgotten was ripe with therapeutic meaning. Sometimes life intervened. An injured child, a traffic accident, a late flight.

But Bob? He'd never missed a scheduled appointment. Never.

I thought about the midnight-blue box with the Kinko's logo that was sitting in the file cabinet near my desk. Bob had said, "Don't read it yet. I'll tell you when."

After he'd handed it to me I thought I'd said, "I'll see you tomorrow then."

I thought Bob had replied, "Sure." Was it possible that Bob had known he wouldn't be showing up for this appointment? With most patients, I would have simply packed up my things, gone home, and not given the missed session another thought. But Bob wasn't most patients: Bob was Doyle's friend, and Bob knew Mallory.

Bob thought he knew what Mallory had been thinking. Bob had been next door the night that Mallory had disappeared.

Bob had written a story about Mallory's disappearance. Bob thought Mallory was scared.

I had a copy of what he had written.

But he'd told me not to read it.

Powered by the pair of fresh batteries that I'd installed that morning, the pager on my hip vibrated with irritating insistence. The number that flashed on the screen was for Raoul's cell.

I dialed immediately. "Raoul, it's me: Alan."

"I'm ready to kill these people. Tell me something: Does Nevada have the death penalty? I think I'm becoming a proponent."

"Which people?"

"Take your pick. The Las Vegas police. The fascists in Venetian security. Even the damn minister at the Love In Las Vegas Wedding Chapel. He might be first."

"What?"

"I gave the housekeeping manager two hundred more bucks to look for Diane's calendar in her room. It wasn't there, but she let me see the notepad by the telephone. Diane was visiting wedding chapels. She wanted to talk with somebody named Rachel at a wedding chapel. She had a list of them on the notepad. I visited

all three. Love In Las Vegas was the most promising."

Without much thought, I said, "I'm glad you found that . . ." I didn't know how to end the sentence.

Raoul did. "On my own, you mean," he said.

"Yes. Did you talk to this . . . Rachel?"

"Nobody at the chapel will tell me anything. But they know her, that's clear enough. The minister is a guy with a fake British accent who prances around like he's on holiday from his day job in the House of Lords. He acted really cagey when I mentioned Rachel's name. I'll find her tomorrow."

"Diane?" I said, hopefully.

"I pray. But I'll find Rachel, and she'll help me find Diane. Despite the neon carnival and depraved World's Fair ambiance of the place, Las Vegas feels like a small town. Money is ammunition here. That works in my favor. I'm well armed."

"The police are uninterested?"

" 'Uninterested' is a generous word."

"And Venetian security?"

"I think they went ahead and looked at the videotapes of whatever happened while Diane was walking out of the casino. When she lost her phone."

"Did you get the impression it seemed significant to them?"

"It raised an eyebrow or two. But they won't tell me why."

"What happens in Vegas stays in Vegas?"

"Like that. There's one woman on the security team who wants to talk with me. I flirted with her a little, and I'm going to see if I can catch up with her later on when she gets off work. Her shift ends at eight."

I tried to imagine Raoul's frustration. His determination was apparent, but whatever he was doing to mask his frustration was admirable. I asked him, "Why aren't you bugging me for more information about Rachel?"

"Diane wouldn't want me to. She didn't talk to me about her clients. One of the things she respects about you is how you've kept your mouth shut through all the . . . difficult situations you've been in over the years. I'm trying to respect what she respects."

"I appreciate that. I'm in another difficult position right now. I'd really like to be more helpful, but Diane's not the only one who's . . ."

"Who's what?"

"Mixed up with Rachel's . . . problems. I've already told you more than I should." I knew I sounded lame. If I were in Raoul's shoes, I think I'd want to string me up by my thumbs.

In a tone that was intended not only to sound calm but also to communicate his increasing desperation, he said, "It's a reprieve, not a pardon, my friend. As soon as I run into a dead end with this Rachel person I'll be back in your face, insisting. Or worse." At the end he managed a little laugh.

"I can't wait," I said.

"I have to go. Before my date with this security lady later I'm going to try to see if I can find any gamblers who remember seeing Diane at the craps tables last night. I hope that some of the same people will be playing again. I'll be in touch. *Adeu*."

"*Adeu*" is Catalonian for good-bye. Other than profanity, the only other Catalonian Raoul had taught me during the many years of our friendship was how to ask if there was a good bar nearby. At that moment, had I been on a beachfront up the coast from Barcelona, I would have been sorely tempted to try out the phrase.

I said, "*Adeu,* Raoul." But he'd already hung up.

After only a moment's hesitation I opened the drawer to the file cabinet and withdrew the Kinko's box that Bob had given me. Almost reverentially, I lifted the lid off the box, and raised the title page in my hands.

My Little Runaway
By R. C. Brandt

A quick, surreptitious glance at the open box revealed that the top sheet in the pile of paper that remained in the box wasn't the beginning of Bob's story. The second page was handwritten. In his familiar, neat, incredibly cramped script, Bob had written me a note.

> *Dr. Gregory,*
> *If I've told you to go ahead and read this, this is the page that I want you to throw away. You can go ahead. If I haven't given you permission, this is where you should stop. Remember, I'm trusting you. I'll tell you when.*
>
> *Bob*

His tiny scrawl seemed indecipherable, a missive intended for selected residents of

Lilliput. I guessed that the first line was my name and the last line was Bob's, but I couldn't read the two lines in between all the way through, not at first. Only by holding the paper farther and farther from my eyes until I got it all the way out to arm's length did the script come sufficiently into focus. "Dr. Gregory," it read. "If I've told you to go ahead and read this, this is the page that I want you to throw away. You can go ahead. If I haven't given you permission, this is where you should stop. Remember, I'm trusting you. I'll tell you when. Bob."

Reluctantly, I replaced both pages — the title page and the warning page — and fit the lid back onto the box.

What could be the harm of reading the damn thing?

Bob's handwritten note had spooked me. How had he anticipated that a second caution to me about not reading his manuscript would be necessary? I decided to ask him. After checking my address book for the number, I called his home.

The phone rang and rang. No answering machine ever kicked in. As I hung up, I admitted to myself that I'd just done something that I rarely, if ever, did. I'd just tried to check in with a patient because they'd

missed a session. What was my typical practice? I usually just let the issue simmer until the next scheduled appointment.

This time, that didn't sound like a judicious plan.

30

I thought she was maybe fifteen years old, but she swore she was seventeen. I didn't have to ask her age; she was apparently accustomed to protesting that she was older than she looked, and before I'd known her for a full minute she'd insisted she was seventeen, really. Her name was Jenifer Donald. The Jenifer was leavened with only one *n*, she'd pointed out — the result not of a spelling failure, but rather, I was guessing, of a momentary lapse in judgment by young parents who were intent on making sure their daughter went through life with a distinctive name.

Jenifer was from Clemson, South Carolina, and was in Boulder visiting her grandparents, who lived on the northern edge of Boulder's original downtown near the intersection of Eighteenth and Pine. "They're so cute. They really are," she said, referring to her grandparents. "Some of my friends' parents are as old as my grand-

parents. But my grandparents are just so cute."

"Clemson? That's where the college is?" I asked.

"The university," she corrected. It was clear that the distinction was important to her. "It's where I want to go. I'm hoping for a scholarship, for band. I'm a drummer. I have a good chance, I think. My PSATs were better than I expected. Much better. I take the SATs next month — I hope, I hope, I hope I do well. My parents and my grandparents want me to look at CU, too. I told them I would. That's why I'm here." She rolled her eyes. As if *anyone* would choose the University of Colorado over Clemson.

I found myself warmed by the unfamiliar melody of her lilting voice and loving the openness with which she'd greeted me at the front door of the brick two-story home. Jenifer's pretty face was as welcoming as her manner. Her blond hair fell in a straight shot well past her shoulders. "What kind of doctor are y'all?" she asked. Her question wasn't at all suspicious, merely friendly.

When she'd opened the front door, I'd introduced myself as "Dr. Gregory," hoping the appellation would grant me some advantage with the kid who'd responded to

the doorbell. I was already regretting having done it; I couldn't very well tell her I was a clinical psychologist without leaving her with the implication that Bob had a reason to be seeing one.

"So Bob's not here?" I asked, changing the subject.

"The guy upstairs in back? That's Bob? Grandpa calls him 'the tenant.' Don't think so." Jenifer said "the tenant" in a deep, gravelly voice, mimicking, I guessed, her grandfather's delivery. "I haven't actually seen him this visit. I just got in to Boulder today — it's so cold here, how do you stand it? My grandparents have an appointment somewhere. Pill-ottos, pill-ah-tees. Those machines? We don't do that much of it in South Carolina."

She laughed; and her laugh made me smile. She really thought her grandparents were cute and that Boulder was exotic. "Yes, those machines," I said.

She smiled back and shook her head. "Would you like to come in and wait for him? I'll fix you something."

"Thank you," I said, stepping past her into the house. "You're a drummer? Marching band?"

"And orchestra," she said.

A short hallway led to the back of the

house. Through a kitchen window I could see the curtained rooms above the garage. "That's Bob's?" I asked.

Jenifer said, "You bet."

"Where are the stairs?"

"Other side, on the alley."

A pile of mail was visible in a basket on the back porch.

Jenifer saw me looking. "See that? I'm sure your friend Bob would have picked up his mail if he was home." She lowered her voice to a whisper before she added, "He sure gets a lot of catalogs."

"I'm sure you're right. He must not be home."

"Hey, I'm a pretty good cook. Y'all like grilled cheese? I make a mean Swiss on rye."

Jenifer managed to make "Swiss on rye" sound almost as alien as blowfish.

I said, "I'm actually kind of worried about him. He and I were going to get together earlier today but he didn't show up, which isn't like him."

"Are you thinking maybe he's sick?" Her voice blossomed with concern.

I shrugged my shoulders. Bob could indeed be ill; it would explain a lot. I asked, "Is it okay for me to go knock, you think?"

She hopped past me and bounded out

the door and across the back porch. "I don't see why not. Knocking never hurt anybody, did it?"

She lifted the rubber-banded stack of mail from the basket, led me around to the alley, ran up the stairs, and knocked on Bob's door. Two sharp raps. She cooed, "Knock, knock," for good measure.

While we were giving Bob much too much time to make his way to the door, Jenifer seemed to be examining my face. She finally scrunched up her nose a little bit and asked, "You really are worried, aren't you?"

I said, "Yes, I am."

"That's so sweet. Wait here." In one fluid motion she jumped down the stairs, and disappeared around the corner. She returned seconds later with a fistful of keys, popped back up the stairs, unlocked the lock, turned the knob, and threw open the door.

"Go have a quick look," she said. "I'm sure he wouldn't mind. I'll just toss this mail in here so nobody —"

Jenifer took a half step into Bob's apartment and immediately screamed, hitting a note that — despite a volume that would have made a siren engineer envious — was so high in pitch that it almost disappeared

into the range undetectable by human ears.

I hurdled up the steps three at a time, "What —"

31

"Detective Sam Purdy, this is Jenifer Donald. She's visiting her grandparents from South Carolina."

"Pleased to meet you," Sam said.

I was tempted to tell Sam that Jenifer was as sweet as an August melon, and warn him that she was older than she looked, but I didn't. He'd figure it all out himself before too long.

He flipped open his badge wallet for her benefit. Jenifer hopped back from it as though it were cocked and loaded.

"So you don't actually live here, Jenifer? This isn't your house?"

"No, sir. Should I call you 'officer'?"

"Detective. Dr. Gregory told me that you're here visiting your grandparents. They are due home when?"

Sam was dressed in new clothes, or at least clothes I'd never seen him wear before. Two factors were at play: One, he'd lost a lot of weight over the last year and

his old stuff didn't fit. Two, he actually seemed to have started caring how he looked. The ensemble he was wearing was composed of a pair of jeans from the Gap and a striped wool v-neck sweater over a white T-shirt that hadn't even considered turning yellow. For Sam, the outfit constituted styling.

Jenifer's acute anxiety that she had done something to lure a police detective to her grandparents' door was making me nervous. She said, "Soon. They're due back soon. Any minute I bet. But I'm not sure. They're out doing that pill . . . thing. Exercise, you know? With those machines?"

Sam sighed. He knew. Eating a healthy diet was something Sam had embraced. Exercise? That had become cool with him, too. But Pilates and yoga? For Sam, they were still on an astral plane with tats and piercings. He wasn't quite there yet. At his partner Lucy's insistence, he'd accompanied her to a solitary session of Bikram yoga — the kind that's basically done in a sauna — and was astonished, and dismayed, to learn that people were physiologically capable of sweating out of their noses.

Profusely.

And that they would pay dearly for the privilege.

I thought it would take him a while to come around to being open-minded about yoga and Pilates.

"And this guy, Bob, is your grandparents' tenant?" he asked Jenifer. "He rents a room?"

"Two rooms. Yes, sir. And he has his own bathroom, of course. Hot plate, microwave. You know. I used to stay up there when I was visiting. It's nice. You can see the mountains real well when the leaves are off the trees. Or is it 'real good'? No, no — it's real well."

We were all standing out near the alley at the foot of the stairs that led up to Bob's rented rooms. Sam looked at me before he asked Jenifer the next question. "And which one of you actually entered Bob's rooms?"

Jenifer swallowed and her eyes got as big and bright as table grapes. "I did. That's when I saw — I shouldn't have done that, should I? Oh my Lord. Am I in trouble? The doctor was worried and I thought that he . . . oh my Lord! Oh my Lord. I'm so sorry. Back home, we'd — but, oh, I really am sorry. I'll never do it again. I promise. Please don't . . ."

She couldn't even bring herself to say "arrest me."

" 'The doctor' " — Sam glared at me — "said you saw some blood when you were inside? And a mess?"

"I did. I'm so sorry. I don't know what I was thinking. I really don't know what I was thinking. Going into a stranger's place like that? We might do it back home, but I'm not — Y'all —" She sighed. "I screamed. The blood, the mess. I'm so, so sorry."

"It's nothing," Sam said, in his best fatherly voice. "Don't you worry; you did what you thought was best." Sam climbed the staircase toward Bob's rooms. He stopped near the top, turned to Jenifer and me, and said, "What I'm going to do is something that law enforcement calls a 'welfare check.' All that means is that I'm going to make a quick walk through his place, make certain that there isn't someone inside needing assistance, then I'm going to come right back out." He focused his eyes on me before he continued. "Just in case anyone's ever curious about exactly what I did in there. Understand?"

"Yes," Jenifer replied, although it hadn't been her understanding Sam had been seeking.

He edged into the flat without touching a single surface and was back out of Bob's rented rooms in a little over a minute. Because of the way the door was situated I wasn't able to follow his progress. Once he was back on the landing at the top of the stairs, he looked at me and shook his head, "Nobody in there. Some blood, not too much. Just what you saw near the door. And it's a mess in there, too, Jenifer, just like you said."

"There they are. *Finally,*" Jenifer said, pointing down the driveway that led out to Pine Street.

A huge dark GMC pickup with a camper shell was pulling into the driveway. We all waited.

The second her grandparents made it out of the truck, Jenifer announced, "The police are here about the tenant. There's blood. I looked inside. I'm so sorry. I am."

32

"Get in," Sam said. He pointed at his Cherokee.

I got in. The consequences of being obstreperous at that moment were too much for me to contemplate.

"There's not that much blood," he said.

"It's relative," I argued. "If it was yours, I think you might consider it a reasonable quantity. Anyway, isn't that exactly what you said about Mallory's blood on the day after Christmas?"

"And it turns out I was right about Mallory's blood on the day after Christmas. Kid got nosebleeds. The splatter in the house was consistent with a sudden nosebleed."

I could have argued the point, but it was clear that Sam was holding trump cards. "What about the mess?"

"You really didn't go in?"

"I peeked, Sam. I was worried."

"Being messy isn't a crime. I see teenag-

ers' rooms that are worse all the time. There's no visible evidence that a crime was committed in the guy's flat. The kid's grandparents heard nothing. There're a few drops of blood on a wall and some bad housekeeping. Hell, he could be over at Community right now getting his finger stitched up. ER doc told me once they see people all the time who slice their hands up while they're cutting bagels. I hadn't known that. Bagels."

"There was blood on the carpet, too," I argued.

"You said you didn't go in."

"You can see it from the door."

"There wasn't that much blood on the carpet."

"Was it fresh?"

"I didn't stop to test it."

I opened my mouth to ask another question, but Sam stopped me. "We have rules, Alan. Bill of Rights ring a bell? I did a welfare check. I didn't find anyone in need of assistance or see any other reason to stay in the man's home uninvited, so I left. Done."

"You're not going to investigate, are you?"

"Investigate what?"

It was exactly the response I'd dreaded. "He's missing. His place was tossed."

"Tossed? So you say. You know any of this for sure?" He waited long enough to see if I was done arguing with him. "Didn't think so." He went on, making his case, "Jenifer's grandparents say that they're sure Bob was home alone when? Last night?"

"Night before, actually. And they said they thought he was alone because he always is. They don't actually know he was alone."

"Okay, they weren't sure about last night. And now it's early evening and he's not home. Big frigging deal. Where's the crime? The only crime I see is that Jenifer's grandparents are in violation of zoning codes for having a tenant and a crappy makeshift second kitchen in those rooms. But I'm going to let that one slide."

"Big of you," I said, trying not to sound too sarcastic. The truth was that I didn't know how to answer any of Sam's questions without telling him things I wasn't allowed to tell him.

Sam probed the contours of my silence and came to the conclusion I figured he would get around to. "He's one of yours, isn't he? Your . . . clients?" Sam asked, not expecting me to answer. "And . . . let me guess, he didn't show up for his appoint-

ment with you. He's usually as reliable as milk of magnesia about showing up on time, so you're worried." Sam didn't even bother to make these statements sound like questions.

I didn't deny anything. Didn't confirm anything.

"You want me to be worried, too," he added.

I was relieved to be given a prompt I could actually respond to. "That would be nice," I said.

"Why didn't you just call nine-one-one? Why'd you call me?"

I stared at Sam for a moment. I could've told him that I called him because I trusted him and didn't call 911 because for all I knew I would end up having to introduce Jenifer, with one *n*, to Jaris Slocum. It would have suggested to Sam that I still wasn't prepared to cut Jaris Slocum any slack, and that was one argument I didn't need rewound.

I played another card instead. I suspected the card I played broke a rule, but I convinced myself that the rules were gray about whether or not I could play that particular card. "I wonder if he has a car. That might help us find him. His car."

Sam gave me about an eighth of a smile.

"You wonder if he has a car?" He lifted his chin half an inch and groomed the grain of his mustache off to the sides with the index finger and thumb of his right hand. "Stay here while I go back inside and ask Bob's landlords a few more questions that I'm sure you could tell me all the answers to if you didn't suffer from such serious constipation."

He added a comment about Jesus before he was out of earshot.

While Sam was gone, I phoned Lauren and told her I was going to be even later than I had told her I was going to be the last time I called. She wanted to know if she should hold dinner, and she wanted to tell me about the new ways that Grace was being cute, and chat about why I was tied up so late, and she wanted to know what was new with Diane and Raoul. I explained I'd fill her in on everything when I got home and told her to give Grace a kiss for me. Dinner? I'd fix something for myself.

Sam returned after about five minutes. He settled onto the driver's seat and crossed his arms. The front of the Cherokee was pointed toward the southwest, and from the shotgun position there was a break in the trees that allowed me to see

the vault of the second Flatiron outlined against the night sky. The light of the fractional moon was reflecting just right.

Sam said, "He has an old muscle car. A Camaro. Keeps it garaged at a house over on Twelfth Street."

I caught myself holding my breath and forced myself to inhale, exhale, act natural. "Where exactly on Twelfth?"

"You're really going to pretend you don't already know all this? Okay, I'll play along. Mr. Donald doesn't know exactly where. But I have a suspicion you might be able to find it for me, you know, like those good ol' boys can find the exact spot you should drill your new well. What are those boys called? The ones with the forked sticks? Are they called dowsers? Ah, who cares? We're going for a little drive."

Sam started the Jeep and made his way across downtown until he got to the Hill and turned on Twelfth Street. We were heading south, paralleling the mountains that loomed a dozen blocks away. He pulled to a gentle stop at the curb halfway between the instantly recognizable home where Mallory Miller had disappeared and the smaller place that was next door on the north side.

Doyle's house.

"I'm guessing that's where this guy Bob keeps his muscle car," Sam said. "Just a suspicion. Call it cop's intuition."

I didn't bite. Sam picked Doyle's house either because the Donalds had actually told him exactly where he could find Bob's car, or he picked it because during our morning jog I'd already mentioned the Millers' neighbor's house to him. Sam didn't misplace much information.

I was busy eyeing the real estate sign in front of the house, trying to cram the listing agent's name — *Virginia Danna, Virginia Danna* — into my memory. I asked, "So are you going to check for a car in the garage?"

"Sure we are. Come on."

The front yard of Doyle's house was terraced. Undulating, mortarless flagstone walls of varying heights supported a series of planting beds that radiated away from the curving center walk like the lines on a topographic map. Dried ornamental grasses were interspersed with globe evergreens and other Xeriscape-y things I didn't recognize.

I stuffed my hands into my pockets to try to ward off the January cold and followed Sam down the front walk until he moved onto a path that intersected with it

314

and led around to the back of the house. After a few more steps, I could see the gable of a single-car garage roof toward the rear property line.

"You're not going to introduce yourself to whoever lives here?" I asked innocently.

"Place is empty. Owner moved away a couple of months ago. Guy's asking way too much is what I hear. You know, given the market and interest rates and all. But who the hell knows what's up with Boulder real estate these days? Did I tell you some agent's been dropping by begging me to sell my place? Says he already has a buyer and can get me a fortune for it. I think he's a developer and wants to scrape my shack and put up a spec. I could take the money but I'd have to move halfway to Wyoming to find someplace new to live. What's the point of that? It would mean commuting for me, and new schools for Simon."

A casual observer might have mistaken Sam's ramblings for whining, or for the opening gambit in a friendly discussion of Boulder County property values and the moral and economic consequences of chasing the appreciated dollar. I knew better. Sam's moves were misdirection. From experience, I knew that he used mis-

direction the same way magicians used it.

So what was it that I was not supposed to notice?

Sam has been in Doyle's yard before.

I was sure of it. Despite the darkness he was leading me across the property as though he'd sat in on the design meetings with the landscape architect. Once we made it to the backyard, he followed a flagstone path over a little wooden bridge that spanned a curving faux streambed. When the path split, Sam chose the fork that ran toward the rear of the lot.

Only the top half of the garage was visible behind a stunning series of man-made granite — for want of a better word — cliffs. At the bottom of the natural-looking walls was a good-sized, but drained, pond that would flow into the streambed we'd crossed earlier. I had no trouble imagining the waterfall that would cascade down those rocks into that pool come spring.

"This way," Sam said. He stopped at a garage window and shined the beam of a flashlight through the glass. The garage was clearly empty.

No cars. No cherry Camaro.

"There you go," Sam said. "Your guy took his car and went somewhere. Free country. Mystery solved. Nothing that re-

quires the services of Boulder's finest."

"You?"

"Me. This is the right house?" Sam asked. He was holding the flashlight between us down near his waist, aiming the beam straight up toward the night sky. With the up light his forest of nose hairs was illuminated with way too much clarity for my taste. His face and head took on eerie contours inside the fog of his steamy breath.

I felt like saying something in reply to his question but couldn't figure out anything that confidentiality permitted me to say.

He smiled, recognizing my conundrum. "Thought so."

Over his shoulder I saw movement in the Millers' home. A silhouette in the upstairs window. I tried to watch it without watching it. I said, "I'm worried about Diane."

"What?"

I had his attention. I repeated my concern.

"Your partner? That Diane?"

"She went to Las Vegas a couple of days ago. I was talking with her on the phone last night from one of the casinos and the call suddenly went dead. She's disappeared. Her husband flew out there a couple of hours later and he can't find a

trace of her. The Vegas cops aren't interested."

Sam moved the flashlight beam away from our faces. A second glance next door revealed the silhouette moving from the Millers' window. In an instant, it was gone.

"Your friend Diane went to Las Vegas?"

Sam knew precisely what I had told him by telling him that fact. With Sam I rarely had to say things twice. "To talk to someone," I said, as a way of underlining my point, just in case.

He nodded, wetting his lower lip with his tongue. "You're looking at something behind me. Don't do it again. Look at me. Eye contact. Good, good. What is it?"

"Somebody watching us in an upstairs window."

"Still there?"

I shook my head.

"Dad?"

"Couldn't say. Just a silhouette."

"Which window?"

"Closest to the street."

He nodded and ran his fingers through his hair before he stuffed his free hand into the back pocket of his jeans. "Diane went to Las Vegas to talk with someone and then yesterday she vanished? Now you have a client you're worried about that you

think may have just vanished, too? You and I are standing in the backyard of a house on Twelfth Street where said client garages his old car. Right next door a young girl happened to disappear on Christmas Day. I got it all right, so far?"

"You're doing pretty well." *The car part is a little off,* I was thinking. *The Camaro may be old, but it's cherry.*

"Great, glad to hear it. Let me add a couple of things to the list, things I've already been a little concerned about. You know something about Mallory Miller's mother that in my book you don't have any reason to know. You probably even know she lives in Vegas. You're way too curious about Reese's aggressive tendencies for my taste. And it was not too long ago that you kind of predicted that you and I were going to knock heads about this house next door to the Millers."

"That's three things, Sam, at least."

"Do me a favor, ignore the arithmetic."

"I can't confirm some of what you're saying. But I can't argue with what you're saying, either."

"From you that's a ringing endorsement."

I shrugged.

With gorgeous understatement, Sam

said, "Well, too many missing pieces. It all sounds too goofy for words to me." He began walking. "Come on. I want to hear more about Diane and what's going on with her in Las Vegas."

He led me back out through the dormant water features of Doyle's yard. Just before we got to Sam's car at the curb I said, employing a voice that was much more measured than I was feeling at that moment, "Diane and I were both there the day that Hannah Grant died."

Without even a glance in my direction, he said, "I know that. Don't you think I fucking know that?"

33

My car was across downtown outside the house where Bob rented rooms from the Donalds. After pressing me for some more details about Diane's disappearance in Las Vegas, Sam headed toward Pine Street to drop me off.

"So what do you know about the owner of the house with the water park?" I asked.

He killed the volume on the radio, squelching some country lament that I didn't really want to hear. While I waited — rating the odds at three out of ten that he'd actually answer my question about Doyle — I was thinking, and not for the first time, that most of Sam's favorite country artists could use a few sessions of psychotherapy.

"Owner's been out of the house for a while; it's vacant now, was vacant over Christmas, too, if that's what you're wondering. And yes, we've talked to him — the owner — got in touch with him right away

through the real estate lady who's listing the house."

Sam paused poignantly. Okay, provocatively. I thought he was waiting to see if my sense of self-preservation was so impaired that I would choose that moment to remind him of something he had once confessed to me about the last time — the Christmas when the little blond beauty queen was murdered three blocks away. That time, Sam admitted one night over beers, eleven long months passed before any cop, any DA's investigator, any FBI agent — anyone in law enforcement — got around to interviewing one of the dead girl's family's nearest neighbors.

For eleven months after a child was viciously murdered, the cops had failed to interview the residents of a house with a perfect view of the crime scene.

To me, unbelievable.

But I didn't remind him. He didn't need reminding.

He went on. "The owner gave us permission to search. No hesitation, no bullshit, totally cooperative. Agent unlocked the place and we searched it. Nothing. And all this happened in the first few hours after Mallory's father reported her missing."

"Is the owner in town?"

Doyle. I wanted to use his name out loud, but I couldn't. I wanted to know if Doyle was in town.

"No."

"You guys thought Mallory might have been in there after she disappeared?"

"Vacant house right next door? It's one of the first places we look."

"But nothing?"

"Just a vacant house. Kitchen's hardly bigger than mine. Terrific yard, sure, but no place to toss a football. Definitely over-priced. Hey, what isn't in this town?"

Sam pondered the inflation of Boulder's housing stock more than I did, but taking that detour didn't seem productive to me. I asked, "Was the Camaro in the garage when you searched the house at Christmas?"

"Now there's a good question. I don't recall that it was. If it had been, somebody would've run the tags and talked to your guy. I'm sure of that. And I don't think we've ever talked to your guy."

I could tell that I had only about half of Sam's attention. He was considering some angle I couldn't see. His answer to my last question was probably in the vicinity of honest but he wasn't telling me all that he could. But then I wasn't telling him all that

I could, either. "Something else is spinning in that big head of yours. What is it?"

He startled a bit at my question as he pulled from Ninth onto Pine. "I'm connecting dots, looking for a damn crime. I need a rationalization I can use."

"What do you mean?"

He didn't answer right away, not until we were almost on the Donalds' block. My car was just ahead. The lights were still off in Bob's rooms; I would have been truly surprised if they weren't.

Sam flashed the Cherokee's headlights at a van coming at us from the other direction. The driver of the van responded by flashing to his low beams for half a second before he went right back to his brights. He beeped his horn to underline his aggravation that another motorist would deign to question his choice of headlamp settings. I couldn't see the van driver through the high-intensity glare but I would have bet he was flipping Sam off, too.

I said, "Asshole's tugging on Superman's cape."

"He's lucky I'm in a good mood."

I smiled out loud.

"There's nothing here for me, Alan. Your guy's been gone, what? A day or two maybe? There's half a thimble's worth of

blood near his door — and some clothes on the floor. No sign of forced entry. No witnesses. Guy's gone. His car's gone. Ergo: He split. People do it all the time without warning anybody, without telling anybody. Even their therapists. I have nothing I can give my bosses that they'll find the least bit interesting. I take this in, I know what I'm going to hear: So far this isn't a police matter. So that's what I tell you: So far this isn't a police matter."

"Okay," I said.

"And your friend, Diane? She's so far out of my jurisdiction it isn't funny. I put myself in the Vegas casino's shoes and I'm not going to give a crap about her welfare until another few days pass and the hotel needs her room for the next convention. I put myself in a Vegas cop's shoes, I feel basically the same way. Grown-ups do what grown-ups do. But say she's really missing? By the time people get worried enough to look for her, it will probably be way too late to do anything to help her. I pray she's okay, but just disappearing off a casino floor like that? I don't like what you're telling me. That's just the truth. I wish it were different."

Sam pulled the Cherokee to a stop nose-to-nose with my wagon and doused the

headlights. The glow from a streetlight washed into the car from the driver's side, silhouetting Sam against the glass.

"The dots I'm connecting are actually way more interesting to me," he said. "See, if I put on my decoder glasses I see your footprints just about everywhere I look, which shouldn't be too surprising considering your history with this kind of thing."

I opened my mouth to disagree. Closed it. What was the point?

Sam went on. "First? I think maybe you and your partner, Diane, have some connection to the Millers — I'm guessing Mrs. Miller, Rachel — that I don't know about. Want me to guess? Okay, I suspect it goes back a few years, maybe more. Could I guess what it is? Yes, I could." He paused, allowing me to digest his conclusion.

"Next? I think that the Camaro man has some connection to the guy who owns the water-park house and for some reason that connection makes you much more nervous than a simple rented garage should make you. So it's something else entirely. I'd like to know exactly what that connection is, but experience tells me I'm not going to get shit from you tonight, so I'm trying not to give myself a headache about it. My assumption at the moment is that you think

it has something to do with Mallory Miller. Frankly, that worries me. It worries me that you're playing detective again, and it worries me just the slightest little bit that you might be on to something that we don't know."

The sound of Sam's stomach complaining that it hadn't seen a meal in a while filled the car. The growl made me realize that I was hungry, too. I wondered if Lauren had saved me some dinner.

"More? We already know that you and Diane were the ones who found that vic on Broadway. And —"

"Sam, you just called Hannah Grant a 'vic.' "

"I shouldn't have said that. She was your friend. My apologies. Habit, I'm sorry."

"That's not what I meant. You think Hannah's a victim? You think her death was a homicide? The coroner called it 'undetermined.' Has that changed?"

"It's Slocum's and Olson's, not mine. I'm not the authority on that case. Manner was undetermined yesterday. Manner is undetermined today. End of story, sorry."

In almost any other circumstance I would have pushed him. But I needed Sam to stay interested in Diane and Bob. We could get back to Hannah later. I couldn't

help but wonder, though: *What do the cops have?*

"What else?" I asked. "You were going to say something else."

"Reese Miller," Sam said. He'd forgotten which finger he'd used to keep track of his last point. By default, he chose his thick thumb to represent Reese Miller. "Why are you so interested in him? Where the heck does he fit into this puzzle?" He turned his head toward me and looked right at me. "Do you even know?"

I opened my mouth, closed it, and emitted some sound that was closer to a sigh than anything else. Reese was an unknown to me. I said, "No, I don't really know anything about him."

"Good," he said. "Listen, I have to get the babysitter home and I promised to help Simon with a poem he's writing. Did you have to write poems at his age? It's a good thing. Getting kids to write a lot. Keep me up to speed on Diane."

I opened the Jeep's door and was freshly surprised by the bitter chill of the January night. "Thanks, Sam."

"Yeah," he said. Then: "Wait."

I leaned back into the car. Sam looked away from me for a couple of seconds before he turned back. "I know you expect

me to find a way to help you. But I can't. There's no hook for me. There has to be something I can grab on to."

"I don't especially want anything to do with this either, Sam. Since the day that Mallory fell off the face of the earth I've tried like hell to make this leave me alone. But it keeps tracking me down. From my point of view, you get close enough to this thing and you'll find it has as many hooks as a square foot of Velcro."

I slammed the door shut and he drove off.

34

The clock read just shy of 8:30 when I walked in the front door of my house. Emily greeted me exuberantly, but I found my other two girls sound asleep in the master bedroom curled into the familiar big spoon/ little spoon configuration. They were surrounded by that night's bedtime books and Grace's favorite stuffed animals. Our not-so-stuffed poodle, Anvil, was curled into a tight ball at Grace's knees.

I was feeling remorse that I'd been missing out on the bedtime ritual so often.

Sound asleep at Grace's bedtime was a little early, even for Lauren, but the energy depletion that she suffered as a result of multiple sclerosis wasn't always easy to predict. If you asked her on a day when she wasn't suffering any of the acute effects of one of the disease's myriad symptoms, she'd tell you that what she hated most about the illness was that it made her days so much shorter. As each successive year

took its toll, Lauren had fewer good hours, fewer strong hours, fewer waking hours, fewer hours when pain or weakness didn't drive her to bed. Ask her what she'd most like to change about having MS, and she'd tell you she wished her days were longer. She'd tell you that on most days her energy lasts about as long as daylight endures on a December day in Anchorage.

This had apparently been one of those Yukon days. That's what she called them. I'd call her from work and find her at her desk at the DA's office. I'd ask how she was doing. Too often she'd say, "You know, babe. It's a Yukon day."

I rearranged the comforter so that it provided some cover for both mother and daughter, kissed the tops of their heads, lifted Anvil from the sheets, and led the dogs outside to pee. Once the odd canine couple had done their thing and our little parade was safely inside the house, I checked for a message from Raoul or, even better, Diane.

Nothing.

I scrambled a couple of eggs, folded them into some honey wheat toast, and carried my plate into the living room. I ate standing up at the big windows that faced down into Boulder, trying to spot the

house where Jenifer Donald was visiting her grandparents, trying to spot the over-priced house with the water park up near the foothills on Twelfth, trying to spot the small house on Broadway where Hannah Grant had died.

Far to the west, on the other side of the vast mountains, I wondered if Raoul was on his date with the woman from Venetian security. Or was he still chatting up gamblers at the craps tables trying to find someone who remembered his wife?

And where the hell in all those lights were Bob and his cherry Camaro?

What answers, if any, were sitting in a Kinko's box in my office?

My impulse was to charge downtown and find out.

I reminded myself that what Bob had written was part of a novel.

Fiction.

Stuff he'd made up.

Stuff I was supposed to wait to read.

35

Diane, in rare moments of candid self-doubt, would express astonishment that she'd ended up with Raoul. "Why me? Look at me. Look at him. Why on earth did he choose me?"

Raoul was an olive-skinned Spaniard with piercing eyes, a prodigious intellect, an entrepreneurial instinct for innovation, and a bloodhound's nose for money. He had a smile as sweet as honey, and his thick hair looked black until the sun hit it just so and lit it up like golden floss. He could give charm lessons to George Clooney, put on continental airs when he felt the situation demanded, or pull on faded jeans and cowboy boots and slide right into a farmhouse discussion of southern Colorado water rights as though it had been his family that had cut the first irrigation canals into the dusty San Luis Valley.

In much the same way that the progeny

of Holocaust survivors have been indelibly scarred by Germany's twentieth-century embrace of the Nazis, Raoul had been bruised deeply — down to the place where tissue ends and the soul takes up corporeal space — by Spain's fifty-year flirtation with fascism. Memories of long-absent relatives, and nightmared imaginings of what had happened to them at the hands of Franco's Falangists, flowed through his blood like perpetual antibodies to authority.

The result? Raoul had wide shoulders, and a chip on them that was sometimes big enough to obscure his handsome head.

My impatience to hear an update finally compelled me to dial Raoul's cell number before I climbed into bed. He answered after three rings.

"Yeah?" he said to the accompaniment of Las Vegas background sounds. Music, traffic. Something else — hissing, muted explosions. I wasn't sure what it was.

The single word he'd spoken as he answered had carried a boatload of hope; every time his phone rang he was praying that the caller was Diane. To me, ironically, his hope meant that he hadn't found her. My own hope, which was hovering like a flat stone skipping on a smooth lake,

sank instantly to the muddy bottom.

"It's me, Raoul. You didn't find her."

He said something in Catalonian. It sounded like *"bandarras."* From the spitting tone he employed, I guessed it had been a profanity and that it didn't really require translation, although I was always more than a little eager to add to my knowledge of the profane spectrum of his native tongue.

"Were you able to talk with that woman from hotel security?" I found myself shouting to be heard above the din.

"Marlina has a story," he said. "Unfortunately, it takes her a while to tell it."

"Yeah?" I didn't get whatever he was saying.

"She's from Mexico. What's on her mind is about her brother and something that happened to him on the way from Chihuahua to Tucson. She needs to talk. With some women, it has to first be about them. She is one of those women. *Fer un solo de flauta.* Trust me, it's the only way."

Raoul spoke about women the way he spoke about IPOs and RAM. With authority. Again, I considered asking him for a translation of the Catalonian, but I didn't.

"You haven't learned anything?" I asked.

"Not yet."

He sounded fried — Raoul's anxiety seemed to be swelling with every conversation we had. The appearance of my voice, and not his wife's, on the line had robbed him of whatever buoyancy had been keeping him afloat. I could feel the deflation in his spirits as hope leaked away; whatever vessel he was in was taking on water and he was getting tired of bailing.

"Did you find anyone playing at the craps tables who remembered Diane?"

"I set up a half-million-dollar credit line. I assumed that would give me a little bit of latitude in the casino."

I couldn't imagine. "Yeah? How much were you betting?"

"Five or ten. Sometimes twenty."

Thousand. "You win anything?" I asked.

"I did all right," he said. Raoul, I knew, would take no joy in a big pile of craps winnings. In his various tech businesses, he played for stakes that would make a huge pile of casino chips seem paltry by comparison. But given the events of the last twenty-four hours, Raoul would take some pleasure in the fact that he had taken the money — if it were a large enough pile — from the coffers of the Venetian.

"How good?

"I'm up eighty or so. The only luck I'm

having in this town is at a craps table."

I whistled. "Thousand?"

"Minus four. I tipped a couple of dealers. I'm hoping they're appreciative, might let me buy them a drink."

Two craps dealers were each a couple of grand richer than they'd been before they'd gone to work that day and met Raoul. With that kind of incentive they might be inclined to have a drink with him after their shifts were over.

I asked, "When are they off?"

"Three hours or so. We'll see what happens. My expectations are low. I gave a woman some money to pass each of them a note that said I wanted to talk with them. She says she did it, but who knows? Their bosses may have warned them off."

"A frustrating day?"

"They're the house. They have the cards; they have the odds. My only advantage is that I'm more motivated than they are. They don't understand that yet. One guy at the craps table slipped me his business card when he heard me ask the woman next to him about Diane. He's a VP for some shopping-center developer. They do malls."

"A gambler?"

"In his heart, that kind of gambler. I waited until he left the table and then I

called his mobile number after about twenty minutes. I told him I was the guy from the craps table. He said, 'Not now.' I asked, 'When?' And he said, 'I have your number now. I'll call you.' Then he hung up.

"*Pastanaga.* I think he was playing with me."

"He hasn't called?"

"In Vegas terms the night is young, right? Me? I'm twenty years older than I was at this time yesterday. A week more of this and I'll be ready to trade in the craps table for some pinochle."

I could almost feel his despair. I was on the portable phone, wandering between the mostly dark kitchen and the mostly dark living room, where I stopped and found myself, once again, searching for Twelfth Street in Boulder's dark grid. Looking for the Millers' house, and for Doyle's.

The noise in my ear was Sinatra and percussion. Traffic, too. A siren.

"Are you in a club?"

"I'm at the Bellagio. Outside, watching the fountains. I like them. I know they're garish, but I like them. Have you ever seen them?"

"Only on TV."

"Someday then."

"Yes." *Maybe.* "With Diane."

"With Diane, *sí*. Alain?"

I was a bit taken aback. He hadn't used the French pronunciation of my name for a long time.

"Yes."

"If there were a man involved — with my wife — you would tell me?"

"What? You mean a —"

"Yes. Un autre. We're grown-ups here, right?"

That Raoul was susceptible to whatever affective tides the prospect of infidelity caused in other people surprised me. Where romance was concerned, Raoul lacked confidence the way Spider-Man lacks grip.

I said, "To the best of my knowledge, this has nothing to do with another man. Nothing."

"Thank you. I had to ask."

"Raoul? The Rachel you're looking for? It's Mallory Miller's mother. That's who Diane went to Vegas to try to find."

He was silent. I hadn't lost him; I could still hear the Sinatra and the fountains and the impatience of the traffic on the Strip, but Raoul wasn't speaking. As the interlude grew longer, I immediately flashed

back to the night before and Diane's abrupt disappearance from the conversation I was having with her in the casino. My heart accelerated like a teenage driver with a lead foot chasing after a pretty girl.

"Raoul? You there?"

"I'm here."

"I was afraid I lost you."

"You didn't lose me; I'm thinking. Diane went to see the missing girl's mother?"

"If you've followed Mallory's story in the news, you may also know that Rachel Miller suffers from mental illness. That might be important for you to know when you finally find her."

"I don't read that kind of thing. Diane tells me, but she didn't tell me that. What kind of mental illness?"

I wasn't sure what the tabloids had reported. "I know the answer to your question, Raoul, but I shouldn't say. It's something serious. Let's leave it at that."

"Is she dangerous?"

"Rachel? Unlikely, highly unlikely."

"Why did Diane want to see her?"

"I found a way to rationalize telling you who Rachel is. Giving you the why part is much harder. I'm sorry. And I'm not sure it will help you to know the an-

swer. If I think it will, I'll tell you, I promise."

The fact that Mallory's mother lived in Vegas, even the fact that she lived in Vegas and suffered from a severe mental illness, had been reported in the news media. I wasn't telling Raoul anything new by telling him that. If a patient tells a psychologist that the sun came up that morning, the news isn't necessarily confidential. The psychologist can share the revelation with others.

Raoul asked, "Is Diane mixed up with whatever happened to Mallory Miller?"

"I can't" — I fumbled for a word that seemed to fit — "address that."

"You could if your answer was no."

To myself, I said, *Thank you*. Raoul was absolutely right. I could tell him if the answer was no. But the answer wasn't no, and he knew exactly what that meant. "I can't argue with your conclusion, Raoul."

"This mess — whatever this mess is — it started with Hannah's death, didn't it?"

I thought for a moment about what I could say in reply. "Hannah's death started a lot of balls rolling."

He responded with, *"Si ma mare fos Espanya, jo seria un fill de puta."* From the cadence and tone, I assumed it was pro-

fane, and from the reference to *Espanya* I guessed that a Spaniard wouldn't be thrilled to hear the phrase cross Raoul's Catalonian lips.

36

I hadn't been on the University of Colorado campus for a while. January wasn't my favorite time for a visit, and the Duane Physical Laboratories wasn't my ideal destination. But when my 11:15 appointment canceled on Thursday, I recognized that if I added the newly freed time to my midday lunch break, I had a seventy-five minute hole in my day. I decided to make the short trip from my office to the university.

The physics building is a large, angular, modern complex on the east side of the Boulder campus, segregated by roadways and by design from the cluster of lovely brick or flagstone structures that form the Mediterranean architectural core of the original university. The newer academic buildings surrounding Duane were, like Duane itself, looming, cast-concrete forms faced with just enough flagstone and roofed with just enough red tile to pay

wink-wink homage to the Tuscan soul of the place.

I'd been aware of Duane for years; the tallest structure on campus, situated right across Colorado Avenue from the Muenzinger Psychology Building, it was hard to miss. But, given my arm's-length relationship with the physical sciences, or at least my arm's-length relationship with the study of the physical sciences, I'd never had reason to go inside Duane. Once I did make my way into the building looking for Bob, my initial impression was that Duane was state-university big and anonymous and that the notices on the bulletin boards were mostly about things I didn't understand and, more to the point, until that moment didn't even know that I didn't understand. A professor was looking for a research assistant to study femtosecond optical frequency combs. Another lab needed help developing microcalorimeters and bolometers based on superconducting thin-films cooled to 0.1 K.

I didn't know what any of it meant, not even close, but I was almost one hundred percent confident that I wasn't their man. The students wandering the flavorless hallways — students who likely deserved my respect because, unlike me, they might

have a prayer of being able to translate the bulletin boards — seemed a bit more serious than those I was accustomed to running into in my usual haunts on campus.

A big, anonymous building full of serious students? I suspected that Bob had gravitated to the physics department by unconscious design and had ended up burrowing into an environment where he could survive — thriving for Bob wasn't really an option — for the many years he'd been putting in his time waiting for whatever would come next.

After a few false starts going to the wrong offices, I learned that Bob was actually a clerk/secretary in the office/lab where plasma physicists did their incomprehensible things. It turned out that Bob's boss, a middle-aged woman named Nora Santangelo who was shaped like a chunk of water main, was as curious as I was about Bob's whereabouts, and had a terrific intuitive sense of the parameters of Bob's peculiarities.

When I introduced myself I omitted the doctor part. I told Ms. Santangelo — she didn't strike me as the type of supervisor that a subordinate, or a visitor like myself, should call "Nora" — that I was a friend of Bob's and that he had missed a rendezvous

we'd planned for the previous evening and wasn't answering his phone.

She responded suspiciously, "You're his friend? I didn't know he had any."

Point, Ms. Santangelo.

It had taken some effort on my part to refocus her on the fact that I didn't know where Bob was. "I called here this morning. The person who answered his phone told me he was out sick. But he's not at home, either. I'm concerned."

"Well, to be honest, I am too. I hadn't called his home — that's not the sort of thing that Bob . . . appreciates. He missed a day of work back during the spring blizzard in 2003, but that's the only other time I can remember."

Bob's previous absence was undoubtedly excused: The infamous March 2003 blizzard had dropped almost four feet of snow on Boulder. "He didn't call in today?"

She shook her head. "Or yesterday. Bob usually eats lunch at his desk. Puts his nose in a book or plays games online. Scrabble. Sometimes chess. He never hangs with the rest of the staff. Never. But Monday? Around eleven in the morning he told me he was going out for lunch. Came right up to my office, walked right up to my desk, and said, 'Mrs. Santangelo, I'm going out

to lunch.' I was so surprised — and so pleased, really — that I told him to enjoy himself, to take a whole hour."

"Did he?"

"Sure as heck did. He never came back at all. Didn't call in. I still don't know where he is."

"Well," I said, while I digested the news that Bob's vanishing act had started even earlier in the week than I'd suspected.

Ms. Santangelo and I were standing in her office and I was finding myself increasingly distracted by the tubular shape of her. I would swear that her thighs, hips, waist, bosom, and shoulders were all the exact same measurement. She wasn't particularly heavy; she just looked like she'd been forced to spend her formative years hibernating in a sausage casing.

"Listen," she said. "Bob is . . . different. Different — different. I inherited him when I came over here from Hellems — the history department? I used to think those folks in history were peculiar, but these physicists? Don't get me started; they're something else. And Bob, he's the oddest ball in the rack. Excuse my honesty, but if you know him then you know that already. He likes to keep his distance. He can be difficult for people to deal with,

people who aren't sensitive to his . . . shall we say, tendencies. But he does his job. No more, mind you, not a scintilla more. Bob does just his job. And I've finally found him a desk in a lab where everybody seems to get along with him okay. What I'm saying is that he's not on a short leash like some of the people here. I'm not going to fire Bob for whatever . . . this is." I watched her expression as her imagination took her someplace she hadn't previously considered. "Within reason, of course."

"Ms. Santangelo, it sounds like you know him well. Do you have any idea where I might look for him?"

She thought for a moment and shook her head. "Sorry," she said, as she took a step toward the door. "But you'll call me if you hear anything? I am concerned. Bob grows on you."

Like a mushroom, I thought. *Or a truffle.* Something parasitic.

"Of course." I scrawled my pager number on a Post-it that I spotted on the desk behind me and handed it to her. "Will you do the same?"

She said she would and I headed out the door. Before I'd cleared the threshold I stopped and turned back to her. "Did Bob take his begonia with him? You know the

one I'm talking about?"

She smiled at me. "Of course I do. You do know him well. But I don't know the answer to your question. Why don't you and I go down to his desk and see about that darn Christmas begonia."

As she led me down the hall toward the administrative area that included Bob's desk, I allowed myself the suspicion that Ms. Santangelo had quite a mouth on her when she was younger, but that a lot of ambition and some determined self-discipline had turned her from a damn-and-hell young woman to a darn-and-heck middle-aged one.

The Christmas begonia was sitting in what his boss said was its usual place on the corner of Bob's desk. The plant's presence told me one thing, but it told Ms. Santangelo two. She explained to me that if Bob anticipated being away from the office for an extended period — anything more than a long weekend constituted an extended period — he would carefully transport the begonia home with him. The transport was an elaborate process involving a beer-case flat and tented brown grocery bags. She also explained that if he anticipated being out of the office for a period even as long as a full day but not

longer than three, he would move the plant and its pebble tray from the corner of his desk to the top of a waist-high bookshelf that sat beside a southeast facing window at the far end of the room.

"Always?" I asked.

"Always," she confirmed, without hesitation. "He never puts the begonia in direct sun. And he always watered it from below, you know, from the pebble tray. He knows what he's doing with it. Bob manages to keep the thing in bloom like that from Thanksgiving until spring break some years. People always comment on it, always."

I'd already noted that the begonia was healthy, its blossoms prodigious. I stated the obvious: "Bob didn't expect to be gone for this long, did he?"

Ms. Santangelo reached down and caressed the petals of one of the delicate begonia flowers. "No, he didn't. I wonder if I should move it over to the bookcase so it can get some light while he's gone. Bob would. I know he would. I just don't know if he would want me to."

I'd followed her hands to the desktop and was scouring the surface for a clue that might tell me something about Bob's destination when he'd left work to go out

to lunch on Monday. Other than the Christmas begonia, though, his desktop was devoid of anything personal. I asked, "When Bob plays games, does he use this computer?" I was pointing at the less-than-state-of-the-art machine that filled a third of his desk.

"No, he doesn't. He has a laptop, he brings it with him to work every day. He asked me a long time ago if it's okay with me for him to hook it up to the university's network over lunch to play his games. I told him to have at it. Bob doesn't cheat. If he's unsure about a rule, he asks."

Her response deflated me a little. "He took his laptop with him to lunch?"

"I don't know, heck," she said, and started rummaging in the drawers of Bob's desk. From my vantage the drawers appeared to have been arranged by a demonic closet organizer.

"Don't see it," she said. "He must have taken it."

"Do you know anything at all that might help me find him?"

"I wish I did," she said. "I really wish to heck that I did." She made her hands into fists and lifted them so that they came together just below her chin. "A few of my people here are totally reliable, you know

what I mean? But some of the rest? Flakes. If they were gone for the amount of time that Bob's been gone — a couple of days — I wouldn't give it a second thought. Par for the darn course is what I'd think. Par for the darn course. But Bob? He's not part of either group. He's not regular, he's not a flake. He's . . .

"You know what? I'll just say it: I don't really like Bob, but I . . . like him. Do you understand? I do hope he's okay."

I understood.

I crammed in a quick stop at Mustard's Last Stand on Broadway, inhaled my hot dogs with only a small side of guilt over the indulgence, and made it back to my office with just a few minutes to spare before my next appointment.

37

Was the after-work plan I cobbled together a good idea? Probably not. But once my workday was done I realized that I was fresh out of good ideas, so I was left to settle for questionable ones.

I assumed that it would take me a day or so to get an appointment arranged to see the inside of Doyle's house, but I was wrong. When I phoned the listing agent asking if she could meet me for a showing, her eyes apparently began flashing dollar signs at the prospect of mining a buyer for a house for which she was already representing the seller. She asked me what time I got off work. I told her I was done at six. Without a moment's hesitation she asked if 6:15 would work for me. "You won't believe the water features in the backyard," she exclaimed. "They are worth the purchase price all by themselves. Trust me, they're . . ."

I didn't tell her that I already knew.

When I called Viv, our part-time nanny, she informed me that Lauren would be late getting home, too. Viv promised me that she was happy to stay with Grace a little longer. In my head I added a small bonus to her monthly check. I also left Lauren a voice mail at her office that I would pick up some Thai takeout for dinner.

The woman I was meeting was named Virginia Danna. She pulled up in front of Doyle's house in a silver Lexus SUV, the big version, the fancy Land Cruiser clone that was all shoulders and hips. I was parked a couple of doors farther north and walked the short distance from my car in time to meet up with her near the front porch.

"Dr. Gregory?" she beamed when she spotted me coming. "You're going to absolutely love this place. The bathrooms need a little work, but oh, oh, the potential with the . . ." She was a tall, thin — the word *svelte* actually came to mind — elegantly dressed woman with just a hint of an accent, as though she'd emigrated to the United States from someplace when she was quite young. Despite her last name, for some reason I was guessing she was from Brazil. Her wardrobe made few concessions to winter. She wore no coat and she

balanced effortlessly on high heels. All in all, very not-Boulder.

"Ms. Danna?"

"Yes, yes. I'm so sorry. My manners sometimes escape me when I'm excited. And this house, it . . ." She reached out to shake my hand. "Will you excuse me for just a moment?" She pressed a speed-dial button on her cell. "Yes, yes. Dr. Gregory is here. We're going in now. Fine, fine. Yes, I'm sure. *Doctor* Gregory. That's right, on Twelfth. Thanks!" Ms. Danna turned back to me. "With what's happened to some poor agents in Denver — I'm sure you heard — we're required to check into the office before all private showings. I hope you understand, it's . . ."

"Of course."

She was in the lockbox in seconds, retrieved the front door key, and held the door open so I could precede her inside. "I don't really like to show houses when they're unfurnished like this one is, but . . ." She sighed. "I tried to get the owner to rent some things, you know, just for . . . The right furniture makes everything seems so much brighter and . . ."

Ms. Danna had an obvious penchant for uncompleted thoughts. Regardless, I was grateful for the opening she'd just offered

355

about Doyle. Offhandedly I asked, "Is the owner in town? Did he move to a larger house?"

She was easing me out of the cramped entryway into an adjacent living room with scratched red-oak floors, the original single-pane metal casement windows, and an undistinguished fireplace. "In town? No, no. Not exactly. But we're in constant touch, constant. I promise I can get a response to an offer in a heartbeat. A day at the outside. He's motivated, he is — he's already dropped the price once. Don't get me wrong; I mean that in all the right ways. Do you live here in Boulder?"

The last question was ripe with raw hope that my answer would be yes and that I might offer her the opportunity for a real estate trifecta: a buyer who purchases a home from a listing agent and then agrees to enlist the same agent to sell his existing home. Three commissions — seller, buyer, seller — and a veritable cascade of closings.

"I do. In Spanish Hills. But I work downtown near the Mall, on Walnut, and with the traffic lately, the drive is getting . . ." I tried to find the right word before I settled on "tiresome."

Her excitement at my disclosure was pal-

pable. A Spanish Hills listing? Although naming one of a few other even more precious local neighborhoods might have earned me an almost orgasmic response, in Boulder it didn't get a whole lot better for local real estate purveyors than Spanish Hills. "Inventory" in Spanish Hills usually meant that there was a single home for sale. With my pronouncement that I lived on one of the rare parcels across the valley, I felt an instantaneous change in the electrical charge in the room.

But Ms. Danna knew that she had to sell me on the house at hand and couldn't risk my getting too sentimental about leaving my current home. She played her hand well. "Don't I know?" she said. "That's the beauty of living right here on the Hill. Everything is so close: Chautauqua, downtown, the greenbelt, the mountains, the turnpike, shopping. The location is so . . ."

Perfect?

I caught her staring down at my left hand and accurately predicted her next question. "You're married?"

"Yes."

"Children?"

"One."

"Spanish Hills?" she mused. "It's so pretty up there. I have clients who have

waited for years to . . . the views are so . . ."

Expansive? And the houses so . . . expensive. I didn't have the heart to tell her that I lived in one of the few modest homes — modest by Boulder standards — in the whole neighborhood. She'd be so disappointed.

"Yes, it is lovely," I said, but I was allowing my eyes to wander the recesses of the bland living room and was beginning to wonder what I'd hoped to gain by traipsing through Doyle's empty house. I moved through an opening from the living room into an equally bland dining room. Ms. Danna followed right behind me.

"Good size, don't you think?" she said. "Plenty of room in here for a . . ."

Table? Family gathering?

The kitchen had been recently renovated and had a nice little built-in breakfast nook with a large window facing the yard. A compact laundry room was stuffed into what had probably once been a butler's pantry. The quality of the remodel wasn't congruous with the asking price for the house; the new cabinetry and appliances were the kind of warehouse stuff you might expect to find in a Boulder rental.

Ms. Danna apparently shared my impression. "Some new countertops in here,

maybe stone, or even cast concrete, and you'd need to do something with that . . ."

What? I couldn't tell. "Yes," I said. I was beginning to recognize her real estate dilemma. She was trying to sell a house in Boulder in winter that's main selling point was its yard. And yards don't show too well when they've been stripped of all their green, and elaborate water features don't show too well when they've been drained of all their H_2O.

We made it through a quick tour of the two upstairs bedrooms and two adjacent cramped bathrooms. She had been correct in her earlier appraisal: The bathrooms were in need of a sledgehammer and a good designer. The master bath was lined with chest-high plastic tile in a color that resembled one of the fluids that Grace emitted from her nose when she had a sinus infection.

As my enthusiasm for the house failed to swell, Ms. Danna's enthusiasm about her prospects seemed to go into decline, but she tenaciously held on to some hope for the finale. "The two highlights of this property are the media room in the basement, and that wonderful backyard. Which would you like to see first?"

She didn't wait for my reply. She hit two

switches on the wall near the back door and instantly the yard lit up like a resort. My eyes were drawn to the granite waterfall that I'd seen in the dark the night before.

"That's nice," I said.

"Nice? Imagine the water splashing over those rocks, the sound of that stream. Fish in the pond. The birds, the flowers. In spring, I think you'll find that it's . . ."

Breathtaking?

"The basement?" I asked. "Where are the stairs?"

The lower level wasn't the same size as the upper level. The media room was big enough — I pegged it at fifteen by twenty feet — but the whole basement wasn't even twice that size. A bland powder room, a mechanical room, and a long, narrow storage room completed the downstairs floor plan. On the top third of the storage room wall was a wide opening with a hinged lid.

"More storage?" I asked.

"Crawl space," Ms. Danna said.

"May I?" I asked, touching the handle on the door.

"Of course."

I opened the awning-style lid and peered into a neat crawl space about three feet high. The floor of the entire space was

lined with thick-mil plastic.

"Radon?" I asked, trying to act like someone who was actually interested.

She nodded. "Nothing to worry about. It's under control. Completely. I have all the reports. It's been mitigated to levels that the neighbors would love to have. Really, it's . . ."

Whatever. I closed the lid on the crawl space.

"Did you see that projector in the media room?" she asked. "It's a top-of-the-line Runco. And, yes . . . yes, it's included. All the theater electronics are included. Audio, video. All of them. Denon, B&O. The furniture, too. I don't have to tell you that those chairs are all recliners, and they're not La-Z-Boys. Custom. Crème de la crème. Electronics, finishes, everything. He spared no expense down here. The owner loved his home theater, he . . ."

I didn't know what she was talking about component-wise, and I didn't really care. I was one of those people who couldn't imagine going down into the basement to watch a DVD so I could pretend I was sitting in a theater. I'd just as soon curl up with my wife and daughter and my dogs and watch a video on the old VCR in the bedroom.

"Wow," I said, trying to sound enthusiastic.

"Oh, I forgot, the screen . . ." She took my hand and led me out to the far wall of the theater. A big white movie screen was hung within an ornately carved frame of polished wood. I was guessing mahogany. "Now, don't you touch it — fingerprints, fingerprints. I forgot who makes it — somebody good, no, somebody great. I have it in my notes. It's the same screen that Spielberg has in his private screening room at his place in . . . The same exact one. It's like . . . the best. I promise I have the name back in the office. I'll get it for you. I will. First . . ."

Thing? "Wow." It looked exactly like a movie screen. Spielberg knew what he was doing.

After what I hoped was a suitable amount of time spent staring at the blank screen, I led Ms. Danna up the stairs and as we walked out the front door I gave her my appraisal of the property. "It's a little small for us, I'm afraid."

She was ready for that argument. "Oh, I know, I know, but the potential? You get a good architect to find a way to cantilever the upstairs a little bit and you could expand that second story in a heartbeat.

Think of the covered porch down below and the views from your new master suite upstairs. Just think! You could have a deck that faces the Flatirons! And closets? Oh, I don't have to tell you, do I? You're a man with . . ."

Vision?

The night was cold and a bitter wind was blowing down from the north with the sharp bite of Saskatchewan.

As Ms. Danna replaced the keys in the lockbox she made it clear that she was eager to show me a couple of other "things," though "the price points are up a notch or two from here." I declined, although I admit that I was curious exactly how many digits constituted a "notch" in Boulder's hyperinflated housing market. Resigned, she gave me her card and asked for one of mine.

"I'm sorry," I said. "I don't have any with me."

It was partly true. I didn't have any with me.

But I wasn't sorry.

I walked her down the serpentine front walk to her big Lexus and shook her hand, thanking her for her time. Over her left shoulder — at the upstairs window of Mallory Miller's house — I spotted what I

thought was the same silhouette I'd seen the night before while I'd been trespassing in the backyard with Sam.

Ms. Danna saw me looking. "Such a tragedy," she said. "That girl's father must feel . . ."

Awful.

38

"Finding reality here is like looking for condoms in a convent. There might be some around, but they're not going to be easy to locate."

Raoul was talking to me about Las Vegas, and about how he'd spent his day. His voice was as tired as my toddler's when she was up past her bedtime. Raoul was an optimist by nature, an entrepreneur by character. Watching him treading water in a sea of despair was so unexpected that it felt surreal.

The Las Vegas cops remained uninterested in Raoul's missing wife. He had pressed them to try to ascertain at what point Diane would be considered "missing." One detective told him that, "Given the circumstances, it would certainly take more than a long weekend. And so far, Mr. Estevez, that's all she's been gone. One long weekend." The hospitals continued to have no inpatients matching

Diane's name or description. As a sign of his desperation, Raoul had hired a local private investigator who was apparently chewing up money much faster than he was uncovering clues about Diane's whereabouts. All he'd learned so far was Rachel's address. When he checked for her there, no one answered.

Marlina, the woman from Venetian security, enticed Raoul to buy her breakfast at a place near downtown that was filled mostly with locals. They spoke Spanish while they ate. Raoul learned that Marlina's brother was in INS detention in Arizona, learned how he got there — or at least Marlina's version of how he got there — and learned in excruciating detail how Marlina felt about the whole affair, but he didn't learn anything about what the casino surveillance tapes revealed.

After the frustrating breakfast, Raoul moved on to an alternative avenue of investigation: The Love In Las Vegas Wedding Chapel. As he told me about it, my impression was that relating the story of what happened there seemed to relax him.

According to Raoul's tale, the minister of the Love In Las Vegas Wedding Chapel was the Rev. Howard J. Horton. By

training he was an actor who had enjoyed some success as a young man on Broadway, even once landing the role as understudy for the lead of some Tommy Tune extravaganza. After a move to California to find fortune on the Left Coast, Horton had actually defied the odds and made a living in Hollywood until his thirty-seventh birthday doing bit parts on sitcoms and lawyer and cop shows and getting occasional throwaway lines on big-budget features. In successive years in his late twenties he had been filmed making cocktails for Sean Connery, being pistol-whipped by Al Pacino, and flirting shamelessly with Sharon Stone just before being pummeled into submission by her leading man.

Raoul didn't think he had caught any of those particular movies.

The bit parts hadn't been enough to provide the foundation for Horton's hoped-for long-term career as a distinguished character actor, and as his face matured the parts he was being offered didn't. To pay the bills he'd eventually gravitated to dinner theater and later on made his way to Vegas, where he did some emceeing at shows on the Strip, fell in love with heroin, heroically managed to "divorce the damn

bitch," and eventually ended up winning a thirty-nine percent stake in the Love In Las Vegas Wedding Chapel in a poker game with some locals that had started one cocktail hour on a Wednesday and ended late in the morning or early in the afternoon — Horton didn't quite remember; it had been that kind of game — the following day.

Horton was forty-seven years old and had been the minister of the moment at the Love In Las Vegas for almost seven years. On bad days he consoled himself that it paid the bills.

The British accent and aristocratic demeanor that Horton employed for the tourists who came to Vegas for matrimony were pure shtick, and the slick Vestimenta suit he wore in the relentless Nevada heat nothing but costume. He'd won the suit from a gay guy from Atlanta in another poker game — that table populated, with the exception of Horton, entirely by out-of-towners — and he told Raoul a hilarious story about them both stripping down to their undies to exchange clothes after the game. Howard had given up his favorite pair of cargo shorts and a well-worn Tommy Bahama silk shirt.

Raoul promised me that he'd get around

to telling me the part about the protracted negotiation for the Atlanta man's thong another time.

"You promise?" I said.

"Absolutely," Raoul assured me.

In a city where visitors were primed to expect spectacle, Horton's wedding show at the Love In Las Vegas was a whisper of sophisticated, or faux-sophisticated, understatement. At the Love In Las Vegas, tourists who were so inclined could be married, not by an Elvis impersonator or a cross-dressing reject from Cirque, but by an ex-patriot British lord who seemed intent on bringing his interpretation of a little bit of the best of the Church of England, whatever that was, to the Nevada desert.

While Raoul waited to get a few minutes alone with the Rev. Horton so he could ask some questions about Diane and Rachel Miller, he had to choose between frying outside in the parking lot in the he-was-told unusual-for-January ninety-three-degree heat or sitting in the air-conditioned comfort of the chapel and observing the nuptials of a young couple that had driven all the way from Spraberry, Texas — that's just outside Midland and not too far from Odessa — to tie the knot in Las Vegas.

The engaged had written their own marriage vows and brought a cassette of the music they wanted played during the ceremony. Her vows ran onto three legal-sized yellow tablet pages.

His didn't.

The bride wore white — an ill-fitting empire-style dress with a long train that her second cousin had scored at the Filene's Basement annual everything-for-$299 wedding dress running-of-the-bulls in Boston. The bride was twenty-two, but didn't look it. She was as innocent as the prairie, and her face was full of the wonder that every woman's face should have before she weds for the first time.

On the final stretch of Highway 95 into Vegas she'd made a valiant attempt to memorize all the vows that she had penned onto the yellow legal pad on the haul from Spraberry to El Paso on Interstate 10, but during the actual ceremony she'd had to consult her notes every few seconds during her long recital of eternal love.

In his retelling, Raoul generously wrote it off to nerves.

Her betrothed was twenty-six years old and was dressed in a tuxedo jacket he'd borrowed from his sister's husband, a ruffled-front tux shirt sans tie, and clean —

and pressed — Wranglers. His hair, greasy from all the road time, was combed into a mullet that was as sleek and shiny as the skin of an under-refrigerated fish. This was his third marriage and his second wedding in Las Vegas — he was once widowed and once divorced — and by demeanor and practice he was a love-honor-and-obey-till-death-do-us-part kind of groom. By history he apparently wasn't exactly a love-honor-and-obey-till-death-do-us-part kind of husband, but he'd promised his fiancée repeatedly — including once during the ceremony — that all that rutting was behind him.

The groom's self-written vows were an obviously plagiarized, parsed version of the popular standard. Raoul's impression was that the guy would have been better off just allowing Rev. Horton to do his almost-Anglican-cleric thing. But, Raoul noted, the bride didn't seem to be at all offended by her husband-to-be's lack of vow-writing prowess.

The wedding music, which was played over and over and over again in a toxic loop, consisted of a single upbeat song by Shania Twain with a lot of *uh, uh, oh*s in the lyrics. Raoul couldn't quite figure out the romantic relevance of the tune, but the

cumulative weight of the pure repetition of the *uh, uh, oh*s eventually rendered him willing to accept the silky voiced singer's implied warning about whatever the hell it was. By the time the ceremony was over and the newlyweds had kissed and kissed again and walked hand-in-hand down the aisle toward the desert inferno that awaited them outside, Raoul knew just about all he wanted to know about the couple from Spraberry whose wedding he had just helped celebrate, and he also knew he never wanted to hear the damn *uh, uh, oh* song again in his life.

Ever.

"He may have divorced 'the bitch' but Reverend Howie still sleeps with her cousin," Raoul said to me. "He drinks a bit, and then he drinks a bit more. We spent most of the afternoon at the kind of saloon the Vegas Chamber of Commerce doesn't want tourists to see. That's when I heard his life story and got all that fascinating background on the happy couple from west Texas. Have to give the guy credit, though — Howie knew I was paying but he got the same crappy well-scotch he drinks in that bar every day. He didn't ask the bartender to dust off the single malts

just because I was running the tab."

"Did you learn anything?"

It was late in Colorado — almost eleven at night — and I was exhausted. Although it was an hour earlier in Nevada, Raoul's voice told me that his long day and long story had left him every bit as tired as I was. Maybe more. But something about his day had at least temporarily softened the edge of his despair.

"He wouldn't talk to me about this Rachel woman. I could tell from his little act that he knew who she was, but he wouldn't answer any of my questions, wouldn't even admit that she hung out at his chapel. When I showed him Diane's photograph he wouldn't admit that he'd ever seen her before. I knew he was lying; wasn't sure exactly about what, or why, but I knew he was lying. I was beginning to think I was going to have to just stake out the damn wedding chapel and wait for Rachel to show up again and lead me to Diane."

"I'm sorry."

"No, no. That's when it hit me. I lowered my voice to a whisper, pulled a little pile of thousand-dollar chips from the Venetian out of my pocket, stacked them up in front of me, and asked Howie exactly how much he was being paid."

"Paid for what?" I said.

"That's just what he said to me. All offended and everything. Reverend Howie's a smart guy. He's on the edge, but he has some pride. I don't think he's too dishonest. At the chapel he makes a living providing a service, as screwy as the service is. He supplements his income by taking people's money, or whatever else they might want to bet, in high-stakes poker games. But he plays those games fair. His MO? He sets people up by being a better actor than they give him credit for, and then he takes their money by being a better poker player than they give him credit for. This time? I already know he's a good enough actor, and I wouldn't think about sitting down to a hand of Texas Hold 'Em with the guy."

"Yeah?" I had one ear focused on Raoul's Las Vegas story, the other tuned to Grace's room. She was making the kinds of nighttime noises that often precede one of those restless nights that end up with one of her parents dozing nearby on the rocker in her room until dawn. I said a silent prayer that my little daughter was merely enduring a troublesome dream.

Raoul said, "Eventually, he told me. I had to make it clear I wasn't going away,

but he finally said, 'Fifty.' "

"I'm sorry, Raoul. I'm too tired. I don't get it."

"I didn't get it at first, either. See, my brainstorm was that I thought that Rachel Miller must be paying him. That that was why he let her attend all the weddings. I figured she might be slipping him five bucks, maybe ten, per ceremony. But he was trying to convince me that she was paying him fifty bucks a pop — fifty — to sit in this tacky chapel while Reverend Howie did his pretentious I-now-declare-you-husband-and-wife song and dance." Raoul paused. "Do you know how many people get married in Las Vegas on an average day? One hundred and fifty-three. That's what Reverend Howie told me."

"If it's people, wouldn't it have to be a hundred and fifty-two or a hundred and fifty-four?" I asked. "Maybe you mean couples; the number can't really be odd."

Raoul sighed. "Alain, your point?"

I did the math. Five weddings a week: two hundred and fifty dollars. Ten weddings a week: five hundred dollars. Five weddings a day, with one day off each week: fifteen hundred dollars. That meant that for Rachel Miller to attend weddings to her heart's content would cost some-

where between two thousand and six thousand dollars a month, or between twenty-four and seventy-plus thousand dollars a year.

Plus gifts. Holy moly. Where the hell would a schizophrenic woman living on the streets of Las Vegas get that kind of money?

I asked Raoul, "Do you believe him?"

"At first, I thought he might be inflating the numbers to see how the negotiations would go with me, that I might be sitting in that saloon watching him drink scotch so that I could try to outbid Rachel for some crazy reason. You know, offer him more than fifty to turn her away."

"He's making pretty good money by allowing her to stick around for weddings."

"That part seems clear. Tell me, how sick is Rachel? No details — I'm not asking for anything confidential — just rate it for me. Do it in a way I can understand."

I couldn't tell him anything specific about Rachel's mental health mostly because I really didn't know anything specific about Rachel's current mental health. "With the kind of disease that someone like Rachel has, with the kind of chronicity she's endured — she could have very visible symptoms. If you were to measure the

disease of a person like that on the figurative ten-scale, say, on a bad day — a day when she's not taking appropriate medicine — she could be approaching double digits."

"On that ten-scale?" Raoul asked.

"Yes."

He emitted a high-pitched whistle. "See, that's what I thought. That kind of sick is scary to people like me. Which means that Rachel is ill enough to be a serious liability at a place like the Love In Las Vegas. What bride wants somebody that disturbed camped out in the front row of her wedding?

"Reverend Howie's fee is insurance: He makes Rachel pay to attend the weddings. Who knows, he may even limit the weddings he lets her attend. Maybe he picks them himself. Makes a judgment about which ones are safe for her to be at, which ones she might create a distraction, cost him some business."

"Raoul, if Rachel were attending all the weddings she wanted and if she were paying that much, it would cost a fortune. Where would she get that kind of money?"

Before the words were out of my mouth, I heard a prolonged whimper from Grace's room. *Damn.*

"This town?" he said. "Too many bad ways to answer that question. Way too many."

I shuddered at the thought of what perverse advantage some people might gain over someone as ill as Rachel Miller. "What did Howie finally admit to you?"

"Just that she gives him money so he'll allow her to attend the ceremonies. And this is the funny part — she doesn't pay him herself — the money comes from someone else, someone who makes Reverend Howie very nervous. He wouldn't give me the person's name. He said, 'You can buy me scotch all day and all night and I'm not going to give you a name.' I even pushed one of the thousand-dollar chips from the Venetian across the table and left it right in front of him. I said, 'Name and phone number, Howard, and it's yours.' He picked it up, flipped it, ran his fingers over the surface, and pushed it back onto my side of the table.

"I added two more and made it a nice little pile. He pushed them all right back to me. I added two more. He did the same thing."

Howie had turned down five grand. I was thinking, *Wow.* "So what are you going to do, Raoul?" I asked.

"I took four chips off the pile and slid the one that remained back across the table. I said, 'Different question. Man or woman?'

" 'Yeah?' Howie asked me. 'For a grand? That's all you want to know?' I said that was the deal and he actually had to think about it. He is so wary of this person that gives him money so Rachel can attend weddings that he actually considered turning down a thousand dollars rather than reveal to me the person's *gender*. Eventually, he picked up the chip and slipped it into his shirt pocket like it was a pack of matches. He said, 'It's a man. Not a man you want to fuck with.' "

"That was it?" I said. "That's all you got for a thousand dollars?"

"In business you don't always get value at the front end of a relationship. At the start you form a bond, establish platforms, ensure access. What I got for my thousand dollars is I got Howie on my payroll. And I reduced the possible suspects by half."

"How do you find the man you're looking for?"

Raoul sighed. "You remember a guy in Denver named Norm Clarke? Use to write for the *Rocky*."

I remembered him. "The gossip colum-

379

nist with the patch on his eye?"

"*Sí*. Well, I know him — he did a story on me back in the tech boom times. He lives in Vegas now, knows everybody. I'm meeting him downstairs a little later for a drink. I'm hoping he can help me find the man Howie was talking about."

Grace's unsettled whimper suddenly blossomed into a wail that was so powerful I could have sworn her lungs had been temporarily replaced by air compressors.

Raoul didn't need to be told our conversation was over. I sprinted in Grace's direction, praying that I could quiet her before Lauren's sleep was shattered.

39

After getting all of four hours' sleep I got all of four hours' warning before the next shoe dropped. I spent most of those four hours wondering whether having any warning at all was a good thing or a bad thing.

I never quite decided.

Patients, when they call my office number, are given a voice-mail instruction to call my pager directly in the case of an emergency. How often do my patients take advantage of the opportunity to reach me on my beeper? Once or twice in a bad month, infrequently enough that the mere sight of an unfamiliar phone number on my pager makes me anxious. So, on Thursday morning, while I was idling at the intersection of Broadway and Baseline on the way to work and my beeper vibrated and displayed an unfamiliar (303) 443- number, I was wary.

The 443 prefix meant the call came from a Boulder address. That's all I knew.

I returned the page as soon as I stepped into my office.

"This is Alan Gregory," I said. "I'm returning a page to this number." I don't use the "Doctor" appellation in those circumstances because I don't know if the person who called me will answer the phone or if someone else will. If it's someone else, discretion might dictate that my profession remain secret.

"Thanks for calling back so soon," the man on the line said. "This is Bill Miller." And then, as if I might not know, he added, "I'm Mallory's dad."

What a sad thing, I mused, that he could use his daughter's unfortunate notoriety as a quick social identifier. And an even sadder thing that he would.

"Mr. Miller," I said, buying some time while I hurriedly chewed and swallowed the ramifications of the simple fact that he had called me. "What can I do for you?"

"Can you squeeze me in for an appointment? It's . . . important."

"Umm," I managed. My eloquence, given the circumstances, was profound.

"Today, if possible," Bill Miller said.

I wondered whether he was asking me to get my tongue untied sometime "today," or whether he was asking for an appointment

with me sometime "today."

If you asked me to write an ethics problem for a psychologists' licensing exam, or to dream up a delicious ethical conundrum for clinical psychology graduate students' comprehensive exams, I don't think I could have come up with something as devious as the dilemma I was facing at that moment.

"Do you have some time available?" he said, kindly pretending not to notice how flummoxed I was. "I'll be as flexible as I need to be."

The problem freezing my communication skills wasn't my schedule. My practice calendar that day was no more or less constricted than usual. On most days, if I was willing to give up a meal or stay late at the office, I could squeeze in an emergency.

The problem I was struggling with was that I didn't know if I could see Bill Miller professionally at all. The issue that was complicating what should have been a simple matter of logistics was a problem of professional ethics.

My initial impulse about the ethical maze? I didn't think that I could see Bill Miller as a clinician. But I wasn't at all sure I was correct in that snap assessment. The circumstances were complex. I quickly

decided that I'd never confronted another set of facts quite as complex in my entire career.

The arguments for agreeing to see Bill Miller for therapy? They were easy. He had once, albeit briefly, been my patient. His present circumstances — or at least the ones I knew about — were so public and so tragic that they might cause someone to seek professional help. Empathy and compassion both argued for me to make myself available to him.

The arguments for refusing to see Bill Miller for therapy? This is where things got messy. Psychologists are under an ethical obligation to avoid what the profession calls "dual relationships." At its heart, this is a conflict-of-interest clause, intended to ensure that a clinician is free to act in the best interest of his or her patient, uncomplicated by competing forces. In practice, the dictum requires that a clinician not wear two different hats in a patient's life.

In simple English, it means I shouldn't do psychotherapy with the woman who cuts my hair. I shouldn't join a book group run by one of my therapy patients.

Simple, right?

Usually, yes. But try to apply those simple guidelines to my relationship with

Bill Miller. That's what I had been trying to do for the hours between his morning phone call and the midday appointment time I'd eventually offered him.

I hadn't gotten very far.

Did the fact that I was a good friend of a Boulder cop who was involved with the investigation of Bill Miller's daughter's Christmas Day disappearance qualify as a dual relationship?

I wasn't sure, but the degrees of separation seemed to be sufficient insulation.

Did the fact that my practice partner was covering the clinical work of a therapist who had died, and possibly been murdered, weeks after seeing Bill Miller's daughter for a single therapy session qualify as a dual relationship?

Once again, blank spaces seemed to separate Bill Miller's place on the board from the space that I was occupying.

Did the fact that I was seeing a patient who parked his car in the garage of the house of the man who lived right next door to the Millers qualify as a dual relationship?

Maybe, maybe not. In isolation, I would lean in the direction of "not." My patient had spoken with Bill Miller's daughter, considered her a friend. That was all I

knew about Bob's relationship to the Millers. It wasn't much of a tie.

Did the fact that my partner and good friend had disappeared while on a trip to Las Vegas to try to arrange a meeting with Bill's estranged wife constitute a dual relationship?

I knew of absolutely nothing that tied Bill Miller to any of those events.

Did the fact that my friend and partner's husband, someone else whom I enthusiastically considered a friend, was busy looking for Bill Miller's estranged wife qualify as a dual relationship?

Probably not, for all of the same reasons.

But I wasn't totally sure. I didn't know if I should be contemplating additive effects. If a wasn't greater than z, and b wasn't greater than z, and c wasn't greater than z, did I have to be concerned whether $a + b + c$ was greater than z?

Ethical algebra hadn't been covered in graduate school.

I interrupted my obsessing over the Bill Miller conundrum to address a practical problem: Diane was still missing, and Thursday was the day she was supposed to be back in her office seeing patients. Although Diane and I shared space, our

practices were separate businesses: I didn't know how many patients she was scheduled to see, nor did I know any of their names.

My problem was that I had to figure out some innocuous yet compassionate way to notify Diane's patients that their doctor would not be in the office that day. My solution was to post a note on the front door, the patient entrance to our little building. It read:

To Anyone With An Appointment With
Dr. Diane Estevez:
Dr. Estevez is unexpectedly away from the office to deal with an urgent situation. She is unable to cancel her appointments personally, but will not be in today. She will contact each of you individually upon her return, and she appreciates your understanding, and your patience.
Dr. Alan Gregory

At the bottom of the note, I belatedly scrawled a handwritten offer that anyone with a clinical emergency should call me, and I left my pager number.

When I'd returned Bill Miller's call, the offer for an appointment that I eventually made to him wasn't any more straightfor-

ward than was the prevaricating note I had left for Diane's patients. "I'm not sure I can see you, Bill. I may have an ethical conflict."

"How?" he said. "We haven't spoken in, well, years."

"It's complicated," I said, lamely. "It's not even clear to me that I actually have a conflict. I'm just concerned that I might."

"Well, how about this," he said. "Let's schedule a time. In the interval between now and then you can think about your ethical problem. We'll talk, I'll run my concerns past you, and you can decide if you're able to help."

He sounded eminently reasonable. I was reminded that even during the session with his wife so many years before, Bill Miller had always seemed levelheaded and reasonable. Almost, I also reminded myself, to a fault.

"How about eleven forty-five?" I asked.

Bill Miller was close to ten minutes late for his appointment. Since I was meeting with him over the brief window in my day that would have constituted my lunch hour, I'd greedily used the free time to devour an energy bar from the emergency stash in my desk.

"Déjà vu, huh?" he said as he settled onto the chair across from me. "It feels odd to be here without Rachel. That was one day that I will never ever forget."

My natural human instinct was to offer condolences to Bill, to be sympathetic about whatever had happened with Mallory, to reflect on the sad outcome of the situation with Rachel. But I didn't. Instead I contemplated the fact that after so many years between visits with me his first association in my presence was to his long-estranged wife, and not to the tragedy of his recently absent daughter.

Ironically, one of the most difficult things about the psychotherapeutic relationship is the necessity for the therapist to, at times, put brakes on reflexive human kindness. Were I to presuppose to start this interaction with Bill Miller with expressions of compassion, or even overt sorrow, at his plight — or by giving him a big hug, a pat on the back, and a hearty "hey, big guy" — I might unwittingly interfere with whatever motivation he'd had for picking up the phone.

So I waited. The truth was that most of the time, when I reached over my shoulder into my therapeutic quiver I ended up drawing out the dullest arrow, the one that

was marked SHUT UP AND WAIT.

"I bet you'd like to know why I'm here," Bill said.

"Yes," I said evenly. "I would. That's a good place to start."

Bill was dressed in wool flannel trousers, good leather loafers, and a crisp blue dress shirt that was the color of his eyes. His sportcoat wasn't new, but it looked like cashmere, and hung on him with the drape of good tailoring. He wore no tie; few men in Boulder did.

"What's your ethical problem?" he asked. The question was neighborly. He could have been inquiring about a problem I said I'd been having with my gutters.

"Explaining the circumstances would lead to a whole different ethical dilemma for me. It's something I'm going to have to deal with on my own. When I reach a determination, I'll let you know."

"But you've obviously dealt with it enough to have this meeting?"

"I'm hoping to get a better understanding about why you've come to see me. That might make my concerns moot, or it might clarify things so I'll have a clearer sense of what I should do." That was the plan, anyway.

Bill closed his eyes for a moment, a long

moment that grew into seconds. Five, then ten. Finally he opened his eyes, looked right at me, and with pain etched in his brow, he said, "You've been at my house twice over the past two days. Why?"

40

In the same way that a boxer who has just absorbed a right uppercut has many options as he's lying on the canvas staring straight up at the klieg lights listening to a referee count "eight, nine," at that moment I had many options.

I could have reached back into my quiver for the safety of my SHUT UP AND WAIT arrow.

Or I could have said something classically therapeutic, and classically arrogant, like, "This isn't about me, Bill. This is about you."

Or, of course, I could have out-and-out lied: *"I don't know what you're talking about."*

Instead, almost purely instinctively, I chose an alternative that I hoped might buy me a moment to think while at the same time it reinforced the separation that existed between, and needed to continue to exist between, my chair and that of my

patient. What I said in reply to Bill's question about why I was at his house was, "And that's why you're here, Bill?"

"Well, I don't think it's a coincidence."

"Excuse me?" I was honestly perplexed by his quick reply. Bill Miller was implying that my appearance at his neighbor's house was coincident with what, exactly? I really wanted to know. "What kind of coincidence are you talking about?"

"Why would you be at my next-door neighbor's house twice in two days with two different people?"

He apparently wasn't eager to answer my question; I was certainly not about to answer his. Discussing with Bill Miller that I'd been at his neighbor's house because I'd been concerned about the apparent disappearance of another one of my patients, and the disappearance of my partner and friend, wasn't about to happen.

"Is this meeting" — I waved my hand between us — "a professional meeting? Did you come to see me for psychotherapy, or for something else?"

He hesitated long enough that I knew he had hesitated, which told me that he'd had to think about how to answer my question.

I said, "The distinction is important. If we're going to work together, the distinc-

tion is important."

"Yes, yes, of course it's professional," he said. "I need your help, Dr. Gregory. But I'm also concerned why you've been . . . so close to my home in the past few days."

Was that a reasonable concern for him to have? I could have argued yes, I could have argued no. But was reasonableness the point? "Go back three days please, Bill. Were you considering calling me for psychotherapy then?"

"What do you mean?" he stammered.

"You said that you've seen me at your neighbor's house twice in the past couple of days. I'm wondering whether that is the reason that we're talking today, or whether you had been considering asking me for help prior to that."

Shit. By babbling on, I'd just given him a road map for how to respond.

No surprise, Bill consulted the map before he replied. "I'd been considering it. Seeing you next door brought everything closer to the surface, a lot of old memories, unresolved, you know, feelings about . . . what's happened, so I decided to call and set something up. But I feel I deserve an explanation as to why you've been in my neighborhood so much. I do."

Did he deserve an explanation? It was an interesting question. Were I truly interested in buying Doyle's house, that would potentially make me Bill Miller's next-door neighbor. If he and I were neighbors, the dual-relationships ethical restriction would definitely kick in: Preexisting therapeutic relationship or no preexisting therapeutic relationship, missing daughter or no missing daughter, I certainly could not provide psychotherapy to my next-door neighbor.

I decided to provide just enough of an explanation to allay his concerns.

"Bill, I can assure you that my presence at your next-door neighbor's house had nothing to do with you or your family."

Was that really true? I actually wasn't sure.

"Are you thinking of buying that house?" Bill asked.

An easy question, finally. "No, I'm not."

"You were there with the woman who is listing that house."

"I'll repeat what I said. I'm not considering buying the house."

"Then why were you with her?"

"My presence had no direct relevance to you or your family." Did it have indirect relevance? The question of indirect rele-

395

vance had to do with Bob Brandt and the conversations he'd had with Mallory through the fence. The answer to the question of indirect relevance was either all chronicled in the pages in the Kinko's box Bob had given me, or it wasn't. My money was still riding on "wasn't." Barely.

I went on. "Assuming for a moment that we each decide that we are comfortable working together . . ."

"Yes," Bill said.

"How can I be of help?" A quick glance at the clock told me we had precious little time remaining until my twelve-thirty showed up in the waiting room.

"I'm under a lot of stress."

I can only imagine.

"I'm not sleeping. I'm losing weight; I don't have any appetite at all."

Likely culprits for that constellation of symptoms? Depression, anxiety, post-traumatic stress. Given the circumstances of Bill's life, there were no surprises on that list. The most natural thing for me to do at that moment would have been to presuppose the source of Bill Miller's symptoms. I cautioned myself not to do it.

I pressed him, wondering aloud what he thought was going on. He responded with generalities about "events" and "the kids"

and "work." I tried for some c
He eluded me.

Was I observing resistance —
psychotherapeutic Great Wall that s
rates so many patients from the issues that
are most tender to them? Possibly. I decided to challenge the resistance a little.
"How was she feeling, Bill?"

"My daughter?"

Not Mallory. *My daughter.* I nodded.

"The holidays are hard for her. Always.
This year, too. They haven't been fun for
her since . . ."

I filled in the blanks with *her mother left.*

"Hard how?" I asked.

"She gets nervous. Withdrawn, irritable.
She's definitely a teenager."

Bill had grown anxious and withdrawn,
too. As I considered the fact that the media
had failed to report any details of
Mallory's troubled holiday mood, and as
the final moments of our appointment
time dripped away, I decided not to test
the flexibility of Bill's resistance any further. We made tentative plans to meet
again the following Monday. I told him
that I'd call him if I ultimately decided that
my ethical concerns were so grave that I
couldn't proceed.

Bill Miller left my office that day without

...ng once spoken aloud his daughter's name.

Was it too painful for him?

I didn't know.

41

To my relief, my note on the door worked and none of Diane's patients camped out in the waiting room.

Until four o'clock.

At four o'clock, I walked out to retrieve my scheduled patient but was greeted not by one person eager to see me, but by two.

The unexpected person was the woman with the cheddar-colored hair who had been so insistent on seeing her therapist on the day that Hannah Grant died. I recalled that Diane had told me that she had begun seeing the woman for psychotherapy. Was she there for her appointment?

I told the young man whom I was scheduled to see at that hour that I would be back with him in just a moment, and invited the Cheetos lady to come down the hall. We walked halfway to my office, far enough to be out of earshot of the waiting room, before I asked, "Did you see my note on the door about Dr. Estevez? She

can't be here today."

"I saw your stupid note. I have a right to know what's going on."

In the weeks since Hannah's death this woman had not shed any of her petulance. "She's unfortunately away unexpectedly," I said, stumbling over the adverbs I was stringing together.

"What does that mean?"

"She'll call you when she's back in the office."

"That's what you said about Hannah."

She was right. That is what I'd said about Hannah.

"I'm sorry." I was sorry. "I don't know what else to say. I'm sure, given what tragically happened with Ms. Grant, that this is especially difficult for you."

I didn't know what else to say. I was also running out of big adverbs.

"How long has she been gone?"

"I'm afraid I'm not in a position to answer that question."

"Then change your damn position."

The top of her frizzy head reached just about to the level of my chin. Her hair had a scent that I associated with bad Indian restaurants. "I'm available for —"

"I don't care what you're available for. Have you checked Diane's office?"

Diane, not Dr. Estevez. "There's no need to check her office."

"Then you know where she is. Tell me what the hell is going on."

"I'm sorry that Dr. Estevez isn't here for your appointment. She'll call you as soon as she is free to do so. I have someone I have to see now. Please excuse me."

I led her back toward the waiting room.

"This isn't going to stop here," the woman said before she left.

Before I retrieved my patient, I rushed back down the hall, grabbed my keys, and opened Diane's office door. I was so relieved that it was empty.

"Jay?" I said to my four o'clock after I'd recovered my composure and returned to the waiting room. "Why don't you come on back? I'm sorry for the late start."

My last appointment of the day was scheduled to begin at five o'clock. I took a deep breath, reassured myself that the finish line of my day's therapy marathon was only forty-five minutes away, and made the stroll down the hallway. Once again, though, I found two people, not one, waiting for me.

One was my five o'clock. She was a thirty-eight-year-old woman whom I'd suc-

cessfully helped with depression a year before, but who was back in my care to try to stave off a recurrence of her profound melancholy after a recent diagnosis of breast cancer. She had a PIC line in her upper arm and was in the interlude between her first and second rounds of chemo. She was sitting in the waiting room with her hands folded in her lap, her eyes closed, meditating, I supposed, on some aspect of life's caprice.

At that moment my empathy for her was even more acute than usual.

The other person in my waiting room was my friend, Sam Purdy. He was dressed in his work clothes — in winter that meant a pair of aging wool trousers, a long-sleeved shirt, a tie that was loose at the collar, and a sportcoat that Goodwill would have tossed into a rag pile had he tried to donate it. The jackets he wore were usually ill-fitting, but with his recent weight loss this coat was to his body what a bad slipcover was to a couch. That day, Sam's trousers were of recent vintage, as was his tie. For years Sam had owned so few neckties that I actually recognized them by their stains, but this one was new, and tasteful, and most surprising, appeared to be made of silk.

I suspected that Sam's new girlfriend had taken him shopping over New Year's. I also bet that he had a pair of silk boxers at home he didn't quite know what to do with.

Sam was reading the *New Yorker*, chuckling at a cartoon. When he looked up at me I made a querulous face at him. He shook his head just a little, flattened his mouth so that his lips disappeared under the umbrella of his mustache, and made a little "everything's cool" gesture with his hand. The gesture closely resembled an insincere "safe" call by a baseball umpire.

I made another querulous face.

He tapped his wristwatch.

I shrugged my shoulders and led the woman back to my office.

Forty-five minutes later my patient departed and I retraced my steps to the waiting room. Sam was asleep on his chair. A half-dozen magazines were in a heap at his feet.

"Hey, Sam," I said.

He didn't reply.

"Sam," I tried, a little louder.

He still didn't say anything.

An image of Hannah Grant's dead body splayed over the leather cube flashed into

my mind with Technicolor brilliance. I said, "Oh shit," and rushed across the room.

"Got you," he said with a sudden smile. The stubble of his beard told me it had been many hours since he'd scraped his face with a razor. He was probably as tired as I was.

"You ass," I said. "What are you doing here?"

"I come by sometimes just to catch up on my magazine reading. You guys have good stuff. Not like my dentist's office. You should see the crap he keeps around."

I made a skeptical face.

He stood up. "I'm buying you dinner," he said. "Come on."

"Sam, Lauren's expecting me to —"

"No, she's not. I already cleared it with her. You have a free go-out-with-the-boys pass for the evening."

"Yeah?" I was suspicious.

"Yeah."

"We walking or driving?"

"We be walking."

Although it was a cold night for a stroll, we hiked to the far side of the Pearl Street Mall toward the Sunflower Restaurant. Before Sam's heart attack I doubted that he'd

ever set foot inside the organic oasis that was the Sunflower, and I was more than a little suspicious that he'd chosen it for a meal for the two of us, but I kept my apprehension to myself. Things definitely weren't what they seemed, so an out-of-the-ordinary restaurant fit right in. We spent the few-block hike catching up on kid talk. Sam was moaning that Simon was making both his parents nuts trying to juggle his hockey and snowboarding schedules, but I could tell that Sam was actually pretty happy about the logistical craziness his son's activities were precipitating.

He declined the hostess's first offer of a table, which was prime territory smack in the middle of the dining room, and instead asked for a booth in the distant corner. Once we were led to his preferred suburban outpost, he took the bench that was facing the big room; I was left with a view of a brick wall that was adorned with a large, quasi-erotic photograph of young eggplants and ripe figs. For some reason I found myself thinking of D. H. Lawrence and Alan Bates.

Then I got it: My association was to the cinematic version of *Women in Love*. I smiled at the memory, and stole another gratuitous glance at the figs. "What is this,

405

really?" I asked.

"Sherry has Simon. I wanted to spend some quality time with you."

"Yeah? At the Sunflower? You really expect me to believe that?"

"I'm hurt," he said, investing all of his energy in the menu. "Can't even do a nice gesture for a friend. What are you hungry for? Look" — he pointed at the entrée list — "everything here's free range and wild and shit. Has to make you happy."

"How's Carmen?" I asked, temporarily giving up on my quest to discover the purpose of the meeting. I wasn't in a hurry; I knew we'd get there eventually. "She buy you that tie?"

Sam looked up and flicked a quick glance at the dining room. I thought I saw him nod his head just the smallest amount.

I had to resist turning and taking a look for myself. Suddenly, Darrell Olson was at my side. Two seconds later, Jaris Slocum was standing right behind him.

42

"Hi, guys," Sam said to the two detectives. He didn't feign surprise. I had to give him credit for that.

I glared at Sam. He made the same little hey-everything's-copacetic face and did the same hey-everything's-cool hand gesture that he'd thrown at me back in my waiting room while I was trying to figure out why he was camping out reading magazines.

"Make some room," he said to me.

I slid over and was immediately pinned against the wall, with no chance of escape, by Darrell Olson.

Sam and Jaris Slocum — their chests and shoulders were much broader than mine and Darrell's — totally filled the space on the other side of the table. A waitress came by and took our drink order. Apparently sensing the tension at the table, she skipped any flirtation and kept her smile under wraps. We all ordered beer.

Four different brands. Just another way of shouting out that we weren't a bunch of buddies sharing a pitcher.

"You guys hungry?" Sam asked.

"You bet," Darrell said. "I love this place."

One mystery solved: Darrell had chosen the restaurant. I slid my menu toward him. My own appetite was wavering. While glaring at Sam, I asked, "What's this about? You should check with my attorney if you want another interview, Detective Slocum. We shouldn't even —"

He snapped back. "I know exactly what —"

Sam interrupted Slocum's interruption. He said, "Call him Jaris, Alan. We're all friends here."

What?

Slocum tried again. "I'm perfectly aware that I need to go through your attorney to discuss . . . that other matter. I'm always eager for a chance to chat with Mr. Maitlin. But Darrell and I aren't here to talk about Hannah Grant."

I might have been offended by the gratuitous sarcasm about Cozy if I wasn't still stuck on Sam's announcement that "We're all friends here." *Since when? And if we're not here to talk about Hannah, what the hell*

are we here to talk about? At that moment I thought of Bob Brandt, and to no one in particular said, "It's your move."

"Hey, allow me," Sam said. "This little party was my idea."

I thought my narrowed eyes and tight brow aptly communicated to Sam that I didn't approve of any of the choreography he'd put into his soiree so far.

"A little background to start," he said, sticking to the charade that we were all just friends having a beer and sharing some crispy tofu triangles. "Jaris and Darrell had a piece of the Mallory Miller investigation. Lucy and I were doing time line. They were assigned to follow up a couple of potentially promising leads: one being the empty house next door — the one that's for sale — and two being the possibility that the girl somehow ended up with her mother."

"This is all about Mallory, then?" I asked. Despite my skepticism, I knew my question was evidence of capitulation on my part. I should have been throwing money on the table for my beer and walking full speed away from the three Boulder cops.

"A little patience, maybe?" Sam said. The drinks arrived. Sam waited until the

waitress was gone again before he continued. "I was thinking about the conversations you and I had, you know, about the guy with the car, that classic Camaro, and about the house next door to the Millers' with the waterfalls and shit, and about your friend, Dr. Estevez, and what happened to her in Las Vegas."

Darrell said, "Sam came to us. We heard his thoughts and started wondering whether there might be some connection, something that tied things together."

"Some connection?" I asked, even more skeptically than before. I already feared a connection among Bob and Mallory and Diane, and I was beyond skeptical that I was hearing about this from Darrell Olson and Jaris Slocum.

"Yeah," said Slocum.

As far as I was concerned he was nothing more than a punk with a shield. "I'm uncomfortable with this," I said, trying hard not to sound petulant. Sam's expression told me that I hadn't quite succeeded. I felt as though all the confidential information that I'd been trying to guard about my patients was in a balloon hovering above the table, and that each of the three detectives was dimpling the latex with the point of a saber.

The worst part? I knew I'd gotten myself into this one by trying to finesse the confidentiality rules with Sam.

"Hear us out," Sam said.

Slocum's mug of beer was almost gone. He'd either been real thirsty, or he was real anxious. He looked toward our waitress and raised the mug and his eyebrows. He wanted a refill.

Darrell said, "We didn't know about the guy with the car. The one who rents the garage next door to the Millers. That was news to us. It could be an important piece of information. We should have picked up on it, but it slipped through the cracks."

I glared at Sam. "Slipped through the cracks, huh?"

Slocum picked up from there. "And the fact that your friend disappeared in Las Vegas? That's curious to us, too."

"Curious?"

"Well, worrisome, of course, but curious, too. Given the circumstances."

"What circumstances are those?" I asked.

"Everything," Slocum replied.

"Everything?"

"Yeah."

I found that I liked him almost as much now that we were all friends having beers and I was calling him "Jaris" as I had when

he was ordering me around outside Hannah Grant's office and I was calling him "Detective." I said, "For old times' sake, Jaris, treat me like you treated me at Hannah's office. You know, like an idiot citizen. Tell me what 'everything' means."

"Alan," Sam said.

I remained unconvinced about the announced agenda for this impromptu meeting. "We're not talking in code about Hannah Grant right now? You're all sure about that? If we are, my lawyer's probably not going to be too happy about it. Come to think about it, neither will my wife." I don't know why I threw in the part about Lauren. It was petty, but then so was my state of mind.

Darrell held up a hand to shush Sam. He said, "Let me, Sam, please." Darrell was using the conciliator's voice that I'd heard him try on with Slocum and later with Cozy Maitlin the night that we found Hannah's body. I suspected that Darrell had been a conciliator at least as long as he'd known how to ride a two-wheeler, and that his initial mediating role had been to intervene before his argumentative parents ripped the flesh from each other's throats.

"Alan — we didn't get off to a good start with you and Dr. Estevez last month —

Jaris and I didn't. Water under the bridge, right? Is that okay? Because based on what Sam's been able to tell us, it sounds like both you and her might have something to do with another situation we're working." He lowered his voice here, and leaned closer to me. "Yes, I'm talking about Mallory. Now, it may just all be coincidence. That's always possible. But it's also possible that everything's related."

I couldn't resist a jab. "If it turns out that everything's related, it sounds like you and Detective Slocum — Jaris — might have missed some important details during your initial investigations."

Sam said, "I'm not sure that's helpful, Alan."

I turned on him. My tone was level. My words? Not as much. "And you're the best judge of that, Sam? Of what's helpful? Please. He" — I pointed at Slocum — "roughed up Diane last month for no reason other than that he'd had a bad day or his feelings were hurt or God knows what else, and now he wants to have a nice dinner with me and down a few beers and he thinks I'll just bow down and help him cover up his mistakes on the" — I caught myself and lowered my voice to a coarse whisper — "Mallory Miller fiasco. Because

413

what I think this is about is ass-covering."

Slocum's face was red. He raised his glass and drained the dregs from the bottom of his first beer — a version of counting to ten to calm himself down, I thought — before he said, "I'm guessing you need help finding her. Not to mention the guy with the old Camaro. Him, too. I don't expect you to like me — to be honest, I don't give a shit — but I'm willing to try to find these people. You want to work something out, or not? Your choice. I don't have time for your sissy-ass games."

Sissy-ass games? I supposed that meant that Jaris and I were no longer friends. "What can you do to help? Last time I looked, Las Vegas was in Nevada."

Sam sighed loudly. I thought he was expressing relief that most of the cards were finally on the table.

The waitress chose that moment to return with Jaris's second beer. She dropped it off in record time and withdrew as though she'd just remembered she'd left the water running in her bathtub.

"If we reach out from here," Darrell said as she retreated, "the Las Vegas police maybe show a little more interest in trying to find out what happened to her. I suspect

414

that could make a significant difference. The current situation — an out-of-state husband who can't find his wife for a couple of days — probably isn't creating a lot of investigative curiosity in Sin City."

Of course he was right. I asked, "And the other guy? The one with the Camaro? How are you going to help with him?"

"One phone call — and one BOLO later — every cop in the state will have an eye peeled for that car," Jaris said.

I hadn't touched my beer. I picked it up and took a long, slow sip. "On what pretense?" I asked.

Across the table, Slocum had already finished half of his second mug. Sam spied Jaris getting ready to jump back into the fray and decided to run interference. He said, "That's our problem. We'll come up with one. It's not as hard as you might think. By the way, BOLO is be-on-the-look—"

"I know what a BOLO is," I snapped, almost spitting my beer. "So what do you want from me, Jaris?"

Sam wasn't done orchestrating. "What do you say let's order first, okay? I don't know about the rest of you, but I'm starving here. Darrell, what's good? Think I'd like the tempeh cutlets?"

Sam's tempeh question was theater-of-the-absurd offered purely for my benefit. Tempeh was so far outside the boundaries of Sam's comfort universe that Hubble couldn't have spotted it.

Sam was thinking that he'd won, and he was pretty darn proud of himself.

43

We'd almost completed a totally silent trek from the Sunflower back up the Mall to my office when he said, "You wouldn't have come out with me if I'd told you what I was up to."

"Damn right," I said.

A few more steps of silence followed. Then, without the slightest bit of animosity in his voice, Sam added, "You should get off your high horse, see what the world looks like from down here with the rest of us."

"And what the hell is that supposed to mean?" I wasn't as careful as Sam was about keeping the animosity out of my voice.

"Your cherished position in life — you know, psych-o-therapist, guardian of all the world's secrets — it's not as special as you think it is. You're just a damn guy doing a damn job. You have trusts to keep. Well, surprise, surprise, other people do, too.

Other people take their responsibilities as seriously as you do.

"Me? Tonight? It turns out I saw a way to get Diane some help for whatever mess she's in. I saw a way to get some serious eyeballs out looking for the guy in the Camaro. You wanted me to find a hook for all this. Well, I found one. The way I see it, call me naive, but no blood gets spilled by my strategy. A few people have to swallow some pride — yeah, you included — but so the fuck what? You think this was an easy meeting for Jaris? The guy has his hands full; trust me on that."

I was inclined to say that I didn't give a ferret fart whether or not it had been a pleasant meeting for Jaris, but I didn't.

Sam had his hands in his pockets and was looking down at the sidewalk as we talked. At Ninth he led us off the curb without looking for traffic in both directions. In half a second a guy heading north on a bike almost creamed him. If the man hadn't screamed a profanity in warning, I'm not sure Sam would have ever noticed.

Even with the profanity, he seemed unfazed. He muttered, "Too cold for a bike."

We started up Walnut toward my office. As we passed the building that was the second or third incarnation of one of Boul-

der's legendary breakfast houses, Sam said, "I miss Nancy's. Those herb cheese omelettes? They were something. Lucile's is great, but I miss Nancy's."

"Me, too." After three or four more steps, I added, "You're right, Sam."

"About Nancy's? Course I am."

I hadn't been talking about Nancy's, but he was right about that, too. "Wonderful biscuits. Remember those biscuits? But I meant that you're right about what you said."

"I know that, too." He exhaled audibly. "The fact that you admit it doesn't change anything, doesn't mean that what happens next is going to be what you want to happen next, or even that what happens next is what I want to happen next. All that's different now is that some people who care about the jobs they do are going to try to find some of these missing people." He pulled his right hand from his pocket and yanked at the knot on his tie. "How bad a thing can that be?"

He was right.

"I'm sorry," I said.

"For what?"

"For being an asshole."

"You mean a sissy-ass?"

I laughed. "That, too."

"Hey," he said.

And that was that.

Almost a block later he climbed into the cradle of the driver's seat of his Cherokee. "Carmen likes to buy me clothes," he said.

It took me a moment to realize that Sam was revisiting the conversation we'd been having in the restaurant at the precise moment when Slocum and Olson ambushed me. I had just asked him about his tie. "I figured," I said.

"What do you think?"

"About the new threads?" I asked. "Or about the fact that Carmen likes to buy them for you?"

Sam shook his head gently, and I could hear the throaty tang of a little chuckle come out of the darkness. "See, that's the thing. I don't know one other guy who would ask me that question. Not one. And that's why I'm okay with the fact that you're an asshole sometimes."

"Goodnight, Sam. Thanks."

I was halfway home before I realized that I'd spaced out telling Sam about my visit to Doyle's house with the Realtor the previous night.

44

My girls were sleeping in separate beds when I got home. The dogs were squirrelly though, and I had to spend ten minutes outside with them before I could get them settled. Emily detected the scent of a critter of some kind while we were walking the lane and once we were back in the door she strolled the entire perimeter of the interior of the upstairs of the house checking to see if an unseen enemy had succeeded in breaching our defenses. Ultimately confident that all of our flanks were protected, she plopped at my feet with a satisfied sigh.

The entire house shook when she landed.

I was thinking about calling Sam to get his inevitable rage over my visit to Doyle's house out of the way, when the phone rang.

I pounced on it: Raoul.

"I'm starting to get somewhere. Couple of pieces," Raoul said.

His tone told me that he hadn't found Diane, so I didn't ask. His words told me that he wanted to confront the practical, so I refrained from asking the question that was second on my list: *How are you doing with all this?* Instead, I said, "What do you have?"

Raoul started with bad news, not, in my mind, a good sign. "Marlina's a dead end. The woman from Venetian security? One more meal with her tomorrow, and I'm done. I know exactly why the woman's been divorced twice though I still haven't figured out how she got married twice. She's playing me."

"Okay, then what pieces do you have?"

"Two. The guy from the craps table? The shopping center developer who was playing craps at the same table as Diane? He finally called me this morning, told me he'd been drunk when I phoned him and he'd forgotten to call me back. He was cleaning out the memory on his mobile and saw my number. Anyway, he said that Diane was his luck at the craps table that night and when she cashed out, he decided to do the same. He said he was right behind her as she was walking through the casino."

"Sounds kind of creepy."

"*Si*. He says as Diane's walking across the casino, two guys walk up to her, say hello. Pretty well dressed. Both of them forty to fifty. One tall, one average. One of them whispered something to her. She seemed happy to hear it and the three of them walked on together, talking. She had her phone in her hand, dropped it trying to shake hands with one of the guys. He picked it up and she stuffed it in her purse. One of the two reached around behind Diane, took the phone right back out of her bag, and tossed it on the floor by a row of slot machines. He said the guy was smooth; he picked Diane like a pro. Until the man dumped her phone, the guy from the craps table thought one of the two guys was Diane's husband, or boyfriend."

"Fits with what I remember, Raoul." I paused before I added, "The guy from the craps table was going to hit on her, wasn't he? That's why he was following her?"

"Yes," said Raoul without any animosity. He understood these things.

"So that was it? He never reported this to anyone?"

"He said that Diane didn't seem to be in any distress. The phone thing was odd, but she went with them voluntarily."

"But he doesn't know where they went?"

"They were walking in the direction of the lobby, but he didn't follow them out of the casino. He went up to his room."

"What are you thinking?" I asked.

"I'm thinking what he said to her had something to do with Rachel Miller. That's why she went with them — she thought she was going to get a chance to talk with Rachel."

"That's what I'm thinking, too." I paused for a moment. "Somebody must have picked the phone up off the floor and put it in the tray of the slot machine where that drunk woman found it."

"It also explains why Venetian security isn't too eager to let me see the surveillance tape. Probably looks a lot like a rendezvous to them. You know, something between . . . adults."

"But they must have a picture of these two guys, right?"

"Right. You can't walk out of a casino without a camera seeing you. No way."

"You said you have a couple of pieces of news. What's the other one?"

"Norm Clarke came through. I should've called him the first day I got here. I can be such a putz."

I was surprised — no, shocked — at the Yiddish. I didn't know it was part of

Raoul's language repertoire. I grabbed a beer from the kitchen so I could sit down and listen to his story about Norm Clarke.

Any good big-city daily newspaper that doesn't take itself too seriously has one, though few are fortunate enough to have that special one that becomes a silk thread in the urban fabric. San Francisco had Herb Caen. Denver has had Bill Husted for as long as I can remember.

What's their role? Gossip columnist? Man about town? If they're good, the phrases don't do them justice. These guys, and a few gals, take the pulse on their city. They tell the rest of us what happens behind closed doors, what happens after the bars close, what's new, what's old, what's coming next. They invite us to the city's water cooler for the latest gossip on the movers and shakers, and they whisper the latest dish over the city's backyard fence. They're the ones who know what local boy has done good, and what local girl has gone bad. What famous visitor has been spotted where, doing what, with whom.

Las Vegas's version was Norm Clarke.

Norm had briefly gone head-to-head with Husted back in Colorado, scrounging the usually dull Front Range of the

Rockies for paltry scoops, but years before he'd moved on to ply his trade at the *Review-Journal* in the much more fertile gossip terrain of Las Vegas. By all the reports that made their way back across the Great Basin and the Rocky Mountains to Denver, Norm soon owned his adopted town.

He knew everybody in Vegas, had spies everywhere, had eaten at every now table, could get backstage at any show, and was escorted to the front of the line and past the velvet rope at any trendy club. After a few years in the desert Norm had, literally, written the book on Las Vegas, and was always busy taking notes for the next edition. His mug, and his column, graced the front page of the paper every weekend.

Celebrities weren't really in Vegas until Norm said they were in Vegas. Some begged him for ink. A few had managers and publicists call and beg him to please, please, please forget what he had seen or heard.

Back in his days at the *Rocky Mountain News*, Norm had done a feature on Raoul, and on Raoul's golden touch incubating Boulder tech companies during the heady days of the early 1990s. Raoul, who generally despised publicity, thought the piece

was on the money, and he and Norm had become casual friends. They'd stayed in touch over the years even as each of their lives grew more complicated.

When Raoul called Norm asking for help in finding Diane, he was asking Norm to do something that Norm wasn't often asked to do: He was asking him to keep a secret.

Raoul's first sit-down with Norm had taken place almost twenty-four hours before in one of the many bars that dot the expansive, expensive acreage on the main floor of the Venetian. After some pleasantries Raoul had told Norm that he had a personal favor to ask, and asked Norm if he could speak off the record. Raoul proceeded to provide only the Vegas pieces of the puzzle: that Diane was in town to talk to a patient's mother, which was as good an excuse as she needed to spend some time playing a little middling-stakes craps. On Monday evening Diane had been talking to a friend on her cell while walking through the Venetian casino, and hadn't been heard from since. She'd disappeared. Hadn't returned to her hotel room. Hadn't called anyone. Nothing.

Earlier in the day she disappeared, Diane

had tried to track down the patient's mother and had ended up at the Love In Las Vegas Wedding Chapel out on Las Vegas Boulevard, where she'd apparently located someone named Rachel Miller — yeah, Raoul told Norm, *that* Rachel Miller — but Raoul hadn't been successful finding her. Raoul also told Norm about his conversation with Reverend Howie at the Love In Las Vegas and about Howie's suggestion that Rachel could possibly be tracked down through an intermediary — a man, someone who apparently made Howie shake in his Savile Row boots. Somebody scary.

Norm admitted to Raoul that he didn't have a clue about the intermediary's identity, but that he suspected the man didn't inhabit the part of Las Vegas that typically interested his column's readers.

"But . . ." Raoul had said, sensing something.

"But," Norm had added quickly, "I think I know somebody who might be able to help."

The way Raoul told it to me later, he and Norm met again at almost exactly the same time that I was finishing my meal with Sam, Darrell, and my new buddy Jaris

at the Sunflower in downtown Boulder.

Norm was on the clock getting ready to chronicle for his column which of-the-moment celebrities were really going to show up at some cocktail-hour charity-do at one of the trendiest of the city's many trendoid restaurants, this one high in the newest tower of the Mandalay Bay. A setup crew was bustling around the still-vacant space, frantically arranging the tiers of a gorgeous raw bar, and test-fitting the blown-glass platters that would soon be heaped with gleaming shellfish, sushi, sashimi, and maki.

Raoul joined Norm at a corner table that had a stunning view of the Strip's neon at dusk. The table in front of Norm was naked except for his ubiquitous mobile phone, a longneck Coors Light that was almost full, and a couple of paper cocktail napkins on which Norm was scribbling notes with a felt-tip pen.

Norm looked up and said, "Raoul, hi. Any luck?"

Raoul shook his head as he sat down.

Norm asked, "You want a drink?"

"No, thank you."

Norm slid the beer aside and leaned forward. "I didn't think you'd have good news. Especially given what I found out

about the guy you're looking for. You ready? His name is Ulysses Paul North. That's U — P — North. Or . . . Up, North. On the street they call him Canada."

Raoul took a second to pull it all together, then he couldn't help himself: He smiled. "Up North? Canada? Really?"

Norm smiled, too. He held up his hand like a Boy Scout taking an oath. "I'm good, but I couldn't make that up." Norm's grin caused his cheekbones to levitate — just a tiny bit — and that motion caused the distinctive black, flat crescent patch that always covered his right eye to rise.

Raoul said, "There's more, yes?"

"There's more. Canada's a facilitator, apparently. A street facilitator of some kind." Norm sipped from his beer. "If this place were Hollywood" — he gazed down at the flashing neon skyline of ersatz New York, and the ejaculating fountains at the Bellagio, and the distant faux icons of Egypt and Paris and Venice — "and if Canada's people were movie stars, he'd probably be called a manager. But this is definitely not Hollywood, and Canada's clients are, well, definitely not movie stars, so there's not exactly a name I know of for exactly what he does."

"He's not a pimp?"

"No. He probably counts some pimps and prostitutes among his . . . clients."

"He's not muscle, protection?"

"Not in any conventional sense. But should the need arise, he has all the muscle he might want. That's what I'm told."

"I assume he gets a percentage of —"

"He does. I was told he advises his . . . clients — I'm sorry, I keep stumbling over that word — on business matters, helps them formulate strategic plans. I swear; that's the party line. He intervenes only when necessary. Tries to keep turf fights in his territory to a minimum. Settles occasional disputes. For those services, he is paid a percentage of his clients' . . . proceeds."

"The clients are crooks?"

Norm took a moment before he decided how to reply. "Let's say they don't report their income to the IRS."

"And Canada's a scary enough man to do this . . . job?"

"He is known to be ruthless when necessary. And sometimes more, when he needs to make a point."

"Your source knows him?"

"Of him."

Raoul sat back. "You have contacts everywhere." He intended it as a compli-

ment, and as a question. Norm read it both ways.

"Everywhere I can. To do my job for the paper, I need all the eyes I can find." He gestured over his shoulder. "When nobody knew where Jacko was after his indictment, I found him. When Britney got married for ten minutes, I knew about it before her mother did. Roy Horn after the tiger mauled him? I knew things his nurses didn't know about how he was doing.

"Tonight? One of the busboys here is going to tell me exactly who shows up for this shindig. Sometimes it's a host who helps me, occasionally a chef. Some of my best sources are people on the fringes of the A-list. They get invited to the hot parties, then tell me who else is there. Rule number one in this business: Everybody knows somebody."

"And one of them knows how I can find this Canada?"

"You won't find Canada. He doesn't like to be found by people outside his orbit. But if you would like, the man who's talking to me will pass the word along on the street that you would like to speak with him. That's how it works, apparently." Norm shrugged, a gesture that at once apologized for the melodrama and ac-

knowledged that the show was totally out of his control.

Raoul sat back. "Canada is what? Nevada's answer to Osama? I get a canvas bag on my head and get driven out to a cave somewhere in the desert?"

Norm's face remained impassive. "I'm a reporter; I don't make this stuff up. I'd never heard of this guy before today. Odds are I'll never hear about him again after today. This is North Vegas stuff. It's way off my beat."

"But you trust your guy? Your source?"

Norm took a long pull from his Coors Light. "I work hard to write my column. It's not a party. To do this right, I have to have great instincts, I have to hustle, and I have to have a good bullshit detector, or I end up becoming a joke. I don't get them all right, Raoul, but I get almost all of them right. My gut says I have this one right.

"I grew up in a middle-of-nowhere town in Montana. Small-world time: Turns out a guy I went to high school with is part of the North Vegas street life. I tracked him down after his photo showed up in the paper one day with a story on the homeless. He's my source on this. He has no reason to lie to me, and it was pretty clear

to me that he's honestly afraid of this guy Canada. He would much rather have been telling me that he knew where I could get serviced by the pope's favorite hooker."

Raoul pondered for a few seconds. "This man you know? Did he tell you anything about Rachel?"

Norm shook his head.

"Diane?"

"No. I'm sorry."

Norm's cell phone rang. He excused himself to Raoul. "Sorry, I have to get this. I'm waiting for a confirmation about an item for tomorrow's column. That thing at The Palms." He opened the phone. "Hello."

Raoul didn't know about the thing at The Palms, and preferred it that way. He'd read it fresh in Norm's column the next morning.

Norm listened for a moment, stood up from the table, faced the window, and said, "Of course, yes." He listened for a longer period, almost a full minute, before he said, "He's with me right now." Beat. "Okay, you know that . . . You want me to ask him?"

Norm set the phone on the table between himself and Raoul. He nodded at it and with an extended thumb and pinky

held up to his face, he mimed that the telephone conversation was continuing.

"It's one of Canada's . . . people. If you agree to leave the police out of this, totally out of this, Canada will talk with you."

In a heartbeat Raoul said, "Agreed. Is my wife safe? Can he tell me that? Please?"

Norm shrugged. He didn't know the answer. He picked up the phone and placed it against his ear. "You heard?" he said. Norm listened some more, nodding, and finally added, "It shouldn't be a problem. He'll be there." Norm folded his phone shut.

"I'll be where?" Raoul asked.

"The tram platform at the Luxor at seven o'clock. That's only twenty minutes from now."

"Is it far?"

"If we could get a real good running start, and if we could jump out those windows over there, we could probably land on it. But from way up here, without flying? It'll take us most of that twenty minutes to get over there."

"You know the way?"

Norm stood up. "Of course."

Raoul threw twenty dollars on the table and they ran.

"We had to hustle," Raoul said to me. "Down the elevator, all the way across the casino, which is like the size of Luxembourg, over to the monorail station. Wait for the train, get onto the train, ride it over to the Luxor. It's a turtle. The thing moves so slowly, you wonder why they bothered to build it. My mother has a cane; she walks faster than the damn tram moves. We finally made it to the platform with only a couple of minutes to spare."

He stopped.

"And?" I asked.

"And nothing. We stood there for half an hour. Nothing. Nobody. Trains came, trains left. Nothing."

"Nobody met you?"

"No."

"Now what?"

"I don't know," Raoul said. "I suppose I'll continue to try to reach out to Canada some other way."

I'd grown increasingly discomfited listening to Raoul's recanting of his meeting with Norm Clarke, especially the parts about the man called Canada. I stood up and began to pace in front of the big windows that faced the mountains. My movement caused Emily to stir. She was so

exhausted that it appeared as though the simple act of lifting her big head to see what I was up to required a monumental effort.

"When I got back here a little bit ago?" Raoul said.

"Yes."

"Marlina had dropped off an envelope. A single grainy screen shot from the casino security tape. Diane with the two guys who walked her out of the casino. They're all in profile."

"How does she look?"

"Fine."

"Any idea who they are?"

"No."

"It's something, right?"

"It's something."

"Raoul, I have some news that I originally thought was good news, but may now be bad news."

"What?"

"The Boulder police are involved. They're asking the Las Vegas police to take Diane's disappearance seriously."

In my ear, I heard one of the familiar Catalonian profanities. Then he said, "I'll have to call Norm, so he can tell Canada."

45

What if this is why she died? . . . What if some-
body killed Hannah because she met with
Mallory that one time?

As my head hit the pillow and I tried to
find the sanctuary of sleep, Diane's original conspiracy theory about Hannah
Grant's death — a hypothesis I recalled I'd
dismissed out of hand at the time —
bounced back and forth inside my skull
like the digitized ball in a game of Pong.

What if this is why she died? . . . What if
somebody killed Hannah because she met with
Mallory that one time?

It didn't take long for my sleep-depriving
musing to move on to cover fresh ground:
If Diane had been right, and Hannah had
been murdered because of something she'd
learned from Mallory, could Diane and
Bob somehow have suffered the same fate,
too?

I shuddered at the thought.

The links were there. Diane had con-

sulted with Hannah about Mallory; Bob had talked to Mallory across the backyard fence.

It was a far-fetched stretch, but could everything — Hannah's death, Mallory's disappearance, Diane's disappearance, and Bob's disappearance — really be related? Could some immense ball have started rolling the December afternoon that Mallory decided she just had to see Hannah Grant?

But why?

And how?

I gave up on sleeping and stumbled back out to the living room in search of a common denominator.

If Diane's theory was true, there had to be a secret in the Miller household. Something that Mallory had revealed during her single session with Hannah. Or at least something that someone thought she'd revealed.

What was it?

During that week after Christmas, the week after Mallory disappeared, Diane had said, *"She said her father was 'up to something,' remember?"*

So what had Bill Miller been up to?

Had he been up to something at home? At work? Planning a career change?

Planning a major change in his parenting?

And why, I wondered, was Bill Miller so curious as to why I had been at Doyle's house?

Yeah, why?

During the psychotherapy session I'd had with Bill Miller earlier that day, I'd been so busy feeling guilty about being caught snooping around at Doyle's house that I'd missed the obvious: Why had Bill Miller been so damn curious about the fact that I'd been looking at the house that was for sale next door?

46

I woke Sam. He wasn't happy that I woke him. Once we managed to blunder past his unhappiness I began to explain to him why I'd interrupted his sleep. I tried to ease into it but his impatience forced me to admit earlier in the conversation than I wanted to that I had been inside Doyle's house. "I pretended I was interested in buying the house; I got the agent to show it to me last night after work."

"You woke me up to talk real estate?"

For a long moment he'd fooled me; I'd thought he'd sounded genuinely befuddled. "Sam, please. That house is at the center of something. It is."

He wasn't done poking at me. "You liked it? I found it overpriced, personally. Kitchen's hardly bigger than mine. I don't think Lauren would go for it, anyway. She'd be fretting about Grace and all that water in the backyard. And that bridge? With a toddler? Alan, you'd never

have a moment's peace."

"Come on, Sam."

"Okay, okay. Just remember that you're the one who woke me up. So why did you feel this compelling need to sneak into the house next door to the Millers? It's an empty friggin' house. We've been in there."

"Given all that's happened, it seemed important to see it. I have this feeling that the Millers' neighbor is key to all this."

"All what?"

"Everything. Mallory, Diane, the guy Bob with the Camaro. The BOLO? Why are all these people missing, Sam? Three people are missing. Don't you wonder about that? I mean, even —" I almost said, "Even Hannah Grant," but I caught myself. The only link I could make to Hannah in all this was through Diane, and that wasn't my privilege to abrogate.

"Three people are missing? Could be two. Could be one. Could be zero. But assuming I buy your premise that three people are missing, what does the neighbor's house have to do with Diane?" Sam asked.

Sam wasn't easily tricked. My obfuscation-by-shotgun-blast hadn't fooled him for long. I stammered, "I don't know. That part is once removed. But there's a con-

nection, there is. I can feel it."

"Once removed? What the hell does that mean?"

"I can't say."

He sighed. "You were about to say something else. You said, 'even' and you stopped. Even what?"

"Everything." Lame, but it was the best that I could do. "I was talking about everything."

Sam yawned. "You know something else, right? Don't you? Something you can't tell me?"

I didn't hesitate. I said, "I do."

"Fuck," he muttered. "What's the point in talking to you about stuff like this? It's all riddles. It's like trying to get a politician to tell you what he really thinks." I took some solace that Sam's profanity had been mumbled and dull, and not sharply carved and poison-tipped. "I can't start an investigation because you have some confidentiality bee in your butt, Alan. You know that. You do. We've been here before."

"What about the snow thing?"

"Dear Lord, not the snow thing again."

"Have you guys thought about those lines that you can string between trees and stuff? What are they called? What if they strung those between Mallory's house and

Doyle's? What if they did that? What if that's how she got out of her house without leaving any footprints?"

"A patient feed you this? She slid down one of those lines? That's your latest theory? Are you nuts?"

Hearing it out loud, it sounded silly. All I was able to say was, "No. Maybe." Sam had no way to know I'd answered his questions in order, skipping the second one and the final one.

"Why?" Sam asked.

"Why what?"

"If she's running away, why would she care if she got out of the house without leaving any footprints? Why go to all that trouble? She didn't know when the snow was going to start and stop; she didn't know Fox was going to have a helicopter overhead. She's a kid. If she runs, she runs. Everything else is crap and you know it."

I hadn't thought of questioning what motivation Mallory might have for trying to leave no trail behind — it was definitely an oversight in my thinking — but I found myself relieved that Sam was using the present tense to describe Mallory.

Sam wasn't done. "Before, you said, 'They'? Who's 'they'?"

"The neighbor and . . ."

"Mallory? Come on? They were in this together? Now you're talking some conspiracy, right? Alan, I'll forgive you for calling. It's late. I know you're upset about your friend."

"Sam —"

"We searched the house. We talked to the neighbor. Nothing came of it. Let it go."

"Remember when we were in the yard and someone was watching us from the upstairs window?"

"Yeah?"

"Well, why? Why was he watching us?"

"He?"

Sam was sharper three minutes after being woken from a sound sleep than I was at the end of a long day. "Has to be a he, right? It's only Bill and his son who live there."

"The Millers aren't allowed to have guests? I didn't know that. Boulder and its laws? Wouldn't want to be a cop here — be arresting people for farting on the wrong side of the street."

We'd moved from amused incredulity to aggravated sarcasm. Where Sam was concerned, that wasn't a healthy progression. With some defensiveness creeping into my voice, I said, "I think it was a he."

"Then what did you mean when you asked 'why?' What's the big deal about somebody watching you from his own bedroom window? Maybe it was a neighborhood watch thing and Bill Miller's the block captain. Who the hell knows? It's not a crime to spy on your neighbor's yard. We'd have to arrest half the old ladies in town if it was."

"Did you talk to the neighbor yourself, Sam? You or Lucy?"

He forced patience into his voice. It was a tight fit. "Lucy and I were doing other things. You know that."

"It was Slocum, wasn't it?"

"Your point?"

"Talk to the neighbor yourself, please. I don't trust Slocum."

"I thought Jaris behaved himself tonight."

"Barely. He was nervous. And you and Darrell were watching everything he did. I still don't trust him."

The silence that ensued suggested to me that Sam was considering saying something else about Jaris Slocum. He didn't. He said, "You talk about this Camaro guy as though he's a victim. You considered that he may be mixed up in all this, like criminally?"

"It doesn't fit," I said. "Psychologically."

"And in your world people never act out of character?"

Sam actually asked that question with only the slightest hint of sarcasm. "Talk to the neighbor, Sam."

"On what pretense do I do that?" he asked.

"You're looking for that Camaro. You wanted a hook? That's your hook. Now that the BOLO is out, you want to tie up a loose end. Slocum himself said he didn't know about the Camaro during the first interview. You just have to make a call, one call, maybe go have a chat with the guy who owns the house and the garage."

Ten minutes later I crawled into bed and sprawled on my side, facing my wife. Silently, Lauren backed toward me until I could feel the warmth from her nighttime flesh on the front of my naked thighs. I'd almost drifted off to sleep when a fresh thought forced me to snap open my eyes in the dark.

Maybe the secret has to do with Rachel Miller, not with Mallory.

Maybe this is all about Rachel.

That's why Diane disappeared.

She knew something about Rachel. Or

she was about to learn something about Rachel.

I climbed back out of bed, pulled on a pair of sweats, and used the kitchen phone to warn Raoul that when he'd walked into the Love In Las Vegas Wedding Chapel and met Reverend Howie he may have inadvertently walked into something that was extremely dangerous.

But Raoul didn't answer his hotel room phone at the Venetian.

He didn't answer his cell, either.

My next thought? Sam was going to kill me when I tried to explain Canada to him.

47

All I told Bill Miller on the phone was that I had some further questions that I needed to address before I could make a commitment to see him for on-going psychotherapy. He readily agreed to come in on Friday morning. I never quite decided how surprised I was that Bill was so accommodating about meeting with me again on such short notice. My indecision, I was sure, was a product of the fact that more than twelve hours had passed and I still hadn't been able to track down Raoul in Las Vegas.

Lauren shared my dismay about Raoul's silence. The look she'd given me that morning when I slowed her down on the way to the bathroom to let her know Raoul wasn't answering his phone was like the look I might expect after I'd told her I'd not only lost my car keys but also managed to misplace the spare set, too. "Diane *and* Raoul?" she'd said, finally. Before shutting the bathroom door behind her, she'd

449

added, "Find him, honey. Today would be good."

Bill settled into the chair across from me and without any visible indications of concern, said, "Shoot. I'm ready. Ask your questions. I'd love to get this whole thing settled."

In typical shrink form, my question wasn't really just a question. "Thanks for being so flexible," I said. "I'd like to know more about your current relationship with your — is it ex-wife? — Rachel."

"Well," he said, sitting back on the chair. "I didn't expect that one." He wasted a moment picking at the crease on his perfectly pressed trousers.

I, of course, grew curious about what question he had expected. But I didn't ask him that. I waited.

"Rachel and I are separated, not . . . divorced. For some reason, I thought you knew that. I feel like I don't have any secrets anymore. We never went through the whole legal process. It just never felt . . . necessary to me. Or even appropriate. Given her difficulties, I couldn't just . . . You know the circumstances back then as well as anyone."

Actually, not as well as Mary Black, I

thought. "Are you legally separated?"

Bill struggled to find the right word before he settled on "Rachel is my wife."

"And the nature of your current relationship?"

He shifted on his chair, crossing his legs, left ankle over right knee. He took a moment to make certain that his cuff was adequately shading the top of his sock. I wasn't sure he was going to answer my question at all, but he finally said, "Rachel's in Las Vegas, still attending weddings, still delusional, still . . . psychotic. Sadly, that hasn't changed." He paused. "She moved there for the weddings. I'm sure you could have guessed that even if you hadn't heard about it. She still feels compelled to . . . There's no shortage of weddings in Las Vegas, that's for sure."

Yes, I know. I know a lot about Reverend Howie and the Love In Las Vegas Wedding Chapel.

"And she's still suffering, that hasn't changed. She's still struggling with her illness, and . . . and with the medicines. She hates the medicines. She hates the new ones as much as she hated the old ones. Sometimes she takes them, more often she doesn't. They help when she takes them, but they don't solve anything. They're not

a cure, not for her." He exhaled through pursed lips. "I hope you don't mind if I ask, but why is this important?"

I went into a matter-of-fact spiel about a psychologist's ethical burden to avoid dual relationships, and explained that it would be difficult for me, as a psychotherapist, to avoid them if I didn't even know they existed. My explanation was intentionally convoluted, but Bill seemed to buy it. I'd figured he would.

I'd counted on the fact that he would. My voice as level as a freshly plumbed door, I said, "Bill, you still haven't told me about your current relationship with Rachel. That's the part that most concerns me."

I thought his eyes narrowed at my use of the word "concerns." Maybe not. I wished I'd said "interests."

"Well," he said, "that's not exactly true, I said that . . ."

Bill's apparent predilection was to argue the point with me, but he changed his mind and seemed to decide that my statement was, in fact, accurate enough that he'd leave it alone.

"We're in touch," he said. "If you can call it that."

No problem, I'll call it that. "Go on," I said.

"We talk about once a week. That's not true. I call Rachel once a week, but we probably only talk about twice a month." He exhaled hard and grimaced. "She doesn't call me . . . often. Sometimes I leave messages. And the truth is that even when I do reach her, I do most of the talking. I fill her in on what's going on here, with the family.

"She's, um . . . I still think that . . . You know, hope's not really the right word. But I have . . . I pray for . . ."

I watched fascinated as Bill's usual unshakable composure disintegrated before my eyes.

"Yes," I said, nudging him on.

"Rachel always asks about the kids. Almost always, anyway. So often she's off in a different . . . you know. Her mind is in other places. The weddings. The brides, the grooms. Their families. It's always like she knows them, and that I know them, too. But usually she gets around to asking how the kids are doing, seems interested in what's going on with them. They don't get any older for her. They don't age. I don't know what else . . . to say."

Although I would have preferred that Bill keep talking on his own without any prompting from me, I decided to go ahead

and ask the money question — literally and figuratively. "Do you still support her, Bill? I mean financially? How does she make ends meet? Given what you're describing right now, I can't see how she would be able to make a living, or even survive on public assistance."

"Well . . ." he said, flustered by my latest query. "I didn't think we were going to talk about this today. I don't see how it has much to do with your . . . ethical concerns."

I waited. Why? I couldn't think of a thing to say.

"I pay the bills," he said, sounding defiant. "I pay the bills. It's something I want to do, I choose to do. I feel a . . . responsibility to her. On our wedding day, I said 'till death do us part' and I meant it. My love for Rachel didn't end when she got sick. It didn't end when she decided she needed to live someplace where she could be closer to more weddings. I take my vows seriously. So, yes, I support her."

Was there a little self-righteousness in his tone? Yes, there was. But the reality was that what Bill had been doing for his wife for almost a decade was extraordinary. Not too many men in the same circumstances would have done it. I was touched by his

compassion and commitment.

"That must be a difficult burden for you," I said.

"I don't look at it that way. Not financially, anyway. Emotionally, yes — it's hard. I miss . . . having my wife. There's been a hole in my heart since she left me. But financially? I look at it that . . . it's our money, Rachel's and mine, and that she needs some of it to live. That's all. Truth be told, I spend more of it than she does. I don't love her any less because she's ill. I tell myself that it could be worse."

She could have cancer, I thought, ironically. *Hoho.*

Again, I waited.

"You can't tell anybody about this, right? I've never . . . admitted to anyone that I still support Rachel. I'm not sure people would understand."

Understand? What, that you're a saint? Why is that such a secret?

"I can't divulge what you've told me, Bill. I won't tell anyone that you support Rachel."

"Good."

"Do the kids know?"

He hesitated before he said, "No. They know I love their mother. That's all they need to know."

I considered the hesitation. *What was that about?* Why would he lie about that?

I couldn't rationalize my follow-up question therapeutically. I knew I couldn't, so I didn't even try. But I asked it anyway. "How expensive is it? To support someone in Rachel's circumstances? It must be a severe burden."

He didn't stumble over the question. "Of course it is. It helps a lot that she's still on my health insurance. Frankly, that's one reason why I would never — even if I felt differently — why I'd never go ahead with a divorce. If we were divorced, Rachel would have to rely on public health. That would be a . . . tragedy for her. The medicine alone . . . The occasional hospitalizations . . . The ER visits?"

Bill looked to me for an acknowledgment. I said, "I can only imagine."

He sighed. "She has an apartment in Vegas, a small one, but it's a nice place in a decent neighborhood. I pay . . . a caretaker . . . to look in on her, make sure she has food, has decent clothes, is clean, you know. And I provide what she needs for . . . the weddings. Dresses, gifts. She's generous — you know that. I don't want her to be living in filth or out on the street. I want my wife to be comfortable, and to be safe."

I almost said, "A caretaker?" but I didn't. I was wondering if Canada was Bill's idea of a caretaker for his schizophrenic wife. Instead, I refocused on the budgetary arithmetic. I said, "It must add up."

"It does," he said. I thought he was going to say something else, but he stopped.

While I waited for him to resume, I revisited the math. Supporting Rachel the way that Bill described must be costing him two, three, maybe even four thousand dollars a month, depending on housing, medical, and pharmacy costs. I figured twenty-five to fifty thousand dollars a year. A lot of money.

If I added that amount to the amount that Reverend Howie told Raoul that Canada was paying him so that Rachel could attend weddings — I figured it was probably a similar amount, actually, another twenty-five to fifty thousand dollars a year — we were talking big money. Potentially very big money, since Canada was probably keeping an additional cut for his services. My gut instinct said that the total, fifty to a hundred thousand dollars annually, had to be more than someone in Bill Miller's circumstances could afford.

Especially since we were talking after-tax dollars.

Bill tried to explain how he handled his generous allowance to his wife. "I make a good living. The company's been good to me over the years. My career's gone well. It would be better if I could make this living in Nevada, but I can't. I consider myself fortunate. The kids and I cut some corners. We live simply. We manage. My car's a lot older than yours."

Bill had noticed my car? That gave me a little chill.

"Rachel's not in treatment?" I asked.

"She's not interested."

"And you don't use a home health care agency?"

"We've tried, but Rachel can be . . . difficult to deal with. Over the years, I've pieced something together, some . . . services that seem to work out. They meet her needs." He smiled at me, just a little sheepish grin. "Is that it? Is that all that you needed to know?"

"No," I said. "I have one more question. It's similar to the first one I asked."

"Shoot."

"What is the nature of your relationship with the man who owns the house next door to yours?"

He nodded. "Doyle?"

I immediately knew that he'd been ready for that question; it was the one he'd been expecting from me all along. It wasn't too surprising; Bill had twice spied me loitering on Doyle's property. But I didn't want to divulge the fact that I knew the name of the house's owner, so I asked, "He owns the house to the north of yours?"

"Yeah, that's Doyle. I barely know him."

"Barely?"

"We were neighbors for . . . almost four years. But we weren't close. He's a loner, a single guy. He kept to himself. He'd be outside working; we'd say hi. That sort of thing. He invited me over once to look at his new waterfall, and his pond. Impressive. That's probably the most time we ever spent together. He moved away before Thanksgiving, maybe even before Halloween. The house is vacant. But you know that."

I noted the dig, but didn't bite. "When's the last time you spoke with him?"

"I'm having trouble understanding why that is any of your business."

Although I knew that the reason Bill Miller was having trouble understanding why it was any of my business was because it wasn't any of my business, I reiterated

my dual-relationship concerns. Not too surprisingly, Bill seemed less satisfied by my explanation than he had been the first time.

He crossed his arms over his chest. His voice grew wary. "So you have some . . . professional relationship with Doyle? And if I'm his friend, you can't have a professional relationship with me? That's the deal?"

"I can't divulge the nature of my current professional relationships. I'm sure you respect that. You asked me for my help with something. Before I'm able to agree to that request, it's my responsibility to be certain that there aren't any impediments."

"Impediments?"

It was a stupid word, born of my anxiety over what I was doing, the tightrope I was trying to cross. But I was stuck with it. "Yes, impediments."

Bill looked at me as though my subterfuge was as transparent as glass. He said, "Last fall sometime. He told me he was going to list the house. That was the last time I talked to Doyle."

A pad of graph paper. A pencil with a fresh eraser. A whole lot of conjecture.

The meeting with Bill Miller was over

and I was busy trying to compute how much it would take to raise two adolescent kids in an overpriced neighborhood in an overpriced town in an overpriced world. I had one small child in a similarly over-priced neighborhood in the same over-priced town, so I could fathom a guess as to what it was costing Bill Miller to support his family in Boulder. Mortgage, property taxes, food, health insurance, car payments, some amount of recreation, teenage whims . . . hell, I hadn't even considered any additional funds that Bill might try to set aside to fund his eventual retirement.

To the sum at the bottom of my sheet of graph paper, I added the approximate costs I'd already computed that it would take to maintain a schizophrenic wife in a gambling and resort town in another state, and somehow simultaneously support her extravagant serial wedding habit.

Total all those amounts, do some rough reverse income-tax calculations, and I would have a guess, admittedly shoddy, as to exactly how many pretax dollars Bill Miller would have to earn to possibly meet all his financial commitments. My conclusion? I was guessing that Bill Miller would need to earn three hundred thousand dol-

lars a year, minimum.

One of the things therapists do every day is listen to people talk about personal things, things like their money. Over the years, hearing various patients discuss their salary ranges for this job and that job, I'd developed a pretty good sense of what kind of living people made doing what kind of work in Boulder County.

There was no way Bill Miller made three hundred grand a year as a district manager of a chain of retail drugstores. What did I think Bill Miller was paid? Low end? Eighty to a hundred thousand dollars. High end? One fifty. One eighty, tops.

Tops.

That was not enough to provide for the two households Bill was supporting, let alone enough to have anything left over for Rachel's nuptial peculiarities, and certainly not at the rates that Reverend Howie charged.

Family money? It was possible that some trust fund somewhere or some generous recently dead relative had come to the rescue to cushion the Millers' financial burdens. But Bill hadn't alluded to anything about any family money softening his financial plight.

So where, I continued to wonder, was

Bill Miller getting the money to support two households, not to mention to make all the payments to Canada and Reverend Howie, and to otherwise endow Rachel's sundry bizarre wedding imperatives?

I didn't know. But I was beginning to think that the answer was crucial.

Mallory says her dad is up to something.

I tossed my pencil onto the desk and watched it skitter across the oak and tumble to the floor.

With some sadness and a lot of resignation, I admitted to myself that I'd just crossed a serious ethical line. The meeting that I'd just completed with Bill Miller hadn't been psychotherapy. I hadn't met with him for his clinical benefit.

I'd met with him for my own purposes, whatever those really were.

48

Grace was usually all mine on Friday mornings, my day off. That morning Lauren was in a trial and Viv had a chemistry class from ten until noon. Viv had kindly agreed to watch Grace while I saw Bill Miller but I had to rush back home to pick up my daughter so Viv could get to class on time.

Grace and I often used our Friday time for outings or errands, but on cold winter mornings we sometimes tossed "usually" out into the snow and snuggled up inside with hot cider, good dogs, and a warm fire. And books.

The temperature had dropped into the single digits overnight and snuggling seemed like a marvelous plan. But my discomfort over Diane and Bob and Rachel and Mallory wouldn't allow me that kind of leisure, so I covered my daughter in multiple layers of cotton, fleece, and Fiberfill, shuttled her out to the Audi, powered up the seat heater, and began mo-

toring west around 9:30. Grace was a good traveler; she seemed cool with our inclement adventure.

In front of us the vertical planes of the Flatirons were draped in a thin fog, as though a designer had decided that a gauzy covering was just what the foothills needed that morning. As we angled closer to the hogbacks north of the city, tiny glistening crystals descended from the frozen mist. "Look, Gracie, it's raining diamonds," I said.

Gracie laughed. On Friday mornings, until she needed a nap, I was almost always funny.

I spent the next mile or so trying to explain the concept of triplets to my daughter. For a moment, I actually thought she got it. But when she started squealing, "Three me, three me," I was pretty sure that she was still in need of a hands-on demonstration.

I hadn't called Mary Black to tell her we were coming by, mostly because I thought she would tell me not to bother, but partly because I was ninety-nine percent certain I would find her at home and that announcing my visit in advance would give her time to get her thoughts in order,

which was something that wasn't necessarily in my best interest. The reason I was so certain I would find her home was that, considering the energy it took to get one small person out of the house in near-zero January temperatures, I thought it was a safe bet that Mary would need a damn good reason to layer up her three bundles of six-week-old joy to lug them outside.

Mary, her husband Gordon, an anesthesiologist, and their triplets lived in a sprawling contemporary ranch in a tony enclave off the Foothills Highway just south of the mouth of Lefthand Canyon. The house hadn't been built for a family with three infants, and its out-of-town, almost-in-the-mountains location wasn't the most convenient for schlepping multiple kids to pediatricians, preschool, and soccer. I wasn't at all surprised to see a FOR SALE sign out front. Babies change things. They just do.

Triplets change everything.

Before I left the car I tried to check my voice mail for word from Raoul but I couldn't get a cell signal in the mountain shadows. Yet another reason for parents of triplets to move closer to town.

I was relieved the Chinooks that the weather people had been forecasting

hadn't yet started blowing. Chinooks are fierce winter downslope winds, cousins of California's fabled devil winds, the Santa Anas. Chinooks warm as they descend from the tallest peaks of the Continental Divide, the gusts compressing and accelerating as they squeeze through mountain canyons before they ultimately rupture out of the foothills onto the communities of Colorado's Front Range in fifty- to one-hundred-mile-an-hour bursts.

A wise man once said that there is definitely a place not to stand when an elephant has gas. In a similar vein, the mouth of Lefthand Canyon was one of the places not to linger in Boulder County during a serious joust with Chinooks.

It took Mary a moment to respond to the doorbell, but my guess was right — she was home.

"Alan, what a surprise."

She looked surprised. That much was clear. Pleased? That would have been a stretch. Mary had a well-rounded son curled in each arm and the third member of the newly born trio was screaming somewhere in one of the back rooms of the house. Mary seemed inured to the wail.

"Hi, Mary, this is Grace. Gracie, this is Dr. Mary Black."

"Hello," Grace said.

"The babies are lovely, Mary," I said.

Mary sighed and forced a smile. "They are. Thanks for reminding me. Come in," she said wistfully as she led us into a living room that had been transformed by necessity into a day nursery. The grown-up furniture — a lot of leather and stone and glass — had been shoved to one end of the long room and most of the remaining space was consumed with infant paraphernalia, including three immense boxes of Huggies from a warehouse store and two matching, side-by-side changing tables.

The memorable aroma of stale diaper pail lingered in the air.

"Let me hand these guys off to the nanny. Hold on a second. Grace? Would you like to come back with me and see all the babies?"

Grace was thrilled. She looked to me for permission — I nodded — before she took Mary's hand and followed her toward the back of the house.

"Sometimes I'm convinced that no one is ever going to come, ever," Mary said when she returned to the living room.

"Do you know why I'm here?"

She shook her head, but I thought her expression said otherwise. Was I mis-

reading? I thought Mary looked beat up. Her hair was ragged, her face hadn't seen makeup in a long while, and the fleece clothing she wore was spotted with some of the fluids that were either intended to go into infants or with some of the fluids that naturally and copiously came back out. Sleep? Not recently, I suspected.

"Triplets are a handful, I take it."

"A handful? A puppy is a handful, Alan. A baby changes everything. You know that. Three? You wouldn't believe what it's like. Entire weeks pass and I don't even notice. Christmas was a blur."

"You know why I'm here?" I asked again.

"No, not at all."

I thought her response was wary, and just a little defensive. "Believe it or not, I'm here for a consultation."

She gave me a you've-got-to-be-kidding look. "I'm really on . . . an extended leave from my practice. I was originally thinking six months, but that no longer feels like a maximum. I have no idea how long it's going to take for life to feel under control again. My consultation is that you go talk to somebody else."

I no longer had any doubt: She was chary. I wondered for a third time if she'd

469

somehow expected my visit and knew what was coming.

Mary and I were colleagues, not friends. We'd already exchanged condolences at Hannah's funeral, and I decided that I didn't need to squander any more time on social niceties. She hadn't exactly concurred with my desire for a consultation, but she hadn't overtly refused, either. I said, "Mary, do you know that Hannah saw Mallory Miller for an intake session not long before she died?"

From the flash in her eyes, I knew instantly that Mary had not known. Her "No" was absolutely superfluous. "You're sure?" she added.

"She consulted with Diane about it right after the session. Diane didn't know who the kid was at the time, but she's put things together since. It was Mallory."

Mary's brain was full of infants and infant things and she seemed to be struggling to shift gears to contemplate the weight of my news. "Anything that relates to what happened to her?" she asked.

"No, not directly."

She changed her expression. "About what happened to Hannah?"

"Diane suspected there was. She went to Las Vegas last weekend to talk to Rachel

Miller about Mallory. Diane thought that Rachel might be able to fill in some pieces." I paused. "You knew Rachel was living in Las Vegas?"

"Of course. Why didn't Diane just talk to Bill?"

Not "Mallory's father." Not "Bill Miller." *Bill.* "Let's say that because of what Hannah told Diane about the session with Mallory, it wasn't an option."

That got her attention. "I'm not sure what you're trying to say, Alan."

I didn't want to give Mary any more information than I had to. "Diane disappeared on Monday evening in a casino and nobody's heard from her since."

"What?"

"She walked out of the casino with two men and she . . . vanished."

"Diane went to Las Vegas because of a discussion she had with Hannah about a single intake session with Mallory?"

"Within two weeks of that intake, Hannah was dead and Mallory was missing. Diane felt she had a responsibility to try to figure out what had happened. You know Diane."

"God." Mary turned her head as though she couldn't bear looking at me. "What do you think I might know that would be . . . pertinent?"

471

"What *do* you know, Mary?"

She walked away and began folding a pile of recently laundered sleepers and impossibly small T-shirts. "I wish it were that easy, Alan. I wish it were that easy." She looked back at me. "You know the rules we play by. Did Diane ever find Rachel? I wonder how she's doing sometimes. She was so resistant to treatment."

"Diane tracked her down, yes. At a wedding chapel in Vegas, not surprisingly. Had she talked with her? I'm not sure about that."

The triplets were quiet. Grace was singing them a Raffi song — "Down by the Bay." From which parent she'd inherited the ability to carry a tune wasn't at all clear. It was a recessive gene, though. Guaranteed.

"What do you want from me?" Mary asked. The question wasn't particularly provocative; Mary seemed sincerely curious.

"I'd like to know what Bill Miller was up to. His daughter told Hannah that he was up to something. I'm worried that Diane has gotten herself in the middle of whatever that was."

"The police?"

"In Las Vegas? No help."

"Up to?" she said. Her breathing had changed. "What do you mean, what Bill was 'up to'?"

"I'm not sure. Bill seems to have access to money he shouldn't have. He's spending a fortune to support Rachel in Las Vegas. I'd like to know where it comes from."

She reacted physically to my words: She stepped back. "Alan, I —"

"Do they have family money?"

"No. They don't. I shouldn't be talking to you about this."

She was right; she shouldn't be talking with me.

It was her problem, one I didn't want to give her time to contemplate. "What do you know about a guy named Canada?"

"Oh God," she said. "You know about Canada? How do you know about Canada?"

"Raoul is in Vegas looking for Diane. He found Canada."

I wasn't about to tell Mary that I was treating Bill Miller. But I found it interesting that Mary knew about Canada, too. Was that good or bad? I couldn't decide.

Was Canada good or bad? I didn't know that either.

"What do you know about him?" I asked.

"Bill asked for some advice about him once. About trusting him. His motives. That's all I know."

"When?"

"Years ago. Not too long after Rachel moved."

"What did you tell him?"

"I told him that, given what he knew about the man's background, it would be hard to predict how reliable a . . . Canada would be. Whether he could be trusted with Rachel's welfare. I told him I could argue it either way, psychologically speaking."

"Background? What do you mean?"

"Canada grew up with a schizophrenic mother. She left him when he was young, like eleven. Took off with a guy she met in a bar. He's haunted by it."

"Makes sense." But in my business, hindsight almost always makes sense. Foresight is the more valuable, but much rarer, commodity. "Which way did you end up arguing it with Bill?"

"Alan, please."

"Help me find Diane, Mary."

"I argued against it. I suggested that Bill use social services to help him with Rachel if he couldn't afford a home health care agency."

I changed tactics. "Do you know why Hannah was in your office the morning she died? Not in her own office?"

"No."

She'd answered quickly, maybe too quickly. It's not that I didn't believe her reply; it was that I wasn't sure if I believed her reply.

"But you've wondered?"

"Of course I've wondered."

"Is there any reason Hannah would have been in your office?"

"I didn't think she'd ever been in there without me. Ever."

"But she had a key?"

"Yes, we each had a key to the other's office."

Diane and I had keys to each other's office, too. "Why would she have left her purse in the middle of her office floor?"

Mary opened her eyes wide and shook her head at that question. "She left her purse on the floor?"

"Yes. Right in the middle of her office. That's where it was when Diane and I got there."

"That's too strange. The police didn't tell me that. It's so not Hannah. She kept it in the back of a drawer in her file cabinet."

"Are your records in your office? I didn't

see them the day that I found Hannah."

"What records?"

"Practice files. Specifically, your case file for Rachel Miller."

"I have cabinets built into the back wall. They look like wainscoting."

I'd been distracted by other things that day. The image of Hannah splayed over the leather cube, hitchhiking her way into death, continued to intrude on my thoughts with some regularity.

"Rachel's chart is there?"

"I assume it is. Why would Hannah's death have anything to do with the Millers, Alan? I still don't see the connection."

I could have told her that I didn't see the connection either. Instead, I tried the truth. "Hannah met with Mallory a couple of weeks before Christmas. Before too long, one of them was dead, the other one was missing."

She pondered for a moment before she said dispassionately, "Correlation doesn't imply causality, Alan."

Ah yes, science.

"I think we both know it doesn't rule it out either, Mary."

49

We agreed to take two cars into town. The nanny would watch the triplets for an hour or two. Grace would stay with me. I ended up parking in the spot behind the small building where Hannah's pristine Passat had been parked the night that Diane and I had found Hannah's body.

Mary's car, a Honda minivan with temporary plates — her new triplet-mobile, I assumed — was already in the other parking slot.

The back door of the old house was unlocked. Gracie and I found Mary standing in the hallway, her hands hanging limp by her upper thighs. The narrow passage was dimly lit and she was silhouetted by the distant front windows. I thought she seemed disoriented. As Grace and I approached she said, "I don't like being here anymore. It's so strange. I never thought I'd feel that way. I used to love being in this space," she said. "Hannah and I were per-

fect together here. Perfect."

"I can only imagine what it's like for you," I said. "Mary, I need to get Grace settled with a book or something. I'll be right back."

I showed Grace where I'd be talking with Mary, and then led her to the waiting room where I made space on the coffee table for her books and for some paper and crayons. She chose to sit on the same location on the green velvet sofa that the Cheetos lady had chosen on the day that Hannah died. Grace settled right in, picking the crayons and paper over the books. Her cooperation didn't surprise me; I was already confident that one of my daughter's enduring skills in life would be her capacity to ride whatever wave rolled her way.

Mary had unlocked her office door and was standing a couple of feet inside. I squeezed in behind her. The leather cube was gone from the room, as was the stained dhurrie. The pine floors looked naked and ancient. The room appeared as cold as it felt.

I spotted the recessed handles for the lateral files that had been built into the rear wall. The three long file cabinets did indeed appear to be part of the beadboard wainscoting.

"I've only been back once, with the police and my attorney. The detectives wanted to know if anything was missing. I looked around and told them I didn't think so. Nothing appeared disturbed to me at the time, but I didn't do an inventory."

I recalled how hard it was to return to my own office years before after Diane had been attacked by a patient's husband. I touched Mary on the arm. She put her hand on my fingers.

"You know where . . . her body was, don't you? I mean, exactly?" she asked.

"Yes, I do. Do you want me to . . ."

"No. Not yet. I'll tell you if I do." She stepped away.

"Okay," I said. "She was wearing a blouse that day, Mary. Button-front, collar, silk, I think. A basic thing."

"So?"

"The front tail on the left side was tucked up underneath her bra when I found her, exposing her abdomen. I've never seen a woman do that before."

"The police didn't tell me that. You're sure?"

"I am."

"That's interesting. Hannah was a Type 1 diabetic — she was insulin dependent. She usually injected into her abdomen. Rather

than unbuttoning her shirt, she had this habit of just tucking it up under the front of her bra to get it out of the way. Did the police find a syringe close by? Had she just taken insulin?"

"I didn't see a syringe, but I suppose it could have been beneath her body."

"Have you seen the results of the autopsy? How was her sugar?" Mary asked.

"I assume it was within normal limits; nobody mentioned it as an anomaly."

"If her shirt was tucked under her bra, then she was preparing to take insulin. There's no other explanation."

"But in your office?"

"That part doesn't make any sense. She kept the insulin in back, in the kitchen. She would load the syringe back there. But she injected herself in her own office. Hannah was modest, and she was very private about her illness."

"Always?"

"Always."

After a poignant pause — I suspected she was still debating whether or not she really wanted to know precisely where Hannah had died — Mary stepped toward the built-ins. "The file is in here."

The key was secreted on the shelves above the cabinets in a ceramic jar, some-

thing small and celadon. Mary retrieved the key and unlocked the middle cabinet. She chose a pillow from the sofa and threw it on the floor before she kneeled down, slid out the top drawer, and began searching for the file. She fingered the brightly colored tabs sequentially, her middle, ring, and index fingers running after each other as though they were skipping over hurdles. After one time through the area that marked the center of the alphabet, she retraced her work.

That's when she found it.

In a calm voice she announced, "It's here. I almost missed it, but it's here." She pulled the dusky red folder and held it up for me to see.

My voice every bit as level as hers — we were both therapists, after all — I suggested, "Why don't you take a few minutes and make sure that it hasn't been . . . I don't know, tampered with."

She crossed her legs and sat on the pillow on the floor. Slowly, she made her way through the inch-and-a-half-thick pile of pages of scrawled notes and medication records and hospital admission papers and discharge summaries.

"It all seems to be here, Alan. I can't be a hundred percent sure, but everything

seems to be here. It looks just the way I left it."

I sighed involuntarily. Relief? Disappointment? I wasn't sure.

She gazed up at me. "You thought someone stole it, didn't you? That someone was in my office that day, that Hannah heard them in here, came in to see what was going on. And that's why she was killed."

"It was one thought. It all depended on what was in that file."

She closed the file and stood. "I can't tell you what's in it. You know how this works."

"If it's a consultation you can."

"What good will that do? You can't tell anyone what I tell you. It won't help."

"I've been looking for Diane all week. I already know other things. Every piece helps. If I can put it all together, I may be able to find her. I'm terrified that time is running out."

"You won't divulge what I tell you?"

I said, "No," and I hoped that I wasn't lying. Was I willing to be lying if it would help Diane?

Yes. Mary had to know that.

"I wouldn't treat her the same way today. Probably wouldn't even diagnose her the same," Mary said remorsefully, while giving Rachel's file a little shake. "We know so

much more now, don't we? Take me out for coffee, Alan. I'm dying to sit down with an adult for coffee."

I made an apologetic face. "Grace will be coming with us." Grace would be thrilled to go out for coffee; she thought a petite espresso cup full of steamed milk foam with shaved chocolate on top was as good as life got.

Mary deflated, took a step, and slumped down on a nearby chair. "I forgot. She's a sweet kid, but she's not an adult."

"Not the last time I looked, no."

A strong wind exploded out of Sunshine Canyon ten blocks to the west. Had the Chinooks arrived? The *whoosh* shook the house, the naked tree branches squinted together and bent to the east. Debris and dust filled the air.

I excused myself and stepped out into the waiting room to check on Grace. She seemed oblivious to the gales; in fact she was so busy coloring that she didn't notice my arrival in the room. A second blast put the first to shame — the century-old glass began to hum in the window at the front of the house. After one more selfish moment observing my daughter's concentration, I returned down the hallway to Mary's office.

She'd moved to the couch, pulled her legs up under her, and tugged a pillow to her chest. She asked, "Did Bill Miller ever mention to you that he'd done something he wasn't proud of? Something that was eating at him?"

"No, doesn't ring a bell. Should it?"

"I'm thinking maybe it might be important. He never really explained it all to me, but it had something to do with a traffic accident he witnessed. A young woman died. He was torn up about it."

I surprised myself by remembering. "She was an orthodontist," I said.

The winds had quieted. Strange.

Mary said, "Yes."

50

Mary had to get back to the demands of the triplets, and the clock said it was almost time to get Grace home for some lunch and a nap. But something Mary had said convinced me to risk squeezing one more errand into our outing. I didn't even try to explain to Grace exactly what business was conducted at the office of the Boulder County coroner; all I told her was that Daddy had another short meeting.

Years before, during my brief stint as a coroner's investigator, my supervisor was a good man named Scott Truscott. I'd always liked Scott and had felt that once I wasn't working for him he'd grown fond of me, too. Grace and I tracked him down at his desk in the Justice Center on Canyon Boulevard. I introduced him to Grace and he and I spent a moment catching up before he asked, "So what's up?"

"I'm hoping I can help you a little with the Hannah Grant thing."

"Yeah?" He seemed interested, but just the slightest bit skeptical. "I'd love to get that one out of the 'undetermined' column."

The words he used — genteelly chosen without overt reference to death or murder — told me that he was happy to edit his part of the conversation for Grace's tender ears.

He added, "Why me and not the detectives handling the case?"

I could've finessed my answer, but with Scott it wasn't necessary. "I have issues with Jaris Slocum."

"Gotcha." Scott wasn't surprised, obviously.

"Will you answer some questions for me, too?" I asked.

"Depends what they are."

That was fair. I said, "Hannah was a diabetic. Type 1. We both know that. How was her blood sugar when, you know?"

"Blood doesn't actually tell us anything about sugar level during a post; natural autolysis renders the numbers meaningless. But because we knew she was insulin dependent, the coroner checked the vitreous fluid."

"From her eye?" I asked, a shiver shooting up my spine. I didn't know what

486

autolysis was, natural or otherwise, but feared that asking would either tug Scott down a blind alley, or leave my daughter with nightmares.

"It's the only way to get a reliable post mortem sugar. I don't have it memorized, but she was within normal limits." His hand reached for his computer mouse. "You want me to check for the exact number, I can pull the labs."

"It's okay. Did the detectives recover a syringe that night?"

"You mean with insulin in it? No. They found fresh supplies in the kitchen. Nothing already prepared for injection though, and nothing recently used."

"Did you hear anything about an open roll of LifeSavers in her coat pocket?"

His shoulders dropped, and he frowned. "No, nobody mentioned LifeSavers to me. It wasn't in any of the reports."

"It was there; I saw it. The package was open, the wrapper was curly-cueing out of her pocket."

Scott appeared perplexed. "She must have thought her sugar was low. Considering her normal levels, though, that's odd."

"It is odd. Did you collect her . . . that night?" I skipped a word intentionally. The

omitted word could have been "body" or "remains."

He filled in the blank and said that he had. One of the tasks of coroner's investigators is to visit death scenes to begin collecting data, and to prepare bodies for transport to the morgue.

I said, "Her shirttail was tucked up under the front of her bra when I found her."

"When I got there, too. Same."

"Ever run across that before at a death scene?"

"Never," he said.

"A good friend of hers just told me that Hannah did that when she was preparing to do an insulin injection in her abdomen. To get her shirt up out of the way."

Scott crossed his arms and sat back. "I didn't consider that, but I should have. Slocum was already thinking homicide when I arrived." He made a sound with his tongue and the roof of his mouth. "You'll make a statement about the LifeSavers?"

"Of course; I bet the crime-scene photos will show that wrapper."

"I'll take a look. Will her friend give a statement about the shirttail?"

"Can't see why not. Why would a diabetic be eating sugar one minute and pre-

paring to take insulin the next?"

"It makes no sense to me. That's one of the things I'm going to have to think about."

We said good-bye. I bundled Grace back up. On the way out to the car she asked, "What are LifeSavers?"

We stopped at a convenience store on the way home and I bought her a roll. I guessed she was a Butter Rum kid.

It turned out that I guessed right.

When we finally weaved across the valley Viv was almost done cooking up a pot of macaroni and cheese. As the three of us were finishing lunch, Virginia Danna, the Realtor whom I'd tricked into showing me the interior of Doyle's house, phoned me on my cell.

After reintroducing herself she proceeded without any further niceties, her tone full of conspiracy. "The rules have changed. They always seem to in situations like this, don't they? With Mr. Chandler dead, buyers are going to come out of the hills looking for a fire sale. Act fast and you might be able to get that house for a . . ."

Song? What house?

I walked out of the kitchen. "Mr. Chandler is dead?" I said.

"Yes! Can you believe it? This world! Sometimes . . ." She sighed. "A detective called me today to find out when I'd last spoken with him. You could have knocked me over with a feather when he told me Mr. Chandler was dead, maybe even murdered. Who knows what happened to him? The poor man! Murdered? It gives me gooseflesh, right up my thighs. Now, I will admit that I'm not privy to the estate situation in this particular circumstance, but sometimes people — heirs — at times like this are truly eager to settle things after a . . . especially after a . . . So if I could persuade you to make . . ."

An offer?

She went on. "Even a lowball offer would be . . ."

Acceptable? Delectable?

I asked, "Ms. Danna, who exactly is Mr. Chandler?"

"What? The owner of the house I showed you on Twelfth. The one with the water features and that yummy media center downstairs? I'm sorry, I thought you knew."

"Doyle?"

"Yes, Doyle Chandler."

"He's dead?"

She was growing impatient with me.

"Mm-hmmm," was all she said in reply to my last question. Then she waited while I caught up.

"What detective phoned you?" I asked. I was thinking *Sam*.

"I don't recall exactly. Mr. Chandler's body was found up near Allenspark. Maybe it was an Allenspark detective."

Allenspark is a small town in the mountains about thirty minutes from Boulder by car, not far from the eastern boundaries of Rocky Mountain National Park. When not swollen with summer tourists, Allenspark's population typically hovered — guessing — somewhere around two hundred people. The village was as likely to have its own homicide detective as it was to have its own traffic helicopter. Any investigator involved in a homicide inquiry in Allenspark would be part of the County Sheriff's department, on loan from a bigger city, like Boulder, or someone assigned from the Colorado Bureau of Investigation.

Rather than argue the point, I said, "I'll talk it over with my wife and get back to you. The house is still a little small for us."

"One word: cantilever. My mobile number is on the card I gave you. Call any time. When news gets out about this . . . situation, there will be other offers, cer-

tainly by close of business tomorrow. You can count on it. There have been four showings of that property this week alone and I don't have to tell you how slow the beginning of January usually is. And that screen in the basement? Remember? Of course you do. I checked. It's a Stewart Filmscreen. I told you, the best. Think hard — a house like that, a location like that, circumstances like . . ."

These.

"I understand," I said. But, of course, I didn't.

I called Lauren. She didn't return my call until midafternoon during a break in her trial. She'd already heard through the law enforcement grapevine about the discovery of the body of an unidentified male in a shallow grave not far from a trail that meandered off Highway 7 in northern Boulder County. She said she thought the location was east of Allenspark, actually closer to Lyons and Hygiene. I asked her to get me whatever information she could and to call me right back.

"Why are you interested in this?" she asked, of course. The tone of her question made it clear she wasn't sure she wanted to hear my reply.

"It might be related to Diane," I said.

"Two minutes," she said.

It took her four. "We don't have much yet. Pending a post, it appears to be a homicide. Animals had gotten to the body. ID found at the scene indicates it may be a man named —"

"Doyle Chandler."

"How did you know? Is he one of your patients?"

I could have said, probably should have said, "You know I can't answer that." Instead, I said, "No." Were the answer yes I would have answered with stony silence. Lauren and I both knew that the silent yes would have been just as declarative as the spoken no had been.

"One of Diane's patients?"

Well, that was a thought. What if Diane had treated Doyle? I didn't think so. I said, "No."

"But you know him?" she asked.

"Personally, I don't. Doyle Chandler owned the house that's next door to Mallory Miller's house on the Hill. When she disappeared he'd already moved away and put the place on the market."

"I don't think the police mentioned that this afternoon. Are you sure?"

"Yes."

"Is this related to Mallory's disappearance?"

"I don't know. You have to wonder."

"Diane's disappearance?"

"I don't know that either."

"But you have reasons to be suspicious?"

"Yes."

"Then this might be important to you: Sam's up there. He asked the sheriff for permission."

"He's up where they found the body?"

"Yes."

"I'll call him."

"Have you heard from Raoul?" Lauren asked.

"No. I'm still worried."

"Keep me informed, okay?"

After we hung up, I sent Sam a text message on his pager: "I know about D. Call me. A."

While I was waiting for Sam to get back to me, I took a call from Scott Truscott at the coroner's office. "Try something on for me?" he said.

"Sure."

"We know that Ms. Grant hit her head when she tripped that morning at Rallysport, right? On the tile floor in the locker room? That's confirmed?"

Hannah Grant, okay. I fought to change

gears. "Yes," I said. "The witnesses apparently agree on that much."

"She tells the women in the locker room she's fine, and she drives straight to her office."

"We think."

"Okay, we think. On the way, or shortly after she gets there, though, she begins to feel that something's not quite right — maybe she has a headache, maybe she's a little confused, lightheaded — but she doesn't put two and two together, doesn't consider that she's just bumped her head and that she might have a concussion, or worse. Instead she decides that after all the exercise she'd done that her sugar's too low. She's in her car by then, she doesn't have any orange juice, so she sucks on a couple of LifeSavers. With me?"

"So far."

"When she gets to her office she's still not herself, not feeling right. The candy didn't help — she's not feeling better yet. How do we know? Easy: She puts her purse in the middle of the floor. All her friends say she's a compulsive person, OCD, truly anal, so the purse? On the floor? That's not like her. Totally out of character. At this point I think she's feeling even worse, not better. Maybe much worse."

"Why much worse, Scott?"

"Post showed two subdural hematomas, remember? One of those two certainly came from a blunt surface — the tile floor — at the health club, during that initial fall."

"Yes."

"So we know she has a subdural from that earlier trauma. My theory is she actually already has both subdurals — one from the impact with the floor, and one from something with a sharper edge, maybe the locker room bench — and she's actively bleeding into one or both of those hematomas. Ms. Grant was on aspirin therapy — you might not know that. Family history of heart disease."

"I didn't."

"Doesn't matter. Pressure's slowly increasing on her brain, and she's gradually getting more symptomatic. Half an hour passes, then an hour, and she's more and more confused, lethargic, maybe vertiginous. Anxious, probably. Not too surprisingly, her thinking's impaired. All she can come up with is that her diabetes is way out of whack, she has a problem with her sugar. The LifeSavers were there, Alan; in her pocket, like you said. I confirmed that with the crime-scene photos. But if she ate

them, they didn't help, so she goes in the other direction, decides maybe she needs insulin.

"But her confusion is severe; she's disoriented — she can't even get her routine quite right. Instead of retrieving her kit from the kitchen to check her sugar, she tucks her shirt up under her bra the way she always does just prior to her injection."

I saw where he was heading. "And instead of going to the kitchen for the insulin, she's lost and she goes to the office across the hall?"

"Exactly. Maybe once she's there she begins to recognize her confusion, and she sits. Maybe not. But that's where she collapses, in that other office. Eventually, she loses consciousness. She's still bleeding into one of those subdurals. Eventually, Ms. Grant dies from the intracranial pressure."

"Go on," I said.

"That's where you find her. Her shirt is tucked up under her bra like she's going to do an injection, but there's no syringe around, no insulin. It's definitely possible she's eaten some candy. No weapon is ever recovered that matches the second trauma to her head. What am I missing?"

I couldn't think of a single thing left un-

explained. "Nothing, Scott. I think maybe you nailed it. No intruders, no assault, no murderer. No second blow to the head."

"And no more 'undetermined.' Hannah Grant's death was accidental."

"I can't tell you how relieved this makes me."

"Do me a favor?"

"What?"

"Sit on this until I can run it by the coroner."

"Of course."

What was I thinking? I couldn't wait to give the news to Diane. She'd be so happy.

It took Sam a couple of hours to reply to my message about Doyle's body, but he did.

"How'd you hear?" Sam asked. Actually, it was more like a demand than a question.

"The real estate lady. She thought I might spot a housing opportunity in the ashes of the tragedy that was unfolding."

"Shit. Who'd you tell?"

"Lauren. How come you guys didn't let the DA know that Doyle Chandler lived next door to Mallory?"

"I've been busy."

Right. "You still near Allenspark?"

"They just wrapped things up. I'm on my way back to Boulder now."

"How long has your guy been dead?"

"My guy?" Sam laughed, turning my question into the melodic refrain of the Mary Wells ditty. "My guy has been dead a while. But it's frigging cold up here, so the body's been pretty well refrigerated. In the meantime, wild animals have been busy doing their wild animal thing. What they nibble on first? Let me tell you, it takes away much of my faith in the natural kingdom. ME's going to have his hands full on this one."

"Homicide?"

"If it's a suicide, he was considerate enough to bury himself first. If it was an accident, he conveniently died by tripping and falling into a shallow grave."

"Why'd you go up there?"

The signal faded and wavered. When it was strong enough to carry Sam's voice again, I heard, ". . . and somebody convinced me that I should be asking this Doyle Chandler about the guy who used his garage in Boulder to store a classic old Camaro. The agent thought that since he moved away from his house in Boulder, Chandler was living out this way. I'd called the sheriff to give them a heads-up that I would be chatting with him as a follow-up to the Mallory Miller thing. When the

sheriff learned that some snowshoers found what appeared to be his body, they gave me a courtesy jingle.

"For what it's worth, this body shouldn't have been discovered, not during the winter anyway. Most years it would've stayed hidden till spring, at least. You'll like this — want to know how it was found? A woman on a snowshoe outing with some girlfriends had gone off by herself to answer nature's call and was finishing taking a crap when she saw part of a hand sticking out from below this log she was crouching behind. Poor crime-scene techs had to collect it as evidence."

"Collect what?"

"Her . . . you know."

I knew. "What's next?"

"I got twenty minutes to get from here to pick up Simon from hockey practice."

"You want me to get him? Meet you at your house? I'm happy to."

"Nice of you, but I think I'm cool. I'll make it in time. Any word on Diane?"

"Nothing. Anything on the BOLO?"

"Nope. Go home, Alan. Stop playing cop."

With that, the signal faded for good and the call dropped off into the great mobile phone ether.

I wasn't ready to stop playing cop. The day's events had shaken me and I was ready to do what I'd been thinking about doing for most of a week. I drove downtown to my office, opened the dark-blue Kinko's box, and prepared to read Bob Brandt's opus, *My Little Runaway*.

A run, run, run, run runaway.

51

The manuscript was, guessing, about a hundred pages long, but the sheets weren't numbered so I didn't have an exact count.

Bob's story started with a single provocative phrase that constituted an entire sentence, an entire paragraph, an entire page, and an entire chapter.

It moved from there into a series of short, essay-like digressions, one having to do with Del Shannon's childhood, another having to do with the mechanics of installing low-maintenance water features.

A page-turner it was not.

More than half of the sheets of paper in the box were blank.

But that solitary phrase on page one was evocative enough that the manuscript lived up to its billing in the most important area: Bob's story did indeed contain a version of what had happened to Mallory on Christmas night, and proposed a fascinating theory about how she'd managed to make

it out of her house without leaving any marks in the fresh snow.

I reminded myself at least five times while I read and reread the few words on the first page that Bob had told me that the work was fiction.

Fiction. Right.

Once I'd completed an initial pass at the manuscript, and after I'd come up with a plan on what to do next, I had some time to kill before I made my next move. I ended up driving home after stopping on the way to buy my girls some of their favorite takeout from Chez Thuy, a little Vietnamese place that Viv — part of Boulder County's Hmong community — had turned us on to. Grace was in a terrific mood while we ate and seemed totally enamored with the way that her rice noodles stuck together.

Over sublime catfish and green onions in a sauce that had more flavors than the sky had stars, I went so far as to tell Lauren that I had some significant news that might impact the investigation of the body that had been discovered that afternoon near Allenspark. She asked for some clarifications that I couldn't provide. But she was kind enough to phone somebody in the

DA's office to confirm my suspicion about what would happen next: The Boulder police had indeed already applied for a warrant to search Doyle Chandler's Twelfth Street home.

"How long will it take to get the warrant?" I asked.

"They'll have it soon," Lauren said. "Judge Heller has the request; I have no doubt she'll comply. This one's a no-brainer. Likely homicide? The police need to search the vic's house."

"I'm going to have to go over there and see Sam in person. Tell him what I know."

"You can't just call?"

"I want to help him find something at Doyle's that I think he might otherwise miss. If I don't tell him what I'm expecting to find there, and then if it turns out that I'm wrong, I won't end up having to breach privilege."

"And you can't tell me how you know what's inside this man's house?"

"I have a hunch based on something — a story a patient . . . told me. I wish I could tell you more. If I'm right, you'll know all about it tomorrow."

I arrived on Doyle's block around 9:30. In order to execute the search warrant the

police department was out in force — I counted five law enforcement vehicles, mostly unmarked, in front of the house. Doyle's neighbors were curious about the commotion; despite the cold night they were congregated in small groups on nearby sidewalks and on front porches watching events unfold. I chose to park around the corner. If it was possible, I preferred not to be spotted by Bill Miller while running this errand.

I dialed Sam's cell phone from my car.

"I thought I told you to go home," he said.

"Yeah, well. You get Simon on time?"

"Barely."

"Who's watching him now?"

Impatiently, he asked, "What's up, Alan? I'm kind of busy."

"I have something to show you."

"I'm working. Maybe tomorrow."

I could tell he was trying hard to be nice, but that his decorum was on its last legs. "I know you're working, Sam. That's why I asked who was watching Simon. I'm right outside. I have something to show you."

"It can't wait?"

He sounded both perplexed and annoyed. I said, "No, it can't. What I want to show you is inside Doyle's house. You'll

505

want to see it. Trust me."

"What? You're outside this house? That's what you meant?"

"Right around the corner."

"I can't bring you in here."

"Sure you can."

"This better be good," Sam said. We were standing in the cramped entryway of Doyle's house. With one deep inhale Sam could have filled the space by himself.

"It'll either be very good, or it won't."

"That second possibility won't leave me feeling great about bringing you in here in front of God and everybody." He gestured toward the interior of the house. "Where do we go to find your treasure?"

"Basement. Where's Lucy?"

Lucy was Sam's longtime detective partner.

"Cabo San Lucas. Cancun. Ixtapa. Someplace like that. Someplace I should be, but I'm not."

I led the way down the hall and through the kitchen to the basement stairs. "An empty house like this makes executing your warrant pretty easy, doesn't it? Don't really have to toss anything."

"We don't 'toss anything.' We're careful."

Sam had apparently forgotten that my

own home had once been the target of a law enforcement search. I was in a position to make an educated argument about the actual neatness of police searches; I decided not to choose that moment to remind him.

"What did you specify on the warrant?" I asked.

Before he followed me down the stairs and into the basement storeroom he smiled wryly at my question but didn't respond. I hadn't really expected him to. I read his smile to mean, "Nice try."

Sam had latex gloves on his hands; I didn't. "You have any more of those?" I asked, pointing to his gloves.

"I don't want you to be tempted to touch anything. Just keep your hands in your pockets; it's a good place for them."

"Then open that door." I pointed at the awning door that led from the basement to the adjacent crawl space.

"Sorry. We haven't been in there yet. I can't go in there until it's been photographed. You certainly can't."

"My fingerprints are already on that handle. I opened it when I was here last time. You know, with the real estate agent."

"Terrific. I'll pass that on. Let's hope your prints aren't flagged by NCIC. It'd

make for a long night."

I shrugged. "I'll just wait until the photographers are free."

Sam had an alternative in mind. "Or you could simply tell me what we're looking for. I really don't have time for your games."

"If what I think is here isn't here, I don't want to blow confidentiality. If it is here, I'll find it, and you'll know."

He thought for a moment about my plan. "If you're wrong about all this you're going to end up making me look like an idiot."

"No, Sam, I'm going to end up making us both look like idiots."

"I don't give a fuck if you look like an idiot. I do care if I look like an idiot." With pronounced reluctance, he called upstairs and redirected a photographer from the top floor of the house into the crawl space.

He parked me on one of the recliners in the fancy theater where Doyle had allowed Bob to watch movies.

"Sit here and don't move," Sam ordered. "I have to go back upstairs for a while. I'll tell you when the photographer's done doing what she needs to do. Then you can go into the crawl space and uncover your

amazing secret." Sam stopped at the door. "I mean it. Stay right here, wait for me to come back. Don't even think about going into that crawl space without me."

I smiled at him. "Do you mind if I put on a DVD? I hear that projector there" — I pointed — "is a top-of-the-line Runco. And the screen is the same one that Spielberg has in his very own personal screening room. It's a Stewart, Sam. An actual Stewart Filmscreen."

Sam gave me the finger and walked upstairs.

It took me about five minutes to get bored. I'd already played with all the levers and buttons on Doyle's fancy leather recliner. In addition to thirty-seven different reclining positions, the thing had a seat heater and a couple of recessed cup holders. All that was missing was a coin slot for a vibrator.

I checked out the vaunted Runco projector that was mounted to the ceiling near the back of the room. Since I didn't even know what I was looking at, that chore managed to use up no more than another twenty seconds.

The recessed speakers? They were only good for ten. There wasn't much to admire

in a recessed speaker with the sound turned off.

Doyle's theater was actually rather spartan considering the big bucks that had been invested in its creation. No popcorn maker. No Old West saloon and mahogany bar to belly-up to on the back wall. No Xbox or souped-up Nintendo setup. The fancy Spielberg screen was all that was left for me to examine. I ambled to the front of the theater and gave it a thorough once-over. My impression of the screen was the same the second time as it had been the first: It looked suspiciously like a movie screen.

I returned to my designated recliner. *Where is the remote control?* I bet myself that Doyle had one of those fancy programmable remotes that operated everything electronic on the whole block, including his neighbors' toasters and microwave ovens. That would be an interesting find, right? That would capture my attention for at least a few minutes. Maybe there was a hockey game on TV. Sam would let me watch hockey.

I couldn't find the device. I checked the other recliners for hidden compartments and secret drawers. Didn't spot a single cubby that was spacious enough to stash a

fancy remote control.

I began searching the perimeter of the room for a panel that might disguise a hidden cupboard. I used my elbow to put pressure on the wall every twelve to eighteen inches, suspecting that the room might have the kind of panel that you have to press on to free the latch.

Nothing budged. Most of the wall panels were padded and fabric-covered. Whatever was beneath them felt rock solid.

Where is the remote? What good are all these electronics without a remote control?

I was about to conclude that someone had pilfered the thing during one of the showings of Doyle's house when I guessed that the storage cabinet I'd been searching for might be secreted behind the Spielberg movie screen. I returned to the front of the room. Careful to use only my fingernails, I pulled on one side of the mahogany molding.

It didn't budge.

I moved to the other side of the screen and did the same.

That side didn't move either.

I tried the hidden latch trick and used my elbow to put pressure on the right vertical section of the frame.

The mahogany slid backward half a cen-

timeter and clicked.

Bingo.

I released the pressure and the screen swung forward from a recessed hinge on the opposite side of the frame.

My mouth dropped open.

Well, I thought, *this part of the book isn't fiction.*

I pulled myself into the opening behind the screen, used my fingernail to flick on a light switch, and stared, trying to drink in every detail before I was banished from the house, because I knew that it was almost certain that I was about to be banished from the house.

I spent about a minute sitting there — examining, figuring, memorizing — before I hopped back down into the theater, flicked off the light switch, swung the screen back into place, and found Sam in the kitchen. He was engaged in a dialogue with a woman dressed in street clothes. I figured she was a detective or a crime-scene tech. I manufactured some fresh surprise for my voice as I interrupted them. "Excuse me. Something to show you in the theater downstairs, Detective Purdy."

The woman with Sam gave me a who-the-hell-are-you look. Sam glared at me, too, and seemed prepared to launch into

some low-velocity attack on my character either because I'd interrupted something important or because I'd ignored his instructions to stay put downstairs.

Or both. Most likely, both.

"Now," I said. "It's important."

"Give me a minute," Sam said. He said it not to me, but to the woman in the street clothes.

52

Earlier that evening, back in my office, I had lifted a dozen or so sheets from the top of the stack inside the blue Kinko's box and placed them in my lap. I'd turned the pages one by one, lingering for a long moment over the handwritten sheet that Bob Brandt had written warning me not to read any further.

Ultimately, I turned that one, too. Considering the transgression I'd committed by arranging the fake-psychotherapy session with Bill Miller that afternoon, breaking my promise to Bob Brandt not to read his manuscript until he gave me permission seemed, by comparison, like a paltry professional sin. Right or wrong, I'd already rationalized that Bob's apparent disappearance was a sufficiently emergent circumstance to void the previous arrangement, anyway.

I was beginning to feel so adept at rationalization that I was considering running for Congress.

The next sheet in the box was the first page of actual text of Bob's book, written in that tiny font he preferred.

No one had considered the possibility
of a tunnel.

Talk about starting your joke with the punch line.

A tunnel? "No one had considered the possibility of a tunnel."

Holy moly.

53

Doyle's excavation was a work of thoughtful engineering.

The length of the subterranean construction wasn't exactly mind-boggling; the distance between the south side of Doyle's basement and the north side of the Miller home was only about fifteen feet. And this wasn't a highway tunnel; the diameter of the mostly round bore ranged from a maximum of about thirty inches a few feet from where it began behind the Spielberg movie screen to as narrow as twenty-four inches or so near the Millers' house. Parallel tracks of angle iron were embedded in the flat floor of the tunnel all the way from one end to the other. A long string of outdoor holiday lights — white only — were stretched along the entire distance to provide illumination.

The slope of the tunnel — it ran downhill at a steeper angle than I would have expected — was curious to me, but my ini-

tial impression was that the slope was deliberate. It appeared that the floor of the tunnel dropped about six or seven feet over its short length. A husky winch was bolted to the outside of Doyle's foundation wall and a sturdy stretch of conduit connected it to the house's electrical system. The stout cable from the winch was hooked to one end of an ingenious contraption that was constructed of four sets of skateboard wheels topped with two narrow, interconnected sections of thick plywood, loosely hinged in the middle. The wheels of the makeshift sled fit perfectly into the angle iron tracks that had been set in the tunnel floor.

A flimsy remote-control unit jerry-rigged from a garage-door opener would have allowed Doyle to operate the winch from any location in the tunnel. By climbing prone onto the sled, hanging on, and pressing the remote-control button, Doyle could either slowly extend or retract the cable on the winch, which would either lower the sled farther into the tunnel toward the Millers' house or pull it back up the slope toward his own house.

Simple. Elegant.

Building the tunnel would have been tedious, no doubt. But if Doyle had man-

aged only six inches of fresh digging a day, he could have completed the excavation in a little over a month. A foot a day and he'd have been done in a fortnight. The dirt that he'd removed from the tunnel was undoubtedly part of the weaving contours and berms of Doyle's personal backyard water park.

And the snow thing?

Mystery solved.

54

"You should close that door," I said, after Sam had followed me back downstairs into Doyle's theater.

He hesitated, his bushy brows burdened more with aggravation than curiosity. But he complied. The chatter from the rest of the house disappeared as the door settled against soundproofing gaskets in the jamb.

I stepped across the room. Without fanfare I raised my elbow and pressed on the edge of the movie screen. The frame swung open on its long hinge, revealing Doyle's portal.

Sam stepped closer and leaned inside. He said, "Holy shit."

"Yeah."

Sam did what I had done, although he pulled on fresh latex first. He lifted himself up into the opening behind the movie screen, flicked on the light switch, and stared. I watched his eyes move from the dirt cave, to the angle iron tracks, to the

string of holiday lights, to the winch, to the sled.

I couldn't be sure, of course, but I thought that he was adding things up the same way I had. He didn't say a word at first; he just shook his head slowly. Admiration? Frustration? Amazement? I couldn't tell.

After a couple of minutes silently going over the specific elements and the implications of Doyle's tunnel, he hopped back down from the opening and stood next to me. "This is what you were looking for?" Sam's voice was only a few decibels above a whisper.

"A tunnel, yeah."

"But you thought it was in the crawl space?"

"That was my guess. I figured that was most likely. I thought we'd find the opening underneath the plastic in there."

"You going to tell me how you knew?" he asked.

"No."

"How did you find it?"

"Boredom. Luck."

"Tell me how you knew about it."

"I probably shouldn't have disclosed the tunnel to you, Sam. I absolutely can't rationalize disclosing how I know about it."

For the time being he appeared to accept that. He put his hand on my shoulder, the act of a friend, and said, "Come on. We need to clear out. It's hurry-up-and-wait time."

"Why?" I didn't want to leave; if he'd let me, I was planning to stay and watch the photographers and crime-scene techs do their thing on whatever they discovered in Doyle's tunnel.

"This isn't exactly covered by the search-warrant request we made. I have to amend it and go back to Judge Heller." He paused, filling his ample cheeks with air and exhaling loudly before he spoke again. "And now I'm going to need a fresh warrant for the Millers' house to see how this thing looks from the other end."

He sounded weary. "I thought you'd be excited about this," I said.

"You're thinking Mallory, right?" He looked back up at the opening in the theater wall. "This is how she got out of her house that night? This is the answer to the snow puzzle?"

"Sure. You have to admit that it adds a whole new dimension."

"I've told you before: The fact that the kid didn't leave any footprints in the snow the night she disappeared doesn't mean

521

anything. What's important about this tunnel isn't that now we know how Mallory got out of the Miller house. That's not why the tunnel's here. What's important about this tunnel is that now we know how Doyle got into the Miller house.

"What we still don't know is why. Why did the guy living next door want this kind of access?"

Sam had a point. "He certainly went to a lot of trouble, didn't he?"

"This is the sort of thing bank robbers used to dig to get into a vault full of cash. But if Doyle Chandler wanted to bust into the Millers' house to steal, why do all this? People bust into houses all the time. And they get away with it, neighbors even. They pick locks, break windows. But this tunnel wasn't built for some one-time burglary. This was built for long-term access. Bill Miller never reported a burglary at that house. If Doyle wasn't stealing from them, why did he want in so badly?"

"Mallory?" I said in reply to Sam's question.

"Yeah, maybe it's that simple, maybe he was a perv. Time will tell."

"What if your underlying assumption is wrong, Sam? What if she didn't run? What if Doyle took Mallory out through the

tunnel? What if that's why he wanted access to the Millers' house?"

Sam closed his eyes and his body stilled as though he were narcoleptic and he'd suddenly started sleeping standing up. For a moment even the act of breathing wasn't apparent. Finally, he opened his eyes and said, "Again, why? There are easier ways, and there's a lot we don't know."

"Like?"

"Like . . . where does this thing come out in the Millers' house? Why didn't we spot it last month? That house got more attention than the new girl at a titty bar."

"You weren't looking for a tunnel. I wouldn't have found this if I didn't suspect it was here." I actually didn't feel like admitting to Sam that what I'd been looking for when I stumbled on the tunnel was Doyle's fancy remote control. "Who would have guessed that somebody had dug a tunnel into his neighbor's house? Who does things like that?"

Sam eyed me suspiciously. "You didn't go down there, did you? To the other end? Tell me you didn't mess with this evidence."

"I went no farther in than you did."

I waited in the vacant living room while

523

Sam went through the house ordering all the search personnel to pack up their equipment and immediately leave Doyle Chandler's home. While he was upstairs I ambled over to the southern window in the living room and checked to see if I could spot the familiar silhouette in the front upstairs window of the Millers' house. I couldn't.

Sam was the last to clear out.

"Not a word," he said to me as we approached the front door.

"What do you mean?"

"I don't want Bill Miller to know we're heading over there. All I've told the team is that I'm modifying the affidavit. They don't know about the tunnel yet."

I made a zip-it motion over my lips.

Sam clarified. "Not even Lauren."

"She's probably asleep. I'll tell her in the morning."

"That's fine. You can tell her in the morning. But you can't tell your source. Your patient, whatever."

I looked at him quizzically.

"Because I know you aren't clairvoyant, I also know that somebody told you about the existence of this tunnel. It wasn't Doyle Chandler since I don't think he's done much chatting to anybody over the

last few days. So it was someone else. Maybe the Camaro guy, maybe not. Doesn't matter. Keep the discovery of the tunnel to yourself."

"I understand."

"Wait." He glared at me. "You weren't seeing the kid for therapy, were you?"

"Mallory? No."

The glare degraded into a face that was merely suspicious. "Was Diane?"

I shook my head. I was glad I wasn't hooked up to a polygraph.

"No bullshit?"

"No bullshit."

"And your guy's still missing, right?"

"Who?"

"The Camaro guy? You haven't talked to him."

For the moment, I'd almost forgotten about Bob's plight. "Yes, he's still missing, and no, I haven't talked to him."

Sam kept his eyes on mine for a few seconds after I answered his question. He was trying, I thought, to decide whether or not he believed me.

"There's something else to wonder about, too," he said.

"What?"

"Say the Camaro guy knew about the tunnel. What's his part in all this? You're

afraid he's a victim. Not me. I'm seeing his name on our list of suspects. Everything's in play again, Alan. Everything from Christmas Day on." He opened his eyes wide in amazement. "And I'm right in the f-ing middle of it."

It was at that moment that I stopped waiting for Sam to thank me for my help in discovering the tunnel. It was apparent he wasn't too happy about being right in the f-ing middle of whatever the tunnel represented.

"Sam, Mallory could be alone somewhere. If you guys have been wrong all along — if she didn't run, if she was abducted by Doyle . . . well, Doyle's dead. She could be locked in some crappy cabin up in the mountains all by herself. She may not have food or water. It's freezing outside. She may need help."

"I know all that."

"Did you guys find out where Doyle's been living since he moved out of here?"

Sam just shook his head. "We have a cell number, that's all. He was pretty intent on keeping his profile low."

"Why?" I asked.

"We don't know."

"You don't know or you won't tell me?"

"We don't know," Sam admitted.

"Did you find his car?"

"Truck, but no."

Finally, he opened the front door and allowed me to walk out in front of him. "Go home. We can do this," he said.

I thought he was trying to convince himself, but I kept that thought to myself.

55

I took advantage of the cover provided by the cluster of crime-scene techs still huddled outside the front door of Doyle's house and immediately cut across the neighbor's front lawn toward my car. I was hoping that Bill Miller hadn't spotted me either arriving or leaving, but I didn't turn around to check for his silhouette at the window.

The night had turned cold, bitter cold, so cold that the snow on the ground squeaked beneath my feet with each step. I raised the collar on my jacket and stuffed my hands as deeply into my pockets as I could. A breeze was blowing down from the north and I lowered my face to retard the harsh chill of the Canadian air. Each fresh gust cut at my skin like a shard of glass.

"I thought that was you over there."

Someone was leaning against the hood of my Audi wagon, bundled in a ski parka, a wool cap pulled all the way down past

the ears. It took me a moment to process the available data — first, that the person was a man, and second, that the man was probably Bill Miller.

"Good evening," I said. I thought I'd managed a pretty fair attempt at disguising my fluster.

"We need to talk," he said.

Politely, I said, "Well, we have a time set up, I think. I don't have my calendar with me." I didn't really expect my parry to work, but mounting it seemed like a necessity.

It didn't work.

"No, now. You're back in my neighborhood. And you're here with a whole shitload of police. That means we talk tonight. Is that too much to ask?"

Shitload? That wasn't a Bill Miller word.

I was starting to shiver from the cold. I was dressed to travel short distances between warm houses and cars with seat heaters. I wasn't dressed warmly enough to linger on a Boulder sidewalk in January in the face of a north wind.

"It's not appropriate for me to see you here, Bill. This isn't the place for a professional meeting."

"You want to come over to my house?"

The tone of the question was appropri-

ately sarcastic. When I didn't reply, he added, "Or I could follow you over to your office. That would be fine with me, too."

My fingers clumsy, I fumbled for the tiny button on the key that would unlock the doors on the Audi. "Let's get out of the cold. At least tell me what's on your mind."

Bill's ski parka was noisy. The nylon or Gore-Tex or whatever the sleek fabric was rustled and crackled as he settled into the front seat of my car. I waited patiently for the crinkling to diminish, and I used the time to put the key in the ignition, start the engine, and flick on the seat heaters. Truth be told, the seat heaters were half the reason I'd bought the Audi. I never knew it before I tried seat heaters for the first time, but it turned out that if my butt was warm, I was warm.

What an epiphany.

I tried to guess what was coming next from Bill Miller. On that front, I was drawing a blank.

Bill pulled his cap back so that it sat high on the crown of his head like a kid's beanie. He stared at me. In another circumstance I would have found the portrait humorous, and might have laughed. Not that day, though. Not those circumstances.

"Yes?" I said.

Bill turned his whole body on the seat, locking his eyes on mine. His parka erupted in fresh crackles and I concluded that the fabric wasn't Gore-Tex. It would be quieter. He said, "In Las Vegas? Where Rachel is? There's this guy named Canada."

Holy moly, I thought. *Holy moly.*

56

I had no way knowing it, of course, and wouldn't learn about it until much later when he told me the story, but at that moment Raoul was in circumstances similar to my own.

Similar, not identical.

The weather, he told me, was warm in Las Vegas, the air in Nevada's southern desert hovering in the low seventies. Needless to say, no one was wearing a ski parka or a wool cap. And no one in his right mind was flicking on an electric seat heater.

But, like me, Raoul was thinking about Canada.

The man sitting in the driver's seat of the car in which Raoul was a passenger was wearing a cap, but Raoul wasn't totally certain what the cap was made of. Not wool. The stuff seemed to be part of the stretchy family of fabrics ideally suited to follow the curves dictated by women's

swimwear. The cap hugged the contours of the man's shaved skull and was a dark enough charcoal to be mistaken for black. His shirt wasn't Gore-Tex; it was a sleeveless, well-ventilated version of the kind of shell that boogie boarders use to retard board rash. Raoul thought the random vertical ventilation slits in the garment had been fashioned with a razor blade. All the man had on his feet were fluorescent orange flip-flops with rubber soles that had been worn almost all the way through at the heels.

"You carrying?" he asked Raoul. "I'm gonna be checking later. Tell me now be better."

Raoul said, "No, nothing."

"Cell phone?"

"The cabbie who dropped me off took it. I'd love to have it back."

"I'll look into it," he said. They pulled to a stop at a red light. "U.P. doesn't fuck around. You have to know that. Just go back home wherever that is, you don't know that. Don't even."

The car was an old VW bug, similar to the first car Raoul purchased in America decades earlier after ignoring the expiration of his student visa. From dashboard clues Raoul guessed that it was a late '60s

vintage, one of the models that came just before what Raoul considered to be the particularly ill-advised bumper design change in '68. The Beetle still had the original beige paint, and the original radio. From the scratchy sound of the hip-hop that was playing, the car had its original speaker, too.

Raoul liked the car. It brought back memories of uncomplicated times.

The man's ethnic background and racial makeup were a puzzle, even to Raoul, who prided himself on his ability to distinguish a Montenegran from a Serb or an Egyptian from an Iraqi across a crowded café. The driver definitely had some Asian blood — Raoul was guessing Tibet — and some African American blood as well, but something else was mixed into his DNA cocktail, too, something Raoul couldn't quite put his finger on.

"U.P. is Canada? Just want to be clear," he asked.

The man nodded. "Don't go talking to him that way. People call him that, but people don't *call* him that. You dig?" He shifted through the car's four gears as though it were as natural as breathing, moving the stick with the middle finger of his right hand or with the webbing at the

base of his thumb, never allowing the engine's RPMs to climb into the whining range.

"Thank you for that advice," Raoul said. "How would you suggest I address him?"

The man seemed honestly perplexed by the question.

"What do you call him?" Raoul asked.

"Boss."

"That doesn't sound appropriate. How about Mr. North?"

He thought for a moment. "That'll work."

"What's your name?"

"Tico."

"Thank you, Tico."

"Hey."

After a few days tracking his wife, Raoul knew enough about Las Vegas to know that the VW was traveling away from whatever version of civilization the Strip represented on the other side of downtown. He also knew he'd never been in that particular neighborhood before. Literally, or figuratively.

After Raoul had called Norm Clarke late on Thursday to ask him to warn Canada that the Vegas cops were going to start se-

riously looking for Diane, Raoul had spent some restless hours waiting to hear back. Norm had finally called Raoul and told him that another meeting was arranged with Canada, and that he should wait in a specific spot outside the meeting-room entrance of the Venetian at 11:30 that night. The man who picked him up had been an old blond guy driving a Vegas cab that was even crappier than the typically crappy Vegas cab. The driver had what appeared to be corn silk growing out of his ears, and he smoked like a crematorium during the Plague. For the short drive down the Strip the taxi was thick with a fetid Marlboro cloud.

Raoul spent much of the next twenty or so hours in a vintage — as in "old," not in "classic" — sixteen-foot Airstream that had been left forlorn in one of the trailer-park slums that stain the arid fields on Tropicana Boulevard just a few blocks from the faux munificence of the Strip. The not-so-mobile villages — anachronistic oases of transiency, poverty, and despair — consumed conspicuously undesirable real estate within spitting distance of the end of the runways at McCarran International. Raoul's Airstream hovel appeared to have been in the same spot in that park

so long that it looked like the rest of the place was choreographed around it.

Raoul had been alone in the trailer since he'd been dropped off. He'd killed off the long hours counting takeoffs and landings, studying a couple of blackjack manuals printed in the late '60s, and watching local Vegas news for nuggets about his wife. The TV was a tiny black-and-white with rabbit ears that reached all the way to the concave ceiling of the Airstream. The view out the filthy awning window at the rear of the trailer was of the blunt end of an old Winnebago. The plates on the RV were long gone, the aluminum skin pitted, the paint faded to nothing, and the bumper stickers so sun-bleached that Raoul could only make out the one that was once a lure for Crater Lake. Raoul tried to get lost in imagining cool, deep water and high country air. Couldn't.

He was trying hard not to think about whatever was happening with Diane. Couldn't do that, either.

Before he'd assured Raoul that someone would come soon to pick him up and take him to see Canada, the cabbie had instructed him not to wander outside the trailer.

"What about food?" Raoul asked.

"Help yourself to whatever's there," the guy had said.

The only food in the Airstream cupboards, it turned out, was a yellow box of cornstarch, a rusty can without a label, and an old margarine tub that was half full of something that resembled ground chilis.

The water from the faucet smelled like a rat had peed in it.

Raoul had decided it was a good day to start a cleansing fast.

Despite his hunger and his impatience and a lot of apprehension, Raoul eventually got it. The last piece of Tico's heritage puzzle?

Pacific islands. Maybe even Hawaii. Raoul smiled to himself, momentarily savoring the unknowable hows and the whys of the lives that had intersected and the passions that had collided and ultimately melded together in the startling mitotic process that had eventually created this Tibetan/Pacific Islander/African American who was driving a classic old German car out into the scruffy desert beyond the urban boundaries of Las Vegas, Nevada.

But, right then, in Tico's VW bug, Raoul was — like me — thinking mostly about Diane, and about Canada.

Canada was never far from his mind.

57

"I don't understand what you're saying, Bill."

I'd actually already made a guess. Bill was continuing the conversation we'd had earlier that day in my office, the one about all he did to support Rachel in her home away from home in Nevada.

"The caretaker for Rachel in Vegas? It's a guy. Canada's a guy. Canada — it's his name. Street name, I don't know. He's, um, kind of adopted Rachel. He looks after her. Keeps her safe. I owe him a lot for what he's done over the years. I'm . . . grateful to him."

Kind of adopted? What does that mean?

Bill's sentences came out in a series of discrete bursts. Each succeeding sentence was tagged on as though it were a complete afterthought to what had come before. The choppy cadence was something I'd never heard before from him, which told me that he was feeling something right

then that he hadn't felt before in my presence. What was that? What was he feeling?

Anxious was the best descriptor I could conjure. As an explanation though, it felt insufficient.

I said, "Okay." I didn't feel anything remotely resembling okay, but that's what I said.

"You know about him already?" he asked me.

"About who?" I stammered.

"Canada?"

"I don't know what you're talking about."

It was a lie. Was it a smooth lie? Probably not. I lie like I ski. Not as well as most people I know, and my form tends to leave a lot to be desired.

"Canada's help doesn't come cheap. These things are expensive."

These things? Was Bill telling me that he had financial issues about Rachel's care after all? I had the good sense to stay quiet while I waited to find out.

But he changed gears. He said, "We've been together, what, three times? You haven't asked me a thing about Mallory. Do you know how weird that is after what I've been through for the last few weeks?"

I thought: *Well, Bill, we've been together,*

what, three times? You haven't really men-
tioned a thing about Mallory, either. Do you
know how weird that is after what you've been
through the last few weeks?

I didn't say that. I said something else that was just as true, though not quite as honest. "It's not my call. I thought you would get there when you were ready."

"Ready? What the hell does that mean? Ready? You've got to be kidding. Hell, what's wrong with you?"

He grew quiet again. I decided to try being a therapist. I said, "You mentioned a man — Canada? — someone you said looks after your wife. And then you obliquely referred to your daughter's situation. Is it possible that there might be a connection of some kind between the two?" I feared that I'd been way too obvious with my question.

"What are you saying?"

"I'm not saying anything. My job as a therapist is to follow closely behind you, see where you're going, look over your shoulder. Hopefully, I can point out things that you don't see or aren't prepared to see."

"And that's what exactly? What are you implying I'm not prepared to see?"

Bill wasn't curious to hear my response,

not in any sincere way. He was challenging me, provoking me, poking a finger into my chest, trying to get me to back off of . . . something.

"You also mentioned money," I added. I added it because I guessed that money was what Bill didn't want to talk about.

"No, you're the one who mentioned money."

"This afternoon, I did. Tonight, you did."

"All I said is that it's expensive."

I was too tired for verbal sparring. I wanted to go home, hug my wife, hold my daughter, play with my dogs. Eat something hot. Drink something with alcohol in it. I wanted to spend a couple of hours without anyone doing any inferring or any implying or any alluding. My impulse to flee felt selfish and cowardly, at least partly because I was certain that I was missing something that a more contemplative person would see, but I tried for an out anyway. "Bill, these are important things for you, obviously. But I don't see any reason that they can't wait until our scheduled appointment time."

Something about my suggestion seemed to shake him free, allow him to change tracks again. Not exactly what I had hoped

for, but at least momentarily I felt the air between us settle.

"What was going on next door?" he asked. "Why all the cops? Nobody will talk to me. I can't reach my lawyer."

"I can't say. The police asked for my help with something."

"Is it about my daughter?"

"I'm sorry. I've promised them that I wouldn't discuss it."

"Is it?"

"Bill, I'm sorry. I can't say what it is. I can't say what it's not. I've been told not to discuss it."

"Doyle gave them permission to go into his house?"

Doyle's dead, Bill. His giving-permission days are behind him, I thought as I replayed Bill's question in my head, tasting for disingenuousness. I was wondering if Bill already knew that Doyle was dead.

"I'm sorry."

"This is bullshit." Bill's voice suddenly became a hoarse whisper and the anger in it was unmistakable. "If this is the way it's going to be, I'm not sure I can continue seeing you."

If that was a threat, it was lame, like holding a rubber knife to my throat. "That's certainly your choice, Bill. I'll be

543

happy to make a referral, if you would like."

"Yeah," he scoffed. "That worked out well last time."

And what does that mean? Mary Black bent over backward to help Rachel.

"Mallory saw a therapist. Did you know that?" he asked.

I was startled. I managed a flustered, "What?"

"The woman who died. Mallory went to see her a couple of weeks before Christmas. She didn't tell me; she left a note about it in her journal."

I had a thousand questions. One of them was: *Have you told the police about that journal?* I chose a different one: "Why did she see a therapist?"

"I don't know that exactly."

"Do the police know? The therapist may have left some . . . records behind."

He didn't answer my question. He cracked open the door of the car and prepared to climb out, but stopped. "Do you know anything about her? Are you keeping something from me? You wouldn't do that, would you?"

Now those were tough questions. I didn't have an immediate answer for any of them.

"I'm talking father to father right now, Alan. Father to father."

"I wish I knew something that could help you find your daughter. I'd tell you if I did."

He considered my words, tasting them for the sweetness of truth. "You're a father. You have a daughter, too. Imagine losing her. You have to understand the vulnerability I'm feeling."

I swallowed. I didn't want to be reminded of that vulnerability.

Bill went on. "A father would do anything to protect his family. Anything. You know that. The things that can happen to kids? Daughters. You wouldn't wish that on me, would you? I wouldn't wish it on you."

I immediately began pondering the question of how truthful my answer had been. Surprisingly, I decided that, other than the existence of the tunnel, and the fact that I knew she'd seen Hannah for a single therapy session, I didn't actually know anything substantive about Mallory. I really didn't. How odd.

"You wouldn't divulge our conversations to the police, would you?"

"Of course not," I said. I wondered how much Bill really knew about Mallory's sit-

uation. "What do you think happened to Mallory? Did she run? Was she abducted?"

"Those are the only options?" he said.

What? Was he taunting me? "I'm not sure what you're saying."

"Why would she run?" Bill asked.

"Kids aren't always rational, Bill. Especially when they're distraught."

"She was distraught. Christmas was always hard for her," Bill said. "Always. But I thought we were doing okay this year."

That's what Bob had said, too — that Christmas was hard for Mallory. *Huh.* I reminded myself that Rachel had deserted her family during the holidays years before, and that it wouldn't be surprising that Mallory was suffering an anniversary reaction.

"You were doing okay, you and she?" I asked.

"What are you asking?"

"Nothing. I'm fishing."

"Fishing?"

Bill hovered, half-in, half-out of my car for a long three-count before he stood. I sat frozen in place, still troubled by Bill's admission that he possessed a diary from his daughter that he hadn't shared with the police. "Let's do this in the morning, Bill. At my office. Is ten okay?"

He held up his gloved right hand and extended two fingers. "Can't do ten. I'll be there at two," he said before he slammed the door.

The bitter air had frosted the hairs inside my nose.

But I did notice that my ass was nice and warm.

58

The same night, at almost the same time, Raoul was still thinking about Diane and Canada.

He told me later that he was surprised to see how Las Vegas bleeds out into the northern desert. There is no natural demarcation, no river, no ridge, no rail at the craps table. There is no single line in the dirt and sand where a visitor would say, well, this here is Las Vegas, and that there isn't. At some point you know you've left town, but even if someone offered you to-die-for odds, you couldn't go back and find the precise spot where it happened.

Raoul looked back over his shoulder at the profile of the distant Strip that stained the near horizon with artificial vertical interruptions and radiating flashes of neon. He guessed that he and Tico were about five miles outside of town. It could have been seven, could have been three, but he was guessing five.

Tico had yanked the VW through a lot of turns to get where they were, many more than Raoul thought should be necessary to get from point A to point B across a landscape of flat, mostly barren land. But the turns had accomplished what Tico had intended: Other than being some number of miles out in the desert north of Las Vegas, Raoul didn't know where he was.

Wide expanses of scruffy land separated the houses. In some other place, somewhere where the soil was arable, such distances between homes might make sense, but in the desert outside Vegas it seemed to Raoul that people lived as far apart as possible simply so that they could feel some separation. In Colorado's mountains, a ridge or an outcropping of rock or a thick stand of lodgepole pine was enough to leave neighbors feeling distinct from one another. Out in this endless desert, though, the geography made no natural allowances for privacy, and separation apparently meant space.

Tico doused the headlights on the VW a few hundred yards before he pulled to a stop at an expensive wrought iron gate in an even more expensive high stucco wall. There wasn't much of a moon and the desert was dark. Raoul couldn't tell where

Tico had taken him, but he was guessing the building was a residence. Tico waved casually toward a security camera mounted on the stucco wall, and seconds later the gates clanked loudly and started to swing inward.

The place wasn't much to look at. It was a sprawling, low-slung ranch with long overhanging rooflines designed to protect inhabitants from the relentless Nevada sun. Raoul dated the construction from the '60s or '70s. Somebody had once tried to do some landscaping, but the effort had been abandoned a long time before. Tall, vaguely Greek planting urns sat forlorn and empty at intervals around the property. Adjacent to the crumbling concrete driveway a swimming pool shaped like a spade was a third filled with murky water. The front of the separate pool house was almost totally obscured by junk. The shadowed symmetry of the red tile roof on the shack was interrupted by broken and absent tiles and what looked to be an abandoned array of solar panels.

Raoul said, "That fence we went through is worth more than the house."

"Boss isn't picky about stuff. Everything's temporary but people. That's what he says, says it all the time."

"I take it he doesn't swim."

"Don't go there, man." Tico smiled. "Don't go there. Uh, uh. No swimming jokes, you dig?"

"Yes," Raoul said. "Thanks. Does he live here?" He didn't expect to get an answer and was surprised when Tico decided to give him one.

"Stays here sometimes. Other places, too. A lot. He lives where he happens to be. At some point soon enough this place will get sold. They be another, and another after that. Like that. He gets 'em. Gets rid of 'em. We move on."

"The Airstream?"

Tico smiled. "Had that one for a while. May be gone now, too." He killed the tiny engine on the bug. For a moment the clatter of the valves was the loudest sound in Raoul's ears.

Raoul said, "Your boss and me have that in common. Buying and selling. I'm a bit of a speculator, too." Initially Raoul thought Tico had been considering saying something in reply, but had thought better of it. "You have some advice for me?"

"Advice?" Tico adjusted the fabric that clung to his shaved skull, pulling it tighter toward his ears, tight enough that a phrenologist could have done a comprehensive

exam without removing the cap. "Whatever you think is about to happen here, bro, you wrong. That's my advice for you. If you think you here 'cause you want to talk to U.P., you wrong. Want to know why you here? You here 'cause U.P. want to talk to you. No other damn reason." He opened the door and hopped out of the car. "I need to pat you down now. No offense."

Raoul joined him on the driveway and lifted his arms. "None taken. I apologize for the smell. The shower in the Airstream wasn't working."

59

A frosty halo was framing what was visible of the moon as I turned east on Baseline toward my house. Most days, late rush-hour traffic would have dictated that I take South Boulder Road across the valley, but that night, because of the hour, I took Baseline. I was stopped at the traffic signal at the Foothills Parkway when my cell chirped in my pocket. I fished it out, managed to hit a tiny button with my almost frozen fingers, and said, "I'll be home soon, I promise. I'm on my way. I'm sorry."

But it wasn't Lauren. It was Sam.

"Sweet," he said. "Total capitulation. I find that so attractive in a man. Where are you?"

"Baseline. Across from Safeway."

"Good, you're close. Come on over to the department. I want to show you something."

"Now?"

"You'll want to see this."

The signal arrow turned green. I checked my mirrors and cut across two lanes of the intersection to make one of the more illegal left turns in Boulder history, and accelerated back toward Arapahoe.

"Tell me," I said.

He of little patience said, "Patience."

I arrived at the Public Safety Building on Thirty-third Street within minutes and parked on the deserted street out front. Sam was pacing in the public lobby, eating the last few bites of a Chipotle burrito that I knew had originally been almost the size of a loaf of Wonder Bread. My stomach growled at the tantalizing smell.

"Chicken?"

"Carnitas. Not too much fat. Niman Ranch pork. No hormones or shit. I get them with no sour cream, no cheese. Living in Boulder is finally starting to rub off on me." He stuffed a final chunk of burrito into his mouth. "Probably too much salt, though. Whatever, it's a treat. A year ago I probably would have been sucking that white shit out of the middle of a Twinkie."

"Got any more?" I asked.

"Ha. Come on," he said, balling up the tinfoil and dropping it into a trash can by the reception counter. He wiped his mus-

tache with a napkin and tossed that away, too.

"You already revise your warrant?" I asked.

"Just waiting on Judge Heller and then we head back to the Hill for round two."

I followed him down the central corridor to a detective's work area that was set up with a video monitor. The detritus of a few other investigations and the refuse of a few other recent fast-food meals littered the surface of three laminated tables that had been pushed into a clumsy U-shape.

Detectives cleaned up crimes; they apparently didn't clean up after themselves.

"Make yourself comfortable," he said, pointing to a chair that didn't scream "comfort."

"I'd be more comfortable home in bed."

"Yeah," he said wistfully, but without any empathy whatsoever.

I sat. "What is it you wanted me to see?"

He gestured at the AV setup. "You tell me."

He flicked on the monitor and used a remote control to start a VCR. After a moment's whirring the familiar logo of the local Fox news affiliate filled the screen.

"We recorded this off the air. TiVo. Somebody upstairs transferred it to tape

for me to play with. VCRs I can handle, barely. TiVo? Sorry, I don't TiVo." He chuckled at something. "Department has frigging TiVo. When I got here we had yellow squad cars."

I ignored the fact that the allusion made no particular sense and smiled at the memory of the banana-colored patrol cars that Boulder's cops had driven around town for a while as part of a short-lived, amusing experiment in community-friendly policing.

I expected I was about to watch tape of the local Fox affiliate's coverage of the discovery of Doyle Chandler's body near Allenspark that afternoon. Why? Sam would tell me when he was ready. Not before. But Sam surprised me, as he often did.

"Christmas night," Sam said as the screen showed Fox's infamous Mallory Miller money shot: the helicopter footage of the Hill on Christmas night, the tape that purportedly showed no footprints or tire tracks leaving the Millers' home after the snow started falling in earnest.

"You oriented?" he asked.

"Yes." I'd seen the footage often enough to know what was what. If you lived in Colorado in the days after Mallory's dis-

appearance and had turned on your TV set, you had seen this film as many times as you'd seen the other little Boulder girl dancing around at beauty pageants.

Sam paused the screen, picked up a laser pointer, and let the red dot settle. "Harts' house."

"Got it." The holiday lights were unmistakable.

"Millers' house and Doyle Chandler's house are over here." He made a dot appear on the wall behind the monitor.

"Right where they've always been."

"Fox has been kind enough to superimpose the time line on the bottom of the screen." He started the tape again. "Here's where the controversy starts: nine-sixteen."

The footage was the enhanced version that Fox had promoted and promoted and promoted a few days after Christmas. It was the clip that started at 9:16 on Christmas night and stopped a couple of minutes later with the famous few seconds that showed no footprints or tire tracks leaving the Millers' home.

"I've seen this," I said.

"Yeah, but have you *seen* it? Start with your eyes at the lower-right corner of the screen — here, Doyle Chandler's garage." He paused the footage momentarily. The

Harts' house was in the center of the screen; Doyle's house, but not the Millers' house, was visible on the lower edge.

I'd never noticed that Doyle's house showed up in the early moments of the Fox footage. Sam said, "That's smooth snow around the garage, right?"

"Yes."

"Fresh? You're sure."

"Yes."

"Well, keep your eye on the garage as the chopper moves around. With the distraction of the Christmas lights and the shadows it's kind of hard to follow, but try."

Sam aided me with his laser pointer; he was remarkably adept at keeping the red dot targeted on the dark mass of Doyle's garage. As the angle of the shot varied with the helicopter's movement the garage would frequently shift totally out of the frame; one long absence lasted for a good half minute, another for almost as long.

I stated the obvious. "Can't see it most of the time, Sam. It goes off the screen."

"I know. It's important that you can't see it. The last few seconds are coming — watch carefully."

Fox hadn't enhanced the area on the footage that included Doyle's garage —

they'd focused all their technological wizardry efforts on the Millers' property — and it wasn't easy to discern much detail in other parts of the frame, especially with the startling bright lights that stayed mostly centered on the screen, lights that were emanating from the garish Christmas display at the Harts' house on the next block.

The Very Hart of Christmas.

"There," Sam said. He paused the tape and allowed the red dot to linger on the short driveway that led from Doyle's garage to the alley. "What do you see now?"

I stood up and moved closer to the monitor. The closer I got, the larger the pixels on the screen appeared. At first I wasn't sure what I was seeing, or even if I was seeing anything at all. Then I was.

I turned and faced Sam. "Are those . . . tire tracks leaving Doyle's garage?" I asked. "Those weren't there at the beginning."

"Yeah, that's what I see, too," Sam said. His tone was understated and self-satisfied.

Bob, I thought. Bob had pulled his Camaro out of Doyle's garage during the second extended period that the garage was out of the frame.

The tunnel. The damn tunnel.

The damn movie in the damn theater in the damn basement.

Did Bob really have something to do with Mallory's disappearance?

I was shocked. "Did he help her leave, Sam? Or did he take her?"

I didn't have to say who "he" was. He knew I was talking about Bob.

"You don't know where he is, do you?" Sam asked.

"No, I told you I didn't. I don't."

"This isn't some therapist nice-nice secret-secret bullshit?"

"I don't know where he is."

"You know where to look for him?"

I hesitated for a split second. "No."

Sam made a guttural noise — okay, he growled at me — and mouthed a dry "f" sound. It didn't take much lip-reading skill to know what exactly he'd thought about saying.

"I really don't, Sam. If I did, I'd tell you. Given what already happened to Doyle, Bob could be in danger, too. I would tell you if I knew."

He wasn't satisfied. "You know something, don't you? You know something that could help me? Something you're not telling me?"

"Sam . . ."

"Man . . ." He stood up quickly, almost knocking his chair over.

Five minutes later Sam walked me back to my car. He seemed impervious to the cold. I bet he didn't even care that his Cherokee didn't have seat heaters.

"Chinooks tomorrow," Sam said.

"They thought they were coming today, too. They're wrong a lot," I replied, wondering why we were talking about the weather. "If the Chinooks do start to blow, at least it will warm things up a little. It's too cold."

"The media isn't going to know what to do with those winds," Sam said. "Should be fun."

"What?"

"They'll be back tomorrow. You know they will. With word of the tunnel and the Doyle Chandler situation? All the trucks and all the cameras — they'll all be back outside the Millers' house doing their stupid live shots. The idiot lawyers on cable will all be saying we blew it again. Us, the Boulder cops. 'It's just like Christmas eight years ago,' that's what they'll say. But then the Chinooks will start blowing late morning and they'll blow the goddamn experts all the goddamn way to

Denver, maybe farther. It'll be too windy to raise the antennas on their trucks. I wish I could be there; it'll be fun to watch."

I checked his expression. He was truly sorry he was going to miss it.

"I'm going to tell Lauren about all this, Sam. The tunnel, Doyle, Bob," I said. "I need some advice from her."

"Tell her to sit on it till morning. Our bases will be pretty well covered in the next couple of hours. Get some sleep for me tonight." He stuffed his hands in his pockets. "I don't think I'll be getting much."

"How did you put this together?" I asked as I clicked open the wagon doors with the key remote. "The Camaro? Why did you decide to go back and look at that tape?"

"This is far from together. The tunnel changes everything. One of the things it changes is which house we should be paying attention to. Where Mallory's disappearance is concerned, we've had our eyes on the Miller house, not on Doyle Chandler's house. On the way back here to amend the warrant app I remembered that you had asked me if there was a car in Doyle's garage when we searched the house the day after Mallory disappeared. I told you I didn't think so, but it's been

something I've been meaning to ask your patient Bob about if we ever caught up with him."

"But you decided to check the Fox footage instead? Smart, Sammy. So do you have a theory to explain all this? Does to-night — the tunnel and this video — does it change your thinking about her disappearance? You still sure she's a runaway?"

"I have a few theories," he said. "How many do you have?"

He waited for me to answer.

When I didn't, he added, "Thought so. I'll show you mine if you'll show me yours."

I left the show-and-tell right there. "You still want to run in the morning? I'm happy to bag it if you're too busy."

"I want to run," he said. "No excuses. Since it's Saturday, I'll let you sleep in. Come outside at seven-thirty — I don't want to ring the bell."

60

I finally made it home from the police station, took the dogs out for a last time, climbed into bed, and rubbed Lauren's back until she awakened. Although I left a few names and a few details out of my story, I told her enough of what I knew that she understood the magnitude of my dilemma. I finished by asking for her advice.

Her counsel was succinct. "Higher, on my neck. Right there."

"That's it?"

"No, that's not it. On one hand you know a lot. On the other hand you don't know much. You need to leverage what you have. Save Diane no matter what it takes, screw the rest."

"It's all that clear to you? I could get censured, lose my license."

She rolled over and faced me. My eyes were adjusting to the dark and I could see the shimmer of her irises. She said, "You'd have to sleep with a patient, kill her, and

then have sacrilegious sex with her dead body before that spineless state board would yank your license, and you know it. But what if they do? You and me and Grace? We'll make it if you have to change careers. We will. Will you make it if you knew you could have done something that might have helped Diane and you didn't do it? I don't think so. You're pussyfooting around this, Alan. The rules need to be broken sometimes. This is one of those times. Break the damn rules, save your friend, suffer the consequences. You won't be able to live with any other choice, you know that."

"Just like that?"

"Just like that."

She reached a warm arm out from under the comforter, put her fingers on the side of my neck, and lowered her voice to a late-night whisper. "There's some things I know about you, sweetie: You're a better cook when you're not too hungry. You're a better dad when you're not feeling too protective. And you're a better lover when you're not too horny."

"You have a point?"

"You want this to be right too much, and it's clouding your judgment. Step back. Take off your therapist hat. Be a friend,

first. You'll know what to do."

I didn't have to think long to know that her advice was sound.

"What?" she said, sensing something.

"I'm a better lover when I'm not too horny? Really?"

She smiled and shrugged. She dropped her hand so that it slid down my bare chest. "You want to prove otherwise?"

The truth was, I didn't. Not right then.

61

The way he told it to me later, Raoul's evening, like mine, ended with just the slightest ray of hope.

More quarry tile than he had seen in a long, long time. Big tiles — eighteen-inch squares. Brick-red, uneven surfaces, with dirty grout lines as fat as a grown man's finger. The tile extended through every doorway, down every hall. This house was apparently where the awful quarry tile from that dubious '70s design burp had gone to die.

Raoul had expected to find a posse surrounding Canada, a jury of pathetic hangers-on. He'd expected to have to weed through a motley assortment of tougher-than-shit Cristal and Courvoisier-and-Coke-drinking parasites.

Instead he found a fit, barefoot man wearing crinkled linen slacks and a faded polo shirt that was the color of the flesh of a ripe mango. The man was sitting on one

of two big armchairs that shared a large, mismatched ottoman and faced floor-to-ceiling sliding glass doors in the living room. His legs were crossed at the ankles. One toenail on his left foot had turned the brown-black of just-roasted coffee beans. It was the toe next to the pinky.

Canada was alone.

"Sit," he said to Raoul.

Tico loitered across the room near the back door where the parking lot of quarry tile started, or ended. He said, "You cool, Boss?"

"Yeah, get yourself something to eat."

Tico saluted with a motion of two fingers flying out from his right nipple. Raoul figured it meant, "Yes, sir." Or something in that vicinity. Tico spun. His flip-flops squealed once before they began a percussive *smack-smack* against the hard floor as he made his way toward the kitchen.

"I can't find her," Canada said. "Come on, sit." He pointed at the chair beside him. "You want something to drink?"

Raoul did, but it could wait. *You can't find whom?* That's what he wanted to know. That couldn't wait. He said, "No, thank you."

He was thinking that U.P. North was late thirties, maybe forty. The man was fair-

skinned with a full head of curly jet-black hair, and he apparently went to some trouble to avoid the desert sun. He was strong. Not I-live-in-the-weight-room strong, but I've-got-a-personal-trainer and I-play-a-heck-of-a-lot-of-tennis strong.

Raoul fought an instinct that was telling him that he knew the man, or at least knew his type. Sometimes in Boulder he met the smug, self-assured, I've-got-shit-going-on-you-don't-even-know-about types at parties. At first impression, U.P. North could be one of them, just another Boulder trust-fund baby. But Raoul cautioned himself that North probably wasn't one of them. Not by a long shot.

Intimidating? Not to Raoul, not yet.

Blood? Northeast U.S., sure. Whatever that means anymore. Some French ancestry, and maybe something else. Could North have some Eastern European blood, maybe Jewish? Raoul wasn't certain. Didn't know if he had enough clues.

Raoul sat. "You can't find her? My wife?"

Three sets of sliding glass doors were open to the night air. The pattern meant that every other panel was glass, every other panel was screen. The prodigious sweat that Raoul had developed while doing time in-

side the Airstream and then compounded in the cramped front seat of Tico's bug wasn't evaporating at all. No breeze was blowing across the wide desert that night.

"I like the heat," the man said as though he'd anticipated Raoul's thoughts. "Hate AC."

Raoul duly noted that his question hadn't been answered and decided not to press it. North wasn't actually talking to Raoul, he was talking to Raoul's reflection in the glass. Raoul adjusted his gaze, found the mirrored image of his host against the black hollow, and did the same. He said, "I changed my mind. I'd love a beer, thank you."

Canada called out, "Tico? A brew for our guest."

Tico came and went. He left behind a long-necked Bud that was sweating even more than Raoul. The bottle immediately left a round tattoo on the table.

"You like the desert?" Canada asked.

"I grew up on the Mediterranean," Raoul said as a way of answering. "Live in the mountains now."

"I grew up on Long Island, not far from Jones Beach. I like the desert better."

"Taste," Raoul said. "It's a personal thing."

North chewed on that for a moment. "There's some shit we do that has nothing to do with taste. It has to do with cycles. Ebb and flow. Moon and tides. Sunrise, sunset. You play golf?"

"Some. I suck," Raoul said.

North laughed. "Bastard game. In golf . . . in business . . . with women . . . dear Lord, with women . . . all the time, I'm big on mulligans. I . . . treasure the living that happens in the echoes. Like to think I do some of my best work in the echoes."

"The echoes?"

"The opportunities that come back around. The do-overs. A man has to learn in life. He has to. In golf, it's not really that satisfying. It's hard to learn enough from one tee shot to the next. If you do better on your mulligan than you did on your first drive, could be dumb luck. Probably is dumb luck. In life, though, the do-overs tend to come around less often. That gives the wise man time to adjust, to be grateful for the opportunity, to make the most of the blessing of the second chance. You're a successful man. You must know about the echoes. Every successful man I've ever met knows about playing the echoes."

Raoul drank enough of the Bud that when he pulled the bottle back down from

his lips the beer leveled off at a line about two thirds of the way down the label. He said, "If I'm understanding you right, I think maybe I do know about the echoes."

"Rachel's one of my echoes." Canada's eyes locked on Raoul's in the black mirror of the glass. He held Raoul's gaze like a strong man holds a handshake — a few beats too long, just to prove that he can do it. "She's a paranoid schizophrenic. You know about that?"

Raoul decided the time was right to once again interject Diane into the conversation. "My wife's a psychologist. I learn some things from her."

North nodded. Raoul translated the nod to mean, "Whatever."

"My mother was one, too. A paranoid schiz. I watched her do her crazy thing most of the time I was growing up. Nobody helped her out. Not really. People laughed, the ones who didn't avoid us took advantage. She ended up running away with some loser she met in a biker bar. Came home with him, grabbed some things, said she'd be back soon. I never saw her again. I still don't like to think about what happened to her next."

Raoul felt the rhythm of the melody that was developing and decided to skip right

to the chorus. "But for Rachel, you're what happened next?"

"There's the echo. When they come back around, you get another chance. Not all the time, but sometimes. When you do, it's important to get it right. The gods count on it. They keep score."

"You take care of her?"

"I watch out for her. Difference. Nobody can protect her from being crazy. I learned that lesson as a kid. Paranoid schizes have the kind of crazy that comes from someplace else. Someplace where the tiniest wires are jumbled, someplace you and I don't ever get to visit. All I do — all I can do — is I protect her from people who prey. That's all. I let them know if they fuck with her, they have to fuck with me. People in town have learned to leave well enough alone; people new to town need lessons. It's what I wished I could have done for my mother."

Raoul lost the visual connection in the pane of glass as Canada shifted the range of focus from Raoul's eyes to the infinity of the desert night. From inside to out.

"That's generous of you," Raoul said, already wondering whether his empathy was being misapplied.

"Is it?"

Raoul didn't want to argue the point. A linguistic chameleon, he adopted his host's vernacular. "Has someone fucked with her lately?"

"People have been coming in from out of town. It's not been welcome. We've had to deal with it."

Raoul felt the reverberation: Diane had come in from out of town. He put his cards on the table. "My wife flew to Las Vegas looking for Rachel. She had some questions about her daughter — Rachel's missing daughter. I'm sure you know that. Before she was able to meet with Rachel, Diane disappeared off the casino floor at the Venetian. That was Monday night. I'm worried about her, very worried. I'd like to know where she is. I'm happy to tell you what I know."

With just the slightest spice of menace added to his tone — a verbal dash of cayenne — North said, "Doesn't make any difference to me whether or not you're happy. But you will tell me what you know. One thing, though, Raoul. May I call you Raoul?"

"Of course. What's that?"

"It's not all about your wife."

Raoul felt some intimidation then. He shrank a little at the words, had to remind

himself not to cower, and had to remind himself that Canada held all the good cards. "Okay," he said.

"Now, like I said, I can't find her — Rachel. You feel the echo there? Yes, me, too." He exhaled through pursed lips. "I'm not happy I can't find her. Are we in the same boat, Raoul? You and me? The not-happy-I-can't-find-her boat?"

"Are we?" Raoul asked.

"I think so. I think we are."

Raoul dove so far into his host's eyes that he was almost submerged. Sensing something there, he took a last look at his cards and went all-in. "Diane was led out of the Venetian casino on Monday evening by two men. They weren't yours?" He pulled the grainy screen shot that Marlina had given him from his pocket, unfolded it, and handed it to Canada.

"You think they were mine?" Canada asked after a quick glance at the photograph of three people walking through the casino at the Venetian.

Totally cognizant of how provocative his words were, Raoul said, "I did."

"If they were mine, you'd be a dead man. You feel like a dead man?"

"I admit I've felt better."

Canada laughed. A stretch of silence

consumed half a minute before he added, "They're not mine." He raised the photograph, grasping it between his thumb and index finger, and rotated it so that it faced Raoul. "You don't recognize the tall guy? I'm surprised; you seem like an observant man."

Raoul leaned over and squinted at the taller of the two men. "Should I?"

"I hear you call him 'Reverend Howie.' "

"What? *Mierda.* His hair . . ."

"That's not his hair. Probably won it in a poker game."

Raoul had participated in a thousand negotiations, some of them involving tens of millions of dollars. In every deal, instinct was his guide. He relied on that intuition and felt around in the dark for whatever direction he was going to get. "Howie didn't take Diane for you?"

Canada hesitated before he shook his head.

"Do you recognize the other man?" Raoul asked.

Canada took another fleeting glance at the paper. "If I admit I do, what happens then?"

Raoul jumped at the bait. "If Diane's okay, I swear I'll —"

Canada held his left hand out. A stop

sign. "No, my friend. No . . . No. The ifs are all mine. You don't get any ifs. These two people weren't working for me. I don't know what they've done, or to whom. That means there are no ifs left over for you. We clear?"

No, Raoul thought. He said, "Yes."

"Good. I repeat, if I admit I do recognize him, what happens then?"

"I will be grateful for your assistance," Raoul said.

"How grateful?"

Raoul wondered momentarily if Canada was trying to extort some money. He recalled Tico's admonition in the car — *Everything's temporary but people. That's what he says, says it all the time* — and decided that it wasn't likely that Canada was squeezing a reward from him. Raoul said, "I will be completely grateful. So grateful you won't be playing any echoes about this."

"Ever?"

"Ever."

"And if you happen to run across Rachel?"

"Goes without saying. You'll know first."

Canada poked at the photograph. "This guy? The one with Howard? Showed up in town a day or so before your wife, went to

577

Rachel's apartment looking for her, failed, then started asking around about how to find her. Howard alerted us that the guy came to the chapel. Howard, it now appears, was playing both ends against the middle. Well, that's a tougher game than Hold 'Em — and soon enough, if he isn't already, Howard will regret he anteed in. We started keeping an eye on the new man. Lost him for a while. Found him again. Eventually he had a traffic accident. Sad thing."

"Serious accident?" Raoul asked.

Canada feigned a sympathetic face. "Misjudged a curve in the mountains. His car had Colorado plates. Tico?" he called.

Tico hustled in carrying a half-eaten piece of cold pizza. His mouth was full. Canada pointed at the photo. "You know where?"

Tico glanced at the picture, then at Raoul, swallowed, and said, "I could probably find it."

"Show our friend."

"Not sure I can do it in the dark, Boss. You tell me to try, though, I will."

Canada tapped his manicured fingernails on the arm of the chair. "Find Raoul a bed for the night, some clean towels, and offer him some food. You can take him out in

the morning. And Raoul?"

"Yes."

"You don't mind that I hold on to this?" He lifted the photograph. "I'd like to show it to Howard."

62

I was wide-eyed and body-weary long before Sam's arrival for our Saturday run, but the winter sky was too black for daybreak and the bedroom too cold to consider popping right out of bed. I waited for the growl of the paper guy's Power Wagon to come and go and for the first unmistakable illuminations of dawn before I rolled reluctantly into the day.

Even the dogs thought I was crazy. Emily sighed at me, but she didn't bother to get up to see what I had planned. Anvil, whose ears were beginning to fail him, didn't acknowledge that I'd moved.

I forced myself to drink some water and I downed a banana after mindlessly trying to peel a plantain that Lauren or Viv had stuck in the fruit bowl. The plantain wasn't ripe and wasn't at all eager to be peeled. I totally mangled the thing before I figured out that I wasn't wrestling with a mutant Chiquita.

New errand: Replace the damn plantain.

I thought I heard a car on the lane and peeked out the front door at 7:25. No Sam. I was hoping he'd spaced out the run or that he'd overslept. Jogging on a fifteen-degree morning didn't sound any more appetizing to me than had eating an under-ripe plantain.

Seven-thirty. No Sam. Out loud, I prayed, "Give it a rest, Sammy. Take a day off." That, of course, is when he drove up the lane. He climbed out of the Cherokee in his fancy running duds and a brand-new pair of trainers. His frosty breath was visible in long, slow rolls. Lauren's advice from the night before felt as sage to me as it had then, but I still hadn't decided exactly what I knew that I could tell Sam that might help Diane. He rescued me from my temporary paralysis by saying, "Let's stretch a minute. I want to tell you about the tunnel search."

The tunnel. The opening that had been excavated from Doyle's basement was cut at a steep enough angle that it actually descended all the way down below the spread footing of the foundation of the Millers' house. At that point the track-and-trolley system terminated and a vertical shaft

about two feet in diameter rose straight up into the Millers' crawl space. The top of the shaft was covered by a fitted piece of one-inch-thick plywood upholstered with an ample amount of dirt that had been glued to the wood with some kind of industrial-strength adhesive.

Were someone to venture into the crawl space, any evidence of the construction project was hidden from view by the thick-milled black-plastic sheeting that stretched from foundation wall to foundation wall over the entire expanse. The plastic was installed to collect the natural radon that was common in soil in Colorado, so the gases could be vented to the outdoors and the lungs of the home's inhabitants could be protected from the toxic consequences of long-term radiation exposure.

Access from the tunnel into the Miller home was ingenious. False sills had been attached to the tops of the foundation walls in the corner closest to the tunnel shaft. The plastic sheeting had been removed from the original sills and reattached to the false sills, where it could be easily lifted and folded back to reveal the opening of the shaft. After an intruder was ready to return to Doyle's house next door, he had only to lock the false sills back in

place — which would return the plastic to its normal location — and then slide the plywood lid back over the shaft.

A cursory examination of the crawl space by someone in the Miller home would reveal no evidence of the tunnel. Once Sam was down in the crawl space, it had taken him a few minutes to figure out exactly how it all worked, despite the fact that he knew almost precisely where the tunnel should be entering the house. The only clue to the location, he said, was a slight interruption in the dust pattern on top of the plastic sheeting.

Bill Miller professed shock and ignorance at the discovery of the tunnel. Although the revised warrant that Sam delivered to Bill's door gave him no choice about the matter, he was totally cooperative with the police about access to his crawl space.

He also rapidly put two and two together and got four. "Where is Doyle?" Bill had demanded. "Have you guys talked to him? Is he under arrest? Somebody tell me something! Does he know where Mallory is?"

Sam made a tactical decision to allow Bill to hover close by during the search — he wanted to observe him — but he wasn't

buying Bill's act. "He knew it was there," Sam told me. "Might even have known Doyle was dead."

"He knew about the tunnel? What makes you think that?"

"You interview enough people you get to know when they're lying. Meryl Streep could lie to me and get away with it, maybe Al Pacino. Definitely what's-his-face, Anthony Hopkins. But Bill Miller? He couldn't even get a bit part with the Flatirons Players. Must be the same for you, you know, in your business."

The truth was that my patients often lied to me with absolute impunity. I rationalized my often embarrassing credulity by trying to convince myself that when my patients lied to me they were lying to themselves as well, and that was why I was so inept at spotting their mistruths.

But the simple reality is that I am gullible. In reply to Sam, I said, "Yeah."

He chuckled. "Exactly what I'm talking about. Exactly."

I asked, "Speaking of being fooled — Jaris Slocum blew it, didn't he? His piece of the investigation."

Sam nodded. I'd expected him to mount a defense of Slocum, but he didn't. He said, "I'll deny this if it's ever repeated, but

Slocum didn't ever lay eyes on the Millers' neighbor. After the initial search of Chandler's house was negative, Slocum did the follow-up interview by phone — by frigging phone — not in person." Sam paused and grimaced like he had a bad tooth. "And he never ran him."

I was incredulous at the last bit. Sam was admitting that the Boulder Police had never put Doyle Chandler's particulars through the NCIC — National Crime Information Center — database.

"He never ran him? If he'd simply run him, you guys might have focused on Doyle a day or two after Christmas?"

"Something like that."

"Would have changed everything. Everything. For Mallory, maybe for Diane," I said. I'm a master of understatement.

"Woulda, coulda."

Sam didn't seem particularly contrite about his support for Jaris Slocum. Did I want him to be? I guess I did. It seemed to me that a whole gaggle of Sam's colleagues had been complicit in covering for Jaris. "Well?" I asked. Sam wasn't looking at me; he was staring at his right hamstring, which was the size of a pork tenderloin.

"Jaris is meeting with the bosses now. They're trying to find a way out of this that

doesn't smell too bad for the department. But no matter what, it's not going to turn out too good for Jaris."

I considered what I'd witnessed at dinner at the Sunflower. "Alcohol?"

"That's part of it." Finally, he looked up from his leg.

"You knew?" I said.

"His wife left him a year ago, got his kids after a nasty custody eval. As you might expect, Jaris had developed a little animosity toward mental health professionals and lawyers after that little fiasco. He should never have been sent out to Hannah Grant's office that night, but that's hindsight — who knew that he'd be spending his evening hanging out with shrinks and lawyers?"

"Sounds like his superiors should have known enough to rein him in. You did. Darrell Olson did."

"This all started right after Sherry left me. Despite the fact that I'd never really liked him, I had sympathy for the guy. I thought he just needed some room, some time to sort through all that was going on. We covered for him, all of us did. Could've been me, Alan. Could just as well have been me. Or you. You done chewing on him? I have other stuff I want to tell you."

"He was still drinking the other night at dinner, Sam."

"Couple of beers."

"That he downed like Gatorade after a marathon."

"And?" he said. He said it provocatively.

"And what?"

"You're doing it again, Alan."

"I'm doing what?"

"Cops are people. Guess what? We have problems. Sometimes we handle them, sometimes we don't. Same as shrinks. Same as teachers. Everybody. Jaris Slocum screwed up. Happens. People cut him some slack. Nice people like Darrell Olson do that. Slocum hung himself with it. Happens. Get over it. Nobody knew he fudged his investigation of Doyle Chandler. And nobody guessed what was going to come of it."

Sam offered me nothing but a stony face that was more punctuation than anything else. I read the punctuation to be a period.

I said, "Okay, I'm done."

"Wise. The partials we found in the search last night? One of them is Bob Brandt's right index finger."

"Oh shit," I said.

"Yeah," Sam said. "Oh shit. We have his fingerprint in the basement theater and we

587

have his car leaving the garage of the house at the other end of the tunnel during the window when Mallory disappeared from her home. Circumstantially speaking, it doesn't look too good."

"But nothing on the BOLO?"

"It's a rare car. It shouldn't be as hard to find as it's turning out to be. I'm thinking it's parked inside someplace. I don't think he's using it; we'd have it by now. We're going back into his place on Spruce later, this time with a warrant. We're going to test that blood."

"Pine."

"Pine then."

"Say hi to Jenifer for me."

"Jenifer?"

"The cute kid? The one who wants to go to Clemson?"

"I'll be sure to send your regards," Sam said sarcastically.

63

Sam wasn't talkative as we ran, nor was I. My lungs were trying to recover from their shock at being forced to process enough oxygen for cardiovascular exercise in Colorado's best impression of a deep freeze. After his initial, "Let's go," we covered a good quarter-mile before Sam grunted anything more. He had been running on my heels, but pulled up astride me and said, "News."

I thought it was a question, that Sam was asking me what I'd heard about Diane. Tapping my pocket I replied, "Nothing. Got my phone with me in case Raoul calls."

"No, I have more news for you. About the neighbor."

"Doyle?"

"You'll hear this soon enough: Doyle Chandler's not Doyle Chandler. It's a stolen identity. We don't know who he is. Was."

"You're kidding." I knew he wasn't kidding.

"The Doyle Chandler whose social security number matches that of the guy we found murdered yesterday died in a car crash with his parents, Renee and Dennis, in 1967 in Roanoke, Virginia. He was six years old at the time. The man who lived next door to the Millers filched the kid's identity. He's been using it for sixteen years."

"So whose body was it?" I suddenly didn't even know what to call Doyle.

"We don't know, and we may not ever know. AFIS doesn't pull a match on the index print he gave for his Colorado driver's license. NCIC has bupkis." Sam paused to allow his breathing to catch up with his talking and running. "Animals had chewed off almost all of the fingertips and most of the face before the body was discovered. We're not going to get usable prints from what's left. We have his teeth, of course, but the guy hadn't seen a dentist in a while."

"What about the house? There must be prints there."

"The techs aren't hopeful — the place had been professionally cleaned after he moved out. Need to match them with something, anyway."

"This case," I said.

"Tell me about it," he agreed, and fell back into position on my heels.

Five minutes later, from the ridge top above the neighborhood, I watched a sedan without headlights approach the junction of dirt lanes that leads toward our house. It wasn't a car I recognized. Light in color, GM in ancestry, its boxy shape dated it back a decade or more. Our neighbor Adrienne's latest nanny? Possibly. I kept an eye on the car as it took the turn onto our lane, but our route carried us down the other side of the ridge and I couldn't see the car's ultimate destination.

Sam passed me on the downhill and increased the pace for the final mile. I was exhausted after the run. He, too, seemed unnaturally winded. We both knew it wasn't just the jog. "Coming in?" I asked. "I'll make you breakfast."

I'd already looked around for the GM sedan. It wasn't at my house or at Adrienne's.

"Have to get to work," Sam said. "Simon's with Sherry."

I was perseverating on Sam's news that Doyle wasn't Doyle. But I had no easy way to digest that news, so I refocused on Sam's implication that Bob might be deeply involved in Mallory's disappearance, but

couldn't get anywhere with that either. Bob was a schizoid personality. He was as schizoid as anyone I'd ever met. Bob kidnapping Mallory — or anyone else — made no more sense to me than a pedophile breaking into an old folks' home.

"You no longer consider Mallory a runaway, do you?"

Sam said, "I go back and forth. If she is, it looks like she had help getting out of the house. If she isn't, we have a different problem. What was the neighbor's role in all this? Did he take her? Did he help her? What was Camaro Bob's? Did he have something to do with it? Looks like he did. What's what exactly, I haven't decided. I still want to know why Doyle dug that tunnel in the first place. Why did he want into the Millers' house so badly?"

The obvious was to me, well, obvious. "He lived next door. People prey on kids, Sam. He could've become obsessed with her."

"A voyeur? That's all you got?"

"I'm thinking worse."

He scowled. "Why dig a tunnel?"

"To do his thing. Access."

"Risky as shit. Three people live in that house. He's bound to get caught wandering around in there trying to get at the

girl. Doesn't work. You live next door, there're much easier ways to spy on a kid."

"Maybe he went in at night when they were asleep."

"There are pervs who like to watch girls sleep?" Sam asked.

After all his years as a cop, Sam's residual naiveté still ambushed me sometimes.

"There are pervs who like just about everything."

He held up his hand. "I don't want to hear it."

I thought about the theater in Doyle's basement. All the top-end electronics. "Did Doyle wire their house? Hide video cameras in Mallory's room? The bathroom? Anything like that?"

"We checked. Fixtures are all clean, attic's clean. No holes drilled where they shouldn't be drilled. There's nothing there, not a single extra cable in the Millers' house, not a single cable coming back through the tunnel to Doyle's. No transmitters. If he put surveillance in, he took it back out when he moved away."

I thought for a moment, forcing myself to go back to basics. Psychology basics. The best predictor of someone's future be-

havior — maybe the only predictor — is his past behavior. I said, "Car thieves steal cars, right? Bank robbers rob banks?"

Sam looked at me as though he'd just realized I was mentally challenged. "Yeah, and psychologists ask stupid questions."

"What do we really know about Doyle Chandler?"

"Not much," Sam admitted. "Did I tell you he was shot?"

"No, you didn't."

"He was shot. Behind the ear, slight upward angle. Shooter wasn't real close, no burns on his skin. Slug looks like a .38. Second and third shots to his back. But they were just insurance. He was already dead with the first slug."

"Suspects?"

"Camaro Bob's on the list."

I didn't want to hear that. I went back to Doyle. "You know one more thing about Doyle for sure, Sam: He steals identities," I said.

"Yeah?"

He knew where I was going. I said, "You were wondering about the motive for the tunnel. There it is."

"Doyle went into the Millers' house to build a new identity?" Sam said.

I noted — with some relief — that his

question was almost entirely devoid of skepticism.

"What better place? Say Doyle went in during the daytime when Bill was at work and the kids were at school. He'd have the run of the house. Personal records, financial records, work stuff that Bill left laying around. Computer files, his e-mails, maybe even passwords. Be like Wal-Mart for an identity thief. With a tunnel he could take all the time he needed to fill in every last blank."

" 'Lying' around. Bill would leave stuff 'lying' around. Not 'laying' around."

I smiled. "Does the gratis English lesson mean you think I got the rest right?"

"Maybe," Sam said. Even though he'd already caught his breath, he put his hands on his hips the way exhausted athletes do, stared at me, and momentarily left any parsimony behind. "We blew it the first time. Eight years ago? We did. I don't care about the public face we tried to put on it, the damn truth is that we fucking blew it. Guess what? I don't want to be the guy who blows it this time. If you have something that'll help me find that girl, I need to hear it. Second chances don't come around too often in life. I have one. We need to redeem ourselves."

In the years since the other little girl's death, I'd never heard Sam be so brutal in his appraisal of law enforcement's role. "Okay, yeah," I said.

"Yeah, you have something? Or, yeah, you understand?"

Did I have something? If I did, I wasn't sure what it looked like. I said, "Yeah, I understand."

He stepped toward the Cherokee. "I don't need your understanding."

64

I tried to stretch out my calves a little more as I pondered Sam's challenge and watched him disappear down the dusty lane. I was just about to go back inside when the square front end of an approaching car came my way. It stopped a hundred yards or so down the road, in a little turnout on the soft shoulder.

The car was the GM sedan I'd seen earlier. The sun had crested the eastern horizon and was reflecting off the windshield. From my vantage point I could tell the car was pale yellow. The hood ornament clued me in that it was a Cadillac.

I stuck my hands in my armpits to warm my fingers, and I waited.

A man climbed out of the driver's seat, stuffed his hands in his pockets, and began walking toward me.

Bob Brandt.

Even at a hundred yards I recognized the denim jacket. My thought? *Thank God you're alive.*

"Somebody's been in my house," he said when he got within fifty feet. His voice was pressured. He didn't say hello.

So what else is new?

"I know," I said. I'd come to the conclusion that it was Doyle who had trashed Bob's place, but I kept the guess to myself.

"Did you read my stuff?" he asked.

That's why Bob was at my house: to chastise me for breaking his trust and spilling his secrets. That was fair — I had broken his trust and spilled his secrets. "Hi, Bob," I said, reframing things, at least for a moment. "I've been worried about you."

"Why?"

Bob's "why" was a classic schizoid question, but perfectly sincere. His disorder left him with only the most rudimentary concept of "concern," at least the person-to-person variety.

"I hadn't heard from you, thought you might be in . . . danger."

"Oh." He played with the notion for a moment before he added, "I went somewhere. Do you know what's going on? Who was in my place?"

"Are you okay?"

"Tired. Drove all night."

"Are you here by yourself?"

He turned his head and looked back at the Cadillac, as though he needed to check to be sure. "Yes. What's going on? Did you read my stuff? I told you not to. You must have seen my note."

"Like I said, I got worried. Anyway, I think you wanted me to read it. Otherwise you wouldn't have given it to me. We can talk about it." It was shrink talk, but it also happened to be true.

"I was just getting started. It's just a story."

"The tunnel part is real."

He swallowed, and his eyes started their disconcerting shimmying. He spit a solitary word: "So?"

Bob's retort was schoolyard bravado, nothing more.

"How can I be of help right now?" I said, trying to sound therapeutic.

He seemed surprised by my offer. After a moment, he said, "That's a good question."

He stepped back, literally and — I feared — figuratively. Instinctively, I sought safer ground for him. "Is that your car?"

His eyes found the Caddy and lingered there. "It's my mother's."

Your mother's? Was Bob being sardonic? I couldn't say. "You like it?"

He'd returned his attention my way, but was looking past me toward the distant turnpike. Finally, he said, "Lots of power. Good cruiser. Cushy. Only fourteen K on it."

"Not as cherry as your Camaro," I said.

"Close," he said. "Pretty close." He made an unfamiliar popping sound with his lips. "Maybe you can help somebody . . . I know."

"A friend?" I asked. *Please tell me Mallory's okay.*

Emily chose that moment to erupt; she'd apparently just realized that her homeland security had been violated and that a stranger was on her doorstep. Her fierce barking — even though it came from inside the house — caused Bob to retreat a few steps.

"She's fine," I said.

"I don't like dogs. You know that."

I didn't think I knew that. "She'll stay inside. Bob?" I waited until I thought I had his attention. "The police are looking for you. They want to talk with you about Mallory. I think you should get a lawyer and go see them. I can put you in touch with someone."

"Sheesh," he said, and did his little half head-shake thing.

I experienced an odd sense of relief that I'd finally lit on something I could share with Sam. I said, "You should know that whatever you decide to do, I'm going to tell the police you were here."

He was puzzled. "Is that some . . . rule? You have to tell?"

"No. It might even be breaking some rule. It's what I think is the right thing to do."

He nodded. "That's what I did, too. What I thought was the right thing."

"You could be in danger. Doyle's dead."

"No, he's not."

Okay. I didn't see a point in arguing. "The police need to talk with you."

"I didn't do anything wrong."

"It'll be fine then. Let me put you in touch with an attorney."

My phone rang. I pulled it from my pocket and checked the screen: Sam. I said to Bob, "Excuse me. This will take just a second." I turned away, putting a dozen feet between us. "Yes," I whispered into the phone.

"I passed that DeVille on the way out of your neighborhood — the one we saw during our jog. Had a funny feeling, so I ran it. Expired tags, but it's registered to somebody named Verna Brandt in —"

"I know."

"He's there?"

"Yes."

"A deputy is on the way. I'll be right behind them."

I turned around. Bob was almost all the way back to the Cadillac. "Don't," I yelled.

He jumped in the car, spun the sedan in the dirt as though he practiced the maneuver on weekends, and was gone within seconds.

A huge gust of wind whooshed from the west. I didn't sense it coming and the blunt force of the gale almost blew me over. When I finally caught my balance I looked toward the mountains the way somebody might look to check the identity of somebody who just sucker punched him. My conclusion? The forecast Chinooks had definitely arrived; the slopes of the Front Range were already haloed in snow that was being whipped off the glacial ice of the distant Divide.

I braced my feet and tried Sam on his cell, but didn't get an answer. I waited until the sheriff's deputy and Sam drove up, told Sam what had happened, and wished I could start the day all over again.

Lauren was planning to hang out with

Grace on Saturday morning and then the two of them were going to do some clothes shopping at Flatiron. Later in the day, winds permitting, they were planning a mother-daughter "tablecloth restaurant" visit someplace Gracie kept insisting was a big secret. I spent the morning hoping to hear from Raoul or Sam. Didn't. I filled the time writing a couple of reports that were long overdue, and did a few chores around the house before I cleaned up, hopped in my car, drove the few miles west to my office, and prepared to see Bill Miller.

I wasn't looking forward to the visit, and half hoped he would bag the session because of the Chinooks.

65

Bill was waiting for me.

His car was parked where Diane usually left her Saab, not too far from the doors that led from our offices to the backyard. He was standing between the taillights, leaning back against the trunk, his arms folded over his chest. The January sun was already low over the southwest mountains and the fierce wind gusts were blowing anything that wasn't bolted down from the west side of town to the east. Some day soon, one of these Chinook events was going to propel our rickety garage from our side of downtown to the other.

I stopped my wagon parallel to his car — but a few feet farther from the rickety garage than usual — and stepped out. I didn't like that his car was parked in back. I didn't like that he wasn't waiting for me by the front door.

He greeted me with, "You knew."

I chose defensiveness. Wise? Probably

not. "I'd given my word to the police, Bill. I also knew you'd find out what happened soon enough. I'm sorry I couldn't tell you. It would have made things easier for both of us."

He nodded; he'd probably traversed that territory himself. "What's your role in all this?" he asked. "Why were you at Doyle's last night? And those other times?"

His voice seemed to carry better in the wind than mine did; mine felt like it was being swallowed up like spit in the ocean. "It has to do with what was making me concerned about the dual-relationship problem I talked about."

Bill nodded as though he understood. But I wondered how he could even hear, let alone understand. The nod must have meant something else.

"When we talked last night did you know that Doyle was dead?" he asked. I had the sense that he was methodically going down a list of questions. I also had the sense that he didn't really expect to learn anything novel in my responses.

"Same situation, Bill; I couldn't talk about it with you. I knew you would find out this morning anyway."

He turned his head momentarily so he was gazing west toward the mountains,

frankly into the wind. His hair flew back behind him like he was a character in the cartoons. "Do you know where my daughter is?" he asked.

I half heard him, half read his lips. "No, I don't. I wish I did," I said.

"You're sure?"

"I am." Almost reflexively, I asked him the same question. "Do you know where she is, Bill?"

"No."

"What's the third option? The other night you suggested the possibility that running and kidnapping weren't the only options."

"Hiding."

"Hiding? From what?"

He surprised me by taking a quick step closer to me, closer than I liked. "Life. Yes, hiding. I have a story to tell you."

In retrospect, that was the point when I should have stopped him. Walked away. Told him therapy was over, or that it had never really begun. Handed him my license and let him use it for a coaster. Given him the phone number of the state board that censures wayward psychologists, like me. Something.

But I didn't. I still had a scintilla of hope that Bill knew something that would

help me find Diane.

"One day last spring," he began, "I came home from work and found Doyle Chandler inside my house, sitting at my kitchen table drinking a beer. My beer. My records — my files, my bills, my checkbook, you name it — were spread out all over the table in front of him."

"Bill, I —" I tried to interrupt him. Why? Something visceral was still telling me to get him to stop.

"I'm not done." He raised both eyebrows and through a hissing exhale said, "Give me this. I deserve this." I stepped back involuntarily. He immediately closed the distance between us. "Doyle knew everything about me. Said he'd spent almost a month going through my things. Paperwork, letters, tax returns, computer files. Passwords. Everything. He knew about Rachel, her . . . problems. He knew the kids' grades, their teachers' names. Knew I have a swollen prostate, that my LDL's too high. Everything that makes our family different from the Crandalls across the street, everything that makes us who we are, he knew."

I had an incongruous impulse to comfort, to tell Bill the truth about Doyle Chandler, his neighbor, and the truth about Doyle Chandler, the boy who'd died

in a car accident in Roanoke with his parents back in 1967. I wanted to try to placate Bill with the fact that he'd been had by a damn good con man.

A blast of wind sandblasted my skin. The impulse passed.

Bill went on. "I was irate. I asked him what he was doing in my house. He just laughed. I demanded that he get out, that the kids were coming home any minute. He stood up and walked over to the refrigerator and pointed at our family calendar. He said, 'No, they're not. Reese is at hockey practice till seven. Coach usually keeps them late, you know that. And it's Kyle's mom's turn to drive, anyway. Last time she stopped and got the kids dinner at Pizza Hut, remember? She'll probably do something like that again — Frannie's like that, such a sweetheart. And Mallory is studying at Kara's. Cute kids, Mallory and Kara. Really cute kids.'

"He knew it all. Everything. Take a minute, try to imagine it. Go ahead, try. What that would be like. He knew every secret. Every intimacy. Every dirty detail. When you think you know how bad it feels, double it. Then double that. That's what it was like."

I tried to digest what that kind of intru-

sion would feel like to a father. Surreal.

A huge piece of Styrofoam jumped the fence to the west and crashed into the side of Bill's car. I ducked; he continued to seem oblivious to the fierce gales. I forced myself to observe him, to try to read what I could about his affect. I wasn't getting a clear sense of where he was at that moment. It was apparent that he had no trouble summoning the rage he felt at Doyle Chandler. But there was something else present in the mix, some other emotional component that I couldn't put a finger on.

"Doyle had already gone through every last thing I owned and decided that simply stealing my identity wasn't enough of a payoff for all his effort. He wanted money, of course," Bill said. "Lots of it."

"Why didn't —"

"— I go to the police? Because I have things to hide. He knew by then that I couldn't go to the police. Same reason I couldn't turn over Mallory's diary when I found it after she disappeared."

"Things to hide?"

"Everybody has something they don't want the world to know. Everybody. For some people, it's something embarrassing. Maybe even humiliating. For some, it's

something . . . worse. To save my family, I did some desperate things years ago. I made hard choices. For me it was something worse."

"Rachel and Canada?" I said, guessing that Bill's secret had to do with money. Instantly, I wished I hadn't guessed, at least not out loud.

"Do you know? I'm not sure . . . doesn't matter. I'll tell you."

"Bill, it's not —"

"Shhhh. I'm not done."

For a fleeting second, right then, I felt menace from him. The scent of peril was fleeting, like a waft of perfume as a lovely woman waltzes by. I allowed myself the luxury of believing that I'd misread him, and I somehow convinced myself that it was okay to dismiss the menace as an illusion, to allow it to be carried away on the wings of the Chinooks. In retrospect, that was a bit of a mistake.

"Rachel's illness almost buried us financially. When we came to see you way back when it was already bad, but after? That year after? Lord. The medicine, the doctors, the hospitals. Not to mention all the damn weddings. There were always more and more damn weddings, always. Rachel was better when she went to weddings,

much better. The voices weren't as frequent, not as scary. So I fed the beast, paying for the outfits, the gifts, everything. I was in so far over my head. Mortgaged to the hilt, credit cards maxed out. Every month I was borrowing from a new Peter to pay an old Paul.

"I was about to declare bankruptcy. I didn't know what else to do. Then the voices began telling Rachel — demanding — that she had to move to Las Vegas or . . ." He took a moment to reflect on some ugly, ugly room in his wife's private hell. "And that meant she would need even more money. I begged her not to go, but the voices were too frightening. I thought I was going to lose everything then. The house, the kids, Rachel.

"Then I got handed a way out. My boss had just been promoted to western regional manager — a big deal for him. His wife threw him a surprise party up at the Flagstaff House just before Christmas. Late, close to two in the morning, I was driving behind him down Baseline and . . ." Bill shook his head, disbelieving. "He was distracted, I guess. I don't know what it was, but a pedestrian was walking from the Hill over to Chautauqua, right across Baseline. I saw her clearly from a block

and a half away — she had her hands in her pockets, her head down against the cold. Walter just mowed her down.

"She must have flown a hundred feet in the air. Turned out she was a young mother, an orthodontist. He never even touched his brakes; he just plowed into her. I still see her body flying. Sometimes, I feel the impact when I'm asleep.

"He killed her, of course. She was dead at the scene."

He paused, and I reminded him that he'd told me about the accident years before when he'd stopped by to thank me for my help with Rachel.

"I didn't tell you the next part. Walter was in shock. Kept saying, 'What happened, Bill? What happened?' I saw an opportunity. I told him to shut up and listen to me. As out-of-it as he was, he did. When the cops came, I told them what I saw. A white van was coming up Baseline in the other direction. The woman walked out from behind it. My boss couldn't have seen the woman. I told them I was right behind him and I didn't see her until she was in the air. It wasn't Walter's fault at all. That was my story."

"You made up the van?" I asked.

"It was two in the morning. I figured I

was the only witness. My boss matched his story to mine. It worked. Why wouldn't it? Turned out his blood alcohol was just a hair below the legal limit so he wasn't even arrested. He was never charged with anything. He didn't go to prison. His promotion was secure. His family . . . was safe."

"You saved his ass?"

"I did it for me, not for him. I was saving my family. I told you I was desperate. I don't even like Walter. He's a prick."

"I don't understand," I said. But I did. Before I'd left her office, Mary Black had suggested enough that I could guess the rest.

"I knew Walter would be grateful." Bill suddenly seemed out of breath.

"The promotion you got," I said, filling in a blank for him. "The one you told me about years ago?"

"Yes, that promotion. My salary went way up, and then it went up again. I began getting regular Christmas bonuses. That was eight years ago. I had a good job, better than I deserved. I was making enough money to make ends meet here and enough to keep Rachel safe in Vegas, barely."

"Until Doyle Chandler showed up at your kitchen table?"

"I'd kept a record about everything that happened in case Walter ever turned on me. When Doyle starting coming into my house he did it simply to steal my identity, but then . . . then he ended up finding every last thing I'd kept about Walter and the orthodontist. Newspaper clippings. Notes. Everything. Once he understood what I'd done, and how vulnerable I was, he changed his plans. Doyle wanted a cut."

"How much?"

"He asked for ten thousand a month. We settled on five at first. But I knew I couldn't do five for long. Canada was demanding more and more money to keep doing what he was doing for Rachel in Las Vegas. As she got sicker he had to pay more people more money so that she would be . . . left alone. What choice did I have? What could I do? I was in so deep.

"When Doyle moved out in the fall and put his house on the market, I thought he might have realized that the till was empty, you know? Hell, he knew my finances as well as I did. Better, maybe. I thought — God, I was naive — I thought things might be over. But that's when Doyle went to Walter and started blackmailing him, too. Walter and I realized he'd moved away so that we couldn't find him. My boss wasn't

happy. He's not a pleasant man when he's not happy."

The sky was getting dark and, despite the warming winds, I felt winter and January all the way to my bones. It wasn't just the temperature, though; I knew that.

"Bill, would you like to come inside?" I said. "Sit down?"

He looked around as though he'd needed to remind himself we were indeed outside, nodded, and followed me to the back door of my office. Once we were in I flicked on some lights and sat across from him as though we were doctor and patient.

Were we? Partly yes, partly no. Mostly no. All the ethical guidelines I'd always held so dear were designed to keep therapists from feeling the ambiguity of roles I was feeling right then, were designed to keep patients from suffering the conflict-of-interest vulnerabilities Bill was floating in right then. What a mess I'd made.

The thing was, I wasn't too upset about it.

Bill crossed his legs, uncrossed them, stood suddenly, and moved to the southern windows. His back was to me, and he seemed to be focused on the advancing sunset that was visible through the skeleton of the ash trees. My sense was that he

wasn't sure how to resume his narrative. I could have drawn the shut-up-and-wait arrow from my quiver. I didn't. To help him find a way to restart his story I chose an option that I thought was a gimme: "That's when you found out he'd dug a tunnel? The day Doyle showed up in your kitchen."

"No, I had no idea that's how he'd gotten in. Learning about the tunnel last night was a complete surprise to me. A tunnel? Never crossed my mind, not for a second. I thought Doyle had a key to our house, that he'd discovered where we hid our spare, or had somehow gotten hold of one of the kids' keys. That's what he'd led me to believe. He had told me not to get an alarm, not to change the locks. Told me I'd regret doing any of those things. When he'd threaten me with what I was going to regret if I didn't cooperate, he'd always mention the kids."

"He threatened them?"

"He tried. I threatened him right back. I told him if he came into my house when the kids were home, I'd kill him. If he so much as talked to them, I'd kill him. I think he believed me."

She was scared. That's what Bob had said about Mallory. *She was scared.*

Was that why she was scared?

"What did Mallory know about all this?" I asked.

"Mallory," he said in a long exhale. His breath temporarily clouded the window glass in front of his mouth. "Mallory."

I thought he was about to cry.

66

"She hasn't had a good Christmas since she was six." Bill said into the glass. "That's eight years, most of her life. She hates Christmas."

She misses her mom. Diane had told me that Mallory missed her mom. The year that Mallory was six was the year that Rachel abandoned her family for the lure of Las Vegas weddings.

Psychotherapy 101: Christmas for Mallory was irrevocably linked to loss.

Finally, I thought I understood why Mallory had felt so compelled to see Hannah Grant for psychotherapy: Mallory hadn't had a good Christmas since she was six. She went to see Hannah because she didn't want to have another bad Christmas, another Christmas when her primary emotion involved desperately missing her mother.

"She'd get so scared," Bill said. "Every year, right after Thanksgiving she'd start to get scared."

Scared? That's what Bob had said about Mallory, too. *She was scared.* Why scared?

"Scared?" I asked. I would have suspected that Mallory would show signs of anxiety or depression on the anniversary of her mother's abandonment. But fear?

Bill wiped at his eyes with his fingertips. "She thought it was going to happen again. She couldn't be comforted. No matter what I tried to do over the years to help her deal with it, nothing worked."

Rachel had deserted her family eight years before. Was Mallory afraid that her father was going to leave, too? Was that the vulnerability she felt? "What, Bill? Mallory thought what was going to happen again?"

He turned back from the window. His face was pink and bright. "What happened eight years ago on Christmas? Mallory thought she'd be next. Every year since that year, she's been afraid that she'd be next. That the same man was coming to get her."

Oh my God, what an idiot I am. Mallory was scared because of the murder of her friend. "They were friends? When they were little?"

"Classmates. A sleep-over or two. You know what it's like for girls when they're that age. That Christmas, Mallory was al-

ready so vulnerable because of . . . what was going on with her mom. What happened that night scared her so much. She used to cry and cry every time she saw the pictures on TV. And those pictures were everywhere.

"She was so determined to confront her fears about Christmas, to grow out of it. She desperately wanted to get past all this, to feel safe."

"The police know all this?"

"Of course; it's why they think she ran. They think she got spooked and left to go find her mom and that something — you know — happened to her on the way."

"Did she know about Doyle? About the blackmail?"

"She knew something was up with me, that I wasn't myself. She'd mentioned it. It's in her journal."

"Did she know about the tunnel?"

"I know what you're thinking — that that's how she got out of the house. But how could she know about it? I didn't know about it until last night. She was terrified of the basement. The basement is where her friend's body was found eight years ago. She never went down there. Never."

"Doyle?"

"Doyle could have shown it to her, I guess. But why? He had too much to lose if he exposed what he was doing. And I think he knew I meant that I'd kill him if he went near the kids."

I thought, *Bob.* That's how she could know. Bob's fingerprint was in the basement. Bob was taking care of Doyle's empty house. Bob knew all about the theater — he had told me that he thought it was a great place to watch movies. And Bob certainly knew about the tunnel.

Bob and Mallory had talked.

Had Bob actually been there on Christmas night, holed up in Doyle's theater watching movies?

Mallory's friend — the other little girl, the tiny blond beauty queen — had died eight years before as Christmas Day became the day after.

She was scared, Bob had said about Mallory.

She thought it was going to happen again, her father had said about Mallory. She feared that someone was going to come into her house and do to her what someone had done to her little friend. She feared that someone was going to bust in and leave her head crushed and her neck garroted, that someone was going to

abandon her alone and dead in her grungy basement on Christmas night.

Doyle? Bob? The man loitering outside? *Who?*

I'm a gullible guy. But I'm aware that I'm a gullible guy, so aware that sometimes I catch myself and pause long enough to question what I'm hearing. Right then, I stopped, and I questioned. *Do I believe what Bill is telling me?*

Yes, kind of.

Is he telling me the truth? No, probably not completely.

I replayed some of the earlier conversation I'd had with Bill Miller. *"When Doyle moved out in the fall and put his house on the market, I thought he might have realized that the till was empty, you know? He knew my finances as well as I did. Better, maybe. I thought — God, I was naive — I thought things might be over. But that's when Doyle went to Walter and started blackmailing him, too. Walter and I realized he'd moved away so that we couldn't find him. My boss wasn't happy. He's not a pleasant man when he's not happy."*

"What," I asked, "did your boss do when Doyle started blackmailing him?"

"Same as me. He paid him off, bought some time. After so many years you don't

expect to get caught."

Content is the aphrodisiac of psychotherapy. For a therapist, it's so tempting to get caught on the wave of the story, to get lost in the facts and the promise and the details of the narrative. What suffers when the therapist succumbs to that seductive lure?

Process. And process — what is going on in the room — is almost always where the truth hides. I forced myself to be a therapist. I returned my attention to the process.

"Why did you decide to tell me all this, Bill?"

"I didn't know what you'd already figured out. I actually thought you might know too much. That would be a whole new problem for us."

"Us?"

"Me and Walter."

"I don't quite understand," I said. But I did.

Bill's voice was almost apologetic as he said, "I've just tied your hands, Alan. You can't tell anyone what I told you. It's confidential, now. I can't afford to have anyone know what I've done. Walter can't either. So, just in case — for some insurance — I've sealed your lips."

Was Bill right?

In his reading of the law, and of my professional responsibilities, yes.

In his reading of me, no. He had no way to know, but I was more than ready to say "screw it." Was I angry? A little. Less than I would have anticipated. "Doyle knew everything," I said. "He may have —"

"Doyle's dead, remember?"

"Did you —"

"Kill him? No. God, no. I would have liked to, I might even have been willing to, but . . . no."

"Did your boss?"

"He's probably capable of it. Walter's in Vegas now trying to find Rachel. To see if Mallory's with her. We have to keep her under control. He and I are in the same boat on this one. Our families are both at risk."

"Rachel knows about the orthodontist?"

"She's my wife; of course she knows. I don't have secrets from Rachel."

I stated the obvious. "You're desperate, then. You and . . . Walter?"

"Yes, we are."

"Why did he go to Vegas?"

"One of us had to get to Rachel. I couldn't — the press might have spotted me. They're everywhere."

I'd noticed. "Do you think Mallory's there?"

"I hope she is." His despair about his daughter was palpable. "The alternatives are so horrifying that I can't even . . ."

My cell phone rang. I checked the screen: Raoul. Thank God. "I need to get this," I said. "It's an emergency. There may even be some news that affects Mallory."

"Go ahead then," Bill said.

"Raoul?" I said. "Any news?"

"I'm at the hospital with her. She's okay."

Diane? "Hold on a second; I'm with someone." I covered the phone and turned to Bill. "Could you please go out to the waiting room while I take this?"

Reluctantly, I thought, he walked out of my office and down the hall. I kept my hand on the phone until I heard the waiting room door open and close.

67

"She's really okay?" I said.

"She's safe. She held my hand. We talked. She had a little food. Now she's sleeping."

"Where has she been? What happened?"

"I was sure Canada had Diane, or he could lead me to her. I had it all wrong."

"What do you mean?"

"None of Canada's people have seen Rachel since Tuesday. Turns out Canada's had me on a leash since I got to Vegas. He's been watching me, concerned I'd be causing him more trouble with Rachel, later on hoping that I'd lead him to her."

"I don't understand. How did you find Diane?"

That's when he took a deep breath and slowed his voice and began relaying the long story about the ratty cab and doing dead time in the Airstream and about the old VW bug and Tico, and about playing the echoes with Canada.

★ ★ ★

Before dawn on the morning after Raoul met with Canada in the walled house in the scruffy desert outside of the city, Tico fired up the VW and drove Raoul into the desolate mountains west of Las Vegas. Raoul recalled seeing a sign for Blue Diamond near their destination — so wherever that is, that wasn't too far from where they ended up. Just as it was beginning to get light Tico stopped the Bug on a mountain curve, and asked Raoul if he was up for a little hike.

"This is where the accident was?" Raoul asked him, recalling Canada's story the night before.

"The guy's driving too fast," Tico said, pointing down the road. "Way too fast, and he comes around the curve — that one — and sees a guy standing in the road with a .45 pointed at his windshield." He held up both hands. "This is what I hear. The man in the road fires a shot — you know, to warn the guy — a little bit over the top of the truck. Driver doesn't handle it good. Freaks." Tico then pantomimed a dive off a cliff before he kicked off his flip-flops and began pulling an ancient pair of orange high-top Keds onto his bare feet.

A moment later Raoul followed him

down a scruffy hillside covered with nothing but scree and big boulders. They went down a hundred feet or more into a narrow wash that had been invisible from the road above. A battered, crushed, bronze Silverado with Colorado plates rested upside down on a rock that was half the size of Tico's VW. Inside was the body of a man. The stink was horrific.

Tico said, "That's the guy, the guy in the picture with Howard, the guy who met your wife in the Venetian. You want me to check for ID?" Raoul wasn't able to come up with an answer for him, but Tico pulled on some work gloves and crawled into the overturned truck. A minute later he handed Raoul a Colorado driver's license.

The name meant nothing to Raoul. "What's farther up the hill? Where was he going?" Raoul asked.

"A couple of old cabins. Might be important. To you, anyway."

"But not to you?"

"This . . . accident? It happened before Rachel lost touch with the boss. We weren't too interested in what was up there. Not our business, you dig. We stay out of things that aren't our business. That's one of the boss's rules."

"Can we look?" Raoul asked him. "At

those two cabins? Now?"

Tico said, "I got a little time."

The second cabin they checked, the last one on the road, was where they found Diane. Raoul went in alone and found her cuffed to an iron bed. She'd been there a long time. She was delirious, almost unconscious.

Tico used his mobile phone to call somebody down in Vegas, asked them to send help. Then he told Raoul, "I gotta go before, you know . . . And my man? The police don't need to know about the Silverado. That'd be better for everybody."

Raoul told him he understood and he promised to come up with a story for the police.

Fifteen minutes later people started showing up to help Raoul save his wife.

I briefly relayed to Raoul most of what I'd told Lauren the night before. I told him about the tunnel and the car that had left Doyle's garage right around the time Mallory disappeared. I told him that Doyle Chandler wasn't Doyle Chandler, and that whoever he really was, he was dead.

"Are you coming home?" I asked.

"As soon as they clear her to travel," he said.

"Can you tell me who the guy in the Silverado was?"

"Does it make a difference?" he asked. "I promised I'd be discreet. The cops didn't find it. It needs to stay that way."

"I think I know."

"Who?"

The irony didn't escape me: Raoul was protecting secrets, too. I gave him the name he already had: "Guy named Walter."

His voice grew tight. "You've known about him for how long?"

"This afternoon. Just now."

"He was a bad guy?"

"He had something important to hide. He was afraid Diane might have learned what it was from Hannah."

"When I get back we'll have a beer, you'll tell me how you know all this."

"I'm looking forward to that, Raoul. Listen, I'm with a . . . patient. Call me back when I can talk with Diane, okay? Please?"

We said good-bye after Raoul asked me if I had any idea how to thank someone for saving his wife's life. "Canada?" I wondered.

"No, Norm Clarke," he said.

I thought I'd read somewhere that Norm

had a weakness for foie gras, but I promised Raoul I'd think more about it and stepped back out to the waiting room to get Bill Miller.

The front door was wide open. The coffee table was tipped over, magazines scattered on the floor.

Bill was gone. *Damn.* Immediately, I regretted leaving him alone for such a long time.

The winds seemed to have stopped.

68

Huh. What did Bill's hasty exit mean? Why the overturned table and the open door? Had something happened while I was talking with Raoul, or was Bill making a statement about his frustration with me, or about his annoyance that I'd interrupted our meeting to take a phone call?

My relief that Diane was okay was so strong at that moment that I wasn't particularly upset about whatever had prompted Bill's departure, but I was perplexed. Why had he taken off so suddenly?

I was becoming more and more convinced that Mallory's Christmas night disappearance had been accomplished with Bob's help. What had happened next? I was guessing that she'd talked Bob into driving her somewhere and I was hoping that she'd somehow made it to Vegas to visit her mother. Where were mother and daughter right then? I didn't know. Raoul's story satisfied me that Bill's boss, the by-

then-dead Walter, hadn't been successful in tracking them down in Vegas.

But where was Bob? If Sam had caught up with him, I was sure he would have called and let me know.

I straightened up the waiting room, walked back to my office, and phoned Bill Miller at his home. No answer. I left a message, and asked him to call me back on my pager. Then I called home. The girls were still out on their excursion. I left Lauren a message that I was going to run a few errands and that I'd be home in time for dinner.

As cold as it can be in Colorado in January, there are always respites, warm days in the high fifties or low sixties when the sun defies its low angle in the southern sky and the blue above is just a little bluer. I was surprised when I stepped outside to discover that the Chinooks had abated and left the day so much warmer than it had been earlier. The seat heaters in the Audi seemed superfluous. I flicked them off and drove east to begin my errands.

I felt the vibration of my pager while I was waiting in line to buy some fish for dinner at Whole Foods. Had Lauren asked for ono or opah? I couldn't remember. I pulled the beeper off my belt and read Bill

Miller's familiar number. My turn at the fish counter had arrived, so I mentally flipped a coin and chose a good-sized piece of opah before I meandered over to the relative quiet of the dairy department to return Bill's call.

"We need to talk," he said.

"I went back out to the waiting room and —"

"I just got a call about Mallory."

"From whom?"

"The Colorado State Patrol. They found a body, a girl, in a ditch near I-70 west of Grand Junction."

"Oh my God," I said. "What can I do?"

"I want to talk to you before whatever happens next. I need to make sure I'm thinking straight."

"Bill, you just admitted that you're using the therapy to shut me up. I don't think I'm the right person to —"

"Fire me tomorrow. Tonight I need some help." He sounded genuinely frantic. I couldn't imagine his terror. I looked at my watch. "My office. Ten minutes," I said.

"I have to be here, at home, if they call back. I can't leave. Can you come over?"

"I'll be right there," I said. I tossed the opah on top of a display of organic butter in the dairy case, and sprinted to my car.

69

Maybe it was the time of day, just past dusk. Or maybe, as Sam predicted, the fierce assault of the Chinook blitzkrieg had scared everyone off. But the media encampment outside the Millers' home was deserted, the street peaceful. Doyle's house was dark.

Bill met me at the front door. I didn't even have to knock.

"Thank you for coming," he said as he ushered me inside. "Can I get you something? Some tea? I make good hot chocolate. That's what the kids tell me, anyway."

"No, thank you."

His cordial greeting left me off-balance as he led me to the back of the house and a battered oak claw-foot table with some mismatched pressed-back chairs. "Sit, please." He pointed me to a seat that faced the service porch and the rear yard. "Thank you," he repeated.

"What can I do to help, Bill?" I wanted to get down to business, whatever it was. I

wanted to get home. I wanted to convince myself that I hadn't made a big mistake by agreeing to this impromptu house call.

"You being here helps."

It wasn't what I wanted to hear from him. "Bill, I'm glad you find my presence comforting. But my advice to you is simple: Tell the police everything you know. The journal, everything. If you have new information, they need to know it. Mallory's welfare is more important than anything else."

"I appreciate your counsel. You were absolutely right about Rachel years ago. But I'm not sure you really understand the dilemma I'm in. Calling the police isn't an option."

"Mallory's safety is the most important thing. Your legal situation is secondary."

"I'm her father. She needs me. Both kids do."

"I'm sure that's true, but —"

"But nothing. If someone had your daughter, or your wife, or both, you would do anything to get them back, wouldn't you? Anything?"

Once I had. Once when a madman was trying to break into my house I'd closed my eyes and pulled a trigger to protect my pregnant wife. I'd do it again if I had to.

And again after that.

Bill had continued talking through my silent reverie; I wasn't sure if I'd missed anything. When I tuned back in he was saying, "Like right now, if you didn't know where your family was, I bet you would do anything to find them, to make sure they were safe. Right?"

"Of course."

"Do you?"

"Do I what?"

"Do you know where your wife and daughter are right now?"

What? "What do you mean?" I was trying to keep my voice level. I was certain I was failing.

"Your family? Do you know where they are right now?"

No, I didn't know where they were. "Right now? What are you saying, Bill?"

"Nothing. I'm just trying to describe my situation in a way that might make sense to another father. The desperation I'm feeling. Do you understand the desperation?"

"Are you threatening my family, Bill?"

"What on earth are you talking about?"

"Have you done something to my wife or daughter?"

"See? That's exactly what I'm talking about. Right now? I think you're beginning

to get it. My desperation. That's good."

"Answer my question." I stood up. "Have you done something to my family?"

A creaking sound pierced through the house. The floor? A door? Had I caused that?

"Did you hear that?" Bill asked. He stood, too.

"Yes. Is someone else here?"

"No. Maybe it was nothing. Old houses, you know."

Was he unconcerned, or merely cavalier? I couldn't tell.

Another creak disturbed the quiet.

"Then again," Bill said. "I'm going to check around a little. You want to call your wife and daughter, ease your mind, you go right ahead."

Bill stood and left the kitchen. Immediately, I pulled out my cell and phoned home. No answer. I tried Lauren's cell. No answer. I placed the phone in front of me on the table. My heart was pounding. Bill came back into the room.

"See anything?"

"No." He spotted the phone on the table. "Don't worry, I'm sure they're fine," he said, as though he knew I hadn't reached Lauren.

Any pretense of patience gone from my

voice, I asked, "What can I do to help, Bill? You said this was about Mallory. Tell me what's going on or I'm leaving."

Certain sounds are as clear as photographs. Glass breaking is one of those sounds. The stark retort of shattering glass filled the house.

"Shit," Bill said. He stood.

I stood, too. "Where?" I whispered.

"Sounded like the basement."

I wasn't so sure, but it wasn't my house.

He moved toward the stairs. "I'm going down. Probably just some neighbor kid trying to scare me. It's been like that around here."

"I'll call nine-one-one."

"No, this is my home. No police. I'll handle it. Stay here."

He flicked on a light and disappeared down the basement stairs. I spotted a rack of knives on the kitchen counter and shuffled a little closer to them.

Before I reached the counter, all the lights in the house flashed off, at once.

70

I stumbled back toward the table to grab my phone and as I reached out I managed to push it over the edge onto the floor. The phone clattered and slid away into the darkness. I dropped down to my hands and knees to try to locate it.

"Alan!" Bill stage-whispered from the basement. "Down here, please, hurry."

"I'm calling for help."

"Please, it's Mallory!"

The tunnel? I scrambled to my feet and felt my way toward the basement stairs, found them, and slowly started descending. A solitary step into the basement I ran into someone. The shock of the collision took my breath away.

"It's me," Bill whispered. I could feel his breath on my face. "Come on."

He took my wrist and led me across a room and through a doorway. "This is where the glass broke, I think."

I couldn't see broken glass. But then, I

couldn't see much. "You said it was Mallory. Where is she?"

"What are you talking about?"

What? "Where's the tunnel?" I asked.

"In the crawl space."

Somewhere nearby, a door closed in the house. Bill released my arm and stepped away from me, back toward the door we'd just come through.

I moved in the same direction.

"Shhh," he said.

"Is there a phone down here?" I whispered.

"Quiet. I need to listen."

The door at the far side of the room we were in opened slowly. A figure paused in the doorway — a black silhouette against an almost black background. Burnt food on a cast-iron skillet.

Mallory? No. Too large, too masculine.

Bob? Maybe.

I was about to call Bob's name when the person's right arm began to rise and a brilliant flash blinded me and a deafening roar blasted my ears. Before I could even process the first explosion, another one erupted. Then, I thought, another. The figure's knees began to buckle and he grasped at the door frame with both hands.

The support did him no good. A second

later he heaved forward and collapsed to the floor.

My hearing temporarily gone, my eyes useless in a basement dark as a moonless night, I was most aware of the smell of the burnt powder from the gun. I was trying to figure out what had just happened. Bill touched my arm and forced a flashlight into my hand. I flicked it on and saw the gun he was holding. It was a revolver. A big thing.

"Over here," Bill said. I pointed the light in the direction of his voice. He'd stepped away from me and was standing in front of a gray electrical panel. With the benefit of the illumination he reached up and pulled hard at the main power circuit.

Instantly the lights in the house came back on.

With great relief I realized that I didn't recognize the man in the heap at the foot of the stairs. It definitely wasn't Bob.

The butt of a pistol had come to rest two inches from the man's nose. Had the man been holding it? I didn't remember hearing it clatter to the floor. I said, "Who is it? Do you know him?"

Bill moved closer. "It's Doyle."

He didn't sound surprised.

71

I was.

"Doyle's already dead, Bill."

"That must have been somebody else they found in the mountains. That's Doyle, right there."

I used the toe of my shoe to move the pistol away, knelt, and placed my quivering fingers on the side of the man's neck. I couldn't find a pulse. I thought of Hannah a month before, the same fingers, the same result.

"Who was it that they found near Allenspark?" I asked.

"I don't know. I don't care. Doyle's dead for sure, now. For me, that's nothing but good news."

Bill wasn't upset.

"Why . . . did you shoot him?"

"He broke into my house. You saw that."

"He's been in your house a dozen times. Why did you shoot him?"

"You saw what happened. A broken

643

window. An intruder in the dark. He was going to shoot me. Us."

He stressed the words "intruder" and "dark." I thought his explanation sounded rehearsed and I immediately questioned whether Bill knew that Doyle was going to be in his house, in his basement. "Did you know he was coming over?"

Bill didn't answer me. "Did you? Did you know he was coming over?"

He still didn't reply. I thought, *Damn, make my day.*

You set this up, you bastard.

Car thieves steal cars. Bank robbers rob banks. For Bill, this was the white van and the orthodontist all over again.

I started up the stairs to get my phone to call 911. When I was about halfway up I heard a woman's voice. "Willy? You down there? What was that noise?"

72

Willy?

Rachel.

"Rachel? Baby?" Bill said.

This time he sounded surprised.

73

Sam didn't arrive first — some patrol cops did — but he was there within fifteen minutes.

He wasn't happy to find me in Bill Miller's house. He wasn't happy to hear Bill Miller claiming that he and I had been having a psychotherapy session when we heard the glass break. He wasn't happy to hear me concur with Bill that what he had told me prior to the shooting had to stay confidential.

What was Sam happy about?

I think he was reasonably pleased that Rachel Miller was there, and that she was insisting that her daughter, Mallory, was fine. "She'll be here any minute. Any minute," Rachel kept saying. "Don't worry, don't worry."

Before he and I were separated by the cops, Bill readily admitted shooting the intruder in his house, whom he continued to insist was the man he knew as his next-

door neighbor, Doyle Chandler.

Sam parked me in the Millers' living room. "You okay?" he asked.

I said I was.

"Good. What about Rachel?" he said to me. "How did she look to you? As a shrink."

"From what little I saw, not too bad. I suspect she's on her meds. I'd have to evaluate her to be sure, but she looks much better than I would have predicted."

"Do you believe what she's saying about Mallory?"

"I think she believes what she's saying about Mallory. It's either delusional, or it's not. I don't know her well enough to tell you which."

"Thank you, Dr. Freud."

"There's a chance she's telling the truth, Sam. That's a good thing. Hope, right? Has she said how she got here?"

" 'With Mallory and her friend.' I'm thinking Bob, the Camaro guy."

"You never found him this morning?"

"No."

"Is Bill claiming the shooting was a 'make my day' thing?"

Colorado has a frontier-justice "Get Out of Jail Free" law that permits citizens to use deadly force to protect personal prop-

647

erty. Intrude on a Coloradan's homestead — and raise enough of a ruckus while you're at it — and you had better hope that the homeowner isn't armed, because he or she has every legal right to blow you to smithereens, even if you're not threatening any imminent bodily harm. The law is popularly known as the "Make My Day" law.

"Yeah," Sam said. "He is. Loudly. Was it?"

"I'm not a lawyer, but probably. Glass broke, power went out, suddenly the guy is there in the basement. Bill shot him. Three times, I think."

"Three?"

"Yeah. I think three. He kept shooting."

"Was the guy armed?"

"It was dark. After the lights were back on, I saw a gun next to him on the floor."

"All sounds pretty convenient."

"Maybe, I don't know. Bill's been through a lot."

"The broken glass? You see it?" Sam asked.

"No."

"Wasn't a window. Somebody put a couple of clear vases or something on the sill in the basement window well. Anyone who opened the window would have

knocked them off. I find that kind of . . . suspicious."

"People put stuff on windowsills all the time."

"Window was unlocked," Sam said. "No sign it was forced."

"A lot of people have been in and out of this house lately."

"You sticking up for him?"

I didn't want to go there. "Bill said the guy he shot was Doyle, Sam. Is that possible?"

"Yeah, I heard. Maybe he has a twin," he said. "Only thing I know for certain about this whole mess is that there are way too many Doyle Chandlers around for my taste." He stood up. "Tell me again, why were you here?"

I looked him in the eye and told him it was privileged, which told him almost all he needed to know.

Diane wasn't in danger anymore. I had secrets to keep.

"Figured." He ran his fingers through his hair while he continued to stare at me. His next sentence surprised me. "Scott Truscott says you solved the Hannah Grant thing."

I shrugged. "I had a thought; I shared it with him. He put it all together; I guess

the coroner agreed."

Sam's raised eyebrows mocked me more than his words did. "A thought? You had a thought? You seem to have a lot of thoughts." He paused. "And a lot of sources."

I took the comment exactly as Sam intended it — as an accusation.

A patrol cop stuck her head into the room and said, "Detective? That Cadillac? The BOLO? We got it."

"Where?"

"CU. Parking lot near the stadium. SWAT's responding."

He looked at me, waiting to see if I was going to be obstinate. I surprised him, I think. I said, "Duane Labs. Plasma physics. Fourth floor."

Sam repeated the location into his radio as he rushed from the room, leaving me alone.

I walked to a beat-up mahogany secretary, picked up the telephone, and called my house. Lauren and Grace were safely home from a wonderful dress-up afternoon, enjoying high tea at the Brown Palace in Denver. Turned out that Gracie loved scones and clotted cream and peppermint tea in china cups, and was absolutely over the moon for cucumber

sandwiches. I gave Lauren a concise version of what was going on in Boulder and assured her I'd be fine. After we hung up I dialed a second number from memory.

"Cozy?" I said. "Hate to ruin your Saturday, but someone I know needs a lawyer."

74

Bob had indeed told Mallory about the tunnel.

She'd used it on Christmas night to get away from the bad guy she had convinced herself was waiting to do to her what had been done eight years before to her young friend. She'd discovered Bob watching movies in Doyle's theater, and had asked him for help in getting away.

Bob had complied.

Mallory had stayed in Bob's flat for the first few days after she'd left home. Once she'd recovered from her Christmas night fright, she ended up mostly terrified about the ruckus she'd caused by running away, and fearful of the repercussions she was sure she would face when she surfaced. She never was quite sure what to make of the fact that the therapist from whom she'd sought help had died.

Out of boredom as much as anything, she finally cajoled Bob into a road trip to

see "our mothers."

Their first stop was Las Vegas, where they picked up Rachel. The second stop was the assisted-living facility in southern Colorado where the trio paid a brief visit to Bob's mother. That's where Bob switched the Camaro — it had developed a problem with its clutch — for his mother's pale-yellow '88 DeVille, which was almost, but not quite, as cherry as Bob's '60s muscle car.

After the real fake Doyle was killed by Bill Miller in his basement, the police didn't have too much difficulty piecing together the identity of the fake fake Doyle. The man whose body had been discovered in the shallow grave near Allenspark turned out to be a homeless man named Eric Brewster whom Doyle had apparently hired to be an unidentifiable corpse rotting in the woods. That probably wasn't the job description he'd offered Brewster when he'd recruited him off the streets of Cheyenne, but that was the job the poor man got. Doyle was ready for the Doyle Chandler identity to die, and he'd picked Brewster carefully, choosing a man about his size and coloring. He gave Brewster some of his own clothes before he led him

out into the woods and shot him in the head. Doyle planted his ID on the body, reasonably figuring that a winter and spring in the elements would destroy any clues, except DNA, as to who the dead man really was. Without a sample for matching, he knew the DNA wouldn't do law enforcement any good.

Doyle Chandler would be dead for at least the second time.

Raoul brought Diane home on a medical jet charter on Monday, the day after he rescued her. Medically she was going to be okay. Psychologically? We held our breaths; time would tell. She'd have love and support, all she needed. Would it be enough? I hoped it would. Diane was tough.

She used Scott Truscott's assessment that Hannah Grant's death was a tragic accident as a crutch to help herself get back on her feet. I wasn't too surprised that Diane was back to work within a week. The first patient she saw on her initial day back?

Fittingly, it was the Cheetos lady. We passed each other in the hall as Diane led the woman from the waiting room to her office. She smiled at me as though we were buddies.

All, apparently, was forgiven.

With Diane safe, and Bob safe, and Mallory safe, I went back to keeping secrets. I was well aware that had Raoul found Diane even half a day later, I probably would have spilled all the beans I had on Bill Miller. With my friend out of harm's way, though, I knew that revealing what I'd learned from my patients would have been nothing more than a self-destructive act of reprisal.

Still, believe me, I had considered it.

I didn't reveal what I knew about Bill and Walter and the orthodontist. I'd initially learned all those things in my role as a psychologist, and couldn't rationalize revealing them. Did I feel good about keeping those secrets? No, I didn't.

Deep down, I'm quite fond of the idea of justice. But, as fond as I am of justice, it's not the business that I'm in.

Walter's family soon reported him missing, but I kept my mouth shut about the location of his body. Raoul did, too. I wouldn't have known anything about Walter if I hadn't been treating Bill, so I considered that information privileged. Was I haunted by the fact that I had knowledge that could help end a family's

fruitless search for a missing husband and father?

Yes, I was.

Nor did I ever publicly share my suspicions that Bill had enticed Doyle back to his house so he could murder him, once and for all, or that I thought he'd arranged for me to be there as his hapless witness. I couldn't prove any of it, but I believed it all to be true. I think Sam did, too. He told me that the police had some phone records that provided circumstantial support to the theory.

But Sam didn't think he could prove it either. Lauren admitted that when the DA reviewed the evidence, she'd concurred.

The Millers became a family again: Mallory was home, Reese came back from his sabbatical with out-of-state relatives, and Rachel moved back into the house. Would the familial bliss last? I had my doubts. Mary Black, still consumed with her triplets, referred Rachel to a psychiatrist in Denver who was having success treating people with symptoms like Rachel's with some innovative pharmaceutical cocktails.

Miracles happen sometimes. Rachel needed one, probably deserved one.

★ ★ ★

Bill?

As the dust was starting to settle I phoned him, and asked politely for one last session.

He declined.

I rephrased my request, turning it into something a little less polite and a little stronger than an invitation. He relented, as I knew he would, and when he came to my office to see me I didn't bother to waste any time on therapeutic niceties. I told him I wanted both of his kids in therapy, and gave him the names of the carefully chosen therapists I wanted each of them to see. I made it clear that I wasn't making a suggestion; the consequences of not heeding my advice would be harsh.

"Yeah?" he said, cocky as shit. His attitude was, "What the hell can you do to me now?"

I had placed my walnut-framed Colorado psychologist's license upside down on the table between us.

"Yeah," I said, failing to match his cockiness.

He crossed his arms. "I don't think so, although I appreciate your concern."

It was readily apparent that he didn't actually appreciate my concern. I reached

down to the table and flipped the frame right-side up. In case he didn't recognize the parchment document, I said, "That's my psychology license."

He looked down at it. "So?"

"I'm willing to lose it."

He eyed me suspiciously. Disbelieving my resolve, I think.

I added, "What are you willing to lose, Bill?"

"You wouldn't."

I handed him a copy of a letter that I'd mailed the day before. "Read this. All it lacks is a name. Your name, actually."

He took a moment to read the letter.

"You release my name like this, you'll never work again."

"Maybe. My colleagues on the state ethics board have always proven themselves to be rather lenient, even to a fault. Regardless, I'm willing to take the risk. If it does come to losing my license, I think I can find work, but something tells me it won't come to that. Why? Because I don't think you really want your role in this whole thing examined by a panel of skeptical strangers with Ph.D.'s."

Was I blackmailing him?

Yes.

Bill knew plenty about blackmail. He'd

seen it from both sides.

Ultimately, he accepted my prescription about his children because he didn't have much choice. How did I know he followed through? Both therapists called and thanked me for referring the kids. I felt some consolation that Reese and Mallory were getting the best mental health care possible. Would it be enough to save them?

In truth, probably not. I wasn't even sure what saving them would look like. But I held out hope for them anyway.

75

The letter that I'd mailed the day before I met with Bill Miller?

The head of the Ethics Committee of the Colorado Psychological Association didn't know exactly what to do with it.

Psychologists don't usually turn themselves in for ethical violations.

But I did; I turned myself in for multiple violations of the ethical code of the American Psychological Association.

There's a psychological phenomenon, an ego defense if you will, called undoing, or sometimes, doing-undoing. A husband sends flowers to his wife the day after he flirts shamelessly with his secretary. A mother makes a special dessert for her daughter after she sentences the kid to death row for not putting the cap back on a tube of toothpaste. It's unconscious psychological misdirection — the substitution of an act that is acceptable to the ego for something that was not. In the world of

psychological defenses, it's the great cosmic chalkboard eraser.

Turning myself in for unethical conduct was my own twisted version of doing-undoing.

What I'd prepared and submitted to the ethics board was a detailed account of my multiple professional transgressions in the clinical care of both Bill Miller and Bob Brandt. Although I had to withhold plenty of specifics — including my patients' names — I put in sufficient evidence of misjudgment to make my myriad ethical lapses crystal clear to my colleagues.

I'd also sought written permission from both Bob and Bill to release their names to the ethics investigators, but both, not surprisingly, chose anonymity and declined to participate in the inquiry. Neither was eager to prolong public scrutiny of their behavior. Without the cooperation of the patients involved the board had little to go on other than my self-damning appraisal of my own professional conduct.

The head of the board phoned and asked me, mildly exasperated, what I thought they should do with me.

I suggested a sanction: a full year's monitored supervision of my practice by a senior, respected psychologist.

The board greedily concurred, content to have the matter behind them.

I felt a little better, but not much. As an ego balm, doing-undoing is a notoriously ineffective palliative. And when you know you're doing it — and employ it without the insulation of unconscious motivation — as I was, undoing amounts to little more than a halfhearted *mea culpa*.

76

Bob?

Our regular Tuesday at 4:15 came around slightly less than forty-eight hours after he and Mallory had been picked up by the police in the plasma physics reception area in the Duane Building at CU. Mallory was watching Bob deadhead his Christmas begonia when the first few SWAT officers burst into the room and scared the crap out of both of them.

Head down, as usual, he walked into my office for his appointment at the regular time. He plopped his backpack onto the floor and sat across from me without a word of greeting.

We'd been there, literally, a hundred times before.

Bob had spent one night stewing in police custody while Cozy Maitlin convinced the authorities that his client was guilty of nothing more than piss-poor judgment.

Mallory had repeatedly denied that Bob had ever coerced her to do anything, denied that he encouraged her to run away, vigorously maintained that the road trip had been her idea, and asserted that he'd never placed a hand on her during their entire time together. Mallory's only actual complaints about Bob were that he wasn't very friendly and hardly ever said a word that wasn't about cars or board games.

Rachel Miller confirmed that Bob had been a well-behaved, if boring, companion to her and her daughter.

The police discovered no evidence to the contrary. None.

I waited only a moment for him to settle onto his chair before I said, "Hello."

He was staring at his hands. I supposed that Bob knew that I had arranged for Cozy to represent him. Although Bob Brandt and Cozier Maitlin were probably the oddest client-attorney pairing since Michael Jackson and anybody, I suspected that Cozy would have told Bob how lucky he was to have him for a lawyer. I doubted Bob would mention it to me, and I wondered if I should bring it up if he didn't.

"Am I going to be charged?" he said, finally breaking the silence, and interrupting

my reverie long before I'd reached anything approximating a decision.

With kidnapping? Didn't look like it, but that was definitely a question that should be directed to Cozy, not to me. It was my turn, though, so I said, "Charged for what?"

"For last week."

Oh. "The session you missed? No, I won't bill you for that."

Bob acknowledged me with a nod, but he didn't thank me. Did I expect him to? No, not really.

When he finally raised his face enough so that I could see it, I spotted a cold sore the size of a lug nut on his lower lip. The rounded wound was fresh and blistered. Had to hurt. I thought, *Stress.* He didn't speak again for a while. Then, "I almost lost my job. It was stupid."

"What was stupid?" I could have asked. But the recent idiocy options were numerous. Too numerous. Plenty by him, plenty by me.

More by him.

I waited. The Kinko's box sat beside me on the small table next to my chair. Had Bob seen it when he walked in? I hadn't noticed him even glancing in my direction.

"She asked. I didn't kidnap her. Sheesh."

No half head-shake, just the "sheesh."

Although technically it was my turn to speak, Bob said, "I shouldn't have shown her the tunnel in the first place."

I could have argued with him at that point, suggesting that maybe what he shouldn't have done was drive a minor who was the subject of a national manhunt across state lines, but time was on my side. An entire year of Tuesdays littered the calendar ahead. Bob and I would get there eventually.

"She was scared after that therapist died," he said. "I thought she should know how to get out of her house."

His tone, I thought, was defensive, which wasn't too surprising. But was Mallory's fear really the way Bob was going to try to rationalize his decision to help her stay hidden when the whole world was frantically looking for her? I suspected not.

Why? Pulling off that argument would require that Bob convince me that he'd suddenly developed a capacity for empathy. Sadly, the events of the previous couple of weeks would no more leave Bob with empathy than they would leave Bill Miller with a well-functioning superego. "Go on," I said.

He sighed before he turned away,

reached down, and rooted around in his rucksack. He lifted out an electronic device about the size of a paperback book and held it up for me to see.

I couldn't help but smile. It was a fancy, programmable remote control. The one from Doyle's basement, no doubt.

"Perhaps you should give that to your attorney," I suggested.

He stuffed the remote back into the daypack and gazed out the window. The southern sky warned of dusk. He said, "She doesn't look fourteen."

My spleen didn't spasm. I allowed the force of gravity to press me solidly against my chair.

"Tell me," I said.

I thought I'd try to be a therapist for a while.

Acknowledgments

As usual, I got a lot of help.

My gratitude to the kind, talented people at Dutton, especially Carole Baron and Brian Tart, and to my agent, Lynn Nesbit.

Jane Davis, Elyse Morgan, and Al Silverman continue to support me in ways that are personal as well as professional. I've said thanks. I'll say it again, knowing it's not enough. Nancy Hall, once more, brought her critical eye to the process.

If I wore one, I'd tip my hat to Virginia Danna and Darrell C. R. Olson, Sr. Call it courage, call it blind faith, but they paid good money to charity to have their names used for characters in this book. I think I'll just call it generosity. Norm Clarke, on the other hand, was a draftee. His gracious, one-of-a-kind introduction to Las Vegas and his willingness to let me give him an important role in the story were much appreciated.

Robert Greer, who does more things well than anyone I've ever met (other than perhaps his late wife, Phyllis), provided some consultation about one of his many specialties. And although I've long been indebted to them for pushing the swing, the Limericks — Jeffrey and Patricia — deserve some fresh credit for one of this book's small secrets.

Xan, Rose, and my mother, Sara White Kellas, continue not to be surprised that I'm able to do this. They believe, and what is better than that?

About the Author

Stephen White is the author of twelve previous suspense novels, including the recent *New York Times* bestsellers *The Best Revenge* and *Warning Signs*. A clinical psychologist, he lives in Colorado.

I

THE SCHOLAR'S BIBLE

THE SCHOLAR'S BIBLE

THE BACKGROUND OF LAND AND HISTORY

OF THE OLD TESTAMENT

H. ST.J. HART

"EPITOMES HAVE BEEN called the moths of just history; they eat out the poetry of it." That sentence will probably soon haunt your mind and speak your thoughts, as you read this chapter. Your attention will be asked for what is little more than tabulated information and lists of dates, for such things as are but the bare bones of ancient history—and behold they are very dry—when you had rather feed your imagination on its warm flesh and blood. But the remedy is in your own hands. Numerous Old Testament passages will be referred to in the hope that you will read them. To make their ancient wealth of men and women come alive in your imagination is a task for you yourself—it cannot be done for you, through the uneasy medium of ink and paper. And remember the limits of our immediate aim. We seek only to chronicle what may quickly enable you to find your way about the Old Testament, and to answer the question, "From whom do we get the Old Testament?" The clues which you most need to this limited end begin in the eighth century B.C., in the time when Amos and Hosea prophesied prophecies of doom, and the shadow of Assyrian expansion and aggrandizement was over all the Near East. But our tale will be more easily told if we begin with some preliminary observations.

Palestine is a small country. The area of the united Hebrew kingdom, over which Solomon reigned in the tenth century B.C., stretching from Dan to Beersheba and including territory east of Jordan, was perhaps between nine and ten thousand square miles . . . . This little land is a land of strong climatic contrasts. Mount Lebanon (6,070 feet above the Mediterranean) and Mount Hermon (9,383 feet above the Mediterranean) are famous for snow. One hundred and forty-three miles away the river Jordan (the name is from a root meaning "to descend"), which is fed by their streams, races through a deep rift in the earth's surface, in tropical heat, into the Dead Sea which is 1,290 feet below Mediterranean level. On either side are rough limestone mountain ranges. Those to the east form the foothills of the vast Arabian desert. Those on the west, broken only by the "plains of Esdraelon" form the bulk of the Hebrew kingdom, and from a height which averages perhaps 2,500 round about Jerusalem get gradually lower as you go southwards towards Egypt. The Jordan has few tributaries, so that cities had to be built near wells. In ancient times there was no important Hebrew seaport on the Mediterranean coast. The overseas trade from the Levant went from Phoenician ports. Solomon, indeed, tried to work a navy, but the Hebrews were no sailors, and Hiram, King of Tyre (a Phoenician city) provided assistance. Solomon's port was far away from the Mediterranean, at Ezion-geber, "which is beside Eloth on the shore of the Red Sea in the land of Edom" (1 Kings ix, 26). His navy brought luxury goods to augment the splendour of his court and harem at Jerusalem. He perhaps also owned ships which sailed the Mediterranean in the fleet of King Hiram of Tyre. But this is disputed. The life of the people was not frequently affected by overseas trade. They depended on flocks and herds, corn, and wine, and olive oil. These gave them their living, and provided sometimes a surplus which their kings could send abroad in payment of their foreign debts (1 Kings v, 10, 11). There seems to have been hardly any private international economic enterprise in the days of the kings of Israel and Judah. Accordingly ancient Hebrew religion is first concerned with the needs of shepherds and farmers, which were increase of flocks and herds, good harvests and good vintages. It has much in common with the so-called "fertility" religions all over that ancient world. In Egypt agriculture depended on the control of the Nile, and its flood-water, manipulated by an elaborate irrigation system. In Palestine Hebrew farmers were less independent of the weather. "For the land whither thou goest in to possess it, is not as the land of Egypt, from whence ye came out, where thou sowedst thy seed, and wateredst it with thy foot, as a garden of herbs: but the land, whither ye go over to possess it, is a land of hills and valleys, and drinketh water of the rain of heaven: a land which Yahweh thy God careth for: the eyes of Yahweh thy God are always upon it, from the beginning of the year even unto the end of the year" (Deuteronomy xi, 10-12). In such a climate it was easy to believe in providence, and the plain man in Israel could not separate his theology from the weather. When he had a bad harvest there were those who told him he should have a bad conscience as well (Deuteronomy xxviii: Amos iv).

It is "a land of hills and valleys." When you lift up your eyes in Palestine you lift them up unto the hills. The country is naturally divided into small compact districts, which tend to be isolated, a circumstance which does much to explain the long time it took the Hebrews to occupy Palestine. The hillsides are not turf-covered but open rock or rough scrub, which afforded pasturage for sheep, goats and allied wild animals. In the plain of Sharon, and southwards to the country which was Philistia (from which the name Palestine comes to us through the Greeks), were the main cornfields between the mountains and the sea. Elsewhere cereals were confined to the lower valleys and such parts as the broken plain of Esdraelon. From the North, East and South, the winds, including the famous Sirocco, brought the heat and dust of the desert. West winds brought rain. The cloud "as small as a man's hand" seen looking out to sea from Carmel heralded the storm of 1 Kings xviii. Winter began in October, which was ploughing time, with "the former rains," and lasted till the spring in March, which was followed by "the latter rains" in April, and the harvest late in that month. The vintage was, of course, much later. From harvest to vintage the summer was hot and dry. You watched your grapes ripen, and men could be spared from the fields for armed service. The wars of the Hebrews and their small neighbours—Edom, Moab, Ammon, Syria—tended to be annual wars—and seasonal in "the time when kings go forth to war" (2 Samuel xi, 1), limited to the summer with its vacation from the demands of agriculture. Only great kings—kings of Egypt, of Assyria, or of Babylon, etc.—could afford a standing army. It was an austere twelve months, save only for the brief and brilliant spring. That spring was dear to the Hebrews who loved bright colours and fresh flowers. It is the time for love (Song of Songs ii, 10-13), and a type of all that is blessed and brings refreshment to toil-weary men (Isaiah xxxv, Palm xviii, 9, etc.). The Hebrew valued his ripening crops and vineyards which were "the precious things of the fruits of the sun" (Deuteronomy xxxiii, 14), but the summer heat

was too much for him, and taught him instinctively to seek the shade.
He dwelt securely "under the defence of the Most High" when he
abode "under the shadow of the Almighty" (Psalm xci, 1). It was
"under the shadow of Yahweh's wings" that he rejoiced (Psalm lxiii).
The water and the shade—those are two things necessary to physical
salvation in the Holy Land. They have left their mark on the language
of Old Testament religion (think for example of Psalm xlii, 1, Isaiah
xxxii, 2, Isaiah xxxv).

But if Palestine was a small country, it was by no means off
the map of the ancient world. The nearer neighbours of the Hebrews,
the "nations round about," as e.g. the Phoenicians, the Aramaeans
or Syrians of Damascus, the Philistines, the Edomites, the Ammonites,
and the Moabites (all are mentioned, with censure, in Amos i, 3-ii, 3)—
these nearer neighbours are very closely allied by race, culture, language,
and religion, with the Hebrews, except for the Philistines who came in
the twelfth century B.C. bringing other customs, which they seem soon
to have lost, from over the seas. But with the others Hebrew connections were close. They spoke very similar dialects—"Hebrew" as it is
in the Old Testament took shape in Palestine as we may judge from
the ways of expressing the points of the compass. They worshipped
very similar gods in very similar ways. If Yahweh had his "high
places," so had Chemosh the god, or Baal (rudely called "the abomination" in 1 Kings xi, 7), of Moab. On the Moabite stone we find
Mesha king of Moab using phrases which if you read "Yahweh" for
"Chemosh" will irresistibly remind you of the books of Samuel and
Kings: we may cite "I made this high place for Chemosh . . ."; "Omri
king of Israel afflicted Moab many days, because Chemosh was angry
with his land"; "I took it [the town of Nebo], and slew the whole of
it . . . for I had devoted it to Ashtor-Chemosh," and so on. In the
same way, if Yahweh had not been on Israel's side there could have
been no conquering of Canaan, no driving away of the Philistines, no
successful wars with Moab or Damascus. The gods and men of these
little kingdoms acted together in history, defeat of the nation was also
defeat for its god—unless as we shall see some other explanation could
be found—perhaps "he was angry with his land."

Hebrew literature bears witness to wider contacts than these, to
meetings with Egyptians, Hittites, Assyrians, Babylonians, Persians,
Greeks, and Romans. With the exception of the Romans whose capital
city in far-away Italy even legend takes back no farther than 753 B.C.,

and of the Persians whose armies do not come west until the sixth century B.C., all these peoples, or groups of peoples conveniently so labelled could have been met with, or at least they and their ideas might have been heard of, by the Hebrews, at almost any time in their Biblical history after the settlement in Palestine. This should be remembered more especially when you speculate on borrowed ideas found in the Old Testament. The cultural world was already one before Israel and Judah learned from their prophets a new and higher doctrine of the nature of Yahweh: and one it continued to be. In itself the tracing of an idea to an Egyptian or Babylonian ancestry does not tell you when the Hebrews first met with it, liked it, and appropriated it. But that is by the way. If you ask why the Hebrews met so many and great nations in addition to the nations round about, the answer is, Look at the map. If we keep to the eastern end of the Mediterranean, the two most important areas of civilization were Egypt and Mesopotamia. In Egypt the Hebrews met first the Pharaohs, and later, after the death of Alexander (323 B.C.), the Greek Ptolemies. Mesopotamia was the home of Babylonians and Assyrians, whose empire at times included Palestine. The lines of trade from Egypt to Mesopotamia, and the lines of war, went the same way. Sometimes the Egyptians, sometimes the men of Mesopotamia, were dominant among the great ones of the earth. Sometimes this compact world was broken into from Asia Minor—as e.g. by the Hittites. Whether for the purposes of peace or for the prosecution of war, the inhabitants of Egypt and Mesopotamia were always exchanging visits. Palestine lay between, the landbridge (narrow between the Mediterranean Sea and the Arabian Desert), from Egypt to Mesopotamia—a buffer, or a "bone of contention" state. So it comes about that we can divide the story of the Biblical history of the Hebrews into convenient periods, according to the dominant power whose armies or policemen might at any time disturb the Hebrew from such peace as he allowed himself to enjoy "under his vine and under his fig tree," when he was not carrying "the sword of Yahweh and of General Such-an-one" against his nearer neighbours.

We may use such a division into periods, according to the dominant power, with very great appropriateness, because the Hebrews came themselves of necessity to be acutely conscious of the succession of world empires which rode roughshod over the Holy Land and people. The scribe-seer of Daniel thinks of all history in such terms and asks, in the name of the faithful, "how long shall these things be?" There is a pathetic retrospect in Jeremiah 1, 17, looking back soon after the Babylonian Exile began, which tells the familiar tale: "Israel is a scattered sheep; the lions have driven him away: first the king of Assyria hath devoured him; and last this Nebuchadrezzar king of Babylon hath broken his bones." Our "periods" may thus have more meaning than a mere enthusiasm for tabulation may seem to give them.

But at first we encounter a difficulty. Long centuries of Hebrew history are problematical and obscure. The interests of such books, or parts of books, in the Old Testament, which we would naturally classify as histories are not the interests which to-day we so classify in other documents. Thus we have seen that the Hebrew Bible classifies Joshua, Judges, Samuel and Kings as the Former Prophets, and our later enquiries will reveal the cogency of this classification. You have as it were a series of photographs, all of them "close-ups." The detail is vivid, the scenes live. But except in the period when information comes from several sources—e.g. from the Latter Prophets, as well as the Former Prophets, and sometimes from sources outside the Bible altogether—you are left without a panorama. Such a confluence of sources is really only available from the eighth century B.C. to the sixth—the period of the Old Testament prophets, of whom the earliest was Amos, who have books known by their names. The last few chapters of 2 Kings set the stage. The foreign chronicles of a Tiglath-pileser, a Sennacherib, or a Nebuchadrezzar, give the background. The prophets speak, and for a few weeks or days or hours you are able to feel as much at home with the ancient Hebrews as books and memories, tales of your grandfather and the sermons that he heard, can ever make you with so remote a past. But of the years and generations before Amos prophesied in the eighth century B.C., and of the years and generations after the exile in the sixth century B.C., the records are not so complete. You see them as in a glass, darkly. Often you cannot be sure who is speaking, or that you hear the authentic accents of those ages at all. Seeing then that we seek now the briefest and clearest answer to the simple question —from whom do we get the Old Testament?—we shall make the time from Amos to the Exile the centre of our tabulated tale, only going before or after when it is absolutely necessary, and attempting no full and continuous account of the Hebrews for any period.

We have all heard of the Twelve Tribes of Israel and Judah, and in a general sense it is the easiest and least exceptionable answer to our question. But as such it would not be very illuminating. Our tabulated story will explain this. Here are our periods:[1]

(i)   "The days of old": before the eighth century confluence of sources illuminates the Hebrew scene.

(ii)   "The Assyrian period": 853 B.C.–612 B.C., overlapping

(iii) "The Egyptian interlude": 612 B.C.–605B.C.

(iv)   "The Babylonian period": 605 B.C.–539 B.C.

(v)   "The Persian Period": 539 B.C.–334 B.C.

(vi)   "The Greek Period": 332/1 B.C.–63 B.C.

(vii) "The Roman Period": 63 B.C. onwards.

When we begin to read Amos (*c.* 760 B.C.) we find that we are well into the Assyrian Period. We also find that there are two Hebrew kingdoms, both serving the same national god. To explain this situation we shall need to go back to Solomon, the last of three kings of an undivided Israel and Judah. But what of the complicated story of what went before, even farther back in "the days of old"? It must suffice to indicate its outline, very briefly indeed, lest our tale come to drive heavily, like the wheels of Pharaoh's chariots. We can put it all, or nearly all, succinctly in this Biblical confession of faith written for use by the Holy People, when Yahweh their God settled them in Palestine:

> A Syrian [R. V. margin: Heb. *Aramaean*] ready to perish was my father, and he went down into Egypt, and sojourned there few in number; and he became there a nation, great, mighty, and populous: and the Egyptians evil entreated us, and afflicted us, and laid upon us hard bondage: and we cried unto Yahweh, the God of our fathers, and Yahweh heard our voice, and saw our affliction, and our toil, and our oppression: and Yahweh brought us forth out of Egypt with a mighty hand, and with an outstretched

---

[1] "In a system of Chronology . . . it is of far greater importance to be correct in the sequence, or order of succession, than to be accurate in the dates; not to mention that the one is practicable, the other not."—S. T. COLERIDGE.

This remark explains our situation in the problems of Old Testament chronology very well. The dates given in Chapter Two, and often elsewhere, are based on those given in Oesterley and Robinson, *A History of Israel*, 2 volumes, Oxford, 1932. The reader is also recommended to consult the chronological tables on pp. 15 and 16 of *The Westminster Historical Atlas*, edited by G. E. Wright and F. V. Filson, London, 1946. The dates found there will exhibit the considerable range of variation in the modern calculations.

arm, and with great terribleness, and with signs, and with wonders: and he hath brought us into this place, and hath given us this land, a land flowing with milk and honey . . . (Deuteronomy xxvi, 5-9).

So "Israel" in Palestine acknowledges a "perishing" or nomadic ancestor of Aramaean stock and surveys the histories of Genesis to Deuteronomy, and much that followed after, in this fine liturgical form. The hero of the exodus from Egypt was Moses. The long story from the nomadic Aramaean (probably Jacob = Israel) to the settlement in Palestine, the struggle with the Philistines which interfered with that achievement, how Israel elected to have a king, like all the nations round about, how Saul was the first king, and David the second, how David captured Jerusalem and made it his royal city, how he on his death-bed declared that his son Solomon should be king after him— these things take you from Genesis to the opening chapters of 1 Kings, a tale of many centuries, with a strange gap of silence of apparently four hundred years between Genesis and Exodus. A continuous history could not be written. Fortunately most of our clues to the making of the Hebrew Bible can be found in later times. And now when we turn to Amos who began to prophesy soon before or soon after 760 B.C. we find that we are well into the Assyrian period, and that there are two Hebrew kingdoms. The larger, northern, kingdom is Israel, its king is Jeroboam son of Joash of the line of Jehu, and his royal city is Samaria. The smaller, southern, kingdom is Judah, its king is of the house and lineage of David, and his royal city is Jerusalem. Why are there two Hebrew kingdoms both worshipping one national god, Yahweh?

Long ago Solomon, son of David, had reigned (*c.* 976-936 B.C.) a great king of Jerusalem, over all the twelve tribes of Israel and Judah, within his large dominions from Dan to Beersheba, supreme. Kings' daughters had been among his numerous wives (1 Kings xi, 1-8), and of these the princess who most marked his importance was the daughter of the Pharaoh of Egypt himself (1 Kings iii, 1). David his father had fought the enemies of Israel, and made the name of Yahweh the god of Israel respected among all the nations round about. During his last illness Solomon was made king by a palace intrigue (1 Kings i) with David's consent. Solomon began his reign with security measures (1 Kings ii) such as were probably necessary if he were to continue king. He then settled down to a long reign of peace and honour, allying himself by marriage to many neighbour countries. He undertook great building schemes in Jerusalem and made himself a new palace, and his god a new Temple. In these projects he was assisted by Hiram king of Tyre—who also assisted him in his naval ventures at Ezion-geber. But it was all very expensive, and the expense of the splendid court and harem at Jerusalem fell on the people of the Hebrews (1 Kings iv, 7 ff.). There was likewise hard labour in the felling of timber, and in the quarrying of stones, and in conveying timber and stones to Jerusalem for the new buildings: and this hard labour also fell on the people of the Hebrews (1 Kings v, 13-18). Only two generations ago they had been independent and scattered farmers who could hardly unite to fight the Philistines under Saul (1 Samuel x, 27). Even the popular David had not been beyond the reach of tribal jealousy, though it could be stated in a friendly way at the end of a revolt (2 Samuel xix, 40-43). David, when he had at last become king of all Israel, had been an elected king, we might almost say a constitutional king, for his subjects "made a league" with him (2 Samuel v, 1-3). But Solomon first and last was a typical oriental despot. And the burden fell on the shoulders of a very independent people.

So Solomon was occasionally uneasy (1 Kings xi, 40). When he died the people went to the ancient sanctuary at Shechem to make his son Rehoboam king. The new shrine at Jerusalem, which Solomon's piety built for Yahweh there, had not yet superseded the older sanctuaries in popular esteem. At Shechem there was trouble. Jeroboam, the son of Nebat, who had fled from the wrath of Solomon reappeared from exile in Egypt. Through him the people sought to make terms with their new king. "Thy father made our yoke grievous: now therefore make thou the grievous service of thy father, and his heavy yoke which he put upon us, lighter, and we will serve thee." Rehoboam was uncompromising. "My father chastized you with whips, but I will chastize you with scorpions." That was the signal for revolt. The story is vigorously told in 1 Kings xii, 1-20. "What portion have we in David? neither have we inheritance in the son of Jesse: to your tents, O Israel" (ibid., verse 16). Finally, as though Jeroboam had not been present in verse 1-19 (which is implied in the Septuagint translation), we read in verse 20: "And it came to pass, when all Israel heard that Jeroboam was returned, that they sent and called him unto the congregation, and made him king over all Israel: there was none that followed the house of David, but the tribe of Judah only." According to the next verse he had also the tribe of Benjamin. So there are two kingdoms, the one of ten tribes, the other of two.

The royal house of David never forgot and never forgave the injury done it by Jeroboam the son of Nebat. Unnatural "civil" wars followed (1 Kings xiv, 30), and all was turmoil and confusion. Two hundred years later the worst that Isaiah could say about an Assyrian invasion was that it would bring such days as have not come since "the day that Ephraim departed from Judah" (Isaiah vii, 17). But Rehoboam had two parts in the Holy People: Jeroboam the son of Nebat had ten. The hostility of the two nations did not end with Rehoboam's death (probably in 919 B.C.). The general calamities had been increased by the invasion of "Shishak, king of Egypt," (1 Kings xiv, 25 ff.) in 930 B.C. or perhaps some years later.

Jeroboam secured his position in Israel, and testified to his loyalty to Yahweh, by making "two calves of gold" for the sanctuaries of Yahweh at Beth-el and Dan. The two images—perhaps bulls rather than calves—for use in the worship of Yahweh, can hardly have been a complete innovation. Certainly Jeroboam cannot have believed that they would move Yahweh to anger, even though he may have been acquainted with the idea that Yahweh might not be worshipped with images. There was obviously more than one point of view on the subject. A commentary on 1 Kings xii, 25-33 should be consulted. Jeroboam made Shechem his royal city (ibid.).

We learn from 1 and 2 Kings that the years between the division of the kingdom and the battle of Karkar when the Assyrian period began, is a period of wars—little wars, annual wars, petty border wars, in the dry season, between such neighbours as Israel and Judah (which had so recently broken the brotherly covenant), and the Aramaean (Syrian) kingdom of Damascus, or the Edomites, Moabites and Ammonites. Always of the two Hebrew kingdoms Israel is the larger and more powerful, lying still on the map of the great world with the major trade routes crossing her land. Judah is a little highland state away from international notice if she does not attract it. In Israel kings win the throne often by violence from the ninth century B.C. to the fall of Samaria in 721 B.C. In Judah, conditions are more stable—there are fewer tribal rivalries to placate—and there will still be a king of the house of David in Jerusalem when Judah is overrun by the Babylonians in 597 and 586 B.C.

The narrative of the period from the division to the battle of Karkar (853 B.C.) in 1 Kings xii-2 Kings viii is largely devoted to stirring accounts of Elijah and Elisha, two fierce prophets of Yahweh who belonged to the Northern Kingdom. The chapters which tell of them are some of the best writing in the Old Testament. They should be read with care, for they are one of the more considerable remaining sections of the Old Testament which emanated from the "Ten Tribes." Politically Omri king of Israel (about 886-874) is important. It was he that built Samaria, and made it his royal city (1 Kings xvi, 24). We hear little of him in the Bible, but there are references to him on the Mesha stone, and later the Assyrians still refer to Israel as the "land of Omri," even after his dynasty had been exterminated by Jehu. The friendly relations between the Hebrews and the Phoenicians were maintained. Ahab son of Omri married a Phoenician princess of Zidon, named Jezebel (1 Kings xvi, 31). With her, naturally, came the worship of the baal of her own land, which Ahab duly established in Samaria, so bringing great trouble on Israel. The chief wars of Omri and Ahab (c. 874-852 B.C.) were against Damascus, disputing possession of districts (e.g. Bashan and Gilead) on the east of the Jordan. You read of them in the Elijah and Elisha stories. It is clear that the alliance of Damascus and Israel and others against Assyria at Karkar in 853 was short-lived. This coalition continued for perhaps ten or eleven years—in fact probably until the "prophetic revolt" in 842 B.C.

The two and a half centuries which began with Karkar (853), when an Assyrian king claimed to have defeated a Palestinian league of states, including Israel, were to see the rise of the Assyrian Empire and its decay and collapse (612). At the height of its power it extended from the Persian Gulf to the borders of Egypt. The desire to control routes to the Mediterranean coast is usually held to explain the western campaigns of the Assyrian kings at the beginning of that period. After the battle of Karkar—which is not mentioned in the Bible—Aram (Syria) and Israel appear to have forgone local hostilities. But Jehu's revolt affected both kingdoms. The worship of the Phoenician baal of Jezebel had become very popular in Yahweh's land. It had even been carried to Judah, for the king of Judah had the daughter of Ahab to wife (2 Kings viii, 18) and Judah was now on good terms with Israel, and probably almost a vassal state. One year (perhaps 842 B.C.) Elisha, the prophet of Yahweh, on whom the fierce and hairy mantle of Elijah had fallen, precipitated what is called "the prophetic revolt," the revolt of Jehu, which aimed at exterminating Jezebel and all her works and all her family, that Yahweh and his prophets might be no more insulted by the worship of a foreign baal in his holy land (2 Kings viii-x). The two Hebrew kings were assassinated; as many of their relatives as could be found, Jezebel, and the prophets of her baal, were also slaughtered. In Judah the queen-mother, Athaliah, daughter of Ahab and Jezebel, turned herself reigning queen to save herself from Jehu, and "destroyed all the seed royal" (2 Kings xi, 1). Joash, son of Ahaziah, alone of the house of David, was saved from her hands. He was a child and was concealed. Eventually Athaliah was assassinated and Joash (= Jehoash) was made king, with appropriate violence against the "house of baal" (2 Kings xi, 17-21) and his priest.

While the Hebrews were thus preoccupied in internal strife, Shalmaneser, king of Assyria, came back to the west. Was Jehu summoned to his presence? "Tribute of Iaua (Jehu) son of Omri" (the irony is perhaps unconscious), says Shalmaneser, by the picture of Jehu doing obeisance before him, on the Black Obelisk,[2] "silver, gold, a golden beaker, golden goblets, golden pitchers, lead, staves for the hand of the king, javelins, I received from him."

Jehu has become king. But his violent beginnings left Israel weak. For nearly half a century Israel is unequal to the struggle against Damascus (Syria's royal city). There is a new "oppression of Israel." Eventually "Yahweh saw the oppression of Israel, how that the king of Syria oppressed them" (2 Kings xiii, 4). The last scene in the life of Elisha promises better things. With trembling hands the sickly prophet who in his day was a host in himself, in himself "the chariots of Israel and the horsemen thereof" (ibid., verse 14), covers the hands of Joash king of Israel as he shoots an arrow in the direction of Aram (Syria). Strong symbolism indeed! "Yahweh's arrow of victory over Syria: for thou shalt smite the Syrians in Aphek, till thou have consumed them" (verse 17). About 802 B.C. Adad-nirari, king of Assyria, took Damascus in a campaign which brought him the submission of Israel and other small states which did not wish to share the fate of Damascus. Then Assyrian armies ceased to come westwards for fifty years. Damascus was weak. Israel once more became strong. Joash and more especially Jeroboam, "son of Joash, king of Israel," restored the prestige and the borders of Israel (2 Kings xiv, 23-29). It was to an Israel proud and rich and confident in these victories, which exultingly looked for "the day of Yahweh" (Amos v, 18) as if that would bring even more of the enemies of Yahweh beneath the heel of Israel, that Amos spoke his hard words. Something was rotten within the state of Israel.

[2]Cited from D. D. Luckenbill, *Ancient Records of Assyria and Babylonia,* Chicago, 1926, volume 1, p. 211.

Can you not read the signs of the times? Do you not remember that recent famine (iv, 6), the drought when it was yet three months to harvest (verse 7), the blasting and mildew, the palmerworm which devoured your vineyards, your fig trees and your olive trees (9)? the "pestilence after the manner of Egypt" (10)? "Woe unto you that desire the day of Yahweh! Wherefore would ye have the day of Yahweh? it is darkness and not light" (v, 18).

So spoke the prophet Amos, first of the prophets of an Age of Conflict. We have passed from the ages whose prophets survive only in the memories of other men, to the age of the Writing Prophets, the prophets who survive not only in the memories of the men who collected and edited their oracles, but whose actual compositions could be incorporated in those memories. What was the religious conflict which made this age the Age of Conflict, what the new conception of God which they taught, how they related that new teaching to men and manners in Israel and Judah—are questions we must reserve for the next chapters. We note in passing that the rise of this strange succession of prophets among the Hebrews in the eighth and seventh centuries was far more important for men in general than the rise of the great kings of Assyria and Babylon. By the power of their gods these marched through the length and breadth of the earth that they might possess dwelling-places which were not theirs. But Nineveh and Babylon have passed away and their gods are honoured no more upon the lips of men. Men of Israel and Judah—Amos, Hosea, Micah, Isaiah, Jeremiah, and the rest of them—men of the least of the lands these great ones' hands had conquered—are living forces in the world to-day. But let us return to our parable.

Amos prophesied the fall of Samaria and captivity for the men of Israel "beyond Damascus" (v, 27). The way from Nineveh to Samaria lay through Damascus. Such a threat therefore meant that Assyrian hosts would come again, and that this time they would not be put off with "silver, gold, a golden beaker, golden goblets, golden pitchers, lead, staves for the hand of a king, and javelins." They would occupy the country, settle new settlers there and deport the old inhabitants "beyond Damascus." By that policy of displacing populations the kings of Assyria, and later those of Babylon, habitually weakened the possibilities of revolt. A subject Israel in the land of Israel which was also the land of its god, might defy the policemen of Assyria. "Beyond Damascus" in an alien land, in the territory of deities whose armies had triumphed over the hosts of Yahweh, the God of Israel, they would be less likely to do so. It was a good policy from the Assyrian point of view. What was strange was that Amos, Hosea, Micah, and Isaiah successively declared that the Assyrian captivity was the work of Yahweh—punishing Israel for her sins. The plain Hebrew must have been disquieted at this. He might acknowledge that temporary reverses —the late Syrian oppression—were the work of Yahweh punishing Israel for her sins. But to be taken from Yahweh's land where alone men offered sacrifice and burnt offerings to him—that should mean that the gods of Assyria were more powerful than Yahweh, that they could take his children out of his presence. Perhaps it meant that Yahweh was no god, powerless to save.

Swiftly, surely, at whatever cost to Yahweh's great name, the prophecies of Amos, Hosea, Micah, and Isaiah, were fulfilled in fact. These prophets could certainly read the signs of the times, whatever you might think of their new teaching. In 745 B.C. a new king reigned in Assyria—Tiglath-pileser, called Pul in 2 Kings xv, 19, 20—and he soon turned his eyes westward. In 738 B.C. Tiglath-pileser took tribute from Menahem, king of Israel. In 734/3 B.C., perhaps in answer to an appeal from the terrified Ahaz, king of Judah, who was shut up in Jerusalem his royal city by a besieging army of Israel and Syria (Isaiah vii, viii), Tiglath-pileser again intervened in Palestine. He invaded the northern territories of the kingdom of Samaria, carried away captives "beyond Damascus," but left a native king—Hoshea—on the throne (2 Kings xv, 29, 30). "The land of Bit Humri (= Beth-Omri, House of Omri)," says the Assyrian record,[3] ". . . all its people together with their gods I carried off to Assyria. Pakaha (= Pekah) they deposed and placed Ausi (= Hoshea) over them as king. Ten talents of gold . . . talents of silver as their tribute I received from them, and to Assyria I carried them."

Soon Hoshea rebelled against the king of Assyria. Samaria was besieged by Shalmaneser (724 B.C.) and fell to Sargon his successor in 721 B.C. The rest of the population—or a large part of it—went into captivity "beyond Damascus." Here is what remains of Sargon's account of the matter:[4] "In my first year of reign . . . Samerinai (= the inhabitants of Samaria) . . . (of Shamash) who causes me to obtain victory . . . 27,290 people who lived there I carried away. The city I rebuilt. I made it greater than it was before; people of the lands my

---

[3]Cited from Luckenbill, *op. cit.,* volume I, p. 293.

[4]Cited from Luckenbill, *op. cit.,* volume II, page 2.

hands had conquered I settled therein. My official I placed over them as governor" (compare 2 Kings xvii, 5, 6, 24 ff.). So ended the Northern Hebrew Kingdom. Samaria became yet another Assyrian province, and its new population had come to terms with the local god (Yahweh, "the god of the land") who had created difficulties to begin with (2 Kings xvii, 24-40). The newcomers no doubt mixed in marriage with what was left of the Hebrew population. They brought their own gods, but had to arrange for the worship of Yahweh as well (2 Kings xvii, 33). Their history thus provides on a small scale an interesting parallel to the earlier settlement of the people of Yahweh in Palestine, and their habit of worshipping the old local gods as well as Yahweh.

But the exiles pass out of history, lost in the populations where Sargon settled them. There are a few later references to them— perhaps some of their descendants met exiles from Judah more than a hundred years later. But whatever the character of their religion it does not seem to have survived the hard fact of history that the gods of Assyria had proved greater than Yahweh, that Yahweh had not been able to deliver Samaria out of his hand. The prophets had spoken on different lines. But who now heard them? The point for us to grasp and ponder here is that the Northern Tribes, representing the bulk of the old Hebrews, pass out of Biblical history in 721. Judah went forward as the Israel of God. To the men of Judah who represent the descendants of but a small section of the Hebrews, over whom Solomon long ago had reigned in all his glory, we owe the Old Testament. The literary legacy of the Northern Tribes survives in the Old Testament only because the men of Judah saw fit to collect, edit, and preserve them. The men of Judah, moreover, had been prejudiced against Israel ever since the "departing of Ephraim from David." They naturally accepted the verdict of the prophets that it was for Israel's sins that she had been carried away "beyond Damascus." The list of sins was added to as the years went by. No ruler of Israel "did that which was right in the eyes of Yahweh," according to 1 and 2 Kings.

Hezekiah, king of Judah (*c.* 725-690 B.C.), pursued a more subservient policy, at least at the beginning of his reign, and so ruled on as a native ruler in Jerusalem, by grace of Sargon, king of Assyria, after 721 B.C. Once Hezekiah took an important part in a revolt against Assyrian power. The revolt was effectively crushed by Sennacherib (perhaps in 701 B.C.), who boasts in these terms:

As for Hezekiah, the Jew, who did not submit to my yoke, forty-six of his strong, walled cities, as well as the small cities in their neighbourhood, which were without number—by escalade and by bringing up siege engines (?), by attacking and storming on foot, by mines, tunnels and breaches (?) I besieged and took (those cities). 200,150 people, great and small, male and female, horses, mules, asses, camels, cattle and sheep, without number I brought away from them and counted as spoil. Himself, like a caged bird, I shut up in Jerusalem, his royal city. Earthworks I threw up against him—the one coming out of his city gate I turned back to his misery. The cities of his, which I had despoiled, I cut off from his land and to Mitinti, king of Ashdod, Padî, king of Ekron, and Selli-bêl, king of Gaza, I gave them. And, (thus) I diminished his land. I added to the former tribute, and laid upon him *(v., them)* as their yearly payment, a tax (in the form of) gifts for my majesty. As for Hezekiah, the terrifying splendour of my majesty overcame him, and the Urbi (Arabs) and his mercenary (?) troops which he had brought in to strengthen Jerusalem, his royal city, deserted him *(lit.* took leave). In addition to 30 talents of gold and 800 talents of silver (there were), gems, antimony, jewels (?), large *sandu*-stones, couches of ivory, house chairs of ivory, elephant's hide, ivory *(lit.* elephant's "teeth"), maple (?), boxwood, all kinds of valuable (heavy) treasures, as well as his daughters, his harem, his male and female musicians (which), he had (them) bring after me to Nineveh, my royal city. To pay tribute and to accept *(lit.* do) servitude he dispatched his messengers. (Luckenbill, *Ancient Records of Assyria and Babylonia,* II, pp. 119ff.)

But what the Jews perhaps chiefly remembered was that although Assyrian armies did besiege Jerusalem, they did not enter it. The sanctuary of Yahweh in Sion (Jerusalem) had thus been inviolate while all his other territory had been overrun. Perhaps no foreign gods could actually take Jerusalem. The revolt was vainly sponsored by Egypt, apparently in search of a defence line against the Assyrian advance (2 Kings xviii-xx—a vivid series of narratives of great interest to any who would see into the logic of these national religions).

Less than a century later the whole world was in uproar and Assyrian power was crumbling away. Josiah, king of Judah, seems to have been left very much to his own devices. On the basis of a mysterious "book of the law" found in the Temple at Jerusalem he instituted a famous religious reformation, purifying the national cult of Yahweh from foreign accretions (2 Kings xxii-xxiii). Its most characteristic regulation was, so it seems, what we call "the law of one sanctuary" according to which the past and then present practice of worshipping Yahweh at many shrines was all wrong. There was one only genuine shrine in which it pleased him to set his name to dwell there. It seems to have gone without saying that that shrine was the royal Temple at Jerusalem. The local high places up and down the Holy Land were to be abolished. Foreign cults at Jerusalem were forbidden too. Things had already gone too far, but perhaps by these means the anger of Yahweh might be mitigated in time to avert calamity. The new views applied for the reformers not only to their own times. The whole story of Hebrew worship at many shrines ever since the building of Solomon's Temple was now seen to be one long story of sin and rebellion against Yahweh. This gave an interesting additional religious explanation of the fate of Samaria in 721 B.C., and was soon to help to explain the end of the Kingdom of Judah (587 /6 B.C.). The presence of foreign cults in Jerusalem also pointed, as the prophets had been preaching many years, to the same end. What could these polytheistic Jews expect if so they publicly provoked Yahweh to anger? The whole reform was marked by a very special celebration of the passover as a public festival for which the men of Judah must go to Jerusalem. So to keep this feast seems also to have been a novelty. Formally and on the surface Josiah was able to impose his will, and by some the new law was kept by conviction. But strange things began to go on underground in dark cellars in Jerusalem out of the king's eye (Ezekiel viii: Jeremiah xliv)—how soon these practices began again after Josiah's reform we do not know—but there is little reason to postulate any length of time. The secret rites mentioned in those two chapters as prevailing early in the sixth century may with probability be read back into the last years of the seventh. In the long account of Josiah's Reform in 2 Kings we find that the local priests, who by the law of one sanctuary were put out of professional employment, "came not up to the altar of Yahweh in Jerusalem, but they did eat unleavened bread among their brethren" (xxiii, 9). It sounds as if the law book had provided that they should share the duties of the Jerusalem priesthood. These few features of the reform should be borne in mind. They may help us when the time comes to try to identify the law book. For our present purpose it suffices to note that we can add to our previous refrain—the Old Testament comes to us not from all the twelve tribes of Israel and Judah, but from the men of Judah; and not from all the men of Judah, but from the men of Judah who accepted Josiah's Reform with its law of one sanctuary, and its assumption that that uniquely orthodox sanctuary was the Temple at Jerusalem.

Josiah died at Megiddo in strange circumstances in 608 B.C., when in what we have called the Egyptian Interlude a Pharaoh marched across Palestine to war beyond Damascus (2 Kings xxiii, 29, 30: compare 2 Chronicles xxxv, 20-24). By 605 B.C. the Babylonians are masters of what had been the Assyrian Empire, and have defeated the Egyptians, who had intervened on the Assyrian side in the struggle, at Carchemish. Nebuchadrezzar, the victorious general, became king (604 B.C.), and was soon discovered to be the new scourge of the people of Yahweh. This Nebuchadrezzar is already well known to you because it is said that, to please his hill-country wife who abhorred Babylon and loved mountain scenery, he adorned his palace with trees so that it was called "the Hanging Gardens of Babylon": it was a miracle of rare device and ancient opulence, one of the seven wonders of the world, in its kind not to be surpassed, except God should make another paradise.

The people of Judah met a harder side of Nebuchadrezzar than that. The prophets of the age are Jeremiah and Ezekiel. Josiah's reforms are still official religion, but underground there is a riot of foreign worships. Jeremiah advised submission to Babylon, to whom Yahweh had given the kingdom of this world. The advice was ignored. The fierce nationalism of the men of Judah made them trust in themselves that they could do great things—and might not help be coming from Egypt? Judah revolted, and this led to a first Babylonian taking of Jerusalem, and a first carrying away captive to Babylon in 597 B.C. Judah is allowed to retain a native ruler—Zedekiah—who is bound by oath to keep faith with Babylon. Jeremiah continues his old theme that to submit to Babylon is to submit to Yahweh (e.g. Jeremiah xxix), and Ezekiel the priest and prophet among the exiles takes up the same message. Their preaching was in vain. Zedekiah sympathized with Jeremiah, but was helpless in the hands of the rough nationalists who looked for Egyptian aid. Judah revolted again. The prophecies change into definite prophecies of doom. In 586 B.C. the siege of Jerusalem ended in the Babylonian triumph and a further carrying away captive to the rivers of Babylon. The throne of David had lost its ancient glory—since Solomon it had not been very great—Yahweh had cast his sinful people out of his presence (2 Kings xxiv, xxv), and the Exilic Age had begun.

Many were unfaithful to Yahweh, and came out openly on the side of other gods whom they had long secretly worshipped (Jeremiah xliv), having drawn their own conclusions from this last catastrophe. But there were others, the men not only of Judah, but of one sanctuary —and that one sanctuary Jerusalem—who accepted the prophets' interpretation of the Babylonian captivity. If indeed Yahweh had used the Babylonians to punish his sinful nation, then he was a great king above all gods, and even away from Jerusalem, although you could not offer sacrifice you could pray to him. It followed also for the fervent few whether far away "by the rivers of Babylon" or in war-devastated Palestine, or in voluntary exile in Egypt, that Yahweh would one day, if only for his name's sake, come home to Jerusalem, and "turn again the captivity of Zion." There are passages in Jeremiah and Ezekiel encouraging you to wait for the redemption of Israel. To that faithful remnant is due the perpetuation of the orthodoxy of the law of one sanctuary and all that went with it—and so ultimately the Old Testament.

The Neo-Babylonian Empire did not last long. Cyrus the Persian—hailed as Yahweh's Messiah or Anointed One (Isaiah xlv, 1) by an unnamed prophet who spoke new words of comfort ("comfort ye my people" (Isaiah xl)) to the faithful—Cyrus the Persian entered Babylon in 539 and took over the Babylonian Empire which he included in his larger dominions. His policy included permission to displaced persons to go home if they wanted to do so. The Jews in Babylonia were comfortable and prosperous: Palestine was disorganized and impoverished (see the Lamentations). The only impulse for a return was a religious impulse, the impulse of the men of one sanctuary who wished to see that one sanctuary restored at Jerusalem. Some perhaps soon after 539, some again about 520 B.C., found their way back to Palestine, to Yahweh's own land. It did not fulfil all their hopes perhaps (Psalm 126), but a beginning was made. Prompted by the preaching of Haggai and Zechariah i-viii, the rebuilding of the Temple was completed in 516 or 515 B.C., and what is usually called the age of the Second Temple began. The rebuilding is perhaps disparaged in Isaiah lxvi, 1, 2. Jerusalem is now a small city state, part of a Persian satrapy, and no doubt paying tribute to Persian kings in far away Susa or Ecbatana "beyond Damascus." At home the Jews are as it were a theocracy, obedient to the accredited priests of Yahweh. There are still Jews in exile who, if they are also men of one sanctuary, still worship Yahweh by prayer and the study, perhaps, of his laws: but sacrifices they leave to the priests of Jerusalem. Few, poor, and politically crushed, these men of Judah became the fathers through many generations of 7 per cent of the population of the Roman Empire some five hundred years later.

But there was to be a further Reformation. Its heroes are Ezra and Nehemiah, and its course is extremely problematical and obscure. It belongs in the main to the second half of the fifth century B.C. Both Ezra and Nehemiah are Jews in Persian service among the exiles who come with special powers to Jerusalem. The movement encourages and widens a growing rift between the "people of the land" whose ancestors had never left Palestine, and "the sons of captivity" who had at various times gone home from Babylonia. An even stricter descendant of prophetic orthodoxy is imposed on Jerusalem. There must be no inter-marriage with foreign nations—and had not the "people of the land" freely married with men of many neighbour nations, including the notoriously sinful people of Samaria, in the exilic age and since? The walls of Jerusalem are rebuilt perhaps that the shutting of gates may keep out any who will not divorce their foreign wives—certainly to keep out profane Phoenician bodies from the sea coast who have been violating the Sabbath by selling fish in Jerusalem on that holy day (Nehemiah xiii). Nehemiah viii tells you of the solemn public reading by Ezra of "the law of Moses." It is a much longer undertaking than the reading of "the book of the law" at Josiah's Reform (2 Kings xxii, xxiii). The occasion is marked by a great public celebration of the feast of Tabernacles (Nehemiah viii, 7) about which you may read in Leviticus xxiii, 39-43. In this form this ancient feast does not appear to have been kept before, a circumstance which may help us later to discover what laws Ezra was introducing.

Obscure in many ways as is the age of Ezra and Nehemiah, the years which follow are obscurer still. In due course the kingdoms of this world were wrested from the Persians by Alexander the Great of Macedon, who arrived in Palestine in 332 B.C. Soon after his death the Jews found themselves until just before 200 B.C., subject to the new Greek dynasty of the Ptolemies who reigned in Egypt. To them tribute must be paid, but, with the exception of a few outrages, religion was unmolested and remained under the High Priests. Rapidly a large Jewish community sprang up in Alexander's new Egyptian city of Alexandria, and in the third century B.C. the Law, and the other sacred books, began to be translated into Greek. About 200 B.C. the Jews of Palestine passed into the Empire of the Greek dynasty of the Seleucids, kings of Syria. In 168/7 B.C. an attempt was made, with much

Jewish encouragement, to force Greek customs and the worship of Zeus—of whom the reigning Seleucid (Antiochus Epiphanes) was supposed to be a manifestation—on the Jews. This led to the Maccabean wars out of which emerged an independent Jewish kingdom, in which the king expected to be high priest. All this time Greek-speaking Jewry was increasing and moving farther west. Already Jerusalem was an oecumenical religious capital, already the Greek-speaking Jews had a larger Bible (including books of our Apocrypha) than their Palestinian brethren.

In 63 B.C. Pompey took Jerusalem and began the story of Roman interference in Jewry which set the stage for the Jewish scene which we meet in the gospels, when Pharisees compassed sea and land to make one proselyte.

From this our tabulated tale we have therefore learned this much so far. The Old Testament comes to us not from all the twelve tribes of Israel and Judah, but from the two tribes of the southern kingdom of Judah: not from all the men of Judah, but from those men of one sanctuary who accepted Josiah's reform: not from all the men of one sanctuary, but from those who also in due time accepted the reforms of Ezra and Nehemiah: and, lastly, not from all these, but from those of them who remained in Palestine, and whose sacred books did not include the Apocrypha. Ultimately of course both Old Testament and Apocrypha came into Christianity in Greek from the Greek-speaking Jews of the dispersion. But the Old Testament as it is owes its limits to the Jews of Palestine. Its books have passed the critical judgment of the priests of the Second Temple, and they have done so for the most part between the reforms of Ezra and Nehemiah and the second century B.C. (compare the Greek prologue to Ecclesiasticus). Each earlier event or controversy which narrowed down the field from which those who should one day determine the limits of the Old Testament might be drawn has left its mark somewhere on the books. Each group which separated itself or was separated from the central stream of Judah and Jerusalem, receives in varying degrees condemnation and reproof. What men from the larger Israel wrote has been preserved in the Old Testament, which is the Jewish Jerusalem Bible, only by their severest critics (pp. 15-38).

THE JEWISH HISTORICAL AND POLITICAL BACKGROUND
OF THE NEW TESTAMENT

KIRSOPP LAKE AND SYLVIA LAKE

TO UNDERSTAND THE NEW TESTAMENT properly, it is well to remember that it is not, like the Old Testament, the story of a people living in a corner of the western edge of the Semitic world, but of a group—not a people—which started from the eastern edge of the Greco-Roman world and spread all over the west. In the Old Testament the background is the world of Babylon or Persia, but in the New Testament it is the Roman Empire. The process of Hellenisation, to say nothing of Romanisation, was by no means complete in the first century, but many Jews were already looking towards the west and not towards the east.

Seven hundred years earlier Syria, Palestine and Trans-Jordan (Per-aea) had been inhabited by a number of Semitic tribes,—Aramites, Phoenicians, Moabites, Ammonites, Edomites, Ishmaelites, Ephraimites and Judahites,—with a non-Semitic race, the Philistines, holding the coast from Carmel to Egypt. These all lived on terms of the most neighbourly enmity, which was broken up when the Assyrians and Babylonians conquered the country. A little later, the Persians took over the whole district, which was divided into Persian satrapies. From this time on, the Jews, who had returned from exile, occupied Jerusalem and a mixed race, the "people of the land," with whom the Jews refused to have friendly relations, occupied the rest. Their world was still Semitic-speaking and Semitic-thinking, for, though the Persians were Iranians and not Semites, the commercial language of their empire was always that which they had inherited from Babylonia.

Within the span of a single life Alexander's conquests changed the whole situation. The Greeks came pouring across Asia Minor, through Syria into Egypt in one direction, and as far as the boundaries of India in the other. Though the Aramaic which the Babylonian empire had spoken did not die out it had, from that moment, a serious rival in Greek,—so that Greek thought, Greek customs, Greek law, and above all the Greek language gradually supplanted the inheritance of Babylon.

But the successors of Alexander were not able to work together. They incessantly quarreled, and the result, among other things, was a rivalry between the house of Seleucus in the north and that of the Ptolemies in Egypt. Palestine fell first under the rule of the Ptolemies, who left the Jews largely alone, and afterwards under that of the House of Seleucus which did not.

The Ptolemaic kings encouraged the growth of the Jewish community in Egypt. In Alexandria it was allowed to have its own laws, its own magistrates and its own quarter of the city. It learnt to use Greek, wrote books in Greek and produced a translation of the Old Testament into Greek (the Septuagint) which differed from our present Hebrew both in text and in contents. Moreover, it became Hellenised in thought, though it will always be a problem how far this Hellenisation spread.

So long as the Ptolemies held Palestine the Jews in Jerusalem were reasonably happy; the kings of the house of Seleucus, on the other hand, as the heirs of Alexander in Syria, endeavoured to go as far as possible in introducing Greek customs and the Greek language throughout the East. They imposed Greek civilisation on Jerusalem, without waiting for the Jews to ask for it, and for a time had some success. But Antiochus Epiphanes endeavoured to force the pace too rapidly, and was handicapped by war and sedition. The result was that he lost his temper at Jewish ingratitude and the Jews lost theirs at Greek oppression; persecution and rebellion mutually encouraged each other.

So long as Antiochus lived, he was able to hold down the Jews by force, but his immediate successors were incompetent and a successful rebellion under the Maccabees first detached Judaea and Galilee and ultimately resulted in the gradual break-up of the whole territory of the Seleucids, to the accompaniment of disorder and civil war. The Maccabees not only succeeded in reconquering for the Jews the Jewish portions of Palestine, including Jerusalem, but destroyed or conquered most of the purely Greek cities such as Samaria, Caesarea (Stratonis Turris) and the Decapolis, and tyrannised over the non-Jewish inhabitants of Palestine.

The inability of the Ptolemies and the house of Seleucus either to control the mixed populations of the East, to conquer one another or to co-operate with one another, opened the way for the Roman Empire to inherit their property. The will of Attalus and the genius of Pompey, Caesar, Antony and Augustus combined to make the Roman Empire the sole legatee of Alexander's conquest.

The Maccabees soon saw their chance of fishing in the troubled waters, solicited alliance with Rome, and took part in the quarrels of the various Roman parties, endeavouring to divine and help the probable winner. When Pompey entered Palestine in 63 B.C. he recognised the Maccabaean kingdom, but freed the Greek cities of Palestine from its rule.

Then followed a strange episode. A man named Antipater, half-Jew half-Arab, made himself the intelligently unscrupulous agent of the Romans and indispensable to the last of the Maccabees. His son, Herod, inherited his ability and convinced Augustus that, although he had supported Antony, he would be a faithful and valuable ally to any one who was successful. A man of infinite talent and unwearied energy, untrammeled by scruples, he was entrusted by Rome with the government of all Palestine. He did not continue the policy of the Maccabees, but adopted that of the Romans, and under his rule Greeks and Jews were equally protected in their own domains.

The animosity not unnaturally felt towards Herod by Josephus and later on by Christian writers has caused many to overlook the great qualities which he showed as a governor. With far-sighted vision, though not without brutality, he suppressed banditry and rebellion and bestowed equal benefits on the Jews in Jerusalem and on the Greeks elsewhere, realising that the business of a ruler of Palestine was to be a Jew in Jerusalem and a Greek in Samaria or Caesarea. He restored Jerusalem to something approaching the glory which it had in the time of the Persians. He greatly enlarged the Temple, adding to it among other things a tower for the garrison, overlooking the whole area, and on the other side of the city built a palace for himself and his soldiers at the spot which is now police headquarters in Jerusalem. He rebuilt Stratonis Turris on the coast and Samaria in the hill country, calling the former Caesarea and the latter Sebaste, in honour of Augustus. In Sebaste he erected a temple to the Emperor and apparently encouraged the worship of Kore.

That this policy secured for him tolerance rather than friendship from both Greeks and Jews was inevitable, but few rulers were ever more successful than he in keeping Palestine in a condition of relative peace, without injuring the reasonable rights of either of the hostile races.

To what extent Herod was in any sense subject to the Roman governor of Syria is open to question. So long as he was successful (and he was throughout his life) he was probably not interfered with, but it may be guessed rather than proved that the Legatus of Syria was his immediate guide, even if not his official superior. In any case, the Legatus of Syria lived a long way off. Syria was an immense province and at the time of Herod, the Romans were more concerned with the northern part of it and with Cilicia, which was attached to it as part of the same province, than they could be with Palestine, which was nominally independent.

With the death of Herod the Great, a new period began. The Romans were forced to choose between permitting internecine strife between Herod's children, of whom he had allowed a few to survive, or of changing the constitution of Palestine. They naturally chose the latter alternative. They abolished the title of King and established one son, Archelaus, as the Tetrarch of Judaea and Samaria, and another, Antipas (the Herod of the greater part of the Gospel story) as Tetrarch in Galilee and Peraea (Trans-Jordan). Archelaus was a failure and in his place a subordinate Roman official with the title of Procurator was sent to take charge of Judaea and Samaria. There were a succession of these officials and at the time of Christ Pontius Pilate was in power.

The Procurator was in fact the High Commissioner of the period and had the same problems to deal with. He had at his disposal a body of troops including legionaries and auxiliaries. These were the Palestinian police of the period and probably there was a centurion (the equivalent of a sergeant) in control of each of the small districts. The Procurator appointed the High Priest, in fact if not wholly in theory, and managed the taxes by means of men who 'farmed' them, so that there was a multitude of collectors, the 'Publicans' of the Gospels. The taxes were partly 'tribute' to Rome, partly 'octroi' for local use.

Thus it came to pass that in the time of Jesus both the Procurator of Judaea, Pontius Pilate, and the Tetrarch of Galilee, Herod Antipas, controlled districts inhabited partly by Jews, partly by non-Jews (who were then called Greeks and now Arabs). Rome expected its delegates to govern in such a way that there should be as few disturbances as possible, but the Jews were at least partially conciliated by being allowed a very large degree of freedom to manage their own affairs. They were curiously divided and their organisation in Jerusalem differed from that in other places.

In Jerusalem, the Temple was the centre of Jewish life. It was nominally under the control of the High Priest, but in practice the High Priest was the temporary representative of a group of great families who quarreled among themselves, but cooperated against all others. These families are often referred to as "the High Priests" and were undoubtedly the richest and most powerful of the Jews. But they were unpopular. They made the Temple a source of wealth by exploiting the rule that sacrifices should be only of perfect animals, which were to be bought from them, and that alms should be paid in Jewish money, which they provided in exchange for Roman coins, charging of course a commission on the exchange. They also levied a tax on all Jews for the upkeep of the Temple which probably included at least some of their own houses. They were inclined to "Hellenise," accept Greco-Roman customs, and be friendly with the Romans. This was, in chief part at least, their ruin. As has always been the case in the East, the people submitted to extortion but rebelled against civilisation.

In addition to his position in the Temple, the High Priest, whose office was no longer held for life, but only during efficient service, was at the head of the Sanhedrin, a Greek word (*synedrion*) meaning 'council'. It was composed, theoretically at least, of seventy members chosen from among the priests, scribes and elders. We know less about it than might be desired, because our information is derived from the Mishna, which was compiled two or three generations after the destruction of Jerusalem, and is primarily a legislative rather than an historical document; it gives, at least in some points, a picture of an ideal Sanhedrin, not of one which ever existed.

In other places where Jews were dominant there may have been minor Sanhedria, but the real centres of local government and of Jewish life generally were the synagogues, the origin of which is not quite clear. They were not only churches, but also law courts, and were controlled by the Rabbis, who were learned in the Law of Israel. In Jerusalem, they were less obviously powerful, and much less wealthy than the priests, for though there were many synagogues in Jerusalem, each with its own rulers, they were overshadowed by the Temple and the Sanhedrin. Outside of Jerusalem, they were really the governing bodies of the Jews, and when the Temple and the Priesthood disappeared in the ruin of Jerusalem, the synagogues continued their work with but little change. Judaism discovered that the Temple and the Priesthood had only an emotional value, and that the Law was an adequate substitute for the sacrifice in the Temple.[1]

Apart from the functional difference between the Priests and the Rabbis (Scribes), the Jews, according to Josephus, recognised in the

[1] Cf. the beautiful story that when leaving Jerusalem Jokanan ben Zakkai said that henceforth the Jews had nothing save the Almighty and his Law—but that would suffice.

first century three chief political or theological parties, the Sadducees, the Pharisees, and the 'fourth Philosophy." The Gospels mention one other, the Herodians (Mark iii.6 and xii.13). Apart from these references, we know nothing about the last.

The Sadducees, whose name may or may not mean 'the followers of Zadok,' were believers in the Law, but not more than the Law. They rejected later developments of Judaism, such as a belief in a resurrection or in angels (cf. Mark xii.18 and Acts xxiii.8).

Most of the priests belonged to this party, which perished with the destruction of the Temple. The generally hostile references in the Talmud suggest that the Sadducees were often Hellenisers, accepting much Greek thought, but it should be remembered that statements about the Sadducees from this source are peculiarly untrustworthy because in the Middle Ages the Censor forbade all hostile reference to Christians and in order to cover their meaning, the Jewish scribes often referred to "the Sadducees" statements which had been originally intended to apply to the Christians. It is, therefore, not always certain whether any one allusion to the Sadducees really applies to them.

The Pharisees were probably the most influential party outside Jerusalem. Their exact origin is not known, but they first appear in the time of the Maccabees and seem to be in some way connected with those who were known as the Chasidim or 'holy ones.'

The word 'Pharisee' is probably connected etymologically with the verb that means to separate, but in what sense it is not clear. The purpose of the Pharisees was to insist upon a life in accordance with the Law, and they devoted much time to interpreting the difficulties in its practice. Their decisions were preserved either by memory or in writing and were formulated in the second century as the Mishna (literally 'repetition') or 'Explanation of the Law.' This again was expounded by still later Rabbis and became the basis of the Talmud, preserved in two forms (the Jerusalem and the Babylonian) which are our main source of information for orthodox Judaism. None of these rules were regarded as additions to the Law, but as explanations intended to render it easier for an ordinary man to avoid transgression.

Those who regarded the Law as positive and found pleasure in living according to it, naturally welcomed the teaching of the Pharisees; and some of these, such as Johanan ben Zacchai, seem to have been men of great spiritual beauty. For those who regarded the Law as chiefly negative,—a series of prohibitions,—the Pharisaic amplifications must have been intolerable. It should, however, be remembered in using the

Talmud that orthodox Judaism as we have known it since the fourth century is not necessarily identical in all respects with the Judaism which was current in Galilee, or even in Jerusalem, in the first century.

It is usually held to be probable that the *Psalms of Solomon* would be more correctly entitled the *Psalms of the Pharisees.* This curious document is remarkable for two things: *a.* it is the most explicit statement (Ps. Sol. xviii) extant of the "Messianic" expectation of a Davidic prince in the first century before Christ, *b.* it constantly distinguishes between the "righteous" and the "sinners," meaning Pharisees and non-Pharisees. This affords an interesting comment on the "sinners" of the gospels.

The 'fourth Philosophy' is a term found in Josephus. He obviously used 'philosophia' in the sense of 'party' (an interesting comment on the deterioration of the word) and by 'fourth Philosophy' he meant the supporters of Judas of Galilee, in the time of the census of Quirinius A.D. 6, and their successors. Agreeing with the Pharisees in general they shared the Apocalyptic hope for a "good time" for the Jews and tried to hasten its coming. They thought it wicked to acknowledge any ruler except God, and advocated strong action to eject the usurping Romans.

From the point of view of Roman officials, the most dangerous phenomenon in Palestine was the existence of this class of patriots. They became prominent in the days immediately preceding and during the Jewish wars, and the name of "Zealot" was given to one part of them,— the followers of John of Gischala. The members of the Patriotic party clashed with the priestly party, especially in regard to Rome. The High Priests were, of course, not wholly favourable to the rule of Rome or of Herod, but, so long as they were allowed to manage the Temple in their own way and accumulate money, they were not actively hostile to the government and cooperated with it in order to keep the people in order. For that reason, in the days immediately preceding the war, the systematic and steady assassination of the Priests was one of the main features of the policy of the Patriotic party.

The party of the 'Herodians' is not mentioned except in the gospels. The termination of the word (-ianos) certainly means "partisan of," but we have only guesses to tell us anything more about the Herodians. Probably they were those who preferred the House of Herod to the Procurator of the Emperor, and ultimately succeeded in securing Herod Agrippa I as king of Judaea. But there is no evidence. (pp. 187-197)

THE BACKGROUND OF THE NEW TESTAMENT IN THE GREEK-SPEAKING WORLD

KIRSOPP LAKE AND SYLVIA LAKE

WITH THE SECOND PART of the Acts of the Apostles, the story of early Christianity passes from Palestine, a little country only partly populated by men of Jewish race and religion, to the Roman Empire, with its many nations and religions.

It was, in the main, a Greek world, not a Roman, except for purposes of government. Rome, the city, not the Empire, was still predominantly Latin; the upper classes, at least, were not Greek, still less Oriental. But for the rest of the Empire, the language was Greek and the thought was Greek; yet not the Greek of Athens, but of that curiously 'Hellenistic' world which started from Macedonia.

If one took a map and painted it in various shades of blue to indicate the extent to which Greek culture had spread, the deepest color would probably be in the cities of Asia Minor or of Egypt, not in Europe at all. But these Asiatic or Egyptian cities, though they were predominantly Greek superstructures, retained Oriental bases. The submerged nations, Phrygians, Syrians, Galatians and Egyptians, remained recognisable by custom and worship, but they were mostly bilingual and had been so impregnated by Greek thought and so overrun by Greek traders, that they had become superficially more Greek than anything else. The weak spot in this cosmopolitan civilisation was that the combination of races produced not a synthesis but a smudge. The Greeks found difficulty in penetrating the East in government, rather than in persuasion or thought: the Romans in persuasion or thought, not in government.

The main feature of the Roman government was its difference from the earlier world empires of Babylon and Assyria, and, though not to the same extent, of Persia. The Babylonians and Assyrians had tried to adopt the policy of the melting-pot and to enforce a homogeneous system. They had desired to have an empire in which all the inhabitants were "100% Babylonian" in despite of language, race, origin and history. To accomplish their purpose, they had made use of enforced migration; Jews had been planted in Mesopotamia and Mesopotamians in Palestine. The experiment had not been very successful; the melting-pot had not melted. It had spoiled Jews for being good Jews, and it made undoubtedly bad Palestinians out of possibly good Mesopotamians.

The Persian kings dropped the experiment; they allowed a considerable amount of local autonomy, and were probably more successful than is realised by any one who looks only through glasses supplied by Herodotus and the Greek tragedians, but in the end their system of government collapsed. First the Greeks and then the Romans took over the empire.

The Romans, consciously or unconsciously, developed and improved the Persian system. They recognised the autonomy, at least in small matters, of every part of the enormous realm which they had inherited, or won, from the peoples of the East. No one was forced to adopt Roman customs or Roman ideas, except in so far as they were necessary for the peace and order of the whole. The various countries retained to a large extent their own forms of government and their own forms of speech. Rome had seen, though she had scarcely formulated, the vision of "a common superior of nations."

The government of the Empire was nominally divided between the Emperor and the Senate. As often happens in history, the position of the Emperor was very different in theory from what it was in practice. The imperial power was nominally held only for a short but undefined period, and the Emperor was therefore "acclaimed" at frequent but irregular intervals. He also held, as a kind of connecting link with the past, the tribunican power, to which he was annually appointed. As Emperor he was in control of all the more recent provinces, which are therefore called 'Imperial.' The other provinces were governed by representatives of the Senate, which appointed a governor of consular rank. These are the Senatorial provinces. In practice, of course, the Emperor's choice was largely instrumental in the Senate's nomination.

The governor of a Senatorial province was called the *Proconsul* in Latin or ἀνθύπατος in Greek; the governor of an Imperial province was called *Propraetor* in Latin or ἀντιστράτηγος in Greek. He might also be called the *Legatus,* or in Greek ἡγέμων.

Each governor of an Imperial province had troops assigned to him, legionaries and auxilaries. These filled the function of police as well as soldiers. The commandant of a legion was a *tribunus,* or in Greek a χιλιάρχος, literally a "captain over a thousand"; his subordinates, who would today be something between subalterns and non-commissioned officers, were the centurions, or "officers over a hundred men." The Greek for 'centurion' was sometimes χεντυρίων and sometimes ἑκατον-τάρχης.

The governor was, of course, the chief magistrate in a province and ruled partly by Roman law, partly by local custom; but it should be remembered that the Romans made much use of *coercitio*—compulsion —which was administrative police action, governed chiefly by the policeman's or the magistrate's idea of what was desirable.

In the various cities of the Empire there were naturally subordinate magistrates, with varying titles regulated largely by local usage. Their general title in the New Testament is ἄοχοντες, but in Philippi they appear to have been also called στρατηγοί, which probably represents *duoviri* rather than praetors. In Thessalonica (Acts xvii.6) they are called πολιτάρχαι,—a characteristically Macedonian name. The officers of these magistrates, at least in some cities, were called *lictors* or in Greek ῥαβδοῦχοι, though they were lictors only in a limited sense,—they carried the fasces but not the axes.

The general practice of Roman administration was to leave all minor cases, not affecting life or fiscal questions, to magistrates whose verdicts were based on local law and custom. It is not quite clear whether Roman citizens were in all respects free from the jurisdiction of native courts, but certainly a Roman citizen could always insist on a hearing before a Roman official.

The strength of the Roman Empire was that, dealing with a very complex and heterogeneous situation, it did not try to be either simple or homogeneous. Each city, with the country surrounding it, was governed by a compromise between the ideas which Roman governors brought with them and the customs which they found obtaining in their provinces. Moreover, there was a noticeable difference between colonies, free cities and cities which were neither colonies nor free. In each case, the practice of government was considered on its merits.

The Jews especially, not only in Palestine but also in at least some of the great cities of the Empire, were in a peculiar position. They were regarded as a separate nation, and were allowed to inflict punishment, including scourging and possibly death, on their compatriots. This was especially true in Alexandria, where the Jews had their own *ethnarch* (also called *alabarch*), their own laws and even their own quarter of the city. The extent to which this Jewish nation in Alexandria was Hellenised is one of the most obscure problems in the history of Judaism and also one of the most important for the understanding of the evolution of early Christianity.

It is obvious, for instance, that this raised the question "When is a Jew not a Jew and therefore excluded from the privileges of his race?" Was the answer "When he is a Christian"? The point is that if Christians were Jews, and they at least claimed to be "the ancient people of God" and "the true Israel," they could claim the privileges of the synagogue, but would then also be subject to its discipline. If, on the other hand, they were free from the synagogue, they were subject to the Roman Empire, which frowned on foreign cults if they could not claim to belong to a recognised nation. Very soon this attitude of Rome led to, or contributed to, the definite condemnation of Christians as such.

The evolution of this process is clearly marked in the New Testament. In the synoptic gospels, Jesus is a Jew; in the Epistles Paul boasts that he is a Jew, and in Acts he is always represented as going to the synagogue first,—the attitude of the writer of Acts is, in effect, that Christians are the true Israel, that their troubles are due to bad Jews, and that reputable magistrates never condemned them. Hostility to the Jews is clear on every page, so that Acts is partly a polemic, partly an apologia. Before long, however, the Romans not unnaturally accepted the opinion of the Jews, that Christians had no claim to Jewish privileges; Christians were told *non licet esse vos,* and to be a Christian became a crime. I Peter and the Apocalypse are as clearly later than this situation as the synoptic gospels and Acts are earlier than it. Unfortunately there is no evidence to enable us to say exactly when the change took place. (pp. 209-213)

BIBLICAL ARCHAEOLOGY

G. ERNEST WRIGHT

AS A RESULT OF THE archaeological investigations of the ancient world during the last one hundred years, it is now possible for scholars to write the history of man's first major effort to erect a complex civilization. Whereas the centre of his second effort lay in Greece and Rome, the earlier drama centred in the lands of Egypt, Syria and Mesopotamia. This is the region where the first domestication of animals and the earliest development of agriculture took place, where the first towns were established (*ca.* 5000 B.C.), methods of writing invented (beginning *ca.* 3500 B.C.), and the material and cultural aspects of civilization developed with exceeding rapidity. This was where the first great states were formed (3000-2000 B.C.), and where the earliest use of the resources of those states for empire-building took place. Possessing new power in knowledge, in community organization, and in natural resources, man promptly set about the task of attempting to control as much of the earth's surface as he could.

This was the epoch when the nation of Israel lived in Palestine, when it was destroyed and scattered among the nations, when it wrote a magnificent testimony to its faith, now preserved as our Old Testament, which in the fullness of time became the soil in which the Christian movement found its roots. Biblical archaeology is the study of this newly exposed history of the ancient world in order to discover the Bible's setting and to clarify its meaning. Archaeology by its very nature must be concerned with a vast mass of detailed data about pottery, architecture, language, documents, and the like, but an overall picture and perspective has been emerging which is of great importance to anyone who would understand the Bible. The following lines represent a sampling of the information now at hand.

Biblical Faith

Of great importance is the fresh understanding of biblical faith which

From *The Twentieth Century Bible Commentary, (a Symposium)*; copyright 1935 by Harper & Brothers. Reprinted by permission.

has come from comparison of it with the rival faiths of its time. It is only in recent years that sufficient information has become available to enable a scholar to write meaningfully and accurately about the theology of the ancient polytheisms (see, e.g., *The O. T. World* by W. F. Albright, *The Interpreter's Bible,* (Vol. I). We must now say, therefore, that while biblical people shared many conceptions with their neighbours, their religion as a whole was radically different at every major point, so much so that we can no longer believe that it was a gradual development out of paganism. It was a new creation; the Unknown God had become Lord indeed.

The gods of the pagans were the personified forces and powers of nature, who had taken on an increasing number of social duties as society had become complex. The great state festivals of worship had at their centre a sympathetic magic wherein the blessings of the cosmic events of nature (the creation of nature's order and stability, of its fertility, and of its death and rebirth in each cycle of the year) were re-enacted so that society, nature and divine life might move together in integrated harmony. The worship of the individual did not proceed from any conception of the called society, or of the Church with a divinely-given mission, but instead from the self-centred desire to be integrated with nature, to find security and protection in the world. Man's attention was thus focused upon nature, whose life was the life of the gods; and his central problem was conceived to be integration. Religion was the buttress of society's *status quo,* but the gods of nature did not control history and they perished with the civilizations of which they were the central supports.

In Israel, on the contrary, the focus of religious attention was not on the plurality of nature, but on the Lord who had created and was governor of all things, who was like nothing in heaven or earth, who was himself, unique, the Holy One, transcendent, and the source of all that is. He was known primarily, however, as Lord of history because he had been encountered in history as the great redeemer. It was inferred that he alone was creator solely because he was known to be Lord. The problem of life was not integration in nature, but the problem of obedience and vocation in history. God was no Lord of the *status quo,* but the dynamic mover, determined that he alone be acknowledged as God; he has destroyed in order to build, for history is to be interpreted as the arena of a great conflict wherein God is in process of redeeming the whole world to the end that it become his kingdom. And man was seen to possess an unheard of dignity and glory because God had dignified him with a personal address and called him to be his agent. Yet the state of civilization reveals man's 'fallen' condition, his rebellion and misuse of his glory. But the living Lord and redeemer is not defeated; he has established on earth his new community. He is in constant struggle with this community that it be faithful, indeed once destroying it completely, only to re-establish it gradually and then to reform it in Christ.

These lines represent a mere sampling of the comparative theology that archaeology has made possible. Considerable work and thought along these lines is needed because without them we cannot penetrate the central emphases of biblical faith with sufficient clarity. These emphases are placed in focus only when we see them over against the religions which were being emphatically rejected.

Hebrew Origins

Israelite tradition traced the nation's origins to a family which had settled in and around the town of Harran in the Upper Euphrates valley during the early part of the second millennium B.C. At that time, we now know, the whole area from the Mediterranean to the Tigris had recently been settled by a people with a common language who are now being called 'the Amorites'. This new civilization belongs to the period which archaeologists designate 'The Middle Bronze Age' (*ca.* 1900-1500 B.C.). The earlier culture of the third millennium had been destroyed by *ca.* 2000 B.C., and the new culture is presumed to have been introduced by a fresh wave of invaders from the Arabian desert who had seized control in the lands of the sown. It seems highly probable now that the ancestors of Israel were a part of that movement. For example, the names 'Abraham' or 'Abram', Jacob, and Benjamin are known to have been used as personal names by these people, and many other personal names of the early Hebrews reflect the language and religious ideas of the Amorites. In Abraham's family appear, among others, Peleg, Serug, Nahor, and Terah (Gen. 11.16ff.), whose names are also names of towns in the Harran area. The Egyptian 'Tale of Sinuhe' (*ca.* 1900 B.C.) and the archives of the Assyrian city of Nuzi (*ca.* 1400 B.C.) furnish considerable information about Amorite patriarchal life and customs during the second millennium B.C., and aid in explaining a number of things in Genesis particularly, which otherwise would have been obscure (e.g. the teraphim as household gods related to the question of the inheritance, Jacob as Laban's adopted son, Esau's sale of his birthright, patriarchal blessings, etc.). We can thus say that the stories in Gen. 12-

36 seem to reflect the 'Amorite' age. Hence it is now possible to view Israel's patriarchs in their proper setting in history.

The Conquest and Settlement of Canaan

God's deliverance of Israel from Egyptian slavery and his gift of the land of Canaan are two of the central articles in Israelite confessions of faith. Archaeology has provided us with the historical background in which the narratives of these events are to be understood. We know that it was common practice for the Egyptians to admit Asiatics into the Nile Delta during times of famine. We also know that foreigners were used by the Egyptian government at times for building projects. Hence there is nothing surprising about the story of Israel's forced labour in the erection of the 'store cities', Pithom and Ramses (Ex. 1.11). These towns have been located and excavated in the Nile Delta, and their construction, we now know, must have taken place during the early part of the nineteenth Egyptian dynasty (that is, after *ca.* 1330 B.C.), because the Pharaohs of the preceding dynasty seem to have done no building in the Delta.

Exploration in Transjordan has revealed that during the thirteenth century the southern part of the country was settled and towns established, following a long period of nomadism during which there were no towns. This evidence is probably to be correlated with the establishment of the kingdoms of Sihon, Moab and Edom, which Israel encountered in her journey through the territory (Num. 20-21). In the north the kingdom of Og appears to have supplanted the system of small city states, ruled by Egypt, which we know to have existed there in the early fourteenth century. In Palestine proper excavations at Bethel, Lachish and Debir have revealed evidence of extremely violent destruction during the course of the thirteenth century, and we infer that this was caused by the Israelites inasmuch as Joshua is said to have taken at least two of these cities. These lines of evidence suggest that Moses and Joshua are to be dated in the thirteenth century.

Yet archaeology at this point confronts us with difficulties. For example, Josh. 7-8 describe Joshua's conquest of Ai (the name in Hebrew means 'The Ruin'). Yet we now know that this town had been destroyed 1,000 years before Joshua's time, and the city of Bethel, 1½ miles away, had been built in its place. Consequently, the great destruction which overtook Bethel during the thirteenth century is evidently the one originally meant in Josh. 7-8 (cf. Judg. 1.22-6), though tradition has evidently shifted the scene of the battle to the great Ruin nearby.

Another difficulty is Jericho (Josh. 6), a city which Dr. John Garstang excavated between 1930 and 1936. Dr. Garstang believed that he had discovered the city of Joshua's time, and that it had been surrounded by a great double wall which had been violently destroyed by earthquake and fire. He dated the destruction about 1400 B.C., though other archaeologists were inclined to date it somewhat later on the basis of the pottery found. (Pottery is a primary means of dating to the archaeologist.) In any case, however, Jericho had fallen, it seemed, too early for Joshua to be dated in the thirteenth century, unless we assume that the tradition is in some measure wrong. The excavations directed by Miss Kathleen Kenyon in 1952, however, appear to have altered some of the previous conclusions. The great walls mentioned above have been found to have been destroyed 1,000 years earlier. Indeed the whole city of Joshua's time, if it existed on this mound, seems to have been eroded and washed away through centuries when the site was unoccupied. All that remains of it (as far as is known now—March, 1953) are a comparatively few pieces of pottery scattered here and there on the mound and in three tombs; in addition there is possibly one building. As a result, we have no certain knowledge as to when the city was destroyed.

Still a third difficulty which scholars have encountered is this: the Book of Joshua implies that the conquest was completed in one great campaign by Joshua, while Judg. 1 suggests that it was a gradual process, extending over a long period of time, during which the individual tribes did most of the fighting. Archaeology appears to suggest that both points of view are in some measure correct. The period of the Judges was a very disturbed and insecure time, and the towns excavated show repeated and often violent destructions between the twelfth and tenth centuries. The evidence we have thus implies that while Joshua captured and destroyed a number of the Canaanite city-states, the attempt to settle and control the land was a difficult process, marked by hard fighting with the Canaanites who remained and with various invaders who are ever ready to move into a 'power vacuum'.

Until the period of the Judges, however, the central hill country had been sparsely populated. From this time on, it was dotted with towns, many of them newly founded. At first the new settlers knew very little about the arts of village life, about architecture, metallurgy, pottery-making and the like. The excavated remains are in marked contrast to the excellence of the preceding Canaanite civilization. In addition, the rapid development of the newly arrived Philistines, whose painted pottery is such a characteristic feature of the areas under their control, almost overwhelmed Israel and prevented any real economic development. By the time of David (early tenth century), however, Philistine power had been broken; the secret of iron-smelting had been wrested from the Philistines; and the new political stability brought about an economic revolution in Israel and a greatly expanded population.

Monarchy and Temple

Tenth-century Israel under David and Solomon marked a radically new departure through the attempt to make Israel a nation like other nations, organized and dominated by two institutions, kingship and temple. Both were conscious importations from surrounding pagan culture. During the preceding period, Israel differed radically in organization from her monarchical neighbours. She believed herself to be a group of tribes, organized by sacred compact (covenant) around a central sanctuary or tabernacle. God ruled his people directly, and no permanent political leader was needed. In time of crisis he raised up a leader ('judge'), and empowered him by the Spirit for a particular task which was finished when the crisis was passed (cf. Gideon's statement, Judg. 8.22-3). Temptation to idolatry, for which the excavations bear eloquent witness, was so great, however, that the covenant unity was broken and the fire of devotion was quenched. Faced with the Philistine menace the institution of the monarchy was established 'that we also may be like all the nations' (I Sam. 8.20). This meant, however, that a theology of monarchy had to be developed, and recent studies of ancient kingship have been revealing how dependent Israel was on Syrian and Mesopotamian conceptions at this point, even when all the major differences are taken into account. This theology of monarchy was not accepted with equal enthusiasm by all sections of the nation. Nevertheless, its core was in a measure preserved in the messianic teaching of the Judean prophets, and fulfilled in the kingship of Christ in the New Testament.

The Temple of Solomon replaced the simple tent or 'tabernacle' of the earlier period, and there is no record of any request made by deity to build it, as was usually the case with pagan temples. On the contrary II Sam. 7 forbids it. Nevertheless it was erected for Solomon by a Phoenician architect and artist. It was thus a typical pagan structure, filled with pagan artistic motifs and symbolism, though the central symbol in the holy of holies was not the visible statue before which a worshipper could feel that he was meeting his God 'face to face', but instead the invisible deity enthroned upon winged sphinxes (Cherubim). Nevertheless, like pagan temples this building was not a 'church' in our sense but the 'house' of deity, the place of his abode. This raised problems to Israel, for how could the cosmic God live in an earthly house (cf. I Kings 8.27ff.)? The pagan solved this problem by means of a rich sacramental magic largely forbidden to Israel. To the Israelite priest God's 'presence' in the Temple could only be understood as his gracious accommodation to his people's need, while his real dwelling was always understood to be in heaven. In deuteronomic circles, on the other hand, there seems to have been a reaction against the doctrine of 'real presence' as understood both by pagans and by the priests. Instead there was an emphasis upon the Temple as a house of prayer with the 'presence' indicated by a conception of the structure as the bearer of God's 'Name' (e.g. Deut. 12.5; I Kings 8.29). Furthermore, to the Israelites the pagan notion of sacrifice and offering as provision for the deity's physical needs had to give way to a conception of the services of worship as something which God did not need but which he had graciously supplied whereby a sincere and faithful people might worship and secure forgiveness of sins. Nevertheless, this Temple of pagan inspiration could not adequately reflect the heart of the faith. It was not an unbreakable bond between heaven and earth (cf. Jer. 7). For this reason the faith could survive without it, and in the Christian Church Christ could be conceived as replacing it.

The Kingdoms of Israel and Judah

The effort of Solomon to make Israel a nation of culture, with great external displays of wealth, is well attested by archaeology, especially in his 'chariot-city' of Megiddo and in his copper and iron refinery at Ezion-geber on the Red Sea. The centuries of the divided monarchy which follow continued many of the architectural and ceramic styles begun in the tenth century, but the progressive weakening and impoverishment of the country at the hands of foreign conquerors is indicated, not only by the destruction of cities, but by the gradual decline in artistic vitality. There is a 'sameness' and monotony about the objects in daily use throughout this period. Styles in pottery, for example, changed slowly, in part because of the introduction of mass production techniques in guilds, techniques perhaps borrowed from Phoenicia. On the other hand, a typical Israelite town of the time indicates by the nature of the houses a different type of social structure from that of the Canaanites before 1200 B.C. There was no feudalism, with the huts of the common people clustered about a palace of the wealthy prince. Instead, there were the well-built homes, fairly regular in size, of a more equalitarian society. Examples of Israelite writing become increasingly common through the period, and suggest a comparatively high literacy rate. Of major interest are the Lachish letters, dating from the final siege of Judah by Nebuchadrezzar, written by the commander of a military outpost to the officer in charge of the defence of Lachish. A large number of seals and seal impressions have been found, among them those which belonged to government officials. For example, an impression of a seal once attached to a papyrus document bears the name of Gedaliah, a prominent man whom the Babylonians made governor of the destroyed country. Three other seal impressions bear the name 'Eliakim, steward of Jehoiachin': That is, Eliakim was evidently the man in charge of the Palestinian property of the youthful king exiled in Babylon.

The importance of the Assyrian and Babylonian inscriptions for the history of the period has long been known. Two of them, the Black Obelisk of Shalmanezer III (859-824 B.C.) and the relief depicting Sennacherib's siege of Lachish in 701 B.C., give contemporary illustration of Israelite and Judean dress, and indicate how wrong it is for us to suppose that the dress of biblical people was the same as that of modern Bedouin.

One of the most striking features of Old Testament archaeology is the vivid evidence of the destruction of Judah by Nebuchadrezzar. So terrible and complete was this event that town after town fell, never again to rise. A veritable dark age descended upon Judah, and recovery can scarcely be said to be complete before two or three centuries had passed. Only as we contemplate this fact can we begin to comprehend the desperate urgency in the prophecies of Jeremiah and Ezekiel, the depth of feeling given expression in Lamentations, and the fierce hatred of Edom for its unjustified share in the division of the spoil.

ARCHAEOLOGY AND OLD TESTAMENT LITERATURE

A comparison of the literature of the Bible with that unearthed in contemporary civilizations has been very rewarding, not only for the aid it has given in understanding the Hebrew, Aramaic and Greek languages, but also for the relation of biblical man to his world. For example, the creation and flood stories in Gen. 1-11 are ultimately based upon Mesopotamian sources. This is especially clear with regard to the flood story.

Nimrod (Gen. 10.8ff), the tower of Babel (Gen. 11), the two lists of pre-flood heroes, composed of seven and ten names respectively (Gen. 4 and 5; the names differ but the numbers are the same in Mesopotamia), and, very indirectly, the creation story itself in Chap. 1. Yet a comparison which reveals relationship also reveals the utter and complete difference. The Mesopotamian material has been demythologized and completely recast in the biblical setting. It is significant that little of this material bears any resemblance whatever to Canaanite conceptions, and we are led to the supposition that the basic traditions may well have been brought from Mesopotamia by the patriarchs and later recast in their present form.

At the present time a great deal of work is being done on Israelite poetry. It is being studied afresh in the light of the Canaanite poems unearthed in Northern Syria at the site of Ras Shamra. Numerous words and expressions, hitherto obscure, have now been explained. In addition, it now appears that Israel learned a great deal about poetic style from the Canaanites, borrowing forms of metre and numerous expressions. Early poetry especially swarms with Canaanitisms, and Ps. 29 has been shown to have been a Canaanite hymn to Baal, adapted for the praise and worship of the Lord of Israel. The wisdom movement, as represented particularly in Proverbs, is now known to have been international in character, and it is probable that many of Israel's colourful sayings dealing with prudential ethics originated in Canaan and in Egypt. The Song of Songs resembles rather closely a collection of love-poems dating from about 1100 B.C. in Egypt, though the liturgical background of the book, if any, is still obscure.

These illustrations may indicate how much Israel learned from the literature of her environment, though all that was learned was ultimately transformed when used in the new context of faith.

Archaeology and the New Testament Period

Because the period of the New Testament covers only a century in which the Church was comparatively very small, the archaeological discoveries bearing directly upon the New Testament history have to do for the most part with numerous details. One major area of discovery has to do with the complexity of the New Testament world. For centuries Greek influences had been penetrating Asia, and both the material and intellectual worlds bear eloquent testimony to the intermingling of two cultures. Herod the Great, for example, rebuilt Caesarea, Samaria, Jericho and Jerusalem, among other cities, filling them with Hellenistic

architecture and art. The introduction of the Greek theatre and hippo-
drome brought new forms of entertainment. The interchange of ideas
produced numerous and peculiar religious sects, and even in Judaism
Hellenism was leaving its mark. In the midst of such complexity the
comparative simplicity, purity and fine sense of balance and proportion
which characterize the New Testament is nothing less than astonishing.

A second major area of discovery has been in the field of biblical
texts and manuscripts. We can now say that no other text from antiquity
is fixed, corrected and attested by manuscript discovery as well as is the
text of the New Testament. While the earliest of the main manuscripts
date from the fourth and fifth centuries A.D., the Chester Beatty papyri
contain some 126 leaves from New Testament books, which are dated
in the third century. In addition, the John Rylands Library in Manchester has a small fragment of the Gospel of John which is dated in the
first third of the second century, or within fifty years of the date commonly given for the book's composition.

By far the most important single discovery in the field of biblical
archaeology has been the recovery since 1947 of a number of manuscripts and bushels of fragments from caves in the cliffs along the north-
western shore of the Dead Sea. Most important is the group from the
area of Khirbet Qumran. They belonged to a Jewish monastic sect who,
their literature tells us, believed themselves to be members of the new
covenant. Their manual of discipline and the area in which they lived
indicates that they were probably a group of the Essenes of whom the
Jewish historian Josephus speaks. Their meeting house and a part of
their vast cemetery has been excavated, and a series of coins found in
the building indicates that they were living there in the time of Christ
but abandoned the area during the first revolt (A.D. 66-70). Their library was packed away in two or more of the caves, but was rifled in
antiquity. What remains is mostly fragments and a few complete or
nearly complete manuscripts. Parts of nearly all of the Old Testament
books have been found, together with a complete manuscript of the
Book of Isaiah, another containing the last third of Isaiah, and a commentary on Habakkuk. In addition, many books among the non-can-
onical literature are represented, including the Testament of the Twelve
Patriarchs, a book of psalms, a document dealing with Holy War, the
Book of Lamech, the Book of Tobit, etc. The importance of this find
can scarcely be overestimated. Not only do we have Hebrew manuscripts nearly 1,000 years older than any previously known, but enough
material has been found to reconstruct to some extent the theology of

the sect. John the Baptist may well have been associated with or influenced by the group; in it we have the earliest datable evidence for pre-Christian baptism; and the influence of its theology upon certain New Testament writings is almost certain to be discovered.

These lines represent only a brief indication of the vast accumulation of new knowledge about the Bible and its background which archaeology has been providing. We are now in a position to understand the Bible far better than any of our forefathers, and the sobering responsibility which is ours is to see to it that this fresh understanding is made available to the Church as it proclaims the gospel to itself and the world. (pp. 36-45)

THE LITERARY GROWTH OF THE OLD TESTAMENT

THE REV. HAROLD HENRY ROWLEY

THE OLD TESTAMENT is puzzling to the reader in part because materials of various ages often lie side by side in the same book, and because there is no chronological order of the books as a whole. In the first part of the Bible there is a broadly chronological arrangement down to the book of Esther, though there are some differences of arrangement in the Hebrew Bible. But this chronological arrangement belongs to the times surveyed and not to the dates of composition of the books. To determine the age of each book is often very difficult, and agreement amongst scholars is far from complete. All that can be attempted here is to offer a summary of the most widely accepted views.

From *The Bible Today—described by Christian Scholars;* Edited by The Times (London), copyright © 1955 by Harper & Brothers, New York, and Eyre & Spottiswoode (Publishers) Ltd., London. Reprinted by permission.

The first five books are known as the Pentateuch, and these comprise the first division of the Hebrew Bible. Behind their present form lies a complicated history. They contain stories of pre-historic times from the Creation to the age of Abraham, stories of the patriarchs, of Moses and the Exodus, together with sections on law and ritual. They are not works of history in the modern sense, though they contain much reliable historical tradition. Our recent growth in knowledge has led to the recognition that the stories of the patriarchal age faithfully represent the culture and custom of the period in which they are set. If these stories are treated with greater respect, the accounts of the age of Moses may be expected to contain even more reliable traditions. Yet the whole is primarily the story of God's relations with the people of Israel.

It has long been recognized that the Pentateuch rests on four main sources, on which the compiler has drawn freely. The extracts have been woven together to read continuously, though they often bear the marks of the diversity of their origin. The four main sources are usually dated *c.* 850 B.C., *c.* 750 B.C., *c.* 680 B.C., and some time in the fifth century B.C. They reveal differences of outlook and idea, as is most natural. The earliest of these sources is believed to have been compiled in Judah, and the second in northern Israel. The third source consists of the major part of Deuteronomy and has many links with northern Israel, but is believed to have been the lawbook found in the Temple in the time of Josiah. The fourth is believed to have been compiled in Babylonia, and to have formed the lawbook of Ezra. None of these sources was the free composition of its author, but all were based on older traditions and records. Even the latest of them contains much very old material. Moreover, we cannot suppose that there was a complete gap from the time of Moses to the date of the first main source. Moses is probably to be dated in the thirteenth century B.C.–400 years before the first of these sources. Oral traditions and probably written collections of traditions coming from this period were drawn on. In addition a number of poetical passages, of varying length and date, were incorporated, and some of these appear to have been collected in written form.

So far as the sections of law and ritual are concerned, there are again four main collections. The earliest is the Book of the Covenant (Exod. xx.–xxiii.), which contains very ancient laws. The second consists of the core of Deuteronomy. The third is known as the Holiness Code, and stands in Lev. xvii–xxvi. The fourth is scattered in Exodus, Leviticus and Numbers, and this belonged to Ezra's lawbook, but contains much that is old.

The second division of the Hebrew Bible consists of Joshua, Judges, Samuel and Kings. All of these books are dominated in their editing by the ideas and outlook of Deuteronomy, which first came to light in 621 B.C., in the time of Josiah, but which may have been composed about half a century earlier. The editing of these four books is therefore placed between 621 B.C. and 561 B.C., when the latest event they record took place. Some later passages have been added, especially in the book of Joshua, but substantially we have a continuous account, though not necessarily the work of a single hand. Once more, however, much older collections of material have been used. There were cycles of stories, collections of poetry, and written sources of various kinds. The snatch of poetry found in Josh. x. 12 f. is from the same collection as David's Lament over Saul and Jonathan (2 Sam. i. 19–26). The Song of Deborah (Judges v.) is probably contemporary with the events it describes.

For the stories in Judges and the account of the founding of the monarchy two main cycles were used, but a lost History of the Ark seems also to have been drawn on. The long section which stands in 2 Sam. ix.–xx. and the first two chapters of 1 Kings is taken from a single source, sometimes called the Court History of David, dating probably from the time of Solomon. This is a historical source of the first importance. In the books of Kings several sources used by the compiler are specified, including annals of the two Israelite kingdoms. Once more, therefore, we must distinguish between the age of our present books and the age of the sources on which they rest, some of which were either contemporary with the events they describe, or very nearly so.

The next division of the Hebrew Bible consists of the prophetic books. These were originally four: Isaiah, Jeremiah, Ezekiel, and the Book of the Twelve–*i.e.,* the Minor Prophets. In these books we find three chief types of material. Sometimes there are isolated oracles, without any indication of the occasion on which they were uttered. Sometimes we have oracles embedded in a narrative written in the third person, telling how the oracle came to be uttered. Sometimes we have oracles in a similar setting, but related in the first person. Various sources seem therefore to have been used by the compilers again, and the editing of the books is to be placed later than the time of the prophets themselves. It is probable that all these four collections were made at about the same time. Since the collection of the minor prophets includes the oracles of Malachi, who lived about 450 B.C., and perhaps of one or two later prophets, we should assign the gathering together of these prophetic collections to a date not earlier than the end of the fifth century B.C., and more probably to the fourth century. The materials collected would all be older, and some much older. Both Isaiah and Jeremiah contain historical extracts from the second book of Kings.

A familiar oracle assigned to Isaiah in Isa. ii. is assigned to Micah in Mic. iv., while about one-third of the little book of Obadiah is also assigned to Jeremiah. Clearly the tradition of authorship was not always sure. It need occasion no surprise, therefore, that other sections of these books must also on internal grounds be believed to be from other authors than the prophets in whose collections they stand. Several of the oracles on foreign nations in the book of Isaiah are so ascribed, while Isa. xxiv.–xxvii. is believed to be the latest part of the whole book, and to come from a post-exilic date. Similarly the magnificent section contained in Isa. xl.–lv. is believed to come from an unknown prophet of the exilic period, usually called for convenience Deutero-Isaiah, while the concluding chapters of the book, Isa. lvi.–lxvi., probably contain the work of some disciples of this unknown prophet, composed during the half century after the return of exiles in the reign of Cyrus. Similarly the second part of the book of Zechariah, Zech. ix.–xiv., is dated much later than the age of Zechariah, and attributed to an unknown author or authors.

The prophets themselves may be put in the following order: Amos *c.* 760 B.C.; Hosea *c.* 740 B.C.; Isaiah 740–700 B.C.; Micah roughly contemporary with Isaiah, but perhaps continuing into the early part of the following century; Zephaniah *c.* 626 B.C.; Jeremiah 626–586 B.C.; Nahum *c.* 612 B.C.; Habakkuk at the end of the seventh and beginning of the sixth centuries; Ezekiel in the first half of the sixth century B.C.; Obadiah after 586 B.C.; Deutero-Isaiah soon after the middle of the sixth century; Haggai and Zechariah 520–516 B.C.; Malachi *c.* 450 B.C.; Joel perhaps the second half of the fifth century; Jonah probably fourth century. It will be seen that the order of the Minor Prophets in the Bible is far from chronological.

Some of the historical books remain to be mentioned, together with various others which stand with them in the final division of the Hebrew Bible. The historical books include the story of Ruth, which was probably written in the fifth century B.C., though it deals with events of the period of the Judges and so stands after Judges in our Bibles. The books of Chronicles cover the same ground as the books of Samuel and Kings, but come from a much later time, probably about 300 B.C. The earlier biblical books formed one of the sources used in this compilation, but others are also mentioned. Often the sources are quoted verbatim, but many changes are made to conform to the compiler's ideas of what was edifying. This work was continued in Ezra and Nehemiah, which were originally a single book. Nehemiah lived in the middle of the fifth century and Ezra perhaps slightly later, or even at the beginning of the fourth century. The editor of these books drew on the memoirs of Ezra and Nehemiah, and also on an Aramaic source which contained some ancient documents. These documents are treated with more respect today than they had from some earlier scholars. The book of Esther cannot be regarded as a historical work, but is a story laid in the age of Xerxes I, but itself most probably to be ascribed to the middle of the second century B.C.

Slightly earlier than Esther is the book of Daniel. This consists of stories about Daniel, whose life is placed in the sixth century B.C., together with visions seen by Daniel, all culminating in the events of the time of Antiochus Epiphanes in the second century B.C. This book is unlike the prophetic books in its literary genre, and is classed as apocalyptic. Within the prophetic books there are some apocalyptic sections, but the transition from prophecy to apocalypse is here carried much farther. There can be no doubt that in its present form this book dates from the second century B.C., though the author used older stories and traditions.

The poetic books all belong to this section of the Hebrew Bible. Of these the Psalter is the best known. This is a collection of sacred poetry, now divided into five books, but once into three. The individual psalms probably come from a wide range of dates, but there is a greater readiness today to admit a considerable pre-exilic element than there used to be. Attention today is concentrated on the types of the psalms and on their probable use in the cultus to accompany ritual acts. The collection of the psalms into the present Psalter was post-exilic, and there are evidences that the collection was the work of two different schools. The headings of the psalms have been much discussed, but no convincing explanation of their meaning has been suggested.

The book of Job rests on an ancient story of a good man who suffered notably; but the story is merely the basis for a discussion on innocent suffering in the dialogue, which lies between the prologue and the epilogue. The prologue offers the setting for the dialogue, while the epilogue is demanded by the prologue to indicate that the test staged in the prologue is ended. It is probable that originally there were three cycles of speeches by Job's three friends with Job's reply to each, preceded by

Job's opening soliloquy and followed by his closing soliloquy, with a single divine speech followed by Job's submission. The third cycle of speeches is in some disorder now, however, and is incomplete. The speeches of Elihu in chapters xxxii–xxxvii interrupt the arrangement of the book and are probably a later addition, as also are the second divine speech and the poem on wisdom in chapter xxviii. The original book of Job without these additions is probably to be dated in the fifth century B.C.

The book of Proverbs consists of at least seven sections, of which the earliest is generally agreed to be pre-exilic and the latest–now found in the first nine chapters of the book–is perhaps as late as the third century B.C.

Of the remaining books only a word can be said. Lamentations consists of five poems, none of which may be credited to Jeremiah, but all of which came from a variety of writers during the period of the exile. Chapters ii. and iv. show the greatest poetic gifts and may come from a single writer who was an eye-witness of the fall of Jerusalem in 586 B.C. The Song of Songs is a collection of love poems of great beauty, most probably dating in its present form from about 400 B.C. Ecclesiastes is dated by most in the Greek period following Alexander the Great. Its general scepticism is interspersed by orthodox observations, which some ascribe to the hand of an interpolator, but which others ascribe to the same writer in a different mood.

Individual scholars could be found to disagree with many of these views. Space alone forbids the attempt to survey all the varying views, and this could only bewilder all but the specialist. What has been set forth here is rather the representative view of present-day scholarship. The frequent use of "perhaps" and "probably" is intended to reflect the writer's reserve, in view of the impossibility of attaining certainty on many points, and also to recognize that there are divergent views.

It will be seen that though few of the books in their present form can be dated earlier than the period of the exile, we have preserved in the Old Testament literary materials which cover a period of about a thousand years. It is always necessary to distinguish between the age of a book and the age of the materials it contains. In recent years greater stress is laid on the antiquity and value of some of these materials, and on the recognition that the analysis of books must be balanced by the study of the purpose which the compiler had in mind and the use he desired to make of the varied materials on which he drew. All of these books are religious books, designed to convey a religious message. It is for that religious message, rather than for history, that they have been preserved, and for this that they are to be read—though this is not to depreciate the genuine historical traditions and records which they contain. (pp. 28-34)

THE CANON OF THE OLD TESTAMENT

WILLIAM O. E. OESTERLEY AND THEODORE HENRY ROBINSON

The Term "Canon"

THE GREEK WORD κανών means, in its original sense, "a straight rod"; it is derived from κάννα, "a reed," for which the Hebrew word is (*Ḳaneh*); in Ezek. xl. 3, 5, *e.g.*, we have *Ḳneh Hammidah*, "a measuring rod"; the Greek word was borrowed from the Hebrew. In its earliest known Greek use (175 B.C.) it is applied to "a level" in reference to the building of a temple.

Its metaphorical use in Greek is equivalent to the Latin *norma*, the "rule" or "standard" of what is right and best; cp. Gal. vi. 16: "And as many as shall walk by this rule (τῷ κανόνι), peace be upon them . . ." (cp. also ii Cor. x. 13 ff.). The title κανόνες was given to the old Greek authors as those who created the best models in literature.

Its use in reference to the books of the Bible—the Old Testament in the first instance—is Christian; derivatives from the word, by the Greek Fathers, occurred before the term itself came into use; as a technical term in reference to the Scriptures it is used for the first time, so far as is known, by Amphilochius, archbishop of Iconium (*circa* A.D. 380).

By the expression "the Canon of the Old Testament," then, is meant the existence of a certain number of books which were held to conform

From *An Introduction to the Books of the Old Testament,* by William O. E. Oesterley and Theodore Henry Robinson; copyright 1934 by The Macmillan Company and The Society for Promoting Christian Knowledge, London. Reprinted by permission.

to a standard; what constituted that norm will become clear as we proceed.

The Purpose of a Canon of Scripture

It is clear that the idea of a Canon necessarily presupposes the existence of a number of books, some of which, for one reason or another, are regarded with special veneration, and which must therefore be authoritative in a pre-eminent sense. Otherwise we should have to assume that what we now call "canonical" books were regarded as "canonical" when they first appeared, and there is nothing to suggest that this was ever the case with any Old Testament writing. Now this *idea* of a "Canon," *i.e.* of some books being more holy than others, could not have arisen all at once; it was only gradually, and by general consensus, that certain books came to have a special sanctity attached to them. The earliest actual designation of the books of the Old Testament as the "holy books," or the "holy writings," is found in Josephus, about A.D. 100; but the formulation of the Canon must have been going on for long before, because the way in which he writes shows that in his time already the Canon as we know it was accepted; and it was regarded as finally fixed, for nothing farther could be added to it. Josephus' words are so important in the present connexion that it is necessary to quote them in full:

"We have not an innumerable multitude of books among us, disagreeing from and contradicting one another; but only twenty-two books, which contain the records of all the past times, and which are rightly believed in. And of these, five belong to Moses, which contain the laws and the tradition of the origin of mankind till his death for a period of nearly three thousand years. From the death of Moses until the reign of Artaxerxes, king of Persia, who reigned after Xerxes, the prophets who came after Moses wrote down the things that were done in their times in thirteen books. The remaining books contain hymns to God and precepts for the conduct of human life. But from Artaxerxes to our times all things have indeed been written down, but are not esteemed worthy of a like authority because the exact succession of the prophets was wanting. And how firmly we have given credit to these books of ours is evident by what we do; for during so many ages which have already passed, no one has been so bold as either to add anything to them, to take anything from them, or to make any change in them. But it is become natural to all Jews, immediately and from their very birth, to esteem these books to contain divine doctrines, and to stand by them, and willingly to die for them."

This passage shows that, according to Josephus, the essential marks attaching to the idea of "canonical Scriptures" were:

(a) that they are θεοῦ δόγματα, of unquestioned authority, and must be believed in *ex animo*; for since they all originate within the prophetical period, they are divinely inspired;

(b) that they are to be distinguished from every other form of literature in that they are holy;

(c) that their number is strictly limited;

(d) that their verbal form is inviolable.

Further, it must also be noted that, according to Josephus' belief, as expressed in this passage, the canonicity of a book depended upon whether it had been written within a clearly defined period, and that period was from Moses to the death of Artaxerxes, *i.e.* within what was held to be the prophetical period. The artificiality of this test is shown by that fact that, as Ryle has pointed out, "the mention of this particular limit seems to be made expressly with reference to the book of *Esther*, in which alone the Artaxerxes of Josephus (the Ahasuerus of the Hebrew book of *Esther*) figures."

This is all entirely in accordance with the teaching of official Judaism as ultimately stereotyped in the Talmud: revelation began with the Patriarchs, all the prophets up to and including Malachi were endowed with the Holy Spirit, so that the words they wrote must be regarded as having been inspired; therefore the Scriptures were "holy writings," the origin and norm of all divine teaching, and no teaching can be recognized as true unless it can be shown to be founded on the holy writings. The Rabbis, like Josephus, maintained that no book could be regarded as canonical unless it had been written within the prophetical period, which they reckoned as from Moses to Ezra.

The holiness of the canonical writings was indicated by the Rabbis by saying that it "defiled the hands"; the phrase denotes an antique conception; what is "holy" is infected by the Deity, according to old-world ideas; but to come into contact with the Deity, even mediately, is dangerous, because everything holy is originally taboo; anyone who touches a holy thing must undergo a ritual washing. Therefore a holy book imparts contagion to him who touches it. This is what lies behind the phrase "defiling the hands" as equivalent to what we understand by canonicity.

The Hebrew Canon

The Hebrew Bible, as we now have it, is divided into three parts; the divisions, which are due to the Rabbis, are artificial, and judged by their respective contents, illogical, as will be seen; they are as follows:

(*a*) *The Law,* called *Torah:* Genesis, Exodus, Leviticus, Numbers, Deuteronomy; five books.

(*b*) *The Prophets,* called *Nebi'im;* these are subdivided into—

> (i) the former prophets, called *Nebi'im Rishonim* viz. Joshua, Judges, i, ii Samuel, i, ii Kings (each of the last two being regarded as one book); and

> (ii) the latter prophets, called *Nebi'im 'Acharonim,* viz. Isaiah, Jeremiah, Ezekiel, and the Twelve Minor Prophets, reckoned as one book; making altogether eight books for this division.

(*c*) *The Writings,* called *Kethubim:* Psalms, Proverbs, Job, Song of Songs, Ruth, Lamentations, Ecclesiastes, Esther, Daniel, Ezra—Nehemiah (reckoned as one book), i, ii Chronicles (reckoned as one book); eleven books. Thus 5 + 8 + 11 = twenty-four books. At first sight this does not seem to agree with the twenty-two of Josephus, 5 + 13 + 4; but there can be little doubt that Josephus' *Ruth* belonged to *Judges,* and *Lamentations* to *Jeremiah.*

The number twenty-four is clearly an artificial one, as can be seen, *e.g.,* by the fact that the books of the Twelve Minor Prophets, belonging to very different times, are treated as one book; on the other hand, *Ezra-Nehemiah* and *Chronicles,* which form one book, are reckoned as two. It is possible that the Rabbinical number twenty-four was chosen because it = 12 + 12; the number twelve "derived its sacred character from the fact that it is the product of three and four, and is the number of the months of the year. There are twelve tribes of Israel and the same number of tribes of Ishmael (Gen. xvii. 20, xxv. 16). The number of many representative men and things was made twelve to accord with the number of the tribes (Exod. xxiv. 4; Num. xvii. 2, 6; Josh. iv., etc.). . ."

That the way in which the books are divided is illogical is also clear, since the first division, the *Law,* consists more of narrative than of legal matter; similarly, the *Prophets,* which is very largely history.

The question now arises as to whether these three collections of holy writings represent three successive stages of canonization. It is usually held that at one time the Hebrew Canon consisted of the Law, *i.e.* the Pentateuch, only; that later the Canon was enlarged by the admission into it of the "Prophets"; and that, finally, the canonicity of the remaining books was recognized, and thus the three-fold Canon came into being. This view Hölscher, in his discerning and discriminating examination of the whole subject, has shown to be based on insufficient and unreliable evidence, and therefore erroneous; there were not three successive stages at which these three collections of books were in turn recognized as canonical in the technical sense; such stages cannot be indicated; the idea is due to post-Christian Rabbinical suppositions. What happened was that the *Torah,* as it grew from the end of the seventh century B.C., was specially venerated; but it was constantly added to until it reached its final shape about the end of the fourth century B.C.; its authoritative character increased, but no idea of canonicity attached to it. As to the *Prophets,* some of these writings existed before the *Torah* became a Law-book, and they were added to from time to time up to the middle of the second century B.C.; but nowhere is there any evidence that they became "canonical." So that, for example, what Ben-Sira says in Ecclus. xliv–l does not indicate anything regarding the Canon as such, i.e. one cannot say that this is evidence that the prophetical canon was closed by that time; it only shows what books had by his day (*circa* 182 B.C.) come to be regarded with special veneration—an important step in the process which ultimately led to the formation of the Canon—but the idea of a Canon had not yet arisen; and this is clearly seen by the fact that Ben-Sira can speak of himself as the latest of the Biblical writers, and therefore regards his book as the most recent addition to the Scriptures: "And I, last of all, awoke (or 'came,' as the Syriac reads), as one that gleaneth after the grape-gatherers. By the blessing of the Lord I made progress, and as a grape-gatherer, filled my winepress" (Ecclus. xxxiii. 16). Again, that Ben-Sira did not regard the books of the Old Testament as what is understood as canonical, in the sense of being separated off from other books to which no addition may be made, is seen from xxiv. 33 of his book, where he writes: "I will yet pour out doctrine as prophecy, and leave it unto eternal generations" (see also verses 30–32, 34); nor would he have taken upon himself, as Hölscher points out, to assume the tone and style of the ancient prophets, as he often does (see, *e.g.,* xlvii. 20, l. 29), if the "unbridgeable cleft of canonicity" had gaped between him and the prophets.

Similarly with the *Writings*; they, too, existed in part before the *Torah* became a Law-book, and went on increasing into Christian times; but there is no evidence to show that they, as a separate collection, obtained an individual *canonicity*.

The underlying and real cause which in course of time forced the idea of forming a Canon to arise was Greek culture and the growth of Greek literature; the more immediate cause—which was, however, to a large extent an outcome of this—was the spread of apocalyptic books written by and circulating among the Jews. To give the reasons for this would take up far too much space here; they are cogently presented by Hölscher. But it became necessary in view of what was regarded by the Jewish religious leaders as erroneous and pernicious literature, to gather out from the mass of current books those which they held to contain the truth; thus the idea of a Canon came into being, and this was towards the end of the second century B.C. But the actual fixing of the Canon did not come until long after this, and it was not piece-meal; there is good reason to believe that the Hebrew Canon as we now know it was an accomplished fact by about A.D. 100.

In what has been said the important thing to bear in mind is the distinction between books which are good and authoritative, and the same books when they have been pronounced canonical, *i.e.* as possessing the marks, mentioned above, attaching to canonicity; the nature of books undergoes by this process, as it were, metamorphosis. But this pronouncement did not take place in three successive stages in respect of what we now call the three divisions of the Canon; on the other hand, it did not, as it were, take place in one act; the discussions as to whether certain of the books "defiled the hands" or not, many remains of which are preserved in the Talmud, show that it must have taken a long time before the final fixing of the Canon was a *fait accompli* in about A.D. 100.

The Greek Canon

By the "Greek Canon" is meant the books of the Old Testament included in the Septuagint Version of the Hebrew Scriptures; the term is used for convenience' sake; in itself it is inaccurate because the books of the Greek Old Testament not represented in the Hebrew Scriptures did not come within the purview of the Jewish religious authorities in their discussions about books which "defiled the hands" or not. So that inasmuch as these books were never even considered from the point of view of canonicity it is not, at any rate from the Jewish point of view, accurate to speak of a Greek Canon. On the other hand, from the Christian standpoint the term is justified, for the early Church regarded all the books of the Greek Bible, whether represented in the Hebrew Scriptures or not, as equally authoritative, and therefore canonical.

When exactly the repudiation by the Jewish Church of the Greek, or "Alexandrian" Canon first began to take shape is uncertain; it would seem in any case to have come gradually, for "about the middle of the first century A.D., when the Greek-speaking Christian community began to break entirely with Judaism, the narrow Pharisaic doctrine of the Canon had certainly not as yet penetrated into the domain of Hellenistic Judaism so deeply as to delete completely, or to exclude from the MSS. of the Septuagint, all the books that Pharisaism refused to recognize." By the time of Josephus, however (end of first century A.D.), the Greek Bible which he used consisted substantially of the books of the Hebrew Canon as we know it; and according to ii (iv) Esdras xiv. 44, 45 (of approximately the same date) the Canon consisted of twenty-four books of the Hebrew Scriptures.

The number of the books in the Greek Old Testament not included in the Hebrew Canon varies in the MSS. and in the lists which have come down to us; but the most complete lists contain the following: i Esdras, Wisdom of Solomon, Wisdom of Sirach (Ecclesiasticus), Judith, Tobit, Baruch and the Ep. of Jeremiah, i-iv Maccabees. In addition, the *Psalms of Solomon* is sometimes included, either among the Solomonic books or at the end of the Canon; and the Greek version of the *Book of Enoch,* "although by some accident it has been excluded from the Greek Bible," was undoubtedly regarded as canonical in the early Church, and must therefore have been included in copies of the Greek Old Testament.

Apart from the last two, these books are comprised in what we now know as the Apocrypha; a final word in regard to this expression is called for. The Greek word *apokryphos* was originally used in a good sense in reference to books which were "hidden" from the outside world because they were too excellent for ordinary mortals. In its technical sense the term "is derived from the practice, common among sects, of embodying their special tenets or formulæ in books withheld from public use, and communicated to an inner circle of believers" (cp. ii [iv] Esdras xiv. 44–47). "Apocryphal" was thus applied originally to books which contained hidden wisdom, and must therefore be kept hidden from the world in general. But Origen used the term in reference to what we know as the pseudepigraphic books; then, in the fourth century, in the Greek Church a distinction was made between "Canonical" books and those which were read "for edification"; but these latter referred to the books of what we now call the Apocrypha; the term "apocryphal" was still used only in reference to pseudepigraphic books.

Jerome (died A.D. 420) in the Latin Church followed the example of the Greek Church in so far that he made a distinction between the "libri canonici" and the "libri ecclesiastici"; the latter referred to those of our Apocrypha, so that these were now "apocryphal" books; Jerome was the first to use this term "apocryphal" in this new sense. It did not become general for some time; St. Augustine, for example, used "apocrypha" in the old sense, in the De Civitate Dei, xv. 23; but by degrees Jerome's usage of the term became generally accepted, and it has continued so to the present day. (pp. 1-10)

THE TEXT OF THE OLD TESTAMENT

WILLIAM O. E. OESTERLEY AND THEODORE HENRY ROBINSON

Hebrew Writing

THE OLD TESTAMENT was originally written in two languages, the greater part being in Hebrew, and portions of *Daniel* and *Ezra* in Aramaic. It has been suggested (*e.g.* by Naville) that the Law was originally written in cuneiform script and in the Akkadian language, being translated into Hebrew at a comparatively late date. This view, however, has not found general favour and lacks direct evidence.

Forms of writing may be divided into three classes. The first is called ideographic, in which the sign represents an idea and not a sound. It is often a little picture of the thing intended, or a conventionalized form of a picture in which only a few lines survive. Examples of ideographic writing may be seen in ancient Sumerian and in modern Chinese, and in

From *An Introduction to the Books of the Old Testament,* by William O E. Oesterley and Theodore Henry Robinson; copyright 1934 by The Macmillan Company and The Society for Promoting Christian Knowledge, London. Reprinted by permission.

the numerals commonly used by us all. The second type of writing represents syllables; to it belong the ancient Akkadian and modern Japanese writing. In the third form the syllables themselves are split up into their constituent sounds, and we have an alphabet. In comparatively early times (*c.* 1400 B.C.) we know that a Semitic dialect resembling Aramaic was written in a kind of alphabet in northern Syria, and such evidence as is available supports the view that, about the same period, a Hebrew alphabet was coming into existence in the south, which proved to be the ancestor of most of the forms of writing now current in the western world.

The shapes of the letters were very different in early days from those which appear in modern printed Hebrew, being much nearer to the early Greek forms. But, in spite of changes which took place between the sixteenth and first centuries B.C., Hebrew writing preserved two characteristics which were not retained in the Indo-European languages. In the first place, the alphabet was always written from right to left, not from left to right. In the second place, it indicated consonantal signs only, like modern reporters' shorthand, and had no means of representing the vowels save by additional signs.

For details of the changes which have taken place, the reader must be referred to special works on epigraphy. The peculiar nature of the Semitic languages (the group to which both Hebrew and Aramaic belong) made it possible to read with fair certainty as long as Hebrew was a spoken language. It was, however, gradually replaced by a form of Aramaic in the post-exilic period, and, by the beginning of the Christian era, apart from the regular reading of Scripture in the synagogues, it was almost confined to a body of learned men. There arose then the need for representing the vowels, in order to safeguard the traditional pronunciation and meaning. The consonantal text was gradually acquiring so high a degree of sanctity that men dared not alter it, even to make its pronunciation clearer, and two systems of vowel-representation were ingeniously devised. One of these consisted of marks placed over the consonants, and was current among Eastern Jews. The other was a system of dots and dashes, mostly placed under the consonants. This was used in the west, and is that normally found in MSS. and printed Hebrew Bibles. It may be remarked that the copies of the Law used in synagogue worship to this day have no vowels indicated at all.

The Hebrew Text

Until the invention of printing, the Hebrew Bible was necessarily copied by hand. The similarity between certain letters made mistakes very easy, but this danger was largely avoided by the extraordinary care bestowed on their work by Jewish scribes. No literature has ever been copied with such absolute fidelity and accuracy as the Old Testament, and there are, probably, not many printed books which contain so few mistakes as did the average MS. of the Hebrew Bible. Among the hundreds of copies known, the variations are only slight, and the great majority of those quoted, *e. g.* by Kennicott, De Rossi and Ginsburg, affect the vowels and not the consonants. Even when scribes were sure that the text before them was wrong, they copied the consonants as they stood, though they wrote a corrected text in the margin. Sometimes the fidelity of the scribes led them to copy ungrammatical or even meaningless sentences, due in the earlier copy to the carelessness or thoughtlessness of an older copyist. But they placed the vowels of their suggested reading in the text, a procedure which often produces a curious appearance, since the vowels of one word seem to be applied to the consonants of another. The most familiar example of the process is to be found in one of the divine names. The consonants were YHWH, probably pronounced *Yahweh*. But the word was too sacred to be uttered, and readers always used the term *'Adonay* = Lord. So the vowels of the latter were actually written with the proper consonants, thus producing the composite form *Yehowah,* whence our familiar word *Jehovah.*

The task of preserving and handing down the sacred text fell to a body of class of men who are commonly known as Massoretes. The name is derived from the Hebrew term Massorah, which means "tradition." But the work of the Massoretes went much farther than merely copying the text accurately and seeing that it was provided with the proper vowel signs. They studied it with the utmost diligence, counting the verses in each book, identifying the middle word, and appending in the margin countless notes, calling attention to anything unusual or remarkable in the text. Even such variations as an abnormally large or small letter were faithfully copied, and a note showed that the peculiarity was traditional, not arbitrary.

A great many MSS. are known, but no complete Bible can be definitely stated to be older than the ninth century A.D., though there are MSS. of portions of it which are as old as the seventh century. Since the process of fixing the text seems to have been complete by the end of the sixth century, it is not surprising that the variants are few and insignificant. One MS., known as GI, in the Library of Trinity College, Cambridge, presents an abnormal number of slight differences, but clearly represents the usual text. Occasional differences of reading are found in other MSS., but, in general, the text is so uniform as to make it possible to cite it comprehensively under the title Massoretic Text (MT).

There is, however, one important group of MSS. giving evidence of the pre-Massoretic text of the Pentateuch. This consists of a few MSS. belonging originally to the Samaritan community, which clearly represent the text as it was some centuries before the beginning of the Christian era. While there are many deliberate alterations, made in the interests of Samaritan as opposed to Judæan orthodoxy, yet, when allowance has been made for these, the number of variants is not extraordinarily large. It is clear that the Samaritan scribes gave to the copying of the Pentateuch almost as much care as did the orthodox Jews, and the general agreement of the two lines of text carries us back with some certainty at least to the second century B.C. Like the MT, the Samaritan text can usually be cited as a general whole.

The Versions

All Hebrew MSS., whether Jewish or Samaritan, belong to that type of tradition which we may call Palestinian. Their practical identity greatly enhances the importance of the Versions, especially when it is clear that these latter were translated from a text far older than the archetype on which all Jewish MSS. were ultimately based. Three of these clearly belong to the Palestinian tradition, and they show how the form of text now current was gradually reached. These are:

1. The Syriac (often cited as the *Peshitta* = "The Simple") made, probably, in the second century A.D.

2. The Targums. These were popular Aramaic renderings, which were often very free, even paraphrastic. The more important, known as the Targum of Onkelos on the Pentateuch and the Targum of Jonathan on the Prophets, reached their present form not later than the end of the second century A.D.

3. The Vulgate; a Latin translation made by St. Jerome in the fourth century A.D. There was an older Latin version, but that was based on the common Greek text, and was not rendered directly from a Hebrew original.

The differences between the text underlying all these translations and the MT are comparatively slight. But it is interesting to notice that the nearest is the Vulgate, which is the latest of the three, while the Syriac diverges more than either of the others. It is thus clear that the fixing of the text was a process which was gradually carried on down to the fourth century A.D., when it was very nearly complete. But it was already far advanced when the Syriac translation was made, a conclusion to which we are forced by the evidence of the standard Greek version. To this we may now turn.

The text which we have been considering up to this point represents, as we have already observed, a Palestinian tradition, even in the Samaritan Pentateuch. But, after the Exile, and especially from the time of Alexander the Great, there were communities of Jews in many places outside Palestine. By far the most important of these lived in Egypt, and Jews formed a considerable element in the population of Alexandria. We may assume that, when they first settled there, they took with them Hebrew copies, at least of the Law, and perhaps of later books, also. Other books were from time to time introduced among them. These would be copied in Hebrew for some time, until, as the Jews forgot their ancestral language, a need for a Greek version would be felt. Probably, also, close contact with the heathen world made the Egyptian Jew anxious to exhibit the treasures of his own literature in a form intelligible to his neighbors. Jewish tradition held that the Law was translated into Greek by the orders of Ptolemy Philadelphus,[1] by seventy-two scribes, whence the version is commonly known as the Septuagint, and is normally indicated as "LXX." It may be remarked that, while the tradition refers only to the Law, the term just mentioned is applied to the whole of the Greek Old Testament, including the books now classed as Apocrypha. Whether the narrative be correct in placing the initiative with the Egyptian king or not, there can be no doubt that the Septuagint Pentateuch dates back to the middle of the third century B.C. Other books followed during the next hundred and fifty years, and it seems that by the opening of the first century B.C., practically the whole of the Old Testament was available in Greek. At the beginning of the Christian era a complete Greek Bible was in existence, largely used by New Testament writers, including, not only the books preserved in the Hebrew Bible, but also some, at least, of those which we now class as apocryphal and apocalyptic. The evidence suggests that in some books, notably in the Pentateuch, the text was from time to time corrected by scribes who were familiar with the Palestinian Hebrew form, though in other cases, especially in Samuel and Jeremiah, it retained practically complete independence.

During the second century A.D. three other Greek versions appeared. These were those of:

i. Aquila, a slavishly literal translation of the Hebrew, designed to

---

[1] 285-246 B. C.

meet the Christian use of the Septuagint in argument. It was claimed that the traditional version did not fairly represent the Hebrew, and the object of this undertaking was to tell the Jews exactly what the Bible really said. It is held by some scholars that Aquila is to be identified with the Onkelos, whose name is associated with the Targum of the Law.

ii. Symmachus. This is a somewhat free translation into Greek of a more elegant literary type than that of the Septuagint.

iii. Theodotion. A very thorough revision of the Septuagint, bringing it to some extent into harmony with the MT as current in the translator's time.

These last three versions (though that of Theodotion is rather a revision than an independent version), like the Syriac, Targums and Vulgate, show comparatively little divergence from the standard Palestinian text preserved in our Bibles. The Septuagint, however, often differs very widely from the MT, and is, therefore, of the highest value for textual criticism. The divergence is smallest in the Pentateuch, and is at its highest point in Samuel, Jeremiah, and Ezekiel.

We are thus able to reconstruct the history of the materials we have for textual criticism, and to represent it in graphic form:

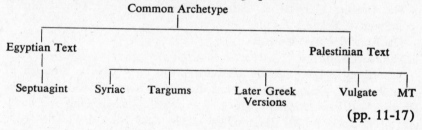

Common Archetype

Egyptian Text — Palestinian Text

Septuagint — Syriac — Targums — Later Greek Versions — Vulgate — MT

(pp. 11-17)

THE NEW TESTAMENT—INTRODUCTION

WILBUR OWEN SYPHERD

Contents. The books of the New Testament are twenty-seven in number, appearing in the King James Version in the following order: The Four Gospels, the Acts of the Apostles, the Epistles (twenty-one), and Revelation. These books may be further classified as:

The Synoptic Gospels—Mark, Matthew, and Luke

The Gospel according to St. John

The Acts of the Apostles

The Letters of Paul: The four great epistles—Romans, Galatians, 1 and 2 Corinthians—indubitably by Paul; 1 Thessalonians, Philippians, Colossians, and Philemon, about which there is hardly less doubt as to Pauline authorship; Ephesians and 2 Thessalonians, about which there is less certainty

The Pastoral Epistles: 1 and 2 Timothy and Titus

The Epistles General or Catholic Epistles: James, Jude, 1 and 2 Peter, 1, 2, and 3 John

The Epistle to the Hebrews

The Revelation

According to their literary characteristics, they may be grouped as (1) Historical—Biographical Narrative, the Synoptic Gospels; (2) Doctrinal—Biographical Narrative, The Fourth Gospel (Gospel according to St. John); (3) Biographical—Historical Narrative, The Acts; (4) Epistles (or letters); and (5) Vision (or Apocalypse), The Revelation.

Process of collecting into one volume. The process of collecting into one volume, to be known later as the New Testament, the separate writings of the Christian church was somewhat analogous to the way in which the writings of the Hebrews were brought together to form their 'scriptures,' to be known later as the Old Testament. This sacred book of the Jews, or Hebrews, was the only Bible of the new religious sect during the first century of the Christian era. The formation of the

From *The Literature of the English Bible,* by Wilbur Owen Sypherd; copyright 1938 by the Oxford University Press. Reprinted by permission of the publishers and the executors of the estate of W. O. Sypherd.

New Testament, which was later to supplement the Old Testament and thus complete the Bible of Christianity, was gradual. The teachings of Jesus, the founder of the new religion, were no doubt transmitted orally from one group of Christians to another, either during the lifetime of Jesus himself or in the years following his death. As we may infer or learn from the Gospels themselves or from other records of the first and second centuries A.D., the desirability of preserving the account of the teachings and deeds of Christ was realized, and thus we have finally brought together in the Gospels what the authors regarded as the main events in the life of Jesus and the significant principles of his religious teaching. These Gospels, in one form or another, were read aloud in the church and thus may be said to constitute the first addition of the Christian religion to the writings of the Old Testament. Supplementing these biographies of the founder of Christianity is the story, as recorded in what was later called The Acts of the Apostles, of the work of the apostles in spreading the new faith from Palestine to Asia Minor, Macedonia, Greece, and Italy. These writings were the latest of the books to be accepted as a part of the Christian scriptures. There were also in existence in the second half of the first century A.D., the letters which were written by Paul and other leaders of the new movement to the churches that had been established or to individuals connected with them. These letters, containing as they do along with personal notes ethical and doctrinal teachings, were also read in the churches and thus in the course of time came to be accepted as an important part of the Christian scriptures. The Revelation of St. John the Divine, through its supposed connection with the apostle of that name and also probably through its greater effectiveness, was the only one of the many Christian apocalypses to find a place in the New Testament. There were many other writings of the first two centuries similar to these four groups which we find today in our New Testament—gospels, acts, epistles, and apocalypses. The selection of sacred writings which was made by the early Christian church may therefore be said to have been somewhat arbitrary, but, as we realize today, as we examine the writings of these kinds which have been preserved, the church succeeded in bringing together and finally canonizing the most valuable of these books as religious and literary documents.

Not however till about the end of the second century was there a decisive movement toward a definite authoritative selection of Christian writings. By that time, all of the writings of the New Testament were in existence, but the limits of the Christian Bible were not strictly defined. These writings existed as separate papyrus rolls. Different collections of these rolls would be in the possession of the different churches. But the New Testament as a book did not exist. With Irenaeus [d. *c.* A.D. 202], Christians began to call these books 'scriptures,' just as they did the Jewish books. The several separate books had for long been spoken of as the books of the New Covenant. The alternative word for covenant, 'testament,' was used because when the writings were translated from Greek into Latin, it was assumed that the word 'covenant' meant 'will' or 'testament.' God had drawn up two 'testaments,' the latter superseding the first. The first man who is known to have called the collection the New Testament is probably an unknown writer of A.D. 192. Tertullian (d. *c.* A.D. 230) also used the term 'the New Testament.' The impetus toward a definite decision as to the books that should be definitely accepted as scripture came from Marcion, the great heretic of the second century. Marcion held that Christianity was a new revelation, that the work of Christ revealed the true God, and that the Old Testament must be abandoned and replaced by a Christian Bible. The Canon of Marcion (*c.* A.D. 140) comprises the Gospel of Luke and ten Epistles of Paul. Although his idea was not accepted by the church, the alarming progress of the Marcion heresy and of other heresies of the second century furthered the idea of putting the authentic Christian writings in permanent form. From about A.D. 200, dates the very interesting Muratorian Fragment, which gives a list of books representing the usage at Rome at that time. All of the books of our New Testament appear except 3 John, Hebrews, 1 and 2 Peter, and James, and added are Wisdom of Solomon, Revelation of John, Revelation of Peter, and, with a reservation, The Shepherd of Hermas. But it was not till A.D. 367, that a final form of the New Testament was definitely established. In that year, Athanasius, Bishop of Alexandria, issued his famous Easter letter (Festal Letter 39) in which he enumerated the books as we now have them. This declaration by Athanasius received official recognition by the church at the Council of Trent (1546) when these 27 books of the New Testament were declared scripture along with the books of the Old Testament as they appeared in the Latin Vulgate of Jerome, but with the addition of the Apocryphal writings.

Preservation of the writings. The printed editions of the New Testament are based mainly on the Uncial Greek manuscripts of the fourth to the sixth century A.D., in number about 170. Of these the three great ones are (1) Codex Sinaiticus, fourth century (British Museum),

(2) Codex Vaticanus, fourth century (Vatican Library), and (3) Codex Alexandrinus, fifth century (British Museum). Of varying importance and interest are the Minuscule manuscripts, dating from the fourth to the tenth century, numbering close to 3000; the Papyrus fragments, of which the most important is the Chester Beatty Papyri, dating from the second or third to the sixth or seventh century; and Lectionaries, Ostraka, and Inscriptions.

Language. The original language of the New Testament was Greek. To this dogmatic statement, certain possible exceptions should be recognized: that the first three Gospels have Aramaic documents behind them, that this may also be true of the earlier part of the Book of Acts, and that there are peculiarities in the style and grammar of the Book of Revelation which would seem to indicate translations from Aramaic, or perhaps from Hebrew. Most biblical scholars do not accept the theory of Greek translation of whole books of the New Testament from Aramaic.

Place of writing, authorship, and date. As to the place of origin of these writings, little is definitely known. Some of Paul's Epistles may be specifically placed. The Gospel of Mark was probably written in Rome, the Gospel of Matthew possibly in Antioch, the Gospels of Luke and John possibly in Ephesus. Not even so much of probability or possibility may be suggested for the other writings, and so the only interest is that of speculation. As to time of composition, reasonable limits are A.D. 50 to A.D. 150. Between these two dates, most Biblical scholars would find approximately definite times of composition for most of the writings. Different suggestions for the dates of composition of the individual books will be referred to in the specific discussions which follow hereafter. As to authorship, little more is known than about the place and date of composition. Of the fifteen or more 'authors,' Paul is the only clearly outlined figure with a definite personality and there is even much uncertainty as to the writings which definitely belong to him. To Luke, the physician, are ascribed, but not unanimously, the Gospel of Luke and the Book of the Acts. The author of the Fourth Gospel and of the three Epistles which bear the name of John was probably the same—but who was he? To John Mark, belongs it seems, the Second Gospel. Matthew is but a name. Great uncertainty prevails as to the identity of 1 and 2 Peter, James, Jude, and the author of the Revelation.

Literary value of the material. A consideration of the literary value of the New Testament suggests at once a comparison with the writings of the Old Testament. The contrast between these two parts of the Bible is most striking. The Old Testament is the literature of a people, a race; the New Testament is the writings of a religious group or sect. The Old Testament is a book of literature, having for its provinces the history, the religion, the ideas and emotions of the Hebrew people; the New Testament is a book of religion, which deals at times with human relations and relates events of history, but presents and interprets this material in the light of its main aim—which is to set forth the significance of this new religion. The Old Testament writings are concerned in the main with showing the hand of God in history; the New Testament writings, with showing the hand of God in establishing a religion which is to save the world through the intercession of Jesus Christ. Old Testament literature deals with the problems of life, of man in relation to God, to his fellows, and to the world in which he lives. In its highest reaches, in its sublime poetry and exalted prose, it is imaginative, creative, universal. New Testament literature treats the one problem of the meaning of the Christian religion as evidenced in the foundation, the development, the teachings of the church which has been set up on earth for the salvation of man from sin. It is informative, didactic, polemical, practical, occasional, immediate. The medium, as befitting its underlying purpose, is prose. It rises to the level of great literature in such works as The Gospel of Luke, the Book of Revelation, and in moments of expression of deep emotion in the Acts of the Apostles and the Epistles—where, to use the admirable phrasing of H. T. Fowler with respect to 1 Thessalonians, we find 'felicitous expression (1) of exalted feeling or (2) of significant thought interpreting the perennial realities of life in terms universally comprehensible.'

The four forms in which the literature of the New Testament appears are: (1) the four narratives—biographical, historical, theological—of the life and work and teachings of Christ; (2) the narrative—historical and biographical—of the work of the apostles in establishing the Church; (3) letters (epistles)—personal, pastoral, doctrinal—dealing with the work of the founders of Christianity and with the doctrines of Jesus; and (4) a vision (apocalypse, revelation) of the reign of Christ in heaven. Interesting general points of resemblance only may be indicated between these writings of the New Testament and some of the books of the Hebrew Bible. Mark, Matthew, Luke, Acts, and John may be looked upon as the Pentateuch of the New Testament, with John representing the Deuteronomic book in relation to the others; the

Epistles are comparable in some respects with the Prophets; Revelation is a counterpart of Daniel; and there is also a New Testament Apocrypha which partly approximates the Apocrypha of the Old Testament. The specific kinds of literature which are comprised in these writings are history, legend, narrative, biography, short story, letters, sermons, orations, parables, doctrinal treatises, and vision.

Almost all of this body of writings is in prose. Exceptions are various fragments, such as the five hymns embedded in Luke (Ave Maria, i:28, Magnificat, i:46-55, Benedictus, i:68-79, Gloria in Excelsis, ii:14, Nunc Dimittis, ii:29-32); Matthew xi:28-30; 1 Corinthians xiii; Ephesians v:14; 1 Timothy iii:16; 2 Timothy ii:11-13; Revelation v:12, vii:10 and 12, xii:10-12, xv:3,4, and xix:5; and the many quotations from the poetry of the Old Testament, such as Matthew ii:6, iii:3, iv:15,16, and xii:18-21; Luke iii:4-6; Acts viii:32,33, xxviii:26,27; Romans iii:10-18; Hebrews i:7-13, ii:6-8; and 1 Peter i:24,25a. The prose of the New Testament is often of a very high order. A good deal of it approaches the rhythm of poetry in its parallelisms of thought and structure, in its cadences, and in its accent. Strength of conviction, intensity of belief, fervour of feeling are revealed in prose of great power and beauty. Simplicity, clarity, conciseness, harmony, rhythmic flow, homely figurative expression, sincerity and earnestness, and a great fundamental theme are the characteristics which elevate much of these writings above the plane of simple narrative or doctrinal exposition to the height of perfect style of its kind and into the realm of literature of universal significance. Such are, to mention some of the notable parts, the whole of the book of Luke, the book of Revelation almost in its entirety despite the incomprehensibility of many of the details of this great work of the imagination, the Gospel according to St. John, Chapters xiv-xvi; Acts xvii:22-31 and xxvi:2-29; Romans viii and xi:33-xii; 1 Thessalonians; and 2 Corinthians xi-xiii. (pp. 151-159.)

THE OLD TESTAMENT LANGUAGES

C. J. MULLO-WEIR

THE OLD TESTAMENT is written in Hebrew with the exception of a few Aramaic passages, namely, Dan. 2^4-7^{28}; Ezra 4^8-6^{18} and 7^{12-26}; Jer. 10^{11} (a gloss); and a few scattered words, including *yĕghar sāhăd-hûthâ* ("heap of witness") in Gen. 31^{47}. In the Old Testament, Hebrew is called "the lip of Canaan" *(sĕphath kĕna'an,* Isa. 19^{18}), and "Jewish" *(yĕhûdhîth,* 2 Kings $18^{26,\ 28}$ and Neh. 13^{24}), while the name "Hebrew" *('ibhrîth)* seems to be a late invention of Palestinian rabbis and occurs first (in its Greek form) in the Prologue of Ecclus. (*c.* 130 B.C.). In the New Testament and Josephus, "Hebrew" is used ambiguously to denote both Hebrew and Aramaic. The Aramaic language *('ărāmîth,* 2 Kings 18^{26}) was called by the Greeks "Syriac" or "Chaldee," the latter name being due to the erroneous supposition that the language spoken in Chaldæa during the time of Daniel was Biblical Aramaic.

The earliest history of the Hebrew language is obscure, but the Hebrews seem to have migrated out of the peninsula of Arabia, and early tradition associates them with Babylonia, North Mesopotamia, Canaan, and Egypt. This tradition is corroborated by an examination of the language which seems to be a mixture of Accadian, proto-Aramæan ("Amorite"), and Canaanite, with a number of Egyptian loan-words. The Canaanite glosses in the El-Amarna letters (*c.* 1400 B.C.) closely resemble Hebrew as does also the Moabite language on the Moabite stone (*c.* 850 B.C.). A comparison of the early Hebrew Siloam inscription (*c.* 700 B.C.) with the Hebrew of Isaiah shows their language to be identical, and since that time the Hebrew language changed remarkably little in Biblical or even post-Biblical times. It began, however, to be supplanted by Aramaic after the Exile, and although Hebrew apparently continued to be a spoken language for some centuries later, it had become unintelligible to the common people by the beginning of the Christian era, so that an Aramaic translation or "Targum" had to be

From *A Companion to the Bible,* ed. by T. W. Manson; copyright 1950. Reprinted by permission of Charles Scribner's Sons and T. & T. Clark, Publishers, Edinburgh.

given in the synagogues after readings of Scripture. Hebrew continued its development as a literary and liturgical language until in the nineteenth century of our era it became again a spoken tongue. Certain dialectal differences seem to have existed within it in Old Testament times (cf. *shibbōleth* and *sibbōleth,* Judg. 12⁶), and some traces of this still survive in the Hebrew text of the Old Testament, but most have been removed by the scribes.

Hebrew and Aramaic belong to the Semitic group of languages, named after Shem, the reputed ancestor of many of them (Gen. 10²¹⁻³¹), and spoken in various parts of South-West Asia and North Africa. These languages, most of which are now dead, may be classified roughly into four main families: (i) Eastern, including Accadian (Assyro-Babylonian); (ii) Northern or Central, including the numerous dialects of Aramaic; (iii) Western, including Canaanite, Hebrew, Moabite, and Phœnician; and (iv) Southern, including Arabic and Ethiopic. Semitic languages have a much closer affinity to one another than have, *e.g.,* Italian, French, and Spanish within the Indo-European group; cf. Acc. *kalbu* ("dog"), Aram. *kĕlebh,* Heb. *kelebh,* Arab. *kelb,* Eth. *kĕleb.* Several consonants, however, undergo permutation in the various languages accordng to fixed laws, *e.g.,* Arab. *dh*=Aram. *d*=Heb. *z;* cf. Arab. *dhahab* ("gold"), Aram. *dĕhabh,* Heb. *zāhābh.*

Semitic languages are distinguished from Indo-European by very noticeable characteristics. The most obvious of these is that with the exception of particles almost all the words are based upon roots containing three letters, all of which are consonants. Only a few roots of two or four consonants are found. It is probable, however, that the tri-consonantal roots are differentiations from originally bi-consonantal roots. Vowels occupy a secondary place in Semitic languages and are generally not represented in writing. In pronunciation, however, they are used to form substantives and verbs according to fixed grammatical patterns. The available number of patterns is increased by such devices as adding a preformative letter (generally *aleph, h, m, n,* or *t*) to the root or by strengthening ("doubling") the middle radical letter. Thus from the root *G-D-L* we have in Hebrew *GāDaL,* "he was great"; *GōDeL, GĕDûLâh,* and *GĕDuLLâh,* "greatness"; *GāDôL,* "great"; *mi-GDāL,* "a tower"; *hiGDîL,* "he magnified"; and *GiDDēL,* "he eulogized."

Another peculiarity of the Semitic languages is that the verb does not distinguish actions as past, present, or future, but indicates them simply as completed (perfect) or not yet completed (imperfect). In contrast to this defectiveness in the tense-system the verb is prolific in means of designating actions as intensive, causative, reciprocal, active, passive, or reflexive. Cf. Hebrew *QāDaSH*, "he was holy"; *QiDDēSH* and *hiQDîSH*, "he sanctified"; *hithQaDDēSH*, "he sanctified himself"; *niQDaSH*, "he showed himself to be holy"; and *QuDDaSH*, "he was sanctified."

Other important features of Semitic languages are these: *(a)* the noun governing a genitive assumes a contracted form known as the Construct State; *(b)* the oblique cases (objective and genitive) of the personal pronouns are expressed by suffixing contracted forms of these to the verb and the noun respectively; *(c)* there are only two genders— masculine and feminine; *(d)* compound words, whether nominal or verbal, are almost non-existent except in proper names, and prepositions are never used to form derivatives; *(e)* adverbs are scarce; *(f)* there are a few additional gutturals and emphatic consonants not found in Indo-European languages; and *(g)* most of the languages, including Hebrew, are written from right to left.

Biblical Hebrew is distinguished from the other principal Semitic languages by having a much smaller vocabulary and a much less developed syntax. It has been computed that the language contains only about 2050 roots and about 5000 words (excluding proper names) of which only about 500 are in frequent use. Many words occur only once and some are of doubtful meaning. Probably in the spoken language many more words existed. Owing to the Hebrew fondness for the literary device of "parallelism" synonyms are numerous, but instead of being used to express different shades of meaning they all seem to mean exactly the same and to be interchangeable. Thus *hāzāk* and *hāzēk* both = "strong" (in its various senses), *hōzek, hēzek, hozkâh,* and *hezkâh* all = "strength"; similarly, *yēsha', yĕshû'âh, tĕshû'âh,* and *môshā'ôth* all = "deliverance" or "victory." On the other hand, a single derivative is used frequently in a variety of different senses, *e.g. bērēkh* = "bless," "greet," "congratulate," "curse," "favour," and "praise," while *ḥayil* = "strength," "courage," "worth," "virtue," "riches," and "army." The word for "law" *(tôrâh)* is the same as that for "instruction" while *tôdhâh* means "thanksgiving," "thank-offering," "praise," and "choir." *Massâ'* (literally = "what is lifted up") means "burden" (physical or metaphorical), "transport," "tribute," and "utterance," while *mishpāt* denotes "judgement," "place of judgement," "verdict," "penalty," "law-suit," "crime," "justice," "ordinance," "prerogative," "duty," "rightness," "custom," and "manner." Translators have sometimes planned to represent a Hebrew word always by the same English word, but this is manifestly impossible, and there is sometimes considerable disagreement as to the exact shade of meaning of the Hebrew term. Further ambiguity arises from the fact that some of the Hebrew consonants, *e.g. H '('ayin)* and *SH* represent two different consonants which have coalesced—*S* represents at least three—so that one triliteral root may have two or more unconnected meanings. Thus the roots *H-P-R* and *H-L-S* both form three verbs of quite different meaning while *'-N-Y* and *'-R-B* both form four.

Nearly all Hebrew roots express some physical action or denote some natural object. Hence, *gāzar* "to decide" originally meant "to cut"; *'āmēn* "to be true" orig. = "to be firmly fixed"; *yāshar* "to be right" orig. = "to be straight"; and *kābhēdh* "to be honourable" orig. = "to be heavy." "Sin" is expressed by roots meaning "to miss the mark," "to be crooked," and "to break bounds." Hebrew is very poor in abstract terms and has often to express intellectual or religious concepts and emotions by metaphors or symbols, this being one cause of the frequent anthropomorphisms. Thus "intellect" or "mind" is rendered by "heart"; "reins" (*i.e.* "kidneys") = "emotions" or "volitions" or "motives." "Bowels" represents "compassion," hence the prophet can address God with the words "the sounding of Thy bowels" (Isa. 63[15]). "Hand," "arm," and "right arm" frequently represent "activity," "action," or "intervention"; "horn" = "vigour," "rule," or "dignity"; "wind" = "spirit"; "breath" = "soul," "life," or "self," *e.g.* "my soul" = "my life" or "myself," just as "his name" = "him" or "himself." "Bones" = "being" (*e.g.* Ps. 35[10]), and the word for "descendants" is "seed," while "anger" is often spoken of as "heat." Similarly, "he was angry" is normally translated by "he burned" or "his nostril burned," and "to cover the face of" is "to reconcile" (Gen. 32[20]), while "to think" must often be rendered by "to say." A "patient" man is "long of breath" and the "obstinate" are "hard of neck." Owing to the limited vocabulary circumlocutions are frequently necessary. Thus for "religion" Hebrew has to substitute "fear of the Lord" (Prov. 8[13]), and "a metropolis" is "a city and mother" (2 Sam. 20[19]). Very common are such phrases as "son of possession" = "heir" (Gen. 15[2]), "sons of valour" = "warriors" (Deut. 3[18]), "sons of pledging" = "hostages" (2 Kings 14[14]), "master of dreams" = "dreamer" (Gen. 37[19]), "masters of a covenant" = "confederates" (Gen. 14[13]), "man of the soil" = "farmer" (Gen. 9[20]), and "men of warfare" = "warriors" (Num. 31[28]). In poetry this usage is still more extended than in prose, but its principal use is to form adjectival phrases, such as "sons of wickedness" (2 Sam. 7[10]), "sons of rebellion" (Num. 17[10]), "sons of tumult" (Jer. 48[45]), "sons of affliction" (Prov. 31[5]), "master of nostril," *i.e.* "of anger" (Prov. 22[24]), "man of form," *i.e.* "of beauty" (1 Sam. 16[18]), "man of blood" (Ps. 5[6]), and "man of courage" (2 Sam. 17[10]).

Hebrew is very deficient in adjectives and often has to make use of cumbrous expressions. "A double heart" is "a heart and a heart" (Ps. 12[2]) and "diverse weights" are "a stone and a stone" (Deut. 25[13]). "The royal family" is "the seed of the kingdom" (2 Kings 11[1]), "a false report" is "a report of falsehood" (Ex. 23[1]), and "an everlasting covenant" is "a covenant of eternity" (Gen. 17[7]). Even when an adjective is available this last construction is often preferred, especially in poetry, *e.g.* "ambassador of faithfulness" (Prov. 13[17]), "God of my righteousness" = "my righteous God" (Ps. 4[1]), "throne of His holiness" (Ps. 47[8]), and "rock of my strength" (Ps. 62[7]). The adjective in Hebrew has no comparative or superlative and no word for "than," but must say "bring your small" (= "youngest") "brother" (Gen. 42[34]), "the serpent was cunning from every beast" (Gen. 3[1]), "Israel loved Joseph from all his sons," (Gen. 37[3]), and "I am not good from" (*i.e.* "better than") "my fathers" (1 Kings 19[4]). The word "too" is similarly represented, *e.g.* "hard from the Lord" = "too hard for the Lord" (Gen. 18[14]). Another method of expressing the superlative is by repetition of a noun, *e.g.* "holy of holies," "song of songs," "king of kings," "to generation and generation," or of an adjective, *e.g.* "talk no more proudly, proudly" = "so very proudly" (I Sam. 2[3]) or "deep, deep" = "very deep" (Eccles. 7[24]).

Hebrew has a poorly-developed tense-system, and the Perfect, Imperfect, and Participle may all indicate past, present, or future time, although normally the Perfect expresses past time. A distinctive and colourful usage is the "Prophetic Perfect," *e.g.* "my people has gone into exile" (Isa. 5[13]), *i.e.* "will inevitably go," but this occasionally leads to ambiguity, as in Isa. 9[1ff.]. More commonly the Imperfect is ambiguous as it not only represents the Indicative Mood (present, past frequentative, past progressive, and future) but may also have a potential, conditional, optative, imperative, or final meaning. Frequently, also, Hebrew does not distinguish a statement from a question.

One of the most characteristic features of Hebrew is its poverty in subordinating conjunctions. Sentences are almost invariably co-ordinated, using the word "and." English translators usually try to show the logical connexion between successive sentences, but this is sometimes uncertain. Hence, in Gen. 1^2-3^1 all except three of the fifty-six verses begin with "and," but the English versions translate this variously as "and" (1^2), "so" (1^{27}), "thus" (2^1), "but" (2^6), and "now" (3^1). Elsewhere we find it rendered "therefore" (Gen. 3^{23}), "as" (Gen. 18^1 R.V.), "then" (Gen. 19^{24}), "although" (Job 2^3), "because" (Ps. 5^{11}) and "(in order) that" (Gen. 19^{32}).

The features above delineated emphasize the desirability of studying the Old Testament with a commentary that suggests alternative interpretations, and preferably of reading it in the original languages. One who has "read himself into" the Semitic mind is often able to "read into" Scripture unnoticed shades of thought which the writer had failed adequately to express, simply because the language possessed no resources for conveying his meaning.

The deficiency in conjunctions coupled with the lack of abstract terms and compound words makes Hebrew an unsuitable language for precise definition or logical reasoning. On the other hand, the co-ordination of clauses adds impressiveness to the denunciations of a prophet and gives to simple narrative a naïve and archaic effect which is heightened by the frequent use of direct speech, the introduction of a new thought or scene by the word "behold" and the device of repeating a phrase superfluously as in Gen. 3^{19}, $6^{6f., 11f.}$, $11^{8f.}$. Vividness and colour are enhanced by the sensuous nature of the vocabulary and the abundant use of metaphor, simile, metonymy, hyperbole, the rhetorical question, and other figures of speech. Very popular is a play on the sound of words which is facilitated by the uniformity of grammatical patterns and inflexions and the vocal resemblance of unrelated roots, but this effect is difficult to reproduce in English.

Two minor features almost peculiar to Hebrew are *(a)* the lengthening or shortening of vowels according to their relation to the accented syllable ("tone-syllable") of the word, and *(b)* the usage of "Waw Consecutive" with Perfect and Imperfect, whereby a series of past events is introduced by a verb in the Perfect and continued by a series of Imperfects each introduced by "and," a series of future events being introduced by an Imperfect and continued by Perfects with "and." Similarly, an Imperative is continued by "and" with the Perfect.

Hebrew verse is characterized chiefly by two types of correspondence, namely, of sound and of thought, known respectively as "rhythm" and "parallelism." The former corresponds roughly to "metre," lines being of approximately equal length but without feet and the rhythm being marked simply by the number of accented syllables in the line. Unaccented syllables are not counted, but the lines are divided into two (or sometimes three) by a strong pause. The commonest rhythms are 3+3, 2+2 and 3+2, the last being called "Elegiac" or *kînah*-rhythm, as it is used by preference for dirges (*e.g.* in the Book of Lamentations). The rhythms cannot satisfactorily be imitated in a translation. It is otherwise with parallelism which assumes chiefly four forms: *(a)* "synonymous" or "repeating," where one line is echoed by the next in different language, *e.g.* "Why art thou cast down, O my soul: and why art thou disquieted within me?" (Ps. 43⁵; *(b)* "antithetic" or "contrasting," where a contrary thought is expressed, *e.g.* "For the Lord knoweth the way of the righteous: but the way of the ungodly shall perish" (Ps. 1⁶); *(c)* "constructive" or "complementary," where the thought is completed by the second line, *e.g.* "My help cometh from the Lord: who made heaven and earth" (Ps. 121²); and *(d)* "climactic" or "ascending" (a much rarer type), where a word or phrase in the first line is taken also into the second and the sentence then completed, *e.g.* "The floods have lifted up, O Lord: the floods have lifted up their voice" (Ps. 93³). Very often groups of lines are arranged in strophes—usually of unequal length—which are sometimes closed by a refrain (*e.g.* Ps. 46 or Ps. 80) and other devices are employed such as alphabetical acrostics where each line (*e.g.* Prov. 31¹⁰⁻³¹), pair of lines (*e.g.* Ps. 37), or group of lines (*e.g.* Lam. 1) begins in Hebrew with a successive letter of the alphabet or each line in a strophe begins with the same letter (*e.g.* Ps. 119). Archaic words and grammatical usages are frequent in poetry and the use of figures of speech is commoner than in prose.

A "golden" and a "silver" age of Biblical Hebrew are generally recognized, the former being the "classical" period which continues to about a century after the Exile and to which belong the JE documents together with Deuteronomy, Judges, Samuel, the older part of Kings, many of the Psalms, and the earlier Prophets. The prose is marked by dignity, lucidity, simplicity, power of dramatic presentation, and life-likeness of portraiture, while the verse is distinguished by terseness and vigour, the vividness and variety of the metaphors, and the smoothness and balance of the rhythm. Among the finest masterpieces in prose are the Joseph-stories in Genesis and the narrative in 2 Sam. 9-20. Some of the best psalms belong to this period as well as Amos, Hosea, and the earlier chapters of Isaiah, but already in Jeremiah the sentences are more laboured and the rhetorical figures lacking in force and originality. Similar signs of decadence appear in Haggai, Zechariah, Malachi, Ezekiel, and the later chapters of Isaiah, while most of the Hagiographa belong definitely to the "silver" age, Chronicles, Esther, Ecclesiastes, and Daniel betraying the most obvious evidences of lateness. The "silver" age in general is characterized not only by the introduction of foreign loan-words from Aramaic and Persian, but also by the use of Hebrew words in new meanings, the abandoning of some classical Hebrew constructions, and the adoption of Aramaic syntactical usages. The verse is artificial and unimaginative and the prose pedestrian, unpolished, and often obscure.

Biblical Aramaic differs from Hebrew chiefly by its preference of dentals to sibilants, its larger vocabulary which includes many loan-words, its greater variety of conjunctions, and its development of an elaborate tense-system through the use of the participle with pronouns or with various parts of the verb "to be." In place of the definite article *ha-* which Hebrew prefixes to nouns, Aramaic suffixes *-â*. The language is less euphonious and poetical than Hebrew but superior as a vehicle of exact expression. Aramaic languages fall into two main groups, an Eastern and a Western, which differ dialectically. Biblical Aramaic belongs to the Western group, that of Ezra having closer affinities with Hebrew than the later Aramaic of Daniel. Closely related to it is the Egyptian Aramaic of the fifth century B.C. The Aramaic of the Targums of Onkelos and Jonathan, dating from the second Christian century, probably closely resembles the language of Jesus. The main dialects of Eastern Aramaic are that of the Babylonian Talmud (A.D. 200-500) and the "Syriac" of Northern Mesopotamia, of which an abundant Christian literature has survived.

The "square" script in which Hebrew is written was borrowed from Aramaic. The "old Hebrew" or "Phœnician" script in which probably the whole of the Old Testament was originally written resembles the "square" script only slightly, although both are apparently modifications of the "Sinaitic" script which seems to have some affinities with ancient Egyptian writing, and which is found in the Sinai peninsula (*c.* 1850 B.C.) and afterwards in Palestine where it presumably evolved into the "Phœnician" script of the Moabite Stone, the Siloam inscription, and numerous inscriptions on potsherds, seals, and coins. The Aramaic script, which is first found about the eighth century B.C. in North Syria, Asia Minor, and Assyria, gradually developed into the present square character, and although it is not known to have been used for Hebrew until the second century B.C., it is conjectured from

Matt. 5[18] that the Old Testament was written in this character by the beginning of the Christian era. The Accadian language and cuneiform script were used by the Canaanites before 1400 B.C. for official purposes, and may have been used afterwards by the Hebrews, since seventh-century documents in cuneiform have been found at Gezer. Cuneiform was written upon clay tablets with a sharp stylus (cf. perhaps Isa. 8[1], Jer. 17[1]), while the alphabetical scripts were written with ink on potsherds or engraved upon stone. Many of the letters mentioned in the Old Testament may have been written on potsherds. The "rolls" or "scrolls" were probably mostly of papyrus (*e.g.* Jer. 36[23]), but perhaps sometimes of sheepskin or goatskin. They were written in ink (Jer. 36[18]) with a pen. The Old Testament text was originally purely consonantal, but at some time after A.D. 200 the letters ' (aleph), *h, w,* and *y* were occasionally inserted to represent long vowels, and after A.D. 500 the Jewish grammarians ("Massoretes") invented and inserted, sometimes inaccurately, a complete system of vowel-signs or "points." (pp. 13-21)

THE LANGUAGE OF THE NEW TESTAMENT

WILBERT FRANCIS HOWARD

The Original Form of the Writings

The visitor to the British Museum can now look at two great codices of the Greek Bible, one dating about the middle of the fourth century, the other about a century later. They are handsome volumes written

From *A Companion to the Bible,* ed. by T. W. Manson; copyright 1950. Reprinted by permission of Charles Scribner's Sons and T. & T. Clark, Publishers, Edinburgh.

by a professional scribe upon vellum, and show the dignity with which the Christian scriptures were treated when Christianity had become the state religion of the Roman Empire. But the books which form the New Testament had a far humbler origin. The earliest of them were letters dictated by a busy missionary, written on papyrus by some friend of his, and then sent by the hand of a trusty messenger to the leader of a community of converts in some distant city. During the lifetime of the Apostle Paul some unknown preachers or catechists were writing down on sheets of papyrus, first in Aramaic and later in Greek, such sayings and stories of Jesus as were treasured in the memory of His disciples or were handed on by word of mouth wherever Christians met together. Stories also gradually became current regarding incidents in the life of Jesus. In due course the good news of Jesus as a whole, His life, teaching, death, and resurrection came to be written down in Greek by various writers. One of these writers also wrote a narrative of the spread of the good news from Jerusalem to Rome. Another writer, embodying both Jewish and Christian material, gave to the Church an Apocalypse, to do for the Christian Church in a time of persecution what a Jewish Apocalypse known as the Book of Daniel had done for the Chosen People during the persecution under Antiochus Epiphanes two and a half centuries before.

If it were possible to recover the autograph, that is the original document which left the hand of the writer, of any of the New Testament writings, we should certainly find that it was written on papyrus. The letter to Philemon, or the Second Epistle of St. John, would probably be written on a single sheet a little more than five inches in width and about ten inches in height. The writing would be in two columns about two inches in width. A sheet of writing material was made of strips of pith taken from the papyrus reed and laid vertically side by side and then covered with strips laid above these horizontally. These were soaked in water from the Nile, treated with some glutinous matter, dried in the sun, and then polished with ivory rollers. The side on which the strips ran horizontally was called the *recto* and provided an easier surface for the stylus or pen. As a rule this side alone was used. But sometimes the *verso* was used as well. Sheets were fastened together side by side to form a roll. It has been calculated that the extreme length of a papyrus roll would be about thirty-two feet, and this represents the size that would be required for each of the writings attributed to St. Luke. In Rev. 5[1] we are told that the Seer was shown "a book written within and on the back, close sealed with seven seals."

Some scholars think that this refers to a papyrus roll in which the woes had overflowed from the *recto* to the *verso*. Others think that a comma should follow the word "within," in which case a papyrus codex, or book, is described, so sealed that only the outside could be seen. Recent discoveries have made it certain that as early as the second century Christian writers used the codex form of book instead of the roll, but we may consider it most probable that all but the shortest books in the New Testament were sent forth originally in the form of rolls.

The Language of the New Testament

There can be little doubt that every book in the New Testament was written in Greek, and this Greek was the common dialect (the *Koine*) spoken throughout the Mediterranean world. It is significant that when Paul sent a letter to the Christians in Rome it was written in Greek, not Latin. In the four centuries that had passed since Alexander made his conquests and bequeathed the world of Hellenism as his legacy, the Greek language had undergone a considerable change. The Attic dialect, in which Thucydides wrote his history, Plato composed his *Dialogues,* and Demosthenes delivered his speeches, belonged to a golden age of literature which had passed away never to return, although in the second century A.D. some writers (known as the Atticists) were to strive unsuccessfully to recapture the secret of an earlier age. Hellenistic Greek was far simpler in inflexions and in syntax. The reader who passes from the great classical authors to the history of Polybius, written in the later middle of the second century B.C., will be struck by the altered meaning of many words, and by many constructions which depart from earlier standards of style. But the student of New Testament Greek recognizes many of these as characteristic of the vocabulary and syntax of the New Testament. So also if he goes forward into the second century A.D. he will often find in the Discourses of Epictetus, and in Plutarch's Lives and Moral Essays, words and idioms that recall the language of the Acts and the Epistles. The tens of thousands of papyri which have been unearthed in Egypt in the last half-century furnish innumerable lexical and grammatical parallels to the Greek Testament.

There is, however, one factor that must never be left out of account when we speak of New Testament Greek. Christianity first sprang to life on Jewish soil. The two languages spoken at different times by the Jews of Palestine have left their mark upon the Christian scriptures. (1) Jesus and His first disciples spoke Aramaic. The earliest traditions of His teaching and of His ministry were handed down in that language. Though the four Gospels were all composed in Greek, some of the sources were probably literal translations from the Aramaic. It is generally recognized that the Gospel of Mark bears strong traces of an Aramaic mind in some of the constructions, as well as of Roman residence in a number of Latinisms of vocabulary. The sayings of Jesus in Matthew and Luke often bear the stamp of the Aramaic original, and there is at least one clear case in which Luke has followed a mistaken, or else a literal, translation from the Aramaic where Matthew avoids the pitfall. In Luke 11[41] we read, "Howbeit give for alms those things which are within, and all things are clean to you." Matt. 23[26] gives the saying in a more intelligible form, "Cleanse first the inside of the cup and of the plate, that the outside thereof may become clean also." Whether the translation followed by Luke mistook two letters which in Aramaic are not unlike *(dakki =* "cleanse," *zakki =* "give alms"), or whether the same Aramaic phrase meaning "to make righteous" was given the meaning "to purify" in one rendering, and "to give alms" (as so often) in the other, we need not determine. In either case an Aramaic original supplies the clue. (2) In the synagogues of the Dispersion the Old Testament was read in the Greek translation made in Alexandria. This translation, known as the Septuagint (LXX), was produced by a succession of scholars at different times, and though the quality of the translation varies greatly in different books, the work as a whole bears the impress of the Hebrew idiom which has been rendered into Greek. This Greek translation of the Old Testament has left its mark inevitably upon the Greek of the New Testament. But it is instructive to observe how differently this influence can be traced in various writers. Luke, who could write (as his Preface shows) in the freest Hellenistic, was so steeped in the idiom of the LXX that many passages in his Gospel might almost be literal translations from a Hebrew original. Some Semitic scholars so explain the hymns in the first two chapters. But "nests of Hebraisms" (as they have been called) can be found throughout the Gospel, and to a much smaller degree Aramaic or Hebrew influence can be traced throughout Acts. Prof. C. C. Torrey would even contend that an Aramaic source lies behind chapters 1–15. Whether this be so or not, from time to time in later chapters phrases recall the language of the LXX.

The Epistle to the Hebrews, on the other hand, although quotations from the LXX abound in every chapter, is written with a rhythm and balance of clauses which is as far as possible removed from the Hebraic structure of these citations. Paul, again, whilst familiar with Aramaic, and steeped in the Old Testament both in its Hebrew and Greek forms, speaks the ordinary Greek of an educated man, though he falls into the use of Biblical phraseology, as might be expected in one who was "a Hebrew sprung from Hebrew parents."

A very different phenomenon meets us in the Revelation of St. John. Ever since R. H. Charles's studies in the language of this book were published it has been impossible to deny the presence of Semitic constructions behind many of the astonishing departures from normal syntax in the Greek of the apocalyptist. We shall perhaps come nearest to a solution of this problem by recognizing three factors: *(a)* a mind that thought in Aramaic and found in the vernacular Greek many idioms sufficiently close to his mother-tongue for his purpose; *(b)* sources in translated Greek and in Hebrew which he worked into his book in Hebraic Greek; and *(c)* a knowledge of the LXX and of Apocalypses already current in a Greek form, which supplied him with a vocabularly and often suggested an idiom. The thorough investigation of the language of the New Testament in the light of Hellenistic syntax and also of Semitic constructions has done much to help the exegete. But the most interesting contributions have been made on the lexical side.

Vocabulary

To understand the meaning of a New Testament word we must not simply assume that a lexicon of classical Greek will supply our need. It is important to know how it is used in the LXX, in writers of the Hellenistic age, and in the inscriptions and the papyri representing the language of everyday life.

"The name that is above every name" (Phil. 2⁹⁻¹¹) was conferred by God upon the Son "that every tongue might confess that Jesus Christ is LORD." This word κύριος is full of meaning. The first Christian creed acknowledged Jesus as Christ. But to the Gentile world that title (the literal translation of the Hebrew word for "Anointed") was meaningless. However, there was an appropriate word at the disposal of the first missionaries, as κύριος was the designation given to the divinities worshipped in the religious cults of the Graeco-Roman world ("My lord Serapis" is found in many papyri). Still, this transposition would have been impossible without the Semitic background of the primitive Church. Κύριος is constantly used in the LXX to translate the sacred tetragrammaton for which the word *Adonai* was substituted when the

Hebrew scriptures were read aloud. Moreover, the urgent prayer of the earliest Aramaic-speaking Church, *Marana tha,* "Our Lord, come!" shows that personal devotion had prepared the way for theological identification. "The highest place that heaven affords is His, is His by right." So "Jesus is Messiah" became "Jesus is Lord," and the two creeds were fused in one title "Our Lord Jesus Christ."

The words δικαιοσύνη (righteousness) and ἐλεημοσύνη (alms) are obviously identical in their use in Matt. $6^{1,2}$. This specialized use of the former word is clearly evident in the Book of Tobit, for the two ideas often found expression in the same Hebrew word for "righteousness." Yet in that book the two Greek words are used twice side by side. It is equally significant that the word δικαιοσύνη is often used in the LXX to render the Hebrew word for "mercy" which also carries the conception of "covenant loyalty." Numerous passages can be cited from the LXX to show that the parallelism of the underlying Hebrew brings δικαιοσύνη into very close affinity with ἔλεος ("mercy") or else with σωτήριον ("salvation"). The bearing of this upon the interpretation of Rom. 3^{25} has been brought out effectively by recent commentators (*e.g.* C. Anderson Scott and C. H. Dodd). The same difficult passage in Romans contains the word ἱλαστήριον (A. V. and R. V. "propitiation"). This word and its cognates bear one set of meanings in classical Greek and also in the *Koine,* but have a different significance in the LXX. Whereas in the former the verb ἱλάσχεσθαι (or its compounds) regularly means "to placate," "to propitiate," with a personal object, and only secondarily means "to expiate," with an impersonal object, it is quite otherwise in the LXX. C. H. Dodd (*The Bible and the Greeks,* ch. iv.) has proved from an examination of the LXX uses of the words from this root that "Hellenistic Judaism, as represented by the LXX, does not regard the cultus as a means of pacifying the displeasure of the Deity, but as a means of delivering man from sin, and it looks in the last resort to God Himself to perform that deliverance, thus evolving a meaning of ἱλάσχεσθαι strange to non-Biblical Greek." The application of this linguistic study to the New Testament passages where these words occur (Luke 18^{13}, Heb. 2^{17}, 8^{12}, 9^5; Rom. 3^{25}; I John 2^2, 4^{10}) leads to the same result. "Propitiation" in the sense of placating an angry God is not in accord with Biblical usage. Christ is sent as the divine means of forgiveness, whereby sin is removed.

These will serve as examples of theological importance of the LXX as a key to the language of the New Testament. Sometimes, however, the papyri warn us that a word may be used in a wider sense than is usual in the Greek Old Testament. Διαθήχη was preferred to the classical συνθήχη as the regular translation of the Hebrew word for "covenant," because the preposition in the latter compound might suggest a contractual agreement made by equals. The covenant idea which plays so large a part in Hebrew religion is of cardinal importance in the New Covenant of our Lord, and so some expositors have wished to retain this meaning wherever the word occurs in the New Testament. Deissmann, on the other hand, seeing that the word always means "will" in the *Koine,* would give the sense "testament" to it in all its New Testament occurrences. The latter meaning seems to be required in Heb. 9[15ff.] and Gal. 3[15]. Probably both meanings are covered by διαθήχη, which is equivalent to the legal term "instrument": in one case an instrument which God draws up and sends to His people to express His will; in the special sense of "instrument" suggesting a disposition made of property in view of ultimate death.

The papyri have illustrated a number of other legal and financial metaphors in the New Testament. The ordinary technical meaning of ὑπόστχσις justifies the definition of faith in Heb. 11[1] as the *title-deeds* of things hoped for . . . ." Καταντάω is so commonly used of property "descending to" an heir, and τέλος of "toll," that there is some justification for translating 1 Cor. 10[11], "who are *heirs* of the *revenues* of the ages," rather than "upon whom the *ends* of the ages are *come.*" Ἀρραβών is often found in agreements, for the "part-payment" as a pledge of what will be fully paid later on. Thus when Paul writes of the *"earnest* of the Spirit in our hearts" (2 Cor. 1[22]; cf. 5[5], Eph. 1[14]) he means that the gift of the Spirit is both a foretaste and a pledge of the inheritance which is not yet fully ours. Paul, again, was probably using a metaphor from accountancy in the famous passage (Phil. 4[8]): "Reckon (λογίζεσθε) these things among your assets," for a little later (v.[15]) he says playfully, "No church communicated with me so as to have a debit and credit account" (εἰς λόγον δόσεως χαὶ λήμψεως), and adds (vv.[17-18]), "It is not your gift that I am looking for, but the interest that is accumulating to your credit (τὸν χάρπον τὸν πλεονάζοντα εἰς λόγον ὑμῶν). *I give you a receipt* for what you owed me. I have been overpaid!" This word ἀπέχω is regularly used in the papyri when a receipt is signed. Those who translated our Lord's sayings into Greek were happy in their choice of this word to bring out the nuance in His condemnations of ostentatious piety. "They have their full reward" (ἀπέχουσι). It is all the reward they will have!

Under this heading we note that λογεία (*"collection,"* 1 Cor. 16[1]), formerly regarded as peculiar to this New Testament occurrence, is very common in the papyri with this meaning. Another word rescued from oblivion by the papyri is the adjective δοχίμιος. Thus the phrase used in James 1³ and 1 Pet. 1⁷ means "the *approved* element in your faith," *i.e.* "what is genuine in your faith." Another obscure phrase has been made intelligible by a study of the *Koine*. The A.V. translates 1 Pet. 2² "the *sincere* milk *of the word*." But ἄδολος which meant "honest," "guileless," in classical prose, was also used by the tragedians of "unadulterated," and in this sense the word is constantly used in the papyri. Λογιχός, which often has the meaning "rational," "spiritual," is found in the vernacular with the sense "metaphorical." Peter therefore is speaking of "pure milk" in the figurative sense.

The word ἡλιχία can mean either "age" or "stature." The latter is evidently the meaning in Luke 19³ and Eph. 4¹³. But the overwhelming evidence of the papyri encourages the other interpretation in the remaining passages. This is specially significant in Matt. 6²⁷, Luke 12²⁵. After all, it is worry that shortens life, and the desire to add eighteen inches to one's height is so rare an eccentricity that Jesus is hardly likely to have deprecated it. (Ps. 39⁵ answers the objection that a spatial measure could not be used of time.)

In earlier Greek, ἀπάτη meant "deceit," in later usage the idea of "pleasure" predominated. Perhaps "beguilement" best renders the word in the New Testament. When the translators of 1611 described Apollos as an "eloquent" man they were guided by the Vulgate rendering *eloquens* (Acts 18²⁴). The Revisers of 1881 followed the classical usage by translating λόγιος "learned." But Jerome was right, as is shown by the protest of Phrynichus—that second-century Atticist who so stubbornly resisted the innovations of the *Koine*.

So also we must abandon the classical meaning "to be ambitious" for φιλοτιμέομαι, given in the R.V. margin for this word in its three occurrences in the New Testament (Rom. 15²⁰, 2 Cor. 5⁹, 1 Thes. 4¹¹). In later Greek the word simply meant "to be zealous," "to strive eagerly." Philological debate has always been busy with the derivation of συχοφαντέω, and the earlier editions of Liddell and Scott actually informed us that one of the etymological theories was a *figment!* The history of the word is interesting. In classical Greek it was used of false accusations, especially for the extortion of money. In the LXX the meaning was rather "to oppress." In the New Testament it occurs in Luke 3¹⁴, 19⁸, where the A.V. gives the meaning "to accuse falsely," and the R.V. "to exact wrongfully." Examples from the papyri favour the former. In the imperial age tax-collectors had no power to collect arrears, but could denounce the defaulter to the proper revenue officials. So that Zacchæus probably said, "If I have falsely accused any defaulter before the government and had him condemned to pay up arrears . . ."

Allusions to the religious and social background of the epistles have been brought to light by inscriptions and papyri. The rendering "for freedom" (Gal. $5^{1,13}$, R.V.) is justified and illustrated by inscriptions showing that ἐπ' ἐλευθερία was a regular formula used in the legal process for the manumission of a slave. So also Ramsay has settled the much discussed meaning of ἐμβατεύω in Col. 2^{18} with the help of inscriptions from Klaros. The verb was a technical term in the mystery religions for "setting foot on" the entrance to the new life of communion with the divinity. Paul is therefore quoting the word from the jargon of those who are causing the trouble in the church at Colossæ. The allusion is to one who is "taking his stand on what he has seen" in the mysteries; he is parading his degree as an initiate. (pp. 22-29)

THE BIBLE IN ENGLISH

GEORGE PHILIP KRAPP

THE STORY OF THE vernacular translation of the scriptures runs back almost to the beginnings of the English race in England. Even before any attempt at specific translation was made, the text of the scriptures was freely drawn upon by the poets who sang in the native tongue. According to Bede, Cædmon composed a versified narrative of practically the whole Bible. Some of the poems of Cynewulf are based,

From *The Rise of English Literary Prose,* by George Philip Krapp; Oxford University Press, 1915. Reprinted by permission of the publishers and Mrs. Elizabeth Krapp.

directly and indirectly, upon the story of the New Testament. Besides these two, doubtless there were many other poets of the Old English period, not now known to us by name, who followed a general custom of paraphrasing Biblical narrative in the terms of native heroic poetry.

All this, however, was very different from translation in the specific sense. The purpose of Old English Christian poetry was literary and devotional, to a very slight extent doctrinal. There was no attempt in these poems to reproduce the text of the scriptures with any verbal exactness. Experiments in more exact translation were made, however, by a number of scholars. Bede, according to the well-known story, completed a translation into English of the Gospel of St. John upon his death-bed, of which unfortunately no manuscript has survived. An Old English translation of the Psalms, however, is still extant, and a number of Biblical manuscripts with glosses in the vernacular are further evidence of early attempts at translation. Towards the end of the Old English period came Aelfric's translation of parts of the Old Testament, and the more important translation of the Gospels into West Saxon by one, or perhaps several, unknown scholars. But there is no evidence of any attempt to translate the whole of the Bible in the Old English period, nor is there any evidence that such translations as were made were intended for popular use. Aelfric expresses his unwillingness to continue with his work of translation for fear that the English version of the text might be put to improper uses by the ignorant of both clergy and laity. And the numerous interlinear versions of and glosses on Latin texts were obviously intended as aids in the reading of Latin, not as a means by which those ignorant of Latin could dispense with the Latin originals.

In the years which immediately followed the readjustment of English life and affairs after the Conquest, no great change appears in the English attitude towards the scriptures. Popular interest continued to be satisfied by versified paraphrases of portions of the Old and New Testaments, which were hardly distinguishable from the general body of current legendary and hagiological literature. Bible paraphrases on a large scale after the manner of the *Historia Scholastica* of Peter Comestor, were written in French, but the nearest parallel to these works in English is the long poem entitled *Cursor Mundi,* to a great extent based upon the *Historia Scholastica,* but including much miscellaneous historical and legendary material. A century earlier, about the year 1200, was written another long poem known from the name of its author as the *Ormulum,* in which Orm intended to translate all the

Gospels for the year, adding expositions on them. The book was designed for the instruction of the people in 'holy Gospel's lore,' but
the poem, although it reaches ten thousand lines in length, does not
carry the plan to completion. As it is, the pearls of the Gospel are
almost completely lost in Orm's ocean of commentary.

Paraphrases of Genesis and of Exodus were also made in a popular
metrical form, and at the beginning of the fourteenth century an
English prose Psalter, the work of a not unskillful translator, appeared
in the West Midland dialect. Biblical texts were of course freely inserted
in homilies and sermons, many sermons being, as Wiclif complained,
nothing more than a string of scriptural quotations with just enough
connecting commentary to make it impossible for the hearer to tell
where the scripture left off and the commentary began. Indeed the
average layman down to the time when printed texts of the Bible began
to be circulated must have had a very confused sense of what was
scripture and what was not. He knew perhaps his Pater Noster and a
certain number of texts, and undoubtedly he was familiar with a great
number of Biblical stories, especially those of the more picturesque
and dramatic kind. But he must have found it difficult, if the thought
ever occurred to him, to distinguish the exempla of profane origin
with which the preacher adorned his sermon from the authentic narratives of the scriptures. The seven deadly sins, the marvels of the Physi-
ologus, in short all the store of pious legend and doctrine which he
heard from the pulpit must have seemed to him of equal authority with
the narrative of the creation or of the atonement and resurrection. For
the scriptures as a book with a definitely limited content he could have
had scarcely any appreciation until such time as the actual pages of the
volume could be held in hand. Only then was it possible to make the
Bible the single and all-sufficient rule of conduct for this life and the
next which it was soon to become.

For the first attempt to construct an English version of the scriptures
with a view to presenting the Bible as a whole, we must turn to the
age of Wiclif. The conception of a complete popular translation of the
scriptures probably originated with Wiclif himself, but before the Wiclifite version was finished, orthodox tendencies in the same direction had
already manifested themselves. These orthodox experiments, however,
differed from Wiclif's in that the translations were intended only for
the use of members of religious orders and others who occupied some
more or less officially recognized position in the church, and who found
difficulty in reading the Latin and French versions already extant. They

were not intended for the use of the common people. An interesting example of this more limited kind of translation is the version made in the latter part of the fourteenth century at the request of the members of some unknown religious house.[1] This book opens with a prologue giving a brief narrative account of the creation, of the fall of Lucifer, and of the story of Adam and Eve. It then takes the form of a dialogue between a "lewed and unkunnynge" brother and sister, that is, monk and nun, on the one hand, and their brother superior on the other. The brother superior acts as instructor and gives a running account of the Old Testament, and more briefly, of the teachings of the New Testament. Then follow translations of the Epistles, Acts, and the first chapter of Matthew. Perhaps the intention was to translate all the Gospels, and indeed this may have been done, although no such complete manuscript has survived. The significance of this translation lies in the fact that it was frankly intended for the orthodox unlearned in the church. The main purpose of the translator was to make the meaning of the text clear, and his English is in general simple and idiomatic. It is not an unreasonable supposition that if the Wiclifite version had not appeared under Lollard auspices and had not consequently brought to a focus and intensified the hostility of ecclesiastical authorities towards vernacular versions of the scripture, the church itself might soon have put forth, as it constantly maintained its intention of doing, an authorized and complete English Bible.

The exact extent of Wiclif's share in the translation which is usually known by his name, cannot now be determined. That the project was inspired by Wiclif was the common opinion of his day and likewise of his successors in the task of making an English Bible. It seems probable that the New Testament was taken up first, and this translation may have been made by Wiclif himself. The Old Testament was in part the work of Nicholas de Hereford, who translated as far as the book of Baruch, where the translation breaks off in the middle of a sentence. The probable date at which Hereford was interrupted in his work was the year 1382.[2] The Old Testament was then completed by a different translator, who again may have been Wiclif himself. Shortly after Wiclif's death the whole translation underwent a revision, probably at the hands of John Purvey, Wiclif's successor in the leadership of the Lollard party. The extraordinary popularity of these translations, all

[1]Paues, *A Fourteenth Century English Biblical Version*, p. xxiv.
[2]Forshall and Madden, *The Holy Bible*, p. xvii.

made from the Latin of the Vulgate, is attested by the large number of manuscripts scattered throughout England which are still extant in various degrees of completeness,[3] and these, it should be remembered, are probably but a relatively small number which survived the wear and tear to which popular books are always subject and the no less destructive zeal of the orthodox party in the early part of the fifteenth century.

Of the many hampering considerations which attended the translation of the scriptures in the fourteenth century, perhaps the most disturbing was the uncertainty which prevailed as to the proper balance to be maintained between literal translation and paraphrase. No such feeling existed when the question was one of the translation of monuments of profane literature into English. In such cases the universal method was that of paraphrase, the purpose of translation being assumed to be the transference of the sense of the original to the forms of English speech. The scriptures themselves had indeed often been paraphrased in this manner. But when it came to the question of translating the Bible as a book, a paraphrastic version of any man's conception of the content or sense of the book could not be regarded as satisfactory. The task before the translator was not that of interpreting the book, but of transferring it literally in body to another language. Two great opposing necessities therefore confronted him. On the one side he must take heed not to do violence to the almost sacred forms of speech in which the original was written, and on the other lay the necessity of making his translation at least intelligible, and if possible, natural and idiomatic. Deficiencies of vocabulary in the native speech and lack of parallelism in grammatical structure and word-order between English and Latin were the main obstacles in the way of the translator who should attempt to produce in English an exact equivalent of the Latin version. At a later period the task of translation was further complicated by questions of the doctrinal coloring of English words, but at the time the Wiclif versions were made, theological discussion had not advanced so far as to make these questions seriously felt. Wiclif's problem was the relatively simple one of finding the safe mean between the extremes of literal translation and of free adaptation of the Latin originals.

Three differing conceptions of the art of translation, which for convenience' sake we may ascribe to Wiclif, Hereford, and Purvey, with

[3]Forshall and Madden, I xxxix-lxiv, give a list of 170.

passing acknowledgement that the exact share of each in the specific work of translation is not altogether certain, may be distinguished in this first English Bible. Of these three, Hereford was the most literal, Purvey was the most idiomatic and free, and Wiclif occupied a middle ground between the two extremes. Hereford's version of the Old Testament is often extremely literal, in this respect going even farther than Wiclif, who not infrequently sacrifices English idiom for the sake of close correspondence between the English and Latin. The principles which Purvey followed in his revision of the whole "were designed to render the version more correct, intelligible and popular; and it manifestly becomes more easy and familiar as the translator advances."[4] In the Prologue to his revision, Purvey has set down some of the rules which governed him in his work. He tells how he first collated many "elde biblis," taking into consideration the statements of the doctors and the glosses in the text in order to make "oo Latyn bible sumdel trewe." Having collected his materials, he then studied them and took counsel of "elde gramariens and elde dyvynis of harde wordis and harde sentencis, hou tho mihten best be undurstonden and translatid." And finally he translated the text as clearly as he could, according to the significance, taking care to have "manie gode felawis and kunnynge at the correcting of the translacioun." Purvey insists strongly upon the necessity of translating not too literally, but according to the thought of the original. The best translation from Latin into English, he says, is to translate "aftir the sentence, and not oneli aftir the wordis, so that the sentence be as opin, either [or] openere, in English as in Latyn"—but he adds the saving clause, "and go not fer fro the lettre." If the letter may not be followed in translating, then let the thought be ever whole and open, for the purpose of words is to express thought and meaning, and if they do not serve this purpose, they are superfluous or false. Specific instances are then cited by Purvey of ways in which the English translation may legitimately vary from the Latin original in order to make the thought more clear. Ablative absolutes may be translated as finite clauses, "the maistir redinge, I stonde" being rendered "while the maistir redith, I stonde," or "if the maistir redith," etc., or "for the maistir," etc. Sometimes the construction may be rendered by *whanne* or *aftirward,* as in "whanne the maistir red, I stood," or "aftir the maistir red, I stood," or it may even be rendered by an independent

4Forshall and Madden, I, xxix.

clause, *arescentibus hominibus prae timore* being translated, "and men shulen wexe drie for drede." In a similar way, a participle, present or past, active or passive, may be resolved into a verb of the same tense, *dicens* being translated "and seith" or "that seith." Or a relative may be resolved into a phrase containing a conjunction and the antecedent of the relative, "which renneth," for example, being equivalent to "and he renneth." When the Latin order of words would be obscure in English, the English order is to be preferred; thus the Latin sentence *Dominum formidabunt adversarii ejus,* would read literally in English, "the Lord hise adversaries shulen drede," but, continues Purvey, "I Englishe it thus bi resolucion, 'the adversaries of the Lord shulen drede him.'" In translating words which may have several meanings in Latin, care should be used to choose the English word which accords with the thought of the sentence in which the Latin word occurs. The Prologue insists a number of times that an English translation may be as clear, or even clearer than the Latin original. It also comments on the necessity of taking figurative speech figuratively, adding the caution that "autouris of hooly scripture usiden moo figuris, that is, mo fyguratif spechis, than gramariens moun gesse, that reden not tho figuris in holy scripture." Purvey then announces the less tenable position, that whatever thing in God's word may not be referred properly to honesty of virtues or to the truth of faith, "it is figuratyf speche."[5] Spiritual interpretations, finally, are commended, but it is pointed out that the literal understanding of the scriptures is the foundation of all spiritual interpretation.

Such were some of the problems to be considered by a fourteenth-century translator of the scriptures who would realize the proper mean between an exact literal translation and the more familiar medieval method of paraphrase. In the light of the later development of the translation of the scriptures into English, the modern reader will feel that neither Wiclif nor Purvey went far enough in accommodating their versions of the Latin to the English idiom. In many instances the later revision improves greatly upon the earlier text, as, for example, in the translation of Mark i, 31-33, where the earlier version reads:

> "And he cummynge to [Vulgate *accedens*], reride hir up, the hond of hir taken [*apprehensa manu ejus*], and anoon the fevere left hire and she mynystride to hem. Forsothe the evenynge maad

---

[5]St. Augustine expressed the same principle, *De Doctrina Christina,* lib. 3, tom. 3, p. 53; Tillotson, *Works,* II, 424.

[*vespere autem facto*], whenne the sone wente doun, thei brouhten to hym alle havynge yvel and havynge develis."

This is more idiomatically, and indeed quite adequately, expressed in the revised version:

"And he cam nyh, and areride hir, and whanne he hadde take hir hoond, anoon the fever left hir, and sche servede hem. But whanne the eventid was come, and the sonne was gon doun, thei brouhten to hym alle that weren of male ese, and hem that hadden fendis."

Often, however, even Purvey's revision is not carried far enough, especially in the books of the Old Testament. Translating Genesis i, 11, the earlier version reads:

"Burion [burgeon] the erthe grene erbe and makynge seed [*facientem semen*], and appletre makynge fruyt [*faciens fructum*] after his kynd, whos seed ben in hym silf, upon the erthe; and maad it so [*et factum est ita*]."

Purvey's translation is only slightly better:

"The earthe brynge forth greene eerbe and makynge seed, and appil tre makynge fruyt bi his kynde, whos seed be in it silf on erthe; and it was doon so."

The inadequacies of the revised translation arise less than the difficulties attaching to words in themselves, for the words of the Vulgate usually find a fairly satisfactory English or Latinized English equivalent, but rather from a disregard of the native idiom. Thus the definite article is often omitted, as in Matt. v, 13, "Ye ben salt of the erthe" [*Vos estis sal terrae*]. In verse 11 of the same chapter the English revision reads, "whanne men schulen curse you . . . for me," where "for me" renders the Vulgate *propter me*. In Matt. v, 25, "Be thou consentynge to thin adversairie soone," the English is a literal translation of the Vulgate, *Esto consentiens adversario tuo cito*. The unidiomatic "Nyle ye" is frequently used as an imperative, translating Latin *nolite,* e.g. Matt. vi, 19, "Nile ye tresoure to you tresouris in erthe, where ruste and mouhte destrieth." Such passages as these are not sporadic, but are so persistent as to give the general tone to the translation. As a work of literary art the Wiclifite Bible cannot be said to have established a new and high standard of English style, nor does it seem probable that it could ever have become a genuinely popular Bible. Nevertheless the work was nobly conceived, and it was carried out with respect for the highest standards of scholarship and of dignity in expression which were possible in its time. Its errors were all on the safe side of caution, and when one considers the difficulties and constraints which must have attended any attempt to translate the scriptures in Wiclif's day, the wonder is not that it failed to be a permanently satisfactory translation, but that it should be as good as it is.

Further growth in the form of this first English version of the Bible was checked shortly after its completion by the hostility which it aroused on the part of the clerical and anti-Lollard authorities in church and state. The attitude of the conservative element in English society towards the vernacular translation of the scriptures is well illustrated by the frequently quoted remarks of the contemporary chronicler, Henry Knighton. Wiclif, he says, has translated the Bible, which Christ gave to clerks and teachers of the church, so that now it is better known to lay men and women who can read than formerly it was to learned clerks. "In this way the pearl of the Gospel is scattered broadcast and trodden under foot by swine. And thus, what is wont to be esteemed by clerks and laity as precious is now become as it were the common joke of both; the jewel of the clerics is turned to the sport of the lay people."[6] Wiclif himself frequently commented on the hostility of the friars towards English versions of the Bible and explicitly defended their use. He often insisted also on the necessity of presenting the Gospel to humble people and dwellers in "litil touns," following the example of Christ who himself "wente to smale uplondishe touns, as to Bethfage and to Cana in Galile." Rich men might possess copies of the English scriptures for themselves, but the inhabitants of the villages and of country communities were dependent upon the poor priests, many of whom doubtless carried with them in their wanderings more or less complete copies of the Wiclifite Bible. In this way the laity not only became acquainted with the idea of an English Bible, but also with a considerable body of the text itself. A movement was thus set on foot which, if it had not been checked, must soon have resulted in further revisions of the English scriptures, and perhaps in the production of a version more completely in accord with the popular feeling for idiomatic expression than was possible in the first experiments of Wiclif, Hereford, and Purvey. Powerful influences were brought to bear, however, to obstruct the popular movement thus begun. In the year 1408 were issued the famous Constitutions of Archbishop Arundel, in which the use of vernacular translations was forbidden, *sub majoris*

---

[6]*Chronicon Henrici Knighton,* ed. Lumby, II, 151-152; quoted by Paues, p. xxxi, whose translation of Knight's Latin is here followed.

excommunicationis poena, unless the translation had been approved by a provincial council of the church. More specifically this prohibition was directed against Wiclif, who is mentioned by name.

There is no reason for supposing that at this early period the use of vernacular translations of the scriptures was absolutely forbidden by the authorities of the church. Men- of high position and members of religious orders probably met with little difficulty in obtaining approved copies of translations of at least parts of the Bible, if they wanted them. But the evidence is conclusive that the orthodox party did not itself father an English translation of the Bible, and that it powerfully discouraged the use of any such translation by common folk and the laity. Sufficient confirmation of this is found in the fact that in the many trials of Lollards for heresy which were held in the early fifteenth century, the possession of a copy of the English Bible, or even attendance upon readings of it, was regarded as damnatory evidence. In 1431, John Stafford, the bishop of Bath and Wells, "threatened with excommunication any who translated the scriptures or copied such translations."[7] In the face of such opposition, the use of the Wiclifite Bible necessarily became more and more limited, and, at least so far as the common people were concerned, more and more furtive. With the gradual changes in English speech which took place in the fifteenth century, important changes in vocabulary, in inflections and in syntax, the language of the Wiclifite Bible must also soon have needed revision in order to make it intelligible to readers of later times. This lack of authoritative support and of revision are in themselves causes sufficient to account for the fact that the Wiclifite Bible did not become the foundation of the English Bible of the Reformation, that by the end of the fifteenth century it was remembered mainly as having established the tradition of an English Bible, and that when Tindale set about the task of creating a new popular version, he carried on his work in almost complete disregard of what Wiclif and his assistants had already done. The influence of Wiclif's English Bible must be sought not by the way of any immediate literary successors, but in the hidden current of popular thought and feeling which it set in motion and which for many years it secretly fed. In a later generation the popular tradition thus established exerted a powerful influence upon the minds of the public leaders of men in politics and religion and upon the forms of English literary art.

Over a hundred years were to pass after the completion of the

[7]Capes, *The English Church in the Fourteenth and Fifteenth Centuries,* p. 129.

Wiclifite Bible before another successful attempt could be made to translate any considerable portion of the scriptures into English. The story of the translation and the publication of Tindale's New Testament, obscure in some minor details, is on the whole clearly known. Tindale submitted himself to a long period of preparatory discipline before he undertook the task which was to be the chief labor of his short life. After a residence at Oxford and Cambridge which covered a period of at least ten years, he removed in 1521 to the country, where he became tutor in the family of a Gloucestershire gentleman. It was not long before his advanced opinions with respect to the use of the scriptures led him into conflict with some of the local clergy, and it was at this time that he is reported to have made his famous answer to one who declared that it were better to be without God's law than the pope's: "If God spare my life, ere many years I will cause a boy that driveth the plow shall know more of the scripture than thou doest."

In pursuance of this purpose, two years later Tindale journeyed to London with the expectation of finding support from Tunstall, the bishop of London, as a scholar and one interested in the translation of the New Testament. As testimony of his ability, he bore with him a translation into English from the Greek of Isocrates. But Tunstall received him coldly and could find no place for him in his household. His hope of episcopal support having proved vain, Tindale soon realized the impossibility of completing in England the work which he had undertaken. "I . . . understode at the laste," he wrote late, "that there was no rowme in my lorde of londons palace to translate the new testament, but also that there was no place to do it in all englande."[8]

In 1524 he sailed for Hamburg, and soon after passed on to Wittenberg, where he almost certainly saw Luther. The work of translation advanced apace, and in 1525 a part of the New Testament was printed at Cologne. Forbidden to continue the printing of the text by the civil authorities of Cologne, Tindale escaped to Worms, where the printer Schoeffer was successful in carrying the work of printing to completion before the end of the year. With the aid of certain of those liberal-minded merchants who throughout were Tindale's chief supporters and patrons, copies were straightway sent over to England and distributed. Tunstall, in a sermon preached at Paul's Cross, October 24, 1526, bitterly denounced the translation, declaring that he had found three

[8]*Preface to Genesis,* Parker Society, p. 396.

thousand errors in it. The translation was condemned to be burned by a conclave of bishops, and this sentence was executed upon as many copies as could be discovered. In this, says Tindale, the bishops did not otherwise than he expected. Having completed his New Testament, Tindale turned his attention to the other parts of the scriptures, publishing a translation of the Pentateuch in 1530, and one of the Book of Jonah in 1531. He also added to a revised edition of his New Testament in 1534, the Epistles from the Old Testament, which included passages from the historical books of the Old Testament as well as from the Pentateuch. No more of Tindale's Old Testament was printed during his life, but his manuscript translation of the books from Joshua to 2 Chronicles was probably used by his friend Rogers in the preparation of the so-called Matthew Bible. A second slighter revision of the New Testament appeared in 1535, and this brought to an end Tindale's work in the English version of the scriptures. He died at Antwerp, at the martyr's stake, in October, 1536, young in years but with the realization of a great task carried nearly to completion.

Two endeavors, not easily combined, were constantly before Tindale in the preparation of his English Bible. On the one side, the ideal of scholarly exactness demanded a truthful, though not a literal, reproduction of the original, and on the other, the translation could be effective, as Tindale meant it to be, only by being intelligible and, still more, by being interesting to the simple folk in whom Tindale was mainly interested. Tindale was convinced that it was impossible "to stablysh the laye people in any truth, excepte the scripture were playnly layde before their eyes in their mother tonge, that they might se the processe, ordre and meaninge of the texte."[9] And this thing only, he declares, moved him to translate the New Testament. At another place he sets forth in greater detail the reasons which justify an English translation of the scriptures.[10] His main points are as follows:

(1) The Old Testament was written in Hebrew, not a learned tongue but the speech of the people: why then may we not have both the Old and the New in our tongue?

(2) "They will say haply, the scripture requireth a pure mind and a quiet mind: and therefore the lay-man, because he is altogether cumbered with worldly business, cannot understand them. If that be the case, then it is a plain case that our prelates understand not the

[9]*Preface,* p. 394.
[10]*Obedience of a Christian Man,* in *Doctrinal Treatises,* pp. 144 ff.

scriptures themselves: for no lay-man is so tangled with worldly business as they are."

(3)   Another objection was that if the scriptures were in the mother tongue, every man would understand them after his own way. "Wherefore serveth the curate," answers Tindale, "but to teach him the right way? Wherefore were the holy days made, but that people should come and learn? Are ye not abhominable schoolmasters, in that ye take so great wages, if ye will not teach?"

(4)   The apostles preached in their mother tongue, and if one preach a good sermon, why may it not as well be written?

(5)   St. Jerome translated the Bible into his mother tongue, and why may we not do the same?

(6)   "They will say it cannot be translated into our tongue, it is so rude. It is not so rude as they are false liars. For the Greek tongue agreeth more with the English than with the Latin. And the properties of the Hebrew tongue agreeth a thousand times more with the English than with the Latin."

(7)   People are wont to follow different authorities, i.e. the various doctors of the church. "Whereby shall I try and judge them [the doctors]? Verily, by God's word, which only is true. But how shall I that do, when thou wilt not let me see the scripture? . . . Nay, say they, the scripture is so hard, that thou couldst never understand it but by the doctors. That is, I must measure the mete-yard by the cloth. Here be twenty cloths [i.e. doctors] of divers lengths and of divers breadths: how shall I be sure of the length of the mete-yard by them?"

(8)   They will say that you cannot understand the scriptures without philosophy, without a knowledge of Aristotle. "Aristotle saith, 'Give a man a law, and he becometh righteous with working righteously.' But Paul and all the scripture saith, 'That the law doth but utter sin only, and helpeth not: neither hath any man power to do the law, till the Spirit of God be given him through faith in Christ.' " Teaching of the scriptures, says Tindale, should be the teaching of God's law, and not the philosophies of nominalists and realists, with their "predicaments, univals, second intentions, quiddities, haecceities, and relatives." Diversity of teaching among the doctors is to be corrected by return to the pure word of the scriptures. "Now whatsoever opinions every man findeth with his doctor, that is his gospel, and that only is true with him, and that holdeth he all his life long; and every man, to maintain his doctor withal, corrupteth the scripture, and fashioneth it after his own imagination, as a potter doth his clay. Of what text thou

provest hell, will another prove purgatory; another limbo patrum; and another the assumption of our lady; and another shall prove of the same text that an ape hath a tail."

(9) "Finally that this threatening and forbidding of the lay people to read the scripture is not for the love of your souls (which they care for as the fox doth for the geese) is evident, and clearer than the sun; inasmuch as they permit and suffer you to read Robin Hood, and Bevis of Hampton, Hercules, Hector and Troilus, with a thousand histories and fables of love and wantonness and of ribaldry, as filthy as heart can think, to corrupt the mind of youth withal, clean contrary to the doctrine of Christ and of his apostles."

(10) "A thousand reasons more might be made, as thou mayest see in *Paracelsi Erasmi,* and in his preface to the *Paraphrase of Matthew,* unto which they should be compelled to hold their peace or to give shameful answers."

The form and manner of expression which Tindale settled upon as adequate to realize his conception of an English Bible for lay readers were of his own invention. He had no predecessors in English who served him as models. In the Epistle to the Reader at the end of the Worms edition of his New Testament, he begs that his readers be not offended at the rudeness of the work and he asks them to consider that he "had no man to counterfeit, neither was helped with English of any that had interpreted the same or such like thing in the scripture before time. . . . Count it as a thing not having his full shape, but as it were born before his time, even as a thing begun rather than finished."[11]

Comparison of Tindale's translation with earlier English versions of the Bible, or parts of it, bears out Tindale's claim to independence. The style of his first New Testament is altogether new in the development of English translations of the Bible; but it was not rudely or imperfectly conceived. By the time Tindale began the actual task of translation he had definitely established the principles of his work, and from these he never greatly departed. The style which he accepted was above all simple and popular. He avoided, not altogether, but with rare exceptions, the use of unidiomatic Latinisms in syntax, and also the use of unfamiliar Anglicized Latin words. Long words were not cultivated as a means of elevating the style, nor were the rolling cadences of liturgical prose imitated. Obvious ornaments of style, such as alliteration, the heaping of synonyms, puns, antitheses, and

[11]*Doctrinal Treatises,* p. 390.

similar mechanical devices of word-play, were not called for by the original and were not added by Tindale. More striking is his avoidance of the quaint and pointed picturesque style of familiar colloquial origin which was the almost universal possession of writers and translators in sixteenth-century England and which Tindale himself frequently employed in his freer and easier prose writings. He made no effort to reach his readers by bringing his translation down to a low level, to color it, as Sir Thomas North did his Plutarch, by broad suggestions of the familiar realistic sides of English life. Striking a happy balance between simplicity and dignity, between the artful structure of a learned style and the easy informality of colloquial speech, Tindale attained a form of expression, *simplex munditiis,* unsurpassed for his purposes. The limits of faithful translation to be sure imposed certain restrictions upon any tendencies towards stylistic exuberance which he may have had, and the quiet tone of the originals from which he translated provided useful models of restraint and propriety in expression. It was no small merit in Tindale, however, that he was content to work within the bounds which his originals and his own purpose established for him. So completely did he realize these limits that he produced a translation which has all the idiomatic propriety and the vitality of original composition. Translation with him became a creative process.

Although Tindale in his first translations of the New Testament had already struck the note which was to become ever afterward the form of expression peculiar to the English scriptures, he did not cease to alter and improve. Many changes were made in the edition of 1534, some for the sake of more exact correspondence in meaning between the English and the originals, some for the sake of brevity, and a multitude of minute corrections for the sake of "more proper English." The great majority of the changes of this latter sort were made in order to avoid a certain meagerness of phrasing, and also to correct rapid and awkward transition from one thought to another. The style which lay at the base of Tindale's translation was the easy, polysyndetic, and naïve style of simple narrative. In his revisions he carefully corrected locutions which interrupted this simple rhythm, and he very often added connectives which improved it. Very frequently he merely added an *and* to a sentence to soften an abrupt beginning, or the simpler logical relations were indicated by other conjunctions, such as *but, or, if* and *though.* Sometimes also he changed the order of words, as, for example, John viii, 45, *beleve ye nott me* (1525), which becomes the more idiomatic, *ye beleve me not* (1534); or again he simplified by omission, as in Luke xiv, 28, *which of you is he that is desposed to bilde a toure* (1525), which reads in the revision, *which of you disposed to bilde a toure* (1534). Numerous changes were made for grammatical reasons, and words more appropriate to the meaning were substituted for others. Nowhere is there any indication that Tindale translated with the desire to interpret the scriptures by paraphrase in favor of any particular set of doctrines. His purpose was above all to make the meaning clear as he understood it, and he translated always "of a pure intent, singly and faithfully." As to vocabulary, he used in the main words which had established themselves in the language and which were in general use. He avoided learned Greek and Latin coinages. His attempts to replace conventionalized ecclesiastical terms by words of familiar and fresher value, such as *seniors* or *elders* for *priests, congregation* for *church* in the sense of the membership, not the physical structure, of the church, *love* for *charity,* are few in number and by no means violent. Sir Thomas More declared that Tindale's New Testament was full of heretical translations, maliciously inserted. But though he charges that over a thousand texts are mistranslated, More limits his illustrations to a very few examples of the kind just mentioned. The truth is that Tindale was not doctrinaire in his translation, and seldom or never forced unusual meanings into words. The differences of opinion between Tindale and More were such as affected ideas and institutions, not merely words, and these differences would have been the same whether the institutions were called by one name or another. In fairness to himself Tindale could not have done otherwise than use the terms which expressed most clearly his understanding of the ideas which the words were supposed to designate. The proof of the essential justice and sanity of Tindale's translation is to be found in the fact that, both in general tone and very largely in detail, it was followed in all important later English versions of the Bible. The Authorized Version derives not merely phrases from Tindale's translation, but whole connected passages. In the history of English prose the origin of the English Bible is consequently to be dated not from the early years of the seventeenth century, but from the second quarter of the sixteenth century when the work in its essentials was both conceived and executed.

The question was formerly much discussed whether Tindale's scholarship was adequate for translation from the Greek of the New Testament and the Hebrew of the Old Testament, and it was often assumed that he translated only from the Vulgate or from Luther's Bible. But this question is now happily and finally settled. It is certain that Tindale was a competent Greek scholar before he began the work of translation, and certain also that he acquired sufficient command over Hebrew to undertake independent translations from that language. His main sources were the original Greek and Hebrew texts. In the mechanical arrangement and in the marginal glosses which accompanied the first fragmentary edition of the New Testament, Tindale followed the model of Luther's Bible. "Tyndale's New Testament is Luther's in miniature; the general appearance of the page is the same; the arrangement of the text is the same; and the appropriation of the margins, the inner one for parallel passages, and the outer for glosses, is also the same."[12] But this statement of the dependence of Tindale upon Luther does not apply to his text. Tindale's New Testament is primarily based on the Greek text of Erasmus, the third edition of which appeared in 1522, accompanied by a Latin translation, occasionally followed by Tindale in preference to the Greek. After Erasmus, Luther seems most to have influenced Tindale's translation, and after Luther the Vulgate. His method in translation was more or less eclectic, but on the whole he followed the most authoritative source for the text, which was the Greek of Erasmus. In the Old Testament as well, comparison of Tindale's translation with the Hebrew, with the Vulgate, and with Luther shows that the Hebrew original was not only consulted, but was carefully studied and followed as the final authority. Tindale's translations have, therefore, not only the distinction of being the first acceptable version in the English idiom, but also of being the first to rest upon an adequate scholarly understanding of the originals.[13]

After the publication of Tindale's translations, the further history of the English Bible must be followed in several directions. In the immediate line of succession come the various adaptations and modifications of Tindale which resulted finally in the Authorized Version of 1611. Before these are discussed, however, it will be convenient to consider several efforts that were made to produce a different kind of English Bible from Tindale's. It was Tindale's desire that every reader, no matter how simple, should understand the text of the scripture without the aid of special knowledge of any kind. So far as possible,

[12]Demaus, *William Tyndale*, pp. 129-130.

[13]Tindale's independence as a translator is amply demonstrated with the aid of comparative tables of illustrations, by Cheney, *The Sources of Tindale's New Testament*, Halle, 1883, and by Westcott, *The History of the English Bible*, 3rd ed., edited by Wright, London, 1905, pp. 131 ff., 152 ff.

therefore, he made his translation speak the language of the normal daily life of English men and women. At heart in sympathy with this theory of translation, Sir Thomas More was in some instances unable to reconcile his feeling for the special and traditional value of the scripture with Tindale's practice. For this reason he protested when Tindale translated the traditional words *church, priest, grace, confession, charity, penance* by *congregation, elder, favor, knowledge, love, repentance,* words in Tindale's mind of a fresher and clearer significance to English people than the ecclesiastical traditional terms, which to the pious implied many irrelevant connotations, and to the thoughtless had lost almost all significance because they were so familiar. This feeling of Sir Thomas More that the Bible by reason of its special distinction among books demanded a form peculiar to itself was shared by many others, and all through the sixteenth century was cherished by the advocates of a more learned and exclusive Bible than the popular English Bible of Tindale. Naturally the higher dignitaries of the church, and in general conservative theorists in matters of church polity, were the chief opponents of the popular English Bible. Frequent protests were uttered by the bishops against the various popular translations as they were made, and promises of a version of their own were given. In the year 1534 the bishops presented a petition to the king for an English Bible to be made "by certain upright and learned men," closing their petition with a request that no layman for the future be permitted to discuss the articles of faith publicly or the scripture and its meaning.[14] What such a Bible would have been if it had ever been made in the spirit of the more conservative scholarship of the time may be inferred from Gardiner, the bishop of Winchester's proposals for the revision of the Great Bible in 1542. At a meeting of Convocation held in that year, Gardiner presented a list of a hundred Latin words which "for their genuine and native meaning, and for the majesty of the matter in them contained" ought to be retained either in their original form, or "fitly Englished with the least alteration."[15] Some of these words were already in general use in slightly Anglicized forms, such as *justice, glory, mystery, communion, prudence, society, apostle,* and others. But apparently Gardiner would have had the Latin origin of even these

[14]Pollard, *Records of the English Bible,* pp. 175-177, reprints the petition.

[15]Moore, *Tudor-Stuart Views on the Growth, Status and Destiny of the English Language,* pp. 89-90. This list of words has been frequently printed, e.g. by Mr. Moore, and conveniently and better in Gairdner, *Lollardy and the Reformation,* II, 296.

words show more plainly, perhaps to distinguish the ecclesiastical from other uses of the words. Many of the words in the list, however, whether in a Latin or in an Anglicized form, would have been unintelligible to most English readers, and a translation of the Bible made in accordance with the principle Gardiner announces would have been in almost as great need of official interpretation as the Greek or Latin originals.

The fullest exemplification of this theory of an ecclesiastical English Bible was to appear a generation later, not under Anglican but under Roman auspices. The Rhemish New Testament, first published in 1582, and the Douai Old Testament, finished earlier but not published until 1609-10, were prepared under the same general direction in order to supply English Roman Catholics with an approved text of the Bible in their native tongue. The translation was published not "upon erroneous opinion of necessitie, that the holy Scriptures should alwaies be in our mother tonge, or that they ought, or were ordained by God, to be read indifferently of all, or could be easily understood of every one that readeth or heareth them in a knowen language," or for any of a number of similar reasons which are specified, but merely as a practical and expedient measure, "profitable and medicinable now, that otherwise in the peace of the Church were neither much requisite, nor perchance wholy tolerable.[16] For reasons which are given in detail, the translation was made from "the old vulgar Latin text, not the common Greek text." The method of the translation was carefully considered and it is specifically defended. The translators declare that they are very precise and religious in following their copy, not only in sense, but also in the very words and phrases, which may seem at first "to the vulgar Reader & to common English eares not yet acquainted therewith, rudenesse or ignorance," but which in time will become familiar and then will be more highly esteemed than if the words were "the common knowen English." From this feeling of the sacredness of the text, the retention of many words in untranslated form is defended. If the older English Bibles retain *Hosanna, Raca,* and *Belial* untranslated, why may not the same be done with *Corbana* and *Parasceve?* "But if *Pentecost,* Act. 2. be yet untranslated in their bibles, and seemeth not strange: why should not *Pasche* and *Azymes* so remaine also, being solemne feastes, as Pentecost was?"[17] And if *proselyte* remain, why

---

[16]Preface to the Rheims New Testament, in Pollard, *Records,* pp. 301-302.
[17]Pollard, *Records,* p. 306.

not also *neophyte,* if *phylacteries* be allowed, why not *prepuce, para-clete,* and such like? The verb *evangelizo* must be translated *evangelize,* not "as the English Bibles do, *I bring you good tydings,* Luc. 2. 10." "Therefore we say *Depositum,* 1 Tim. 6. and, He *exinanited* him self, Philip. 2. and, You have *reflorished,* Philip. 4. and, *to exhaust,* Hebr. 9. 28. because we can not possibly attaine to expresse these words fully in English, and we thinke much better, that the reader staying at the difficultie of them, should take an occasion to looke in the table folowing, or otherwise to aske the ful meaning of them, then by putting some usual English wordes that expresse them not, so to deceive the reader."[18] Moreover, continue the translators we presume not in hard places to mollify the speeches or phrases, but religiously keep them word for word, and point for point, "for feare of missing or restraining the sense of the holy Ghost to our phantasie." If the meaning is not transparent in the Latin or Greek original, according to the logic of the translators, there is no reason why it should be made clear in an English translation. The extreme learned bias of the translators is emphatically expressed in this concluding remark: "And why should we be squamish at new wordes or phrases in the Scripture, which are necessarie, when we do easily admit and folow new wordes coyned in court and in courtly or other secular writings?"[19]

If the translation were to be used only by learned and courtly readers there was indeed little reason why the translators should not invent as many learned words as they pleased. And in fact the authors of the Rhemish Bible are much less extreme in their treatment of vocabulary than many a contemporary secular writer with a passion for aureate diction. The important question in this instance was not whether this or that new word should be accepted, but whether the whole project of a learned English Bible should be approved. In answering this question, by the end of the sixteenth century theoretical considerations carried little weight. By that time it had been deter-mined once and for all that the accepted English Bible for protestant readers was to be a popular and not a learned book, that the text was to be as frank and open as possible, not recondite and cryptic. In justice to the Rhemish translation it should be said, however, that the effect of the whole is not as grotesque as might be inferred from the more extreme examples of learned locutions just cited. Consecutive

[18]Ibid., pp. 307-308.
[19]Pollard, *Records,* p. 310.

passages of some length are frequently found which differ but slightly from the earlier English translations based on Tindale, and many readings which differ in the Rhemish translation from the earlier translations are familiar to us now because they were incorporated in the Authorized Version of 1611. The Rhemish Bible was an unsuccessful, but not an uninfluential experiment. In a revised form it remains to this day one of the standard English Bibles for Roman Catholic readers, but it has never been regarded as a fountain of pure English in the same degree as Tindale's popular English Bible.

Several other translations which fall outside the main line of descent of the English Bible must be noticed. In general the tendency in the development of English translations was in the direction which the Rhemish translation followed to the extreme, that is, in the direction of more exact and scholarly translation. Several efforts were made, however, to develop an English biblical style which should be more popular, or at least less learned, even than Tindale's. The first of these found expression in the English Bible of R. Taverner, published in 1539, the year of the Great Bible. A lawyer by profession and a not incompetent Greek scholar, Taverner makes no pretension to being an original translator. His work is based upon the so-called Matthew Bible, and his alterations are mainly made for the purpose of securing what he regarded as a more idiomatic English phrasing and vocabulary. Thus in I John ii, 1, where the other versions read *advocate,* Taverner uses the native word *spokesman;* and in the following verse, where the earlier versions follow Tindale in translating ἱλασμὸς by *he it is that obtaineth grace for our sins* (the Rhemish version followed by the Authorized Version reading, *he is the propitiation for our sins*), Taverner invents an entirely new native word, *he is a mercystock for our sins.* Similar changes are the substitution of *wickedness* for *iniquity* (Matt. xiii, 41); *ended* for *finished,* (Matt. xiii, 53); *break* for *transgress* (Matt. xv, 2); *lodged* for *had his abiding* (Matt. xxi, 17); *and because of the abundance of wickedness, the charity of many shall wax cold* for Tindale's *and because iniquity shall have the upper hand, the love of many shall abate* (Matt. xxiv, 12); *age* for *generation* (Matt. xxiv, 34); *nailed to the cross* for *crucified* (Matt. xxvi, 2); *to the forgiveness* for *for the remission* (Matt. xxvi, 28). Taverner's Bible, however, is interesting merely as an experiment; it was crowded out of use by the Great Bible and it seems not to have exerted any influence upon later revisions of the text.[20] Another experiment similar to that of Taverner,

[20]The above illustrations are taken from Westcott, *History of the English Bible,* pp. 208-211.

though much more extreme, was the English translation of St. Matthew and the beginning of St. Mark, made by Sir John Cheke, in his own day regarded as the chief defender of the purity of the English language as opposed to those who would enrich, or according to the purists, corrupt, the language by freely borrowing words of foreign origin. This translation was never published in Cheke's lifetime,[21] and it is interesting mainly as an illustration of the form which extreme respect for the native idiom took in the time when it was made. Cheke's endeavor was to use only such words as had an immediately intelligible meaning in the English language. The older ecclesiastical words he consequently translates by means either of popular native words, or frequently by means of new coinages made up from native elements. Thus he translates *apostle* by *fro-sent, parable* by *by-word, regeneration* by *gain-birth, resurrection* by *uprising* or *gainrising, money-changers* by *tablers, publicans* by *tollers, proselyte* by *freshman, crucified* by *crossed, centurion* by *hundreder, founded* by *groundwrought,* etc. Though Cheke's strange vocabulary is for the most part readily intelligible, the general effect produced by it is of an artificial and unidiomatic language, in its way quite as pedantic as the English of the extreme Latinists. Cheke was the victim of a theory in the making of his translation, and his fantastic English brings out the more clearly the effectiveness of Tindale's simple and natural Biblical style.

After Tindale the next important figure in the development of the English Bible from the point of view of its literary form was Miles Coverdale. In his own Bible, published in 1535, Coverdale for the first time presented to the English people a complete Bible in their native tongue between two covers. This translation Coverdale declares to have been made with the help of "sondrye translacions, not onely in latyn, but also of the Douche interpreters."[22] At another place he states that he has "with a cleare conscience purely & faythfully translated this out of fyve sundry interpreters, having onely the manyfest trueth of the scriptures before myne eyes."[23] The Latin version which Coverdale followed was the translation of Pagninus, 1528, though he used also the Vulgate; and his German interpreters were first of all the Swiss-German version of Zwingli, known as the Zurich Version, completed in 1529, and secondarily, Luther's Bible. The Zurich version provided the basis for Coverdale's Old Testament, and Tindale, who was probably the fifth of the interpreters mentioned by Coverdale, is

[21]First printed and published by Goodwin, Cambridge, 1843.
[22]Pollard, *Records,* p. 203.
[23]Ibid., p. 201.

closely followed in the New Testament. Coverdale also used such parts of the Old Testament as Tindale had already published, that is, the Pentateuch and the Book of Jonah. Coverdale's Bible can consequently lay claim to no distinction from the point of view of original translation. Its merit consists first of all in assembling the different parts of the Bible into one complete volume, and secondly in the addition of a multitude of minute changes which do not indeed replace Tindale's Biblical style with a new one, but which in many instances result in a freer and ampler manner of expression than Tindale, severe because of his earnestness, permitted himself.

But Coverdale's influence upon the text of the English scriptures was exerted also through another channel. Following the publication of the Matthew Bible in 1537, a compilation made by Tindale's friend, John Rogers, from the translations of Coverdale and Tindale, the next important Bible was the Great Bible of 1539, the second edition of which appearing the following year with a preface by Cranmer, is often referred to as Cranmer's Bible. It was the first authorized English Bible, and is thus often known as the Bishops' Bible. The work of revision in the Great Bible was intrusted to Coverdale, who returned more or less to the originals in the formation of his text, but who in the main revised on the basis of his own earlier translations and of Tindale's.

This list of the important revisions of the text is completed by the two later versions, the Genevan version of 1560 and the Authorized Version of 1611. The Genevan Bible was the joint work of a number of Puritan exiles temporarily resident at Geneva during the reign of Queen Mary. The revision was thorough, both for details of scholarship and for style, but the basis of it was the Great Bible and the effort in the preparation of it was distinctly not to make a new translation, but to revise the old one. Like the Genevan version, the Authorized Version was the work of a number of different scholars, "to the number of four and fifty," according to King James' letter of instructions,[24] who carried on the task of revision more or less independently but following a set of principles agreed upon beforehand. First of all they agreed that "an entirely new version was not to be furnished, but an old version, long received by the Church, to be purged from all blemishes and faults; to this end there was to be no departure from the ancient translation, unless the truth of the original text or emphasis demanded."[25] 'Truly (good

[24]Pollard, *Records*, p. 331.

[25]*Report on the Making of the Version of 1611 Presented to the Synod of Dort*, in Pollard, *Records*, p. 339.

Christian Reader)," the translators declare in their Preface, "wee never thought from the beginning, that we should neede to make a new Translation, nor yet to make of a bad one a good one . . . but to make a good one better, or out of many good ones, one principall good one, not justly to be excepted against; that hath bene our indeavour, that our marke."[26] Their task was to make the gold of the English scriptures shine more brightly, "being rubbed and polished." The text of the Great Bible, accepted as standard, was continually before them, and departures from it, though numerous, were made only for good and definite reasons. On the whole one must admire the restraint of these four and fifty scholars, who zealously guarded the language of the scriptures to the end that they might "bee understood even of the very vulgar." It was one of the avowed principles of their translation not to use words in special and limited ecclesiastical senses. They would not say to certain words, "Stand up higher, have a place in the Bible alwayes, and to others of like qualitie, Get ye hence, be banished for ever." Niceness in words they counted to be the next step to trifling. How easy it would have been for them to indulge in literary preciosity, the fine writing of their own Preface clearly shows. "In a word," so runs their panegyric on the Bible, "it is a Panary of holesome foode, against fenowed traditions; a Physions-shop (Saint *Basill* calleth it) of preservatives against poisoned heresies; a Pandect of profitable lawes, against rebellious spirits; a treasurie of most costly jewels, against beggarly rudiments; Finally a fountaine of most pure water springing up unto everlasting life."[27] Only in the last clause of this sentence were the authors of this Preface subdued to that in which they worked.

Reviewing these several stages through which the English Bible passed, one finds that after Tindale the most significant contributions to it were made by Coverdale. Especially in the Old Testament Coverdale treated the text very freely, at times, under the influence of the Zurich version producing paraphrase rather than translation. Most of Coverdale's expansions have been replaced in the Authorized Version by more exact translations, and the scholarly Genevan version occupies an important middle position between Coverdale's Old Testament and the Authorized Version of 1611. Coverdale did not think of himself as primarily a scholar, but in the modern term, as a popularizer. A variety of translations does not, he declares, make for "divisyon in the fayth and in the people of God."[28] On the contrary, the more translations the

[26]*Preface,* in Pollard, *Records,* p. 369.
[27]Pollard, *Records,* p. 248.
[28]Ibid., p. 203.

better. One man cannot always hit the mark, but now this shooter and now that comes nearest. In accordance with this spirit of eclecticism, Coverdale varied his translation, sometimes using Tindale's words, sometimes the traditional ecclesiastical words of the conservative translators. The particular mark which Coverdale himself attempted to hit was not so much that of literal exactness as ease and fluency in phrasing. Unlike Tindale, Coverdale was an experienced and successful popular preacher and exhorter, and some of the feeling for the round style of spoken discourse may be observed in his modification of Tindale's compact and sometimes angular English. Many of these stylistic expansions were removed by later, especially by the Genevan translators, but in the Psalter of the Prayer Book they have persisted to the present day. The psalms in the Prayer Book were originally taken directly from the Great Bible, and on the ground that Coverdale's psalms were "smoother and more easy to sing" than any of the later revisions, they have remained unaltered in the Prayer Book. One notes in these psalms not only a fuller phrasing than that of the version of 1611, but also a slightly stronger flavor of the broad popular style, as in Psalm x, 14, *Tush, thou God carest not for it,* which the Authorized Version renders more sedately, *thou wilt not require it* (Ps. x, 13).

In the New Testament Coverdale followed the model of Tindale very closely, but even here he made a great many minor additions which in a surprising number of instances were retained in the version of 1611. A few illustrations from the first Gospel will show how Tindale's texts were gradually made more easy and pliable.

Tindale, in Matt. i, 25, reads, *tyll she had brought forth hir fyrst sonne, and called hys name Jesus,* but Coverdale, translating the Greek πρωτότοχον more at length, has *fyrst borne sonne.* This is changed in the Great Bible to *hyr fyrst begotten sonne,* but the Authorized Version returns to Coverdale's first rendering. In Matt. iii, 4, Tindale translates, *This Jhon had hys garment of camels heer and a gerdell of a skynne aboute his loynes,* where Coverdale, again more literally and also more smoothly, reads, *a lethren gerdell.* The Great Bible, the Genevan and the Rhemish New Testament all return to Tindale's rendering, but the Authorized Version retains Coverdale's first translation. A striking illustration of the gradual formation of a smooth phrasing is afforded by Matt. vi, 34. Tindale reads here: *Care not then for the morow, but let the morow care for it selfe: for the daye present hath ever ynough of his awne trouble.* In Coverdale's Bible of 1535 this last clause reads, *Every daye hath ynough of his owne travayll,* which is improved in the Great Bible: *Care not then for the morow, for to morowe day shall care for it selfe: sufficient unto the daye is the travayle therof.* The Genevan New Testament alters the first half of the verse for the better: *Care not then for the morow: for the morow shal care for it selfe: The day present hath ever inough to do with it owne grief.* The Rhemish version changes slightly: *Be not careful therfore for the morow. For the morow day shal be careful for it self: sufficient for the day is the evil thereof.* And the Authorized Version, accepting the best from the preceding versions and giving the whole a somewhat ampler rhythm, reads: *Take therefore no thought for the morrow: for the morrow shall take thought for the things of it selfe: sufficient unto the day is the evill thereof.* A further illustration may be cited from this Gospel. In Matt. xxv, 21, Tindale reads: *Then his master sayde unto him: well good servant and faithfull. Thou hast bene faithfull in lytell, I will make the ruler over moche: enter in into thy masters ioye.* Coverdale's rendering, as represented by the Great Bible, is as follows: *His lorde saide unto him: well thou good and faithfull servant. Thou hast bene faythfull over fewe thinges. I will make the ruler over many thinges. Entre thou into the ioye of thy lorde.* The Genevan Testament returns to Tindale, but the Rhemish version, with slight modification, follows Coverdale. And the Authorized Version, with one helpful change, also follows Coverdale: *His lord said unto him, Well done, good and faithfull servant, thous hast bene faithfull over a few things, I will make thee ruler over many things: enter thou into the joy of thy lord.* In Luke xviii, 13, Tindale reads: *And the publican stode afarre of and wolde not lyfte up his eyes to heven,* a close translation of the Greek. Coverdale, in the Great Bible, followed by the Rhemish and the Authorized Versions, changes the syntax for the sake of rhythm: *And the publycan stondyng a farre of, wolde not lyfte up hys eyes to heaven.* The play of the texts back and forth is interestingly illustrated by the translations of Luke xviii, 23. Tindale reads here: *When he heard that, he was hevy: for he was very ryche.* The Great Bible changes *hevy* to *sory,* which becomes in the Authorized Version, *very sorowfull.* The Genevan translation reads *very hevy* and *marvelous ryche,* and the Rhemish version is different from all others: *He hearing these things, was stroken sad: because he was very riche.* But in the succeeding verse the Authorized Version owes its reading, *How hardly shal they that have riches, enter into the kingdome of God?* mainly to the Rhemish translation, Tindale reading here, *with what difficulte shall they that have ryches enter into the kingdome of God?* It is interesting to note, however, that the Rhemish version reads *money* instead of *riches,* agreeing in this with the Great Bible. In Luke xviii, 26, Tindale translates, rather awkwardly, *Then sayde they that hearde that,* which reads more smoothly in the Great Bible and the Authorized Version, *And they that hearde it sayd.* One final illustration of the minute changes by means of which stylistic effect was gained may be cited from Luke xviii, 38. Tindale gives here a literal translation of the Greek, except that the pronoun subject of the verb is only implied in the form of the Greek verb, not specifically expressed: *And he cryed sayinge: Jesus the sonne of David, have thou mercy on me.* The Great Bible gains in dramatic force: *And he cryed, sayinge: Jesu thou sonne of David, have mercy on me.* The Genevan version as usual follows Tindale except that it changes the first word to *Then.* The Rhemish version also agrees with Tindale except that it omits the vocative pronoun altogether. And the Authorized Version follows the Great Bible exactly.

These illustrations have been cited to show the changes which Coverdale and the Authorized Version made in the text of Tindale's translation. Compared with the whole, they are relatively slight, and it is much easier to find passages in which the later versions agree with Tindale than passages in which they differ. Verse after verse of the Authorized Version follows Tindale almost without change, and such changes as are made, though as a whole they are improvements both in style and scholarly exactness, do not greatly alter the character of the book as it was first established by Tindale. Of a good book the later revisers made a better, as it was always their purpose to do, not a new translation. (pp. 220-256)

II

THE GENERAL READER'S BIBLE

THE GENERAL READER'S BIBLE

THE RENAISSANCE

In the sixteenth and seventeenth centuries Englishmen's criticism of the Bible as literature was made from a rather special viewpoint, expounded some years ago by Dr. Israel Baroway.[1] In a period when all literature of the imagination, all fiction and poetry, was under attack from serious men, one line of defense was to demonstrate that Biblical writers or heroes, whose practice could not be objected to, had used all the literary forms and devices which were being attacked. The classic example of this defense is in Sidney's The Defense of Poesy.[2] *The passages on the parables of Nathan and of Christ are particularly apposite as justifying the use of "fiction" for teaching virtue or doctrine.*

A much more extended treatment of the literary devices in the Psalms is contained in George Wither's Preparation to the Psalter.[3] *Of special interest here, in addition to the passages quoted below, is a long defense of the opinion that Hebrew Psalms were poetical. Wither admits, as had Sidney, that the form of the verse is now unknown, but he makes the very sound suggestion that it might be learned through "the tongues of the Eastern parts; Arabic, Chaldean, or the old Punic, which was a dialect of the Hebrew; and more anciently called the Phoenician tongue."[4] Wither's surmises as to "why the holy Ghost should commend*

[1]Israel Baroway, "The Bible as Poetry in the English Renaissance," Journal of English and Germanic Philology, 32 (1933), 447-480. I am indebted to Dr. Baroway for calling my attention to Wither's book, and to the significance of the passage in Paradise Regained.

[2]See pp. 117-119.

[3]See pp. 120-124.

[4]George Wither, A Preparation to the Psalter, 1619, Printed for the Spenser Society, 1884, p. 61. Both here and in the extended passages below I have modernized spelling, the use of capitals and italics, and some punctuation.

them [*the Psalms*] *unto us, rather in verse than prose"* contain the heart of his argument with regard to poetry. It will be noted that Wither's position is bound up with a strictly orthodox view of the inspiration of the Scriptures; indeed the orthodox view is the heart of his argument: The Scriptures were inspired by the Holy Ghost; the Psalms were poetical in form; hence, poetry has been sanctified by God. The extent of Wither's orthodoxy may be seen in Chapter XII of his book, where he sets forth the doctrinal positions necessary to a proper reading of the Psalms.[5]

When we come to Milton there is one suggestion of a different view.[6] While his references to specific books of the Bible are still in terms of literary classification, the general description of literary activity is for a moment different. Milton implies that, humanly speaking, Hebrew literature developed from the desire of *"those Hebrews of old"* to be *"interpreter and relater of the best and sagest things"* among their own people and in their own language. This suggests that the Old Testament was a national literature produced by men motivated as Milton was motivated. Further developed and applied, this concept might have resulted in much more extensive comment on the literature of the Bible than we see in the work of either Sidney or Wither. But it was not part of the spirit and habit of the age so to develop and apply it, and the passage from Paradise Regained[7] shows Milton's later adherence to the orthodox seventeenth century view of literary devices in the Bible.

[5]A Preparation to the Psalter, *pp. 89-102.*
[6]*See pp. 125-127.*
[7]*See pp. 127-128.*

THE DEFENSE OF POESY
(excerpts)

SIR PHILIP SIDNEY

This short book, probably written about 1580, is a defence of poetry against "Puritan" suspicion and attack. It was first published in 1595, after Sidney's death, in two editions, one titled The Defence of Poesie *and the other* An Apologie for Poetrie.

At this point Sidney is defending poetry on the basis of the honor implied in the various names given to the poet and poetry by the Romans and the Greeks.

On the Psalms as Poetry.

And may not I presume a little further to show the reasonableness of this word *vates,* and say that the holy David's Psalms are a divine poem? If I do, I shall not do it without the testimony of great learned men, both ancient and modern. But even the name of Psalms will speak for me, which, being interpreted, is nothing but Songs; then, that it is fully written in metre, as all learned Hebricians agree, although the rules be not yet fully found; lastly and principally, his handling his prophecy, which is merely poetical. For what else is the awaking his musical instruments, the often and free changing of persons, his notable Prosopopœias, when he maketh you, as it were, see God coming in His majesty, his telling of the beasts' joyfulness, and hills' leaping, but a heavenly poesy, wherein almost he showeth himself a passionate lover of that unspeakable and everlasting beauty to be seen by the eyes of the

From *The Defense of Poesy*, by Sir Philip Sidney, ed. Albert S. Cook, Ginn & Company, 1890.

mind, only cleared by faith? But truly now having named him, I fear I seem to profane that holy name, applying it to poetry, which is among us thrown down to so ridiculous an estimation. But they that with quiet judgments will look a little deeper into it, shall find the end and working of it such as, being rightly applied, deserveth not to be scourged out of the Church of God. (p. 6)

On Sacred Poetry (Psalms, Wisdom books, Songs of Moses and Deborah) as "imitating" the "inconceivable excellencies of GOD."

Poesy, therefore, is an art of imitation, for so Aristotle termeth it in his word μίμησις, that is to say, a representing, counterfeiting, or figuring forth; to speak metaphorically, a speaking picture, with this end—to teach and delight.

Of this have been three general kinds. The chief, both in antiquity and excellency, were they that did imitate the inconceivable excellencies of God. Such were David in his Psalms; Solomon in his Song of Songs, in his Ecclesiastes and Proverbs; Moses and Deborah in their Hymns, and the writer of Job; which, beside other, the learned Emanuel Tremellius and Franciscus Junius do entitle the poetical part of the Scripture. Against these none will speak that hath the Holy Ghost in due holy reverence. (p. 9)

On Nathan's Parable

Here Sidney is arguing the superiority of "poetry" (i.e., fiction) to philosophy as a method of moral teaching.

For even those hard-hearted evil men who think virtue a school-name, and know no other good but *indulgere genio,* and therefore despise the austere admonitions of the philosopher, and feel not the inward reason they stand upon, yet will be content to be delighted, which is all the good-fellow poet seemeth to promise; and so steal to see the form of goodness—which seen, they cannot but love—ere themselves be aware, as if they took a medicine of cherries.

Infinite proofs of the strange effects of this poetical invention might be alleged; only two shall serve, which are so often remembered as I think all men know them. The one of Menenius Agrippa . . . .

The other is of Nathan the prophet, who, when the holy David had so far forsaken God as to confirm adultery with murder, when he was to do the tenderest office of a friend, in laying his own shame before his eyes,— sent by God to call again so chosen a servant, how doth he it but by telling of a man whose beloved lamb was ungratefully taken from his bosom? The application most divinely true, but the discourse itself feigned; which made David (I speak of the second and instrumental cause)[1] as in a glass to see his own filthiness, as that heavenly Psalm of Mercy[2] well testifieth. (pp. 24-26)

On the Parables of Jesus

. . . For the question is, whether the feigned image of poesy, or the regular instruction of philosophy, hath the more force in teaching. Wherein if the philosophers have more rightly showed themselves philosophers than the poets have obtained to the high top of their profession, —as in truth,

> Mediocribus esse poetis,
> Non Dii, non homines, non concessere columnae,—

it is, I say again, not the fault of the art, but that by few men that art can be accomplished.

Certainly, even our Saviour Christ could as well have given the moral commonplaces of uncharitableness and humbleness as the divine narration of Dives and Lazarus; or of disobedience and mercy, as that heavenly discourse of the lost child and the gracious father; but that his through-searching wisdom knew the estate of Dives burning in hell, and of Lazarus in Abraham's bosom, would more constantly, as it were, inhabit both the memory and judgment. Truly, for myself, me seems I see before my eyes the lost child's disdainfull prodigality, turned to envy a swine's dinner; which by the learned divines are thought not historical acts, but instructing parables. (pp. 17-18)

[1]The first and final cause is, of course, God.
[2]Psalm 51.

A PREPARATION TO THE PSALTER

(excerpts)

GEORGE WITHER

George Wither (1558-1667) was a minor poet and satirist of the seventeenth century. His treatise was intended as an introduction to a translation of and comment on all the 150 Psalms, arranged in fifteen "decades"; a few of the translations he published with the treatise. The general plan was not carried out as projected. The recognition that the Hebrew Psalms were poetry, though the exact poetic form was unknown, the need for versions adapted for musical settings, and the desire to justify poetry itself may account in part for the poetic translations of the Psalms in this age. If they were poetry in the original, it was a laudable exercise to give them the marks of poetry in the translation. We now feel that the true nature of Hebrew poetry was better conveyed in the prose of the great translations from Tyndale down, but in the early seventeenth century a version of the Psalms made to convey their literary beauty was almost inevitably made in verse.

Defence of Translating the Psalms into Verse.

Since I began to take in hand the version of the Psalter, I have heard so many publish a dislike of turning holy Scripture, of what kind soever, into verse, that if the habit, or show of grave sanctity without reason, had been sufficient to have disheartened a young versifier, from his resolution, not only had the translation of the *Psalms* been long before this time left off, but I had also renounced verse; and (as some do) should have abhorred it, as the most profane language of the Devil.

From *A Preparation to the Psalter,* by George Wither, 1619. Printed for the Spenser Society, 1884.

But, I thank God, I have hitherto escaped that disease; there is not yet that antipathy between me and poetry: and I hope I shall never be so over-wise, as to grow out of love with it, whilst I live. Nay, if our verse-whippers be not obstinate in their heresies against the divinities of the *Muses,* I rather persuade myself that I shall reclaim some of them; and bring that which they wrongfully held in contempt, into a just and more reverend esteem.

For I have found, that the principal cause, why they disallow the sacred Word should be expressed in verse, is partly for that they imagine poesy to be the vain invention of man; and partly by reason they are ignorant, that verse is the form of speech which the holy Ghost hath often chosen to express his mysteries in, when they were first penned in the Hebrew tongue. Such there be (some of them Scholars; yea, and professed Divines) that have so little acquaintance with the worth or quality of David's poems, that when in defence of my undertaking, I have told them that both the Psalms, and other books of holy Scripture, are originally Hebrew verse, they wondered at me; as if they either thought it blasphemy, or that I had slandered the Bible. And when they heard me intitle my author, *The divine Poet,* that sacred (though much abused) name was so odious unto them, that I think they supposed it as little to his honour, as if, for his exercising the harp, I had termed him a fiddler. (pp. 57-58)

Protest against Refusing the Name of Poetry to the Psalms because of the Strangeness of the Poetic Form.

For if we should think, that all verse were corrupted, which is not answerable to that in use with later writers; we must say, that the ancient comic, and tragic poems, both of Greeks and Latins (with all the old poets of other languages) are also corrupted, because they have either some strange measures, or use more liberty than we: whereas I believe, that they are rather to be thought such, as the authors intended, and those times best approved. But whatsoever we imagine of those, questionless, it is impiety, and against all reason, that men, to hide their own ignorance, should impute corruption to the Word of God: which is so firmly established, that though heaven and earth pass away, not one jot nor tittle thereof shall perish. For my part I believe their authority, who have affirmed, that these Psalms, and holy mysteries, were first delivered by the holy Ghost in verse. And as I persuade my self, they were then such as best fitted those times, and the elegancy of that tongue: so I am also out of doubt, that they are yet uncorrupted, though we cannot bring them within the compass of rules. Yea, I am assured (and upon good reason) that there is a propriety in this Hebrew poesy, which cannot be truly searched into, by those rules which the same art hath in other languages. (p. 63)

A Suggestion of why God Caused the Psalms to be written in Verse.

Saint Basil helps yet with another reason; and saith, that the Spirit of God seeing mankind so enclinable to pleasure and delights, that they were hardly drawn to virtue or religion, which were enemies to sensuality: He mingled his heavenly precepts, with the sweet and pleasing strains of music and numbers; that so the ear, having that which delighted, might without tediousness listen, whilst wholesome and profitable instructions were unaware infused into us.[1] In which, God hath shown exceeding great mercy, and a wondrous fatherly care: even in this, that it hath pleased him so to inform us, that his word might not seem over austere, by reason of our childishness. For as a wise physician being to give some wholesome, but unpleasing medicine to children, prepares it with sweet syrups, or anoints the cup with honey, that the bitterness of the potion being unperceived, they may by the taste of sweetness be allured to receive it: So the divine wisdom, hath for those who are children in spiritual things, in the sweetness of verse, offered his divine mysteries; that being by that means the more listened unto, they might work in their souls for their spiritual health, and purge out those carnal corruptions, which would make them sick to eternal death. And indeed by this means, many who had else never given heed to the word of God, have been in some measure delighted with it; and divers, whose dullness could remember nothing out of the books of the law, prophets, nor apostles, can yet retain somewhat of the Psalms: and we may often hear those sing them amid their daily labours; though not always with that zeal and understanding which is required. (p. 65)

An examination of the literary qualities of specific passages.
Psalm 104: 1-13

But whatsoever it appears, to some ears, the poesy of the *Psalter* is exceeding elegant. And because I would not seem to speak of things that I had by imagination only, or be thought to feed you with words, I heartily desire such as have understanding, to examine the poesy of

---

[1]The passage in St. Basil is cited in Milton's Commonplace Book. See *The Works of John Milton,* New York, Columbia University Press, 1938, vol. 18, p. 139.

these Psalms. And (though I would not any man should conceit, that the power or majesty of them consisteth in their outward eloquence) because they are accused by many to be defective that way; I could wish that their exquisiteness were a little better heeded. For in my opinion, they are the most excellent lyric poesy that ever was invented, and come not short in any of those elegancies which may be proper to that kind. I think rather, that it hath many more exact and powerful ways of expression, than are to be obseryed in other authors: and I would make it appear by demonstration, if I feared not that my words would hardly equall my apprehension. But if you have respect to those things which are the ordinary ornaments of other men's poesy, as similies, metaphors, hyperboles, comparisons, and such like: how barren soever this book seems to be of them to some readers, I dare maintain that no volume of the same bigness, hath so many as this. For there be scarce two verses together, but they have some or other ornament of speech; yea, in many Psalms, almost every verse hath his flowers of poesy. (p. 71)

Psalm 18: 7-15

Consider this I pray you, and tell me, where have you found in any poet more lively or heroical descriptions? Where can you read more stately expressions? Or how were it possible better to insinuate into the understanding the apprehension of the incomprehensible and inexpressible majesty of GOD. For, that which is unseen, and beyond the apprehension of the senses, is admirably made here as it were visible to the eye. And what is this, but poesy? Nay, what is it but the most excellent kind of poesy? Believe me, I am of opinion, that in the ornaments of speech, and elegancies of poesy also, as well as in dignity of matter, it hath at least equalled, if not exceeded the best that I have any where read. And I am persuaded, that if our adorers of profane poesy, had instead of their Horace or Martial carried those Odes about them; they had been able to have spoken ten times more in their commendations, if malice or contempt of God blinded them not.

Observe here, how marvelously he hath set forth the majesty, the wisdom, the power, the providence, and the terrible wrath of God. Note also how many lofty words, and what store of elegant and significant metaphors there be in these few lines: but withal, consider I pray, that they are in a manner *verbatim* and nakedly turned out of their own natural ornaments, into a language wherein all the facetiae of the original can never be so retained, but that some matter of ornament will be omitted. Moreover, our divine Poet is not so sterile as to wear thread-bare his descriptions; but very often and exceeding properly varieth his expressions, when he hath occasion to speak more than once of one thing. (pp. 72-73)

Psalm 107: 23-27 (the description of the storm at sea).

There are yet many other Psalms nothing inferior to the best of these; as you shall find in perusing them. But to say truth, there is no Psalm that hath not the same excellency, considering what the nature of the subject requires: for, where the matter is heroical, I find as high strains of poesy as may be; and where it is of another nature, I see it fitted with expressions most suitable thereunto. But I would not have you over-pass without heed, how excellently David hath, by this last example, in a few words set forth the sudden violence of a storm, the rage of the seas, the amazement of the mariners, and the working of a poor ship ready to be wrackt. In my mind, it is set forth with hyper-boles and metaphors, far beyond that in Ovid,

> *Me miserum! quanti Montes volvuntur aquarum!*
> *Iam-iam tacturos sydera summa putes.*
> *Quantae diducto subsidunt aequore valles!*
> *Iam-iam tactur as tartara nigra putes.*

Or this in Virgil,

> *Tollimur in coelum curuato gurgite: et idem*
> *Subducta ad manes imos descendimus unda.*

But why do I stand thus upon particulars, when the whole book is full of elegancies? Yea, as I said before, every Psalm hath his proper loveliness. And were I pleased to enter into such a task, I dare both promise and perform, even from hence to bring examples of every rhe-torical figure which may be found in any learned poet among the Greeks or Latins; unless it be where they have over-vainly played with the words or letters to no purpose. Nay, I could show you strains of poesy, and such flowers of rhetoric, as among them could never yet be found. But some there be that are not expressible, and I may resemble them to the purest sort of lightning. For, as that passeth through a purse, which is a porous body, and there melts the Coin, without leaving any impression or sign upon the leather: So, there be certain rhetorical passages in these Psalms, so pure from sensibility, that they can and do convey things through the senses, unperceived; and yet melt the heart, and work strange operations in the soul, such as no man can imagine, but he that hath felt them. (pp. 74-75)

THE REASON OF CHURCH GOVERNMENT
(excerpt)

JOHN MILTON

The general subject of this pamphlet has nothing to do with the theme we are tracing. But in the course of it Milton tells of the literary activities and plans from which he had turned aside to take part in the controversy on the form of church government. He speaks of the promise of his early poetry, a promise recognized by his masters at home and in the academies of Italy, and of his dedication to the task of leaving "something so written to aftertimes, as they should not willingly let it die." Then, à propos of his decision to write in English ("the adorning of my native tongue") he uses, to illustrate his hopes for his own writing, the literature he knew and loved—classical, modern Italian, and Hebrew. Milton sees the ancient Hebrew writers as like himself and like the classical writers in their purposes, and in the choice of the forms in which they wrote.

Decision to write in English for Englishmen, and debate with himself on what literary form to adopt.

. . . . THESE THOUGHTS at once possessed me, and these other; that if I were certain to write as men buy leases, for three lives and downward, there ought no regard be sooner had than to God's glory, by the honour and instruction of my country. For which cause, and not only for that I knew it would be hard to arrive at the second rank among the Latins, I applied myself to that resolution, which Ariosto followed against the persuasions of Bembo, to fix all the industry and art I could unite to the

From *The Reason of Church Government,* by John Milton, in *English Prose Writings of John Milton,* ed. Henry Morley, George Routledge and Sons, 1899.

adorning of my native tongue; not to make verbal curiosities the end—
that were a toilsome vanity,—but to be an interpreter and relater of the
best and sagest things among mine own citizens throughout this island
in the mother dialect. That what the greatest and choicest wits of
Athens, Rome, or modern Italy, and those Hebrews of old did for their
country, I, in my proportion, with this over and above, of being a
Christian, might do for mine; not caring to be once named abroad,
though perhaps I could attain to that, but content with these British
islands as my world; whose fortune hath hitherto been, that if the
Athenians, as some say, made their small deeds great and renowned by
their eloquent writers, England hath had her noble achievements made
small by the unskilful handling of monks and mechanics.

Time serves not now, and perhaps I might seem too profuse, to give
any certain account of what the mind at home, in the spacious circuits
of her musing, hath liberty to propose to herself, though of highest hope
and hardest attempting; whether that epic form whereof the two poems
of Homer, and those other two of Virgil and Tasso, are a diffuse, and
the book of Job a brief model . . . . The Scripture also affords us a
divine pastoral drama in the Song of Solomon, consisting of two persons
and a double chorus, as Origen rightly judges. And the Apocalypse of
St. John is the majestic image of a high and stately tragedy, shutting up
and intermingling her solemn scenes and acts with a sevenfold chorus
of hallelujahs and harping symphonies: and this my opinion the grave
authority of Pareus, commenting that book, is sufficient to confirm. Or
if occasion shall lead, to imitate those magnific odes and hymns, wherein
Pindarus and Callimachus are in most things worthy, some others in
their frame judicious, in their matter most an end faulty. But those frequent songs throughout the Law and Prophets beyond all these, not in
their divine argument alone, but in the very critical art of composition,
may be easily made appear over all the kinds of lyric poesy to be incomparable. These abilities, wheresoever they be found, are the inspired gift of God, rarely bestowed, but yet to some—though most
abuse—in every nation; and are of power, beside the office of a pulpit,
to imbreed and cherish in a great people the seeds of virtue and public
civility, to allay the perturbations of the mind, and set the affections in
right tune; to celebrate in glorious and lofty hymns the throne and
equipage of God's Almightiness, and what He works, and what He
suffers to be wrought with high providence in His Church: to sing
victorious agonies of martyrs and saints, the deeds and triumphs of just
and pious nations, doing valiantly through faith against the enemies of

Christ; to deplore the general relapses of kingdoms and states from justice and God's true worship. Lastly, whatsoever in religion is holy and sublime, in virtue amiable or grave, whatsoever hath passion or admiration in all the changes of that which is called fortune from without, or the wily subtleties and refluxes of man's thoughts from within; all these things with a solid and treatable smoothness to paint out and describe. (pp. 150-152)

PARADISE REGAINED

(excerpt)

JOHN MILTON

These lines were written nearly thirty years later than the preceding passage. They form part of the story of the Temptation in the Wilderness, the event which Milton makes the basis of his poem on salvation. He is here treating the third temptation, to win the power of wisdom or knowledge by admitting the superiority of Satan. What is noteworthy from the standpoint of this anthology is of course the claim that the Old Testament is superior to Greek writings not only as embodying truth but as using all the arts of literature.

Satan: . . . . Be famous then
By wisdom; as thy empire must extend,
So let extend thy mind o'er all the world,
In knowledge, all things in it comprehend.

From *Paradise Regained*, in *The Poems of John Milton*, Second Edition, ed. James Holly Hanford. Copyright 1953. The Ronald Press Company. Reprinted by permission.

All knowledge is not couched in Moses' law,
The Pentateuch or what the Prophets wrote;
The Gentiles also know, and write, and teach
To admiration, led by Nature's light;
And with the Gentiles much thou must converse,
Ruling them by persuasion as thou mean'st,
Without their learning, how wilt thou with them,
Or they with thee hold conversation meet?
How wilt thou reason with them, how refute
Their idolisms, traditions, paradoxes?
Error by his own arms is best evinced.

Christel: . . . .

Or if I would delight my private hours
With music or with poem, where so soon
As in our native language can I find
That solace? All our law and story strewed
With hymns, our Psalms with artful terms inscribed,
Our Hebrew songs and harps in Babylon,
That pleased so well our victors' ear, declare
That rather Greece from us these arts derived;
Ill imitated, while they loudest sing
The vices of their deities, and their own,
In fable, hymn, or song, so personating
Their gods ridiculous, and themselves past shame.
Remove their swelling epithets thick laid
As varnish on a harlot's cheek, the rest,
Thin sown with aught of profit or delight,
Will far be found unworthy to compare
With Sion's songs, to all true tastes excelling,
Where God is praised aright, and godlike men,
The Holiest of Holies, and his saints;
Such are from God inspired, not such from thee;
Unless where moral virtue is expressed
By light of Nature, not in all quite lost.

(Book IV, ll. 221-235, 331-352)

THE ROMANTIC PERIOD

In the latter half of the eighteenth century the consideration of the Bible as literature became more common and more important.[1] Perhaps the earliest treatment of this sort, certainly a very influential one, was the lectures delivered by Robert Lowth (later Bishop of London) as Professor of Poetry at Oxford, and published in 1753. These Latin lectures, "De Sacra Poesi Hebraeorum Praelectiones Academicae," were translated into English by George Gregory in 1787 as Lectures on the Sacred Poetry of the Hebrews, *forming what became one of the best known books on the Bible.[2]*

The purpose governing the lectures can best be conveyed in a few passages from the second lecture, "The Design and Arrangement of these Lectures":

> *I have determined, therefore, in the first place, to treat of sacred poetry, that species, I mean, which was cultivated by the ancient Hebrews, and which is peculiarly appropriated to subjects the most solemn and sublime. . . . For since the university, when it gave its sanction to this species of discipline by a special degree, recommended the study of poetry, particularly because it might conduce to the improvement of the more important sciences, as well sacred as profane, nothing could certainly appear more useful in itself, or more agreeable to the purpose of this institution, and the design of its learned patrons, than to treat of that species of poetry, which*

[1]See C. S. Lewis, The Literary Impact of the Authorized Version, pp. 358-361.

[2]*Johnson, advising Boswell to read the Bible with a commentary, recommended Lowth on the Old Testament (Boswell's* Life of Johnson, *ed. G. B. Hill, revised L. F. Powell, Oxford, Clarendon Press, 1934, III, 58). It had been translated into German in 1758-1761 by the Orientalist Michaelis, and supplied with many learned notes, which were incorporated into Gregory's English translation. An interesting American edition of Gregory's translation was published by Calvin Stowe in 1829. He includes a preface containing an account of the work of Lowth, Michaelis, and Herder. He also restores Lowth's Latin translation of passages of Hebrew poetry in place of Gregory's English.*

constitutes so considerable a part of sacred literature, and excels all other poetry, not less in the sublimity of the style, than in the dignity of the subject.

It would not be easy, indeed, to assign a reason, why the writings of Homer, of Pindar, and of Horace, should engross our attention and monopolize our praise, while those of Moses, of David and Isaiah pass totally unregarded. . . .[3] It is indeed most true, that sacred poetry, if we contemplate its origin alone, is far superior to both nature and art; but if we would rightly estimate its excellencies, that is, if we wish to understand its power in exciting the human affections, we must have recourse to both: for we must consider what those affections are, and by what means they are to be excited. Moreover, as in all other branches of science, so in poetry, art or theory consists in a certain knowledge derived from the careful observation of nature, and confirmed by practice and experience; for men of learning having remarked in things what was graceful, what was fit, what was conducive to the attainment of certain ends, they digested such discoveries as had been casually made, and reduced them to an established order or method: whence it is evident, that art deduces its origin from the works of genius, not that genius has been formed or directed by art; and that it is properly applied in illustrating the works of even those writers, who were either ignorant of its rules, or inattentive to them. Since then it is the purpose of sacred poetry to form the human mind to the constant habit of true virtue and piety, and to excite the more ardent affections of the soul, in order to direct them to their proper end; whoever has a clear insight into the instruments, the machinery as it were, by which this end is effected, will certainly contribute not a little to the critical art. . . .

Since, therefore, in the sacred writings the only specimens of the primeval and genuine poetry are to be found, and since they are not less venerable for their antiquity than for their divine original, I conceived it my duty in the first place to investigate the nature of these writings, as far as might be consistent with the design of this institution: in other words, it is not my intention to expound to the student of theology the oracles of divine truth; but to recommend to the notice of the youth who is addicted to the politer sciences, and studious of the elegancies of composition, some of the first and choicest specimens of poetic taste.[4]

[3]*The persistence of this view is illustrated in one of Professor Quiller-Couch's Cambridge lectures. For he complains that the student of English literature must read Chaucer, Shakespeare, Milton, Pope, but not* Job; *and Goldsmith and Gray, but not* Ruth, Isaiah, Ecclesiasticus, *or* The Wisdom of Solomon. (On the Art of Reading, *G. Putnam's Sons, New York and London, 1920, p. 152).*

[4]*Robert Lowth, D.D.,* Lectures on the Sacred Poetry of the Hebrews, *translated from the original Latin by G. Gregory. A new edition with notes by Calvin E. Stowe, A. M. Crocker and Brewster, Boston and J. Leavitt, New York, 1829, pp. 25-27, 29.*

An even more significant writer about the Bible in this period was Johann Gottfried von Herder (1744-1803). Herder's interest in the poetry of the Old Testament is only one branch of his interest in primitive and popular poetry. The reference to a boy's appreciation of Hebrew poetry as possibly equaling his interest in Homer and Ossian illustrates the point[5]. Herder's feeling for literature as a manifestation of national life lies behind this interest in early popular literature. One of his first critical works was a prize-winning essay On the Effects of Poetry on the Customs and Morals of the Nations in Ancient and Modern Times. *Here he used Hebrew poetry as one example of literature having an organic relationship with the life of the nation which produced it. He had also written on* The Song of Songs *as a collection of folk poetry.*

Herder also shows very clearly the position of the literary enthusiasts towards the Bible, their departure from the attitude of orthodox piety and yet their reaction against the contempt for the Bible shown by some of the men of the Enlightenment.

Thus for two reasons, the interest in primitive national literature and the reaction against the taste of the Enlightenment, Herder's reading of the Bible departs more sharply from earlier interpretations than that of Lowth. His defence of his attitude is well expressed in a quotation from Letters concerning the Study of Theology, *published in 1780-1781, a few years before* The Spirit of Hebrew Poetry:

> *One must read the Bible in a human way: for it is a book written through human agency for human beings; human is the language, human were the external means whereby it was written and preserved; human, finally, is the sense with which it must be grasped and every aid that elucidates it, as well as the entire purpose and use to which it should be applied. You can, therefore safely believe that the more humanly (in the best sense of the word) you read the Word of God, the closer you will come to the purpose of its Artificer, who created man in His image and acts humanly for us in all works and benefices in which He shows himself to us as God.[6]*

The second major figure represented in this section is Goethe.

In a brief passage of his autobiographical work, Poetry **and** Truth, *Goethe has paid tribute to what Herder contributed to his appreciation of Hebrew poetry. The passage refers to the year 1770, when the two*

[5]*See p. 133.*
[6]*Quoted in Robert T. Clark, Jr.,* Herder: His Life and Thought, *University of California Press, 1955, p. 233.*

men were associated in Strassburg, Herder aged twenty-six, and Goethe twenty-one.

> I learnt to know poetry from quite a different side, and in another light than heretofore, one, too, which suited me well. Hebrew poetry, which he had treated in a masterly manner on the lines of his predecessor Lowth—popular songs such as he urged me to search for in Alsace; and the poetry of the oldest extant records— all bear witness that all poetry is a gift to the world and to nations, and not the private inheritance of a few refined and cultivated men.

But Goethe's interest in the Old Testament goes back to a period a few years earlier. When he was in his teens he had entered upon the study of Hebrew through the back door of Yiddish; much of the study consisted of semi-independent explorations into the Old Testament. The stories of the patriarchs in particular made a strong appeal to his imagination.

Like Herder, Goethe was repelled by the attitude towards the Bible taken by men of the Enlightenment. He retained a marked loyalty to it as an element in his education and his view of life.

In writing about the Bible Herder the preacher was concerned to bring other men to share his enthusiasm, Herder the critic to use it to support his beliefs about primitive national poetry. Goethe, the philosophical poet, writing about it in his autobiography, was concerned with its place in his own development.

THE SPIRIT OF HEBREW POETRY
(excerpts)

JOHANN GOTTFRIED VON HERDER

The Spirit of Hebrew Poetry *was published in two parts in 1782 and 1783. The first is a dialogue between Alciphron, representing the Enlightenment, rationalistic and at the outset contemptuous of the poetry of the Bible, and Euthyphron, representing Herder himself, enthusiastic over the poetry of the Old Testament. Euthyphron is early and completely successful in converting Alciphron, and the second part of the book consists of comment on various aspects and books of Hebrew poetry.*

James Marsh, the only translator of this important book into English, is an interesting person in his own right. He was instrumental in making Coleridge known in New England, and this translation of Herder is said to have been a favorite book of Emerson and of his aunt, Mary Moody Emerson.[1]

In the first dialogue Euthyphron defends first, Hebrew as a poetical language against Alciphron's charge that it is "poor and barbarous," and second, the system of parallelism which is the basis of its poetic form. Finally Alciphron, while not so confident as Euthyphron that boys properly taught Hebrew "would hold their Bible as dear, as their Homer or Ossian," thinks that he may in time come to share his friend's enthusiasm.

From *The Spirit of Hebrew Poetry*, by Johann Gottfried von Herder, translated by James Marsh, Burlington, Vermont, E. Smith, 1833.

[1]*See Marjorie Nicolson, "James Marsh and the Vermont Transcendentalists,"* The Philosophical Review, *XXXIV (1925), 28-50; John Dewey, "James Marsh and American Philosophy," (1941) in* Problems of Men, *Philosophical Library, New York, 1946.*

The second dialogue is concerned with the earliest conceptions of God and of the Elohim, and their representation in poetry.

The third dialogue, the one included here, treats of the Hebrews' concepts of the world in which they lived, and the poetical use of those concepts: pre-existence, light, clouds, storm, the heavens and the earth, plants and herbs, sun, moon, and stars, wild animals. By the end of this dialogue, it will be noted, Alciphron is reciting Hebrew poetry with enthusiasm.

In the second part of his book Herder abandoned the dialogue form, and turned to an examination of the poems in the Old Testament up to the time of David. He has chapters on the origin and general character of Hebrew poetry, the office of the prophet, the leadership and teaching of Moses, the blessings pronounced by Jacob and Moses upon the tribes, the triumphal songs of the Hebrews, their riddles, etc., and finally the songs of David, i.e., the Psalms. The selections here include Discourse VII, "Triumphal Songs of the Israelites," with the long note on the story of Sampson appended, and the brief section on fables and riddles.

From the Author's Preface

. . . . The general purpose of the work, required that this part should embrace the general and characteristick traits of Hebrew poetry. . . . It must contain also, especially, the traditions of the patriarchs, which, as among all nations, so peculiarly among this people, were the source from which were derived all the peculiarities of their modes of thinking, consequently also the genius of their poetry. To set forth these, and unfold them correctly, was here so much the more necessary, since most traditions of this kind have themselves more or less of poetical colouring, and what is worse, are often greatly misapprehended. In doing this, I have aimed as much as possible at brevity, have endeavoured not unnecessarily to say for the hundredth time, what had been repeated ninety-nine times already, and where on account of the connexion I was obliged to do so, have passed over it as briefly as possible; for where in common-place matters we cannot read with interest, we can much less write with it.

I sought, therefore, rather to set in their true light, the obscure and misinterpreted histories of Paradise, of the fall, of the tower of Babel, of the wrestling with the Elohim, etc., together with particular mythological representations, and personifications, which show most clearly the character of Hebrew poetry, and will at the same time prove of the greatest service to us hereafter; for before one can say much, either of the beauty or deformity of an object, he must first learn to understand it. A right understanding of words, of figurative language, and of things, will give, without long discourses and a tedious explication of it, the conception of beauty to one who has the capability of emotion. To one who is destitute of this, it can hardly be communicated by exclamations, and repetitions of similar passages from other poets, and much less by abstract discussions respecting the nature of poetry, and its various kinds. From all this, therefore, the present work will be free.

If I have occupied as much as I could of the work with the translation of select passages, no one, I hope, will think it too much, for these are in fact, the very purpose and subject of the work. They are the stars in an otherwise empty space. They are the fruit, and my book is only the shell. Could I have succeeded fairly in setting forth the specimens which I have here given, in all their ancient dignity and simplicity, I should not, at the least, have failed altogether of my aim; for in regard to this, I am of Luther's opinion, "that we must let the Prophets sit as teachers, and at their feet listen with humility to what they say, and not say what they must hear," as if we were their teachers. . . . Ardua res est, vetustis novitatem dare, novis auctoritatem, obsoletis nitorem, obscuris lucem, fastiditis gratiam, dubiis fidem, omnibus vero naturam et naturae suae omnia. Something of this I would have attained, in what I have said of the patriarchs, of Job, and of Moses. With mere learning and the characters of a foreign language, I could not consent to burden my pages. To the unlearned they are of no use, and the scholar who has the original language and the ancient translations at hand, can easily accommodate himself with them; for him indeed, especially for the young scholar, it is a source of pleasure to supply for himself the grounds of the opinions which he is taught, and to have something left for him to search out, to compare, and weigh by his own reflections. Hence, I have availed myself of the rich helps of more recent philologists, where I could do so, without making a display of it, or seeking credit by disputing them. To those whose aid I have experienced, my silent use of it will be my thank-offering; and where I could not adopt their opinion, there—I had my own opinion.

And in order to advance this always in the mildest terms, and in the clearest light, I have chosen the form of dialogue, though unusual, I am aware, in subjects of this sort. . . . The aim here was not to invent in general, but to elucidate, to exhibit, and point out to view, to find what is already before us. The only speakers admissible, therefore, are the demonstrator, and he to whom he demonstrates, friend with friend, teacher and scholar. My pattern for the general plan of the dialogue was not Plato, but the book of Corsi, or indeed the catechism. . . . In the form which I have adopted, the speakers are Alciphron and Euthyphron. The former speaks very much such sentiments as are uttered by the publick with its hundred heads, but they speak to one another lone, teach and controvert nobody in the world besides themselves. Whoever does not agree with Euthyphron, may retain the opinion of Alciphron, or—have his own opinion. Finally, I venture to confess, that the older I become, the more difficult for me is the tone of an instructer. Whom does one teach, moreover, when he teaches the publick as a mass? Where does this publick dwell? and in what style should we address it, that we may neither assume too lofty nor sink to too humble a tone? Here two individuals speak, and whoever will, may listen, improve what they say, and be either learner or teacher.

Let me venture to say, however, whom I would most gladly choose for readers of this work. Alciphron is a youth; he studies this poetry not from compulsion, not from the necessity of his profession, or of bread, but from a love of it. Young men then like him, and lovers of Scripture, lovers of the most ancient, the most simple, perhaps of the most truely heart-felt poetry in the world; lovers, in a word of the most ancient records of the human mind and heart,—unbiased, fresh, and ardent men of the same character, I would choose before all others for my readers. Of the childhood and youth of the human race, we can best speak with children and youth. The times antecedent to the Mosaick bond-service those feel with most congeniality whom the yoke of rules has never oppressed, and in whom the dawn of the world harmonizes with the dawning of their own souls. If my book contains any thing of worth, he is my best friend, who without either praise or censure procures for it readers of this description. Each one can always omit, what does not suit his taste, and for this purpose the contents of the dialogues are prefixed to them.

And if, as I could wish, there be among these youth, those engaged in the study of theology, I venture to say a word more particularly to them. The basis of theology is the Bible, and that of the New Testament is the Old. It is impossible to understand the former aright without a previous understanding of the latter; for Christianity proceeded from Judaism, and the genius of the language is in both books the same. And this genius of the language we can no where study better, that is, with more truth, depth, comprehensiveness, and satisfaction, than in its poetry, and indeed, as far as possible, in its most ancient poetry. It produces a false impression and misleads the young theologian to commend to him the New Testament to the exclusion of the Old. Without this, that can never be understood in a scholar-like and satisfactory manner. In the Old Testament we find as an aid to this, a rich interchange of history, of figurative representation, of characters, and of scenery; and we see in it the many coloured dawn, the beautiful going forth of the sun in his milder radiance. In the New Testament it stands in the highest heavens, and in meridian splendour, and every one knows which period of the day to the natural eye of sense imparts most life and strength. Let the scholar then study the Old Testament, even if it be only as a human book full of ancient poetry, with kindred feeling and affection, and thus will the New come forth to us of itself in its purity, its sublime glory, and more than earthly beauty. Let a man gather into his own mind, the abundant riches of the former, and he will be in the latter also, none of those smatterers, who, barren, and without taste or feeling, desecrate these sacred things. (vol. I, pp. 17-23)

Dialogue III

ON THE FOLLOWING DAY Alciphron did not fail to be punctual at the morning hour of poetry. We must not dwell to day, as we did yesterday, said Euthyphron, when they met together, on individual ideas, but I will direct you to a more general picture, and at the same time richer, than the tablet of Cebes. Is not one suggested to you by this fearful obscurity, in which all beings are at this moment involved, as if impatiently waiting for the light.

A. Do you mean the state of the dead among the Orientals?

E. This is not the topic, with which to begin our conversation. I was thinking indeed, of Sheol, but rather as the state of things yet unborn, which are waiting for the light, and hoping to find along with it unmingled joy. Recollect, for illustration, the night to which Job doomed in his imprecations the hour of his birth. There sleep unborn nights and days. God looks down from his elevation, and calls forth this or that as he pleases, and it comes forth with exultation to join the choir of its companions in the circular dance of the year.

Perish the day, in which I was born;
The night when they said, a son is brought forth.
Let that day be darkness,
Let not God inquire after it from above,
And let no light shine upon it.
Let darkness and death-shade seize it,
The clouds ever rest upon it,
The blackness of misfortune terrify it.
That night! Let darkness take it away,
That it join not the days of the year,
Nor come into the number of the months.
Let that night be set apart by itself;
Let no song of joy resound in it.
May those curse it, who curse the day,
Who can call up the monsters of the deep.
May the stars of its twilight be dark
Let it wait for the light, and light come not;
Nor let it see the eyelids of the dawn,
Because it shut not up my mother's womb,
Nor hid evil from my eyes.

Where have you seen the ancient night to which this unhappy man consigned his birth-day, or the gloom of a starless, rayless, and horrible darkness, that waits in vain for the morning, more fearfully described? No song of gladness cheers it, and its silence is interrupted only by the muttered spells of those, at whose enchantments the day goes not forth to interrupt them in their works of darkness. You know how Shakespeare describes a night like this.

A. He does not yield to the Orientals. But you said something of the state of unborn souls. The passage you have repeated seems to me to have no reference to such a state.

E. The realms that contain them, however, are silent and formless as the night. They are shaped in the deepest obscurity, in the centre of the earth, and there wait the light, as at this moment all creatures wait for it. The hour of their birth is struck—God calls them forth.

A. The representation is remarkably adapted to the senses.

E. Like all the poetical fictions of the Hebrews. They knew nothing for example of a chaos, in which before the formation of our world the atoms that compose it, were driven about, as chance directed; a fiction, for which we are indebted to the Greeks. In their minds its place was supplied by a dark gloomy sea, upon which the wind of the Almighty was hovering with an agitating effect; and the picture, as it appears to me, is so much the finer for being true. Such was in fact the first condition of our earth, as the structure of it shows, and so it must have stood for ages, until, by the wonders of creation, it became inhabitable. This picture has something in it natural and conceivable; that formless chaos has neither.

A. The spirit, to which you allude, that brooded over the waste and fathomless abyss, is to me peculiarly striking, and never fails to inspire me with awe.

E. It was to the Orientals the first and most natural image of that which constitutes life, power, impulse in creation; for the idea of a spirit seems originally to have been formed from the feeling of the wind, especially at night, and combined with power, and the sound of a voice.

A. You remind me of the appearance of an apparition in Job. There is form and yet no form; a gentle whisper, a murmuring like the voice of the wind, but with it also the power of the wind, the energy of spirit. It raises the hair on end, and rouses all the terrors of the soul. "It harrows up the soul with fear and wonder."

> A word stole secretly to me,
> Its whispers caught my ear;
> At the hour of night visions,
> When deep sleep falleth upon man,
> I was seized with fear and shuddering,
> And terrors shook my frame.
> A spirit was passing before me.
> All my hair stood on end.
> He stood still, but I saw not his form,
> A shadowy image was before my eyes;
> It was silently whispered to me,
> How can man, etc.

E. There is as you say a form without form, silence, and yet a voice, and after all the powerful effect alone indicates the formless figure, and so it must be. The more closely defined its features, the feebler would their effect become. Form and definiteness are incompatible with our notions of spirit: it is the offspring of the wind, and must preserve the character of its origin. But look! yonder come the glories of the morning. Let us leave the visions of night to their repose, while we adore the Father of Light.

> Jehovah, my God, thou art full of majesty,

Thou art clothed with dignity and glory.
He putteth on the light, as a garment,
He spreadeth out the heavens as a tent.

When the first morning beam shot forth, thou, the creator, didst declare the light to be good, and didst consecrate it to be an eternal emblem of thy presence, and of thy divine glory, of all delight and purity, of all wisdom, goodness, and blessedness. God dwells in light, and his countenance beams with paternal goodness, and paternal joy. He enlightens the hearts of all good men, and illuminates their path. In their original darkness he sent them the first ray of light, in the night of affliction and death he sends into their hearts a beam of unceasing joy and hope. As God, he displayed his glory in the creation of light, as the father of the universe in irradiating with its beams the souls of men, and leading us onward from this twilight of existence to brighter habitations. Is there any created existence, that would better deserve to be the garment of Jehovah, who, as to the essence of his nature, dwells in eternal obscurity? Light is his swiftest messenger, winged almost with the pinions of his omnipresence, and the emblem of Divine purposes and joys.

A. The poetry of the Hebrews has consequently fine imagery drawn from this source.

E. Perhaps no poetry in the world has drawn from it with more beautiful effect. The very name of light has in this language a lofty and noble sound, the emblem of all that is joyous and transporting. While it paints darkness in images of fear and horror, it places in animating contrast, the bright eye of day, the eyelids of the opening dawn. All the pictures of the dawn associate with it the idea of waiting, of expectation, of desire, and its appearance brings fruition. The morning star, which we see before us, is here a fair son of the twilight; for like every thing else, light and darkness has each its palace, its peculiar and inaccessible dwelling. The dawn appears in Job as a hero, who scatters the bands of misdoers, deprives the robber of the covering of darkness that protects him, gives to all things their form, and stamps them, as it were, with a new impression of his seal. From the womb of the morning dawn, is born the dew, her numerous host of glittering children. See you not there the fair mother before you, in that beautiful blending of light and darkness? observe too, how the Eternal Father is gradually expanding and arching over us the tent of his azure heavens.

He sits above the circle of the earth,

the inhabitants of the world are grasshoppers before him.
He stretcheth out the heavens as a curtain,
He spreadeth it out as a tent to dwell in.

But let us pass, if you please, to the mythology of the heavens themselves.

A. The Orientalists must have, I fear, great disputes to decide what Moses meant by his firmament between the waters and the waters. Whether it be a tent, an arched covering above, or a chrystal firmament on which the waters rested, it seems difficult to determine.

E. No disputes are necessary, for the pictures are all common, and, rightly understood, are also suitable and dignified. The most ancient idea is certainly not of a firmament or foundation of glass, since glass was unknown till a late period. The most ancient mythology represents the heavens, as an arch of water, and even the throne of God as begirt with darkness in the midst of the waters. In the celebrated song of David even it is said,

He stretcheth out the heavens as a tent,
He placeth amid the waters the arch of this dwelling.
He maketh the clouds his chariots,
He goeth forth on the wings of the wind.

Even at this late period we see nothing of the chrystal firmament, but a tent, a sublime palace arched over with the waters of heaven. Such also is the tradition of the Arabians—God called forth the heavens from the waters, and formed them for a habitation. The beautiful correspondence with truth too, in these representations, considered as pictures of natural history, is matter of wonder.

A. I have always admired it, and also the descriptions of the clouds, of the lightning and the rain, as peculiarly beautiful. The droughty Orientals, seem to look upon the heavens only as a store-house for their refreshments, a supply of the blessings, which their earth so often denied them.

E. And they have clothed this beautiful idea in a variety of imagery. At one time he binds up the waters in the clouds, as in leathern bags, and their airy tissue is not broken. In them is the water of life for man and beast. At another he drives them, filled with the stores of his bounty, hither and thither, to refresh the thirsty regions of the earth, and pours them out with a profusion, that overflows even the deserts, where no man dwells, nor blade of grass springs. He is often described, as going forth majestically in these waters, passing from land to land, for its relief, and treading upon the swelling floods of heaven. There he has his treasures of waters, and traces furrows in heaven, and opens channels, by which to conduct them. Again he rends asunder his tent, and lets the rain descend, divides the heavens, or opens the windows of his royal palace, and deluges the earth with torrents. The last were probably conceptions of a late period, when God was represented as the king of heaven.

A. And was he not so represented at an early period?

E. Whether early or not, he was still earlier represented as the father of a family, who extended his parental care to man and beast. Observe the numerous passages of this kind in the Psalms and prophets. What heartfelt prayer for rain and refreshing waters ascend to heaven! How do all eyes wait, and the parched tongue, now animated anew, abound in thanksgiving! The finest images of the bounty, the universal goodness, and providence of God are borrowed from the rain and the dew. So also the most earnest prayer and cordial longing after God, are represented under the image of burning and consuming thirst:

> As the hart panteth for the fresh fountain,
> So panteth my soul after thee,
> My soul thirsteth for God,
> For the living God.
> When shall I come to him,
> And behold his face?

Images of this kind give to poetry a community of feeling and sympathy between brute animals, men, plants, and all that has life; the Supreme and Eternal Father, is the father of all.

A. But how then were the heavens represented as solid?

E. It was on account of their sapphire appearance, their glowing splendour, their unchangeableness, and their beauty. Perhaps the most ancient notion was, that this solid firmament was ice, from which the hail descended. The Arabs have pictures, according to which the lightnings are but sparks, that fly off from the sapphire firmament. Finally, when the heavens came to be represented as a temple and palace of God, this pure azure of the sky was the ground floor of his, and the covering of our habitation. To those who dwelt in tents, however, the idea of a heavenly tent seems to me to have been the greatest favorite. They represent God as daily spreading it out, and making it fast to the mountains, the pillars of heaven. It is to them, an emblem of security, of rest, and of the paternal intercourse and friendship, in which God lives with his creatures.

A. And how do they treat the earth?

E. You will learn from their own words, if you go on with the psalm, in which David has given a picture of the creation.

A.

> He hath established the earth upon its foundation,
> It shall not be moved for ever and ever.
> He hath covered it with floods, as with a robe;
> The waters stood above the mountains;
> At thy rebuke they fled,
> At the voice of thy thunders they hasted away.
>
> Then rose up the mountains, the valleys sunk down,
> To the place which thou didst appoint for them.
> Thou settest boundaries to the floods,
> They shall not pass over and return
> To deluge the earth.
>
> Thou sendest forth springs in the valleys,
> They run between the mountains,
> They give drink to the beasts of the field,
> The wild beasts quench their thirst.
> Above them dwell the fowls of heaven,
> They sing among the branches.
>
> Thou waterest the hills from thy store-house above,
> From the fruits of thy works thou satisfiest the earth,
> Makest grass to grow for cattle,
> And seed for the service of man,
> That he may bring forth bread from the earth,
> And make his face to shine with plenty,
> Wine also that maketh glad the heart of man,
> And bread, that strengtheneth man's heart.
>
> The trees of God are full of sap,
> The cedars of Lebanon, which he hath planted,
> Where the birds build their nests,
> And the fir trees the house of the heron.
> The mountains he made for the wild goats,
> The rocks as a refuge for the conies.

E. With what a joyful expression that poet surveys the earth! It is a green mountain of Jehovah, which he has raised up from the waters; an Elysian field, which he has established above the seas for the habitation of his living multitudes. The series of images, which the poet has made use of, contain exactly the natural history of the earth. At first the waters stand above the mountains, at the command of God they shrink beneath. Now the mountains rise up, the valleys sink, as the waters rush through and level them. Finally God sets bounds to the floods, and makes fast the earth—Then the fountains break forth in the valleys, the streams run between the mountains, where their beds are already hollowed out; to them the beasts resort, and above them the birds sing, for the banks of streams were first covered with trees. We shall find in Job more sublime pictures of the formation of the earth; more true or beautiful are scarcely possible.

A. And in truth whatever is most consonant to nature is most perfect in beauty. What are all the mythologies to me, if they teach me nothing? What profit do I gain, for example, when the Northern Edda represents heaven, as the skull of a slaughtered giant, the earth as formed from his bones, and the rivers from his blood? Poetry, in order to affect the heart and the understanding, must combine beauty with truth, and animate both with sympathetic feeling.

E. The poetry of the Orientals seems to me to combine all these. What sympathy, for example, does it exhibit with flowers, plants and herbs? As it ascribes to all in a certain degree the principles of life, and more than figuratively personifies them, so God is represented as their father, who bestows his blessings upon them, who nourishes them with rain, and serves them with the breath of spring. Their restoration and the renewal of their verdure was a beautiful emblem of the resurrection of the dead, as their preservation was a memorial of his universal providence. The leaves of plants seem to have been early remarked, and the palm tree, the cedar, the vine and the olive have furnished beautiful and sublime images to the poetry of the Hebrews— But this, alas! is all which they have furnished. Had we more of their pastoral fables like that of Jotham, or of the class to which the Song of Solomon belongs, what fine poetry and personifications should we find in them! Perhaps more beautiful and diversified, than the dialogue of our own poet between the rose and the zephyr, or those in the Persian between the rose and the nightingale, the wanderer and the turtle dove. As it is we must content ourselves with a single collection of such songs, but one that breathes throughout the fragrance of the rose, and brings back the musical notes of the turtle; I mean the Songs of Solomon. But the sun, my friend, is rising high.

A. Be not in haste. Point me rather to some examples of fine personification and hymns addressed to the sun. The Hebrews I believe have none of these.

E. Hymns addressed to these, or to any other object of nature, this poetry could not have. It would be idolatry, and you are aware how conscientiously this was avoided. Job says,

> Had I looked at the sun, when it shone forth,
> And the moon going abroad in its beauty,
> So that my heart had burned in secret,
> And I had kissed my hand for them,
> This would have been an abomination,
> For I should have denied the God of Heaven.

When this feeling was so sincere and earnest, no hymns to the hosts of heaven were possible. The Hebrew poetry guarded against this species of idolatry with the more extreme caution, because the Orientals in general were not so much attracted by any inferior idols, as by the king and queen of heaven, and to these their hearts were very greatly inclined. It became therefore a direct object of this poetry to represent the sun and moon as the servants of God, and to ascribe to him also all glory and truth, righteousness and beauty.

> God said, Let there be two great lights in Heaven
> To rule over the seasons.
> He placed them in the firmament
> To have dominion over the seasons.

They are kings of the world, but only subordinate to God, his representatives, his creatures and messengers. In those characters alone the Hebrew poetry has employed them.

A. It has used them you mean but little?

E. Yes, much and appropriately too. The sun, moon and stars also were animated. They had their dwelling places and tents in heaven, as they still have in the minds of the Arabians and other nations. You know the beautiful passage, for which you may seek a parallel among the Greeks in vain.

> For the sun he hath pitched a tent in the heavens,
> From which he goeth forth as a bridegroom
> Out of his chamber,
> And rejoiceth as a hero
> In the career of victory.
> He goeth forth from the end of heaven,
> And goeth onward to the end of it.
> And filleth the world with his beams.

The moon and stars also have their dwellings, in which, when they are to be darkened, God seals them up, or in which they timidly shrink and hide themselves, when the glory of Jehovah appears. Thus in Habakkuk, for example, God comes forth in his war-chariot to conquer and divide the land; the sun and moon come in astonishment to the doors of their tents; his lightnings are shot forth, his arrows fly round him, and they hide themselves in confusion before the presence of his greater glory.

> The mountains saw thee and trembled,
> The waters passed away,
> The deep uttered its voice,
> And lifted up its hands on high.
> The sun and moon stood still in their tents;
> When they saw the brightness of thine arrows,
> The glittering splendour of thy lightnings,
> They hasted away.

A more sublime personification I consider hardly possible. All nature listens; its swiftest objects stand still, its brightest are obscured. In the same spirit the stars are made the martial host, the exulting children of God.—Whatever is pure, fair, and immortal, is compared with the stars, and the angels are often personified in them.

A. But for what purposes are these glittering hosts sent and employed?

E. Those for which God employs his servants. The sun, as even its name indicates, is a messenger, but never the original fountain of blessedness and beauty. Even the nourishment of plants is not ascribed to it, but to the Supreme Father, who refreshes and waters them with the air, the dew, and the rain: it only brings about the seasons—a king of the earth, but in subordination to the King of kings. The stars as his army go out and engage in battle. To them were ascribed the water-spouts and the overflowing of rivers; and in the song of Deborah they are beautifully personified in this character. In their character of angelick messengers they are capable of failure. He discovers them out of the way, and does not trust them with confidence. He finds imperfection in their brilliancy, and the heavens are not pure in his sight. But finally, when the future days of his own peculiar reign shall arrive, then shall the sun shine with sevenfold brightness, and the light of the moon shall be as the light of the sun. That poetry, which so profoundly comprehends the nature of things; which binds all the objects of creation together in such admirable order, and, in a sublime choral song which represents God as the great shepherd of heaven, who knows and calls for the stars by name as his sheep, and feeds them under a variety of images on the azure fields of the sky; who girds Orion, and consoles the nightly wanderer for the loss of her children; who binds together the seven stars in their sisterly union, and hides his secret treasures in the South; such poetry is the daughter of heaven and earth. When we come to treat of the book of Job, what elevated views of the stars will it furnish us.

A. I anticipate it with delight, and am for ever reconciled to the most ancient poetry of the world. I have been particularly, struck by its perfect sympathy with brutes, and the whole animate creation, and was delighted even in childhood to find, that it treated the brute animals (so called because they are dumb) as the brothers of man, who wanted nothing but the power of speech. The wild beasts it denominates living creatures, or the *living,* because the domestic animals are, in the comparison, as it were still and dead. I was delighted, when I found the voice and language of brutes so forcibly expressed in the language; when the prophet coos with the crane and the turtle dove, and mourns with the ostrich in the wilderness. I rejoiced at finding the form of the stag, the lion, and the ox, sometimes their strength, stateliness, and velocity, at others, the acuteness of their senses, their habits of life, and their character described and painted in appropriate terms, and wished that in place of some of the sacred songs we had more of its fables, parables, riddles respecting the brute creation, in short, more of the poetry of nature; for this seems to me to be among this people the most happy, and of the most perfect simplicity.

E. The name of God, however, must always belong to it, as a necessary accompaniment, for he is the parental head of this whole animate creation. He gives to every creature its food;—all eyes wait upon him, and he lights them up with joy. The young and hateful raven does not cry unheard, and the wild chamois goat experiences his parental care, and is delivered in her time of need. He lives as it were with every animal in its peculiar sphere, feels its wants, and fulfills its wishes, because he has given to all their natures. To him nothing is wild, nothing dumb and despised. He roars with the lion after his prey, and looks down from his mountain eyry with the glance of the eagle. The wild ass lives upon his pastures, and the hawk flies by his wisdom. He too is the great deep, the realm of monsters. The hated crocodile is the object of his paternal love, and behemoth is the beginning of the ways of

God, the most magnificent of his works on earth. In short, this poetry
is full of natural feeling, full of the universal providence and goodness
of God in his wide empire. It was nourished in the bosom of nature,
and cherished in the lap of our mother earth.

A. I now discover (what I have often wondered at with some perplexity) why it is, that in this poetry a preference is sometimes given to
the brutes over men, and the ass of Balaam has more influence with
the angel, than the prophet who rode her. In the book of Job, God is
represented as delighting in the horse, and the lion, as being proud of
behemoth and leviathan, but is silent respecting man.

E. It does not however pass over man with neglect; he is the image
of God, the masterpiece of his works, and one of the visible Elohim
here upon the earth. But of this at another time. Finish now your
song of praise, and I will close with one to correspond with it.

A.

He made the moon to divide the seasons,
The sun knoweth his going down.
Thou makest darkness, and it is night,
In which every beast of the forest creeps forth;
The young lions roar after their prey,
And seek their food from God.
The sun riseth, they hurry away,
And lay themselves down in their dens.
Then man goeth forth to his labour,
And to his work in the field until evening.
How manifold are thy works, O God,
In wisdom hast thou made them all;
The earth is full of thy treasures.
The sea too, so vast, so wide in extent,
There are swarms innumerable,
Living things small and great.
There go the ships,
There sports the leviathan,
Which thou hast made to play therein.
These all wait on thee,
To give them meat in its season;
Thou givest it them, they gather it;
Thou openest thine hand, they are satisfied with good.
Thou turnest away thy countenance,
They are filled with terror;

Thou takest away their breath,
They return back to their dust;
Thou sendest forth thy breath,
They are created anew,
And thou renewest the face of the earth.
   The glory of Jehovah endureth for ever.
Jehovah rejoiceth in his works,
He looketh upon the earth, and it trembleth,
He toucheth the mountains, and they smoke.
I will sing to Jehovah as long as I live,
I will praise my God, while I have being.
My song of him shall be sweet,
I will be joyful in Jehovah.
Praise the Lord, O my soul,
Hallelujah.

E. I remain pledged for a corresponding specimen; but since you prefer hymns, here is one entirely in the Oriental style. In my opinion there is indeed but one style in this class of poetry in all the living European languages, and that is the style of Job, the Prophets and the Psalms. Milton has especially interwoven it in the composition of his immortal poem. Thompson has trodden with feeble steps in the same path, and among us Kleist has very philosophically adorned it. For this style and this imagery we are indebted to the simplicity of the Hebrew poetry.[2] (vol. I, pp. 64-79)

The Song of Deborah

THE WHOLE BOOK OF JUDGES is animated with the spirit of heroic poetry. It breathes the spirit of the age, the youthful vigour of a newly settled race of mountaineers, who indeed were often subdued and oppressed for want of organization and government among themselves, but whose heroism and love of liberty now and then kindled up in the heroick souls of individuals, and broke out into a flame. I might denominate this the poetical age of Israel, and will explain myself on the point more at large.

*   *   *   *   *

[2]Reference is had in the last paragraph to Milton's morning Hymn of Adam in the 5th Book of Paradise Lost, which it is not thought necessary to copy in the translation. TR.

A period of civil and political order, of peaceful security, and established moral customs, is certainly the happiest for a nation, but not the most favourable for producing poetry, that is filled with life and action. This delights rather in bold and striking incidents, in the prevalence of passion, of the marvellous, and of liberty. "At that period there was no king in Israel, and every man did what was right in his own eyes," and often, therefore, the most savage and cruel wrong, as we see from many traces of their history. He acted according to the impulse of ardent and unrestrained desire, and in relation to all heroic deeds it is said, "the spirit of the Lord, that is, the national spirit of the Israelites impelled him, or the national God aroused and armed him, the spirit of Jehovah began to drive him here and there," even when the actor was by no means a man of moral worth. It is painful to read the objections, that are multiplied against this book and its marvellous events without regard to the time and circumstances, in which it was written. Every one knows, that all ancient nations in their wars permitted themselves the use of artifice and deception; all rude nations do so at the present day, and, where in other respects magnanimity exists, prefer craft to force. A disorganized and oppressed people, whose national power exists only in individual enterprise, have more especial need of such weapons. For how can an individual even the strongest and bravest, if we mean to speak rationally, maintain himself against a multitude, if he does not gain an advantage by the arts of war? And what are these arts, but skilful artifices? Or is there a less ingenious artifice, a less heroic heroism, than that which breathes from the mouth of the cannon? Let Ehud go, then, excited by Jehovah, and with his dagger pierce the foreign tyrants of his country. It was more decisive than a victory with us, which is purchased by the blood of thousands. Every thing then depended on individual heroism and prowess. The rude dweller in tents, Jael the wife of Eber, who, uniting with her people, pierced through the commander of a foreign foe in her tent, could make, indeed, but little claim to rank in our orders of military merit, yet deserved, according to the spirit of the age, the national praise awarded her in the song of Deborah. We must first convert the hordes, which made war upon Israel to well ordered nations, and their times into ours, if we would apply our principles of right in war to them.

Thus do I picture to myself the deeds of Deborah, of Gideon, of Jephthah, and of Samson, and I hold no more prolonged vindication of particular circumstances on the grounds of morals and natural rights to be necessary. The whole stands forth, even in respect to the tone of the narrative, in the light and costume of poetry. Some of the narratives, indeed, as the capturing of Samson in the lap of Delilah, are arranged with poetical symmetry. Individual expressions have a remarkable force, the language of the heroes is full of the spirit of Jehovah, i.e. of enthusiasm, resolution and boldness. The annunciation of some of them before their birth, the appearance of an *angel, or a nameless Prophet,* the singular proofs, whether of the calling or of the courage of these men, the riddles, the play upon words, the youthful rashness for example of all the enterprises of Samson—all this gives to these narratives more poetry, than many heroic poems have been able to exhibit with all the marvels of their fabulous machinery. Each of these heroes too is so characteristic, so like himself, in the slightest features of his history, that in the brief space of one or two chapters allotted to it he stands forth a living hero.

To this poetical age belongs also the finest heroic song of the Hebrews, the song of Deborah. The 68th Psalm will approach nearest to it, but is still far behind. In the song of Deborah all is present, living action. In that of David an ancient heroic narrative is to become the embellishment of a solemn state ceremony which still remains only a ceremonial procession. Forgive me, thou heroine, beneath thy native palms, that I mingle in the dance of thy nation's jubilee, and in feeble tones re-echo thy triumphal song.

Triumphal Song of Deborah and Barak

Then sang Deborah, and Barak, Abinoam's son,
On the day of their triumph they sang.
   Give ye praise to the Lord,
That Israel hath taken her revenge,
That the people came freely to battle.
   Here ye kings, give ear ye princes,
I will sing, I will sing unto Jehovah.
I will sing unto Jehovah, God of Israel.
   Jehovah, when thou wentest out from Seir,
And marchedst from the hills of Edom,
Then the earth quaked, the heavens dropped,
The clouds poured streams of water,
The mountains melted before Jehovah,
Sinai before Jehovah God of Israel.
   In the days of Shamgar son of Anath,

In the days of Joel the highways were empty,
And travellers sought the winding paths.
The assemblies of Israel were no more,
They ceased, until I Deborah arose,
Till I arose the mother of Israel.

They had chosen them new Gods,
Then war was raging at the gates,
And no shield or spear was seen
Among the forty thousands of Israel.
My heart turns to you, ye leaders of Israel,
And to you ye volunteers among the people.
Sing praises with me to Jehovah.
Ye that ride on asses richly harnessed
That sit on costly coverings,
And who walk on foot in the streets,
Meditate and utter a song,

An ode for the herdsmen[3] to sing—
Who water their herds among the wells,
That there they may praise the goodness of Jehovah,
His goodness to the people of Israel,
For there the people of Jehovah were in straits.
Arouse thee! arouse thee, Deborah!
Awake! awake! give a song of triumph,
Arise Barak, bring forth thy captives,
Thou son of Abinoam.
Then went a remnant against the strong,
Jehovah with me against the mighty.
From Ephraim came the first to Amalek,
Then camest thou Benjamin with thy people,
From Machir came over the leaders,
From Zebulon those that muster for battle.

---

[3]The interpretation of this difficult verse commends itself, I think, by its facility, and the connexion of the whole. The battle occurred among the rivers and torrents of Mount Tabor, (compare v. 21. and chap. iv. 6-7.) and here, therefore, the victory is forever to be celebrated. The battle was fought in the rainy season, when the fountains and rivulets were swollen, and according to v. 21. swept away the Canaanites. On this account Deborah begins with the dropping heavens, introduces the constellations, which bring rain as combatants. In like manner are the narrow passes of Tabor conceived, in which the people were placed, and thus the scene of battle is accurately defined.

The princes of Issachar were with Deborah,
Issachar, in bravery like Barak,
Sprang forth into the valley.

By Reuben's brooks was much consulting.[4]
Why sittest thou there among the stalls?
To hear the bleating of the herds?
By Reuben's brooks is great consulting.

Gilead beyond Jordan stayed unmoved,
Dan also, or why should he dwell in ships,
Asher was safe by the shore of the sea,
And lingered by his bays and creeks.
Only Zebulon jeoparded their lives,
And Naphtali on the mountain heights.[5]
But the kings they came and fought,[6]
There fought the kings of Canaan,
At Tanach by the waters of Megiddo,
But money, their desire, they received not.

From heaven they fought (against them),
The stars from their courses fought with Sisera.
The river Kishon swept them away,
The winding river, the river Kishon.
March on my soul in thy might.

Then stamped the hoofs of the horses,
In the fleeing, in the fleeing of heroes.
Curse Meroz, said the angel of Jehovah,[7]
Utter curses upon the inhabitants thereof,
They came not to the help of Jehovah,

[4]Here begins the sarcasm upon the tribes, which remained behind to v. 17.

[5]They were the first, whom Deborah committed to Barak, (iv. 6) and in whose heroism she confided, and who are here also honoured with the last and highest praise. They with the Northern tribes of Judaea were heroic mountaineers. Zebulon it seems is contrasted with Asher and Dan, because like them it was by the sea, and yet joined the expedition.

[6]In every word of this description there is sarcastic raillery. She honours them with titles, that she may annul them; and this tone continues in what is said of the mother of Sisera and her women.

[7]In the whole book of Judges the voice of God is called the *angel of Jehovah*. (Chap. ii. 1-4. vi. 12-22. xiii. 3-21.) The denomination here is probably from the first of the passages, for the angel of the Lord, which appeared there, commanded to conquer the land. The song speaks in the name of God, i.e., as the voice of the nation.

To the help of Jehovah in his host of heroes.
    Blessed above women be Jael,
The wife of Heber the Kenite,
Blessed above the dwellers in tents,
He asked water, she gave him milk,[8]
She brought curdled milk in a lordly dish.—
She seized with her hand upon the nail,
With her right hand the heavy hammer.
    And with the hammer she smote Sisera,
She smote him through the head,
She pierced and struck through his temples,
Under her feet he bowed himself,
He fell, he lay down,
At her feet he bowed, he fell.
Where he bowed, there he fell down—dead.
    The mother of Sisera looked from a window.[9]
She cried through the lattice,
"Why are his chariots so long in coming?
Why tarry the wheels of his chariots?"
    Her wise ladies answered her,
Yea, she quickly returned answer to herself.
"Are they not then to find and divide the spoil,
To every man a damsel or two,
And variegated garments for Sisera,[10]
A prey of bright embroidered garments,
Doubly embroidered, variegated clothing,
The triumphal procession of the spoil.
    So let all thine enemies perish, O Jehovah,
But let them, that love thee, be as the sun,
When he goeth forth in his glory.[11] (vol. II, pp. 182-191)

[8]This, too, is irony and imitative representation to the last breath of the smitten Sisera. The picture is beautifully poetical, and characterizes the age in a lively manner. That it was intoxicating milk, is plain from a multitude of Oriental books of travels. He concealed himself in the interior gynacaeum of the tent, and there in profound sleep found his death.

[9]The contrasts of the picture render the irony perfect.

[10]This wise lady of the harem was not desirous, that Sisera should acquire any damsels. She wished only for variegated garments and showy trappings for the triumphal procession of her lord.

[11]This short sentence is, as it were, a seal of the whole song, and shows that it is as methodically arranged, as it is consistent with the age and suited to the people and the place.

Samson[12]

I will endeavor to show this by a few particulars in the history of Samson. Good humour, levity and arrogance pervade his whole life. Wine and strong drink are forbidden him, but he yields himself the more devotedly to love, which more than once led him into a snare, and at length deprived him of his prowess, his liberty, and his eyes. "I will seek a wife among my enemies that I may find occasion against them" was a foolish thought, and yet how entirely in the spirit of a headlong youth, who, conscious of his superior power, knows not how to direct it, and divides his heart between love and bold adventure. The riddle at his marriage feast, and its consequences, show the same characteristic. In opposing men he was a man, in opposing women he was but a woman, as many similar heroes in history have been. He answers with levity those, who through his own means had solved his riddle, goes forth and slays thirty Philistines, that his thirty marriage guests might receive their prize, deserts his wife, and returns with a kid for a present, and as if nothing had happened, goes directly to her chamber. When he learns, that she has become the wife of another, he says "now at length I shall have just cause against the Philistines, I will do them mischief," as if he had been waiting for such an occasion. The story of the three hundred foxes with the firebrands between their tails is entirely after his manner; and the objections, that have been made to it are not worthy of reputation. The foxes or rather jackals of that country enter into houses, are easily taken, and an idle, frolicksome adventurer like this would not fail to engage merry accomplices enough to carry it into effect. They had the sport. He looked to the result. So also with the gate of Gaza, which to the reproach of the Gazites he drew off to the mountain. So with the jaw-bone of the ass, the pun upon which was strictly in character for Samson. The place where he made the attack was called Lechi, Jawbone, and as clearly appears from chap. xv, 13. 14. 19. this was a narrow pass, a sort of hollow shaped probably like a jaw-bone. He had made an arrangement with his countrymen, that when they had fulfilled the part which their cowardice led them to take, of binding and delivering him to his enemies, they should remain quiet, since they could not have been excited to any thing more. And when in passing he came into this winding and narrow pass, to Lechi, he chose his opportunity, seized upon the jawbone of an ass, which lay there, and accomplished his work. He then

[12]This passage is Herder's note on the material on pp. 150-151 above.

congratulated himself respecting it in a double play upon words, to which still another is added, that God showed to the fainting warrior, who after his bold adventure longed for a cool draught of water, a fountain in the same winding rock, Lechi, where the battle was fought. The fountain, as the narrator tells us, is called to this day the caller's fountain or the fountain of invocation. (Here too the fountain could not have flowed from the jaw-bone, which he wielded in his hand, but from something that remained to aftertimes, obviously the winding rock, Lechi, v. 14.) All this is told with an animated brevity, which shows the genuis of Samson. The same is true of the sad history of his reposing in the lap of Delilah. His two great weaknesses, love and levity, deprived him of his secret. For he knew nothing more, than that he was dedicated to his national God, whose strength would remain so long as he kept his inviolable vow. This he knew from his name, his education and mode of life, which might perhaps be sufficiently self-denying. Suddenly he lost his courage, when his vow was broken and felt that the assistance of God was withdrawn from him. But as his hair grew he found his cheerfulness and courage revive. His enemies knew this, and when he was to furnish them with amusement, probably in an old, widely extended, and lightly built house of idol worship, he amused himself by trying his renewed youthful energies upon the pillars of the house, thus seeking a joyful death. He died as he had lived, an irreconcilable enemy of the Philistines, and rejoiced in uniting their death with his own. I will not ask, whether a narrative so characteristick, and self-consistent, could have been the work of fiction? I only say, that it is strikingly correspondent to the age, and beautifully told. Precisely that, which is most the object of sarcasm, or most absurdly defended, is the finest. And so generally with the narratives of the book of Judges. (vol. II, pp. 185-186)

Additional Fragments
From the youthful period of Hebrew Poetry

TO THE POETICAL AGE of Israel's liberty belongs also the beautiful fable of Jotham. Like the fables of Aesop and Menenius Agrippa, it was spoken to the people for their instruction respecting an actual event, and such is the truest and best origin and aim of fabulous compositions. In this fable trees speak and act, for Israel then lived beneath the trees the life of herdsmen or cultivators of the soil. The youngest

son of a worthy father, who alone was left after the murder of all his
brothers, goes upon the top of the mountain, raises his voice, and
addresses in the following language the people, who had made the
oppressor of his family and the murderer of all his brothers their chosen
king.

> Hearken unto me, ye men of Shechem,
> That God may hearken unto you.
>   The trees went forth upon a time
> To anoint a king to rule them.
> They said unto the olive tree,
> "Be thou the king over us."
> But the olive tree said to them,
> "Shall I give up my oily sap,
> For which both God and man respect me,
> And go to wave above the trees?
>   Then the trees said to the fig-tree,
> "Come thou be our king."
> But the fig-tree answered them,
> "Shall I give up my sweetness,
> And my rich annual fruits,
> And go to wave above the trees?"
>   Then said the trees unto the vine,
> "Come thou and be our king."
> The vine made answer to them,
> "Shall I forsake my wine,
> Which cheereth God and man,
> And go to wave above the trees?"
>   Then said all the trees unto the bramble,
> "Come thou and be our king."
> The bramble said unto the trees,
> "If in truth ye anoint me over you,
> Come and put your trust in my shadow.
> But if it be not so,
> Let fire come out of the bramble,
> And devour the cedars of Lebanon!"

The fable, as a species of composition, lives wholly in the wild
period of uncontrolled liberty. In the spirit and feeling of such freedom
it represents the quiet happiness of the several fruitful and luxuriant
trees, none of which are desirous of the proposed elevation. It clearly
exhibits the gifts and qualifications, by which the bramble attains the

royal dignity, and of which on the first proposal it is conscious in itself. It shows the inward and essential character of the kingly office, as cold and barren, without oil and joyless, to wave above the blooming trees. Finally it relates the first gracious acts of the bramble, the conditions offered to the cedars of Lebanon, either to come and place themselves under the shadow of the bramble, or be consumed by it with fire. Beautiful fable! full of sad truth for more than one age!

The East is full of such ethico-political fables. What the historians of European nations propose in aphorisms, the Orientals clothe in the dress of fiction or fable. The tyrant, who took from them their freedom of speech, must at least leave them their fables, their proverbs, their wild and romantic tales. These not only commended themselves to the minds of the common people, but sometimes ventured in humble guise to approach the ear of the monarch. Thus Nathan related to David, the king after God's own heart, a little story of the one ewe lamb of the poor man.[13] Thus too, Isaiah[14] sung to his well beloved, the people, a fabulous song of another beloved, the sentiment of which is simply that the former is an unfruitful and unprofitable vineyard, which the latter, the Lord of the vineyard threatens with immediate destruction. The Prophets paint symbols upon the wall, or themselves become symbols, living fables, and when curiosity prompted the enquiry, what is this? what does this witless figure mean? the Prophet explained its pregnant import. Often, too, this is given dressed in verbal conceits.

> What seest thou Jeremiah?
> "A rod of an almond tree."
> Thou sawest truly!
> For I will watch over my word
> Till I accomplish it,

where the words in the original exhibit a paronomasia.

What play of words, too, in regard to proper names, monuments, and historical events, do we find abounding in the historical and poetical writings of the Hebrews.—And as the riddles and puns of Samson belong here, it may, perhaps, be the most fitting occasion to illustrate more at large both these topics, which are so great favourites in Oriental poetry.

When Samson celebrated his marriage festival, he knew of no better

[13]Sam, xii, 1.
[14]Isa. v, 1.

way to entertain his guests than by a riddle, which he propounded in verse.[15]

Samson.

> I will put forth now a riddle to you,
> And ye shall interpret it.

Answer.

> Put forth thy riddle then,
> That we may hear it.

Samson.

> Out of the eater came forth meat,
> Out of the strong came forth sweetness.

Answer.

> Nothing is sweeter than honey,
> Nothing is stronger than a lion.

Samson.

> If ye had ploughed with my heifer,
> Ye had not found out my riddle.

All these sentences in the original are in parallelism, or in a word, rhymes. The question is formally proposed, and formally answered. Seven days were given for reflection, and a liberal reward offered for the solution; clear proofs of the value set upon such trials of wit in these times.

We find this respect and fondness for riddles even in later books. The queen of Sheba came to test the wisdom of Solomon by trials of the same kind, and the last chapter but one of his proverbs contains little else but riddles,[16] though, indeed, in a different and higher style.

The Words of Agur the Son of Jakeh.

> In lofty phrase the man to Itheil spake,
> To Itheil and Uchal spake he thus.
> > More brutish surely am I than a man.
> What men call prudence I have not.
> I have not learned their wisdom,
> And should I know the knowledge of the Holy?
> > Who up to heaven ascended or came down?
> Who gathered up the wind within his fist?
> Who bound the waters in a garment?

[15]Jud. vix, 12-18.
[16]Prov. xxx.

> Who gave the earth its several bounds?
> What is his name? and what his son's?
> Inform me, if thou knowest?

I have already ventured, and I fear without success, an explanation of this enigmatical passage. It is, perhaps, more simple, than one is apt at first to suppose, and the reason we fail to discover the meaning, is in fact, that we look too deep for it. The sage Agur is to discourse lofty sentiments to his pupils, but he begins with modesty, that too exalted wisdom may not be expected from him. How shall he, who in understanding and knowledge is inferior to his race, and confesses, that he is not versed in human wisdom, be supposed to possess that knowledge, which belongs to those, who are entrusted with the truth of God, to the holy ones. The wisdom of men is obviously placed in contrast here with a higher science; and the holy, therefore, are such as may boast of a higher light, and admission to the Divine counsels, as he himself at the same time explains by his questions. The true sage must have ascended to heaven and returned thence, he must know the depths of creation, and understand the whole compass of the world, or he deserves not the name.[17] "And what," asks Agur, "is the name of the man, who can venture to say this of himself? Where does he live, and who are the disciples whom he hath taught. Tell me his name?" In other words, none such is found on earth.—Obviously this commencement is but an echo of what is said of wisdom in Job, where in the same language, and on the same grounds, it is said, that God alone is wise, because he alone knows the whole broad creation, hath weighted the winds, and marked the boundaries of the earth. To man belongs only a different wisdom, and it is precisely that, which Agur gives. He proceeds on.

> What God enjoins is wisdom pure as gold,
> He is a shield to them, who trust in him.
> Add nothing to the words of God,
> Lest he reprove, and thou be found a liar.

The same sentiment, which Job also expresses, that "the fear of God is for man the only divine wisdom."—In the introduction of Agur, therefore, there is nothing enigmatical. Some of his other sayings are more nearly so.

---

[17]That this is the ideal of wisdom among the Orientals, we see from Gen. iii. 5. Job. xxviii. Prov. iii. 8. 20. viii. 22-31.

Two Wishes with Respect to Human Life.

But two things only have I asked of thee,
Deny me not, so long as I shall live.
Put far from me idolatry and lying,
Allot me neither poverty nor riches,
But give me food in just allowance,
Lest I, too full, become a liar,
And say, who is Jehovah?
Or lest, too poor, I steal,
And take the name of God in vain.

How beautifully are the two objects here related to each other in life! how true and convincing the mode of presenting them!

The Evil Race.

There is a race, who curse their father,
And bring no blessings on their mother,
A race, in their own eyes forever pure,
But yet not washed from their own filth.
A race, whose eyes are carried loftily,
And eyelids lifted up with pride.
A race, whose teeth like daggers
And forward teeth, like knives
Devour the poor from off the land,
The needy from among mankind.

The last two lines contain the solution of the riddle, whether spoken by the poet, or added by another.

The Insatiable, a Riddle

Two daughters hath the Halukah,
That cry "bring hither, bring hither."
Three things are never satisfied,
And four say not "it is enough."
The realm of death,
The womb, that never bears,
The earth, insaturate with water,
And fire, that never saith, "enough."

The Halukah is the Parcae of Oriental fable, probably the mother of the realm of death, and the abyss, which according to Prov. xxvii.

20. are never satiated.[18] It is here placed as an introduction, and by way of comparison with the four things, which like it are never satisfied. In the passage above referred to, the eyes of men are also included.

> Hell and the abyss are never full,
> The eyes of men are never satisfied.

Four Hidden Things.

> Three things are too mysterious for me,
> And four I cannot comprehend.
> 　The way of an eagle in the clouds,
> The way of a serpent on the rocks,
> The way of a ship amid the waves,
> The way of a man with a maiden.

The three first are very probably used only to introduce the last. It is the manner of the Oriental enigma, thus to prepare the way for a sentiment. But since the fourth has an ambiguity in the translation, which does not belong to the Hebrew, I will add here a kindred passage,[19] which will remove the ambiguity.

> As thou knowest not the way of the wind,
> Nor how the bones are formed within the womb,
> Even so thou knowest not the works of God,
> Which he performeth.

The manner, in which man is formed in the womb, was to the Orientals the most unsearchable mystery, the most insolvable enigma, and is it not so among natural philosophers to the present hour? To this, then, the proposition was directed with its far-sought comparisons. It was probably another hand, which added to these four unsearchable things still a fifth.

> Such also is the way of an adulteress,
> She eateth, and then wipeth her mouth,
> And saith, "I've done no wrong."

We see here the humourous conceit of arranging together things

---

[18]In several poetical passages they are placed together as personified beings, as Prov. xv, 11. Job xxvi. 6. xxviii. 22.

[19]Eccles. xi. 5.

very different, which yet come under some one general conception.
The more diverse they are, according to the taste of the Orientals, the
more acuteness do they show, and are, therefore, so much the better.
Especially were they fond of tracing analogies between the kingdom
of nature and human customs.

Things Oppressive and Intolerable.

Three things are ever to the earth oppressive,
And four are found intolerable to it.
    The slave, when he becomes a king,
The fool, when filled with meat,
An odious woman, when she's married.
The maid, who is her mistress's heir.

Four Small, but Very Active Things.

Four things are little on the earth,
But wiser than the wisest.
    The ant race are a people without strength,
Yet they prepare their meat in summer,
The conies are a feeble race,
Yet built their houses in the rocks,
The locusts have no king to rule them,
Yet all of them go forth by bands,
The lizard; one may seize it with his hand,
And yet it dwells in royal palaces.

The whole comparison was perhaps made on account of the last,
when an animal of that sort, (which in warm climates live in the
walls, and are very annoying,) made its appearance; for the Orientals
are fond of such conceits, and involved propositions, especially in
company; as they often indeed assembled for the purpose of enjoying
them.

Things Stately in Their Motion.

Three things are stately in their going,
Yea, four, move with comeliness,
    A lion, the heroic king of brutes,
That turns not before his enemy,

> A cock, that proudly treads his dunghill,[20]
> A ram, that moves before his flock,
> A king, when marching with his people.

But enough on the subject of these conceits. We see what is their aim; to seize upon the resemblances of things, and unite them under a moral or artificial point of view. All nations in the early stages of their cultivation are fond of enigmatical conceits, as children are also upon the same grounds. Their wit and acuteness of discrimination, their powers of observation and invention, are exerted in this way respecting particular objects, with the greatest facility, and the praise, which the inventor as well as the interpreter of a good riddle receives for it in his own circle, is to them as it were the prize of battle, the harmless crown of victory. I could wish, that we possessed from the corresponding period, the sensuous age, of more nations instead of descriptions of their spirit, the actual proofs and examples of their childlike wit, of their acuteness exercising itself in proverbs, verbal conceits, and riddles; for with these we should have the peculiar current of their minds, the indications of their peculiar spirit. For every ancient people, with whose records I am acquainted, exhibit, in the discovery of such resemblances among their favourite objects and ideas, their own entirely peculiar method. We have such however from but few nations, because these are the very things, which belong to the inner sanctuary of each language, and are often as difficult to be understood, as incapable of being conveyed in another language.

We come now from riddles to puns. Of these the jovial Samson seems to have been peculiarly fond, and makes three or more of them on a single occasion.[21]

> With jaw-bone of an ass a mighty heap,[22]
> With jaw-bone of an ass I slew a thousand men.

How idle and fruitless the task for us to analyze and vindicate every point of such a punning conceit in the mouth of a lighthearted hero intoxicated with victory! The word thousand too involves a double meaning, since the word signifies also a troop. Who then would take pains to number the slain, and determine, whether the punning hero had not made them more than they were?

---

[20]The second and third I have supplied from the ancient versions, for in the Hebrew text the subject of the second and predicate of the third are wanting.
[21]Jud. xv. 16.
[22]Ass and heap are the same word in the original.

When in his melancholy blindness he was about to die with his enemies, he embraced the pillars of the house and said,[23]

> Jehovah God, look down yet once upon me.
> I pray thee strengthen me this once again,
> I pray thee, that I yet may be avenged
> With one revenge for my two eyes.

The bitterest emotion here gave him, what on other occasions was the offspring of sport and irony, a verbal conceit. (vol. II, pp. 200-210)

[23]Jud. xvi. 28.

POETRY AND TRUTH
(excerpts)

JOHANN WOLFGANG VON GOETHE

The first three parts of Poetry and Truth, *from which the passages below are taken, were published in 1811, 1812, and 1814. They represent an elderly man's view of his youth, for in 1811 Goethe was over sixty years old. The first three long passages here relate to the period of Goethe's early study of the Bible, in the years 1762-1768. They show how the stories appealed to the boy's imagination, but also include the mature man's reflection on the subject of his earlier enthusiasms, and show Goethe, like Herder, reacting against the "scoffing, and perversive attacks upon the Scriptures, though still eager to put the Bible in a natural light." The fourth passage relates to a period some years later.*

LET A MAN turn whither he will, and take in hand whatsoever he please,

From Johann Wolfgang von Goethe, *Poetry and Truth,* revised translation by Minna-Steele Smith, London, G. Bell and Sons, 1911.

he will always return to the path marked out for him by nature. So it fared with me, too, in the present case. My endeavours with regard to the language, to the contents of the Sacred Scriptures even, finally resulted in producing in my imagination a more vivid picture of that beautiful and highly praised land, its surroundings and neighbouring countries, as well as of the people and events which shed a glory over that little spot of earth for thousands of years. (vol. I, pp. 110-111)

The Patriarchs: Abraham

Now the prophecies of an unending posterity are renewed, nay, they assume a wider and wider scope. From the waters of the Euphrates to the River of Egypt all the lands are promised him; but yet the prospect of immediate heirs is still doubtful. He is eighty years of age, and has no son. Sarai, less trustful of the heavenly powers than he, becomes impatient; she desires, after the oriental fashion, to have a descendant by her maid. But no sooner is Hagar given up to the master of the house, no sooner is there hope of a son, than dissension breaks out in the household. The wife treats her own dependant ill enough, and Hagar flees to seek a happier lot among other tribes. At a sign from on high she returns, and Ishmael is born.

Abraham is now ninety-nine years old, and still promises of a numerous posterity are repeated, so that in the end both husband and wife regard them as ridiculous. And yet at last Sarai conceives and brings forth a son, to whom the name of Isaac is given.

History, for the most part, rests upon the legitimate propagation of the human race. The most momentous historical events have to be traced back to the privacy of family life: and thus it is that the marriages of the patriarchs give rise to peculiar reflections. It is as if the Divinity, who deigned to guide the destiny of mankind, wished here to show us, as it were, types of the various forms of marital relationships. Abraham, so long united in childless marriage to a beautiful woman whom many coveted, finds himself, in his hundredth year, the husband of two women, the father of two sons; and at this moment his domestic peace is disturbed. Two women and two sons by different mothers cannot possibly agree. The party less favoured by law, usage, and opinion, must yield. Abraham must sacrifice his attachment to Hagar and Ishmael. Both are dismissed, and Hagar is now compelled, against her will, to traverse a road which she had previously taken in voluntary flight, it would at first seem to her own destruction and that of her child; but the angel of the Lord, who had before turned her back, rescues her once again, that Ishmael also may become a great people, and that the most improbable of all promises may be fulfilled even beyond its first scope.

Two parents in advanced years, and one son of their old age— here, at last, domestic peace and earthly happiness might be looked for. But not so. Heaven has still the heaviest trial in store for the patriarch. But of this we cannot speak without premising several reflections.

If a natural universal religion was to arise, and from it a special revealed religion was to be developed, the countries in which our imagination has hitherto lingered, the mode of life, the race of men, were best fitted for the purpose. At least, nowhere else in the whole world do we find a setting so favourable and auspicious. Even natural religion, if we ascribe to it a prior origin in the human mind, presupposes great refinement of feeling; for it is based upon the conviction of an universal providence, which controls the order of the world as a whole. A particular religion, revealed by Heaven to this or that people, carries with it the belief in a special providence which the Divine Being vouchsafes to certain favoured men, families, races, and peoples. It is difficult for man to evolve this faith out of his inner consciousness. It requires tradition, custom, a guarantee dating from ancient times.

Beautiful it is, therefore, to find Israelitish tradition representing the very first men who trusted in this special providence as heroes of faith, acknowledging their dependence on that Supreme Being, whose commands they follow with an obedience as blind as is the faith unquestioning with which they await the tardy fulfilment of His promises.

As a particular revealed religion is based upon the conception that one man can be more favoured by Heaven than another, in like manner it originates primarily in the differentiation of social conditions. The first men appeared closely allied; but their occupations soon divided them. The hunter was the freest of all; from him was developed the warrior and the ruler. Those who tilled the field bound themselves to the soil, erected dwellings and barns to preserve the fruits of their toil, and had cause to think well of themselves, in that their manner of life promised permanence and security. The herdsman's lot, on the other hand, knew no limitations of space or wealth. The increase of herds proceeded without end, and the space necessary to support them widened out on all sides. These three classes seem from the very first to have regarded each other with dislike and contempt; and as the herdsman was an abomination to the townsman, once more a separation took place from the latter. The hunters vanish from our sight among the hills, and re-appear only as conquerors.

The patriarchs belonged to the shepherd class. Their manner of life upon the ocean of desert and pasture-land gave breadth and freedom to their minds; the vault of heaven, under which they dwelt, with all its nightly stars, elevated their feelings; and they, more than the active, skilful huntsman, more than the secure, careful, domesticated husband-man, had need of the immovable faith that a God walked beside them, visited them, cared for them, guided and saved them. (vol. I, pp. 114-116)

Joseph

Perhaps someone may ask why I have chosen this opportunity to elaborately re-tell these well-known stories which have been repeated and explained so many times. Let the inquirer be satisfied with the answer that in no other way could I make clear how, in spite of my varied life and fragmentary studies, I yet succeeded in concentrating my mind and feelings on one point with tranquilizing effect; in no other way could I describe the peace that enveloped me, however tumultuous and incomprehensible the outer world. When my restless imagination, to which my fairytale bears witness, strayed from one field to another, when the medley of fable and history, mythology and religion, threatened to bewilder me, I loved to take refuge in those oriental regions, and be-come absorbed in the first Books of Moses, and there, amid the scat-tered shepherd-tribes, I dwelt in the greatest solitude and yet with my greatest friends.

These family scenes, before they become merged in a history of the Jewish nation, finally bring before us a figure of peculiar attractiveness for the hopes and fancies of the young: Joseph, the child of the most passionate wedded love. He seems to us tranquil and clear-sighted, and predicts for himself the advantages which are to elevate him above his family. Cast into misfortune by his brothers, he remains steadfast and upright in slavery, resists the most dangerous temptations, rescues him-self by prophecy, and is elevated according to his deserts to high honours. He shows himself serviceable and useful, first to a great king-dom, then to his own kindred. He is like his ancestor Abraham in dignity and magnanimity, like his grandfather Isaac in quietness and resignation. He exercises on a large scale the talent for traffic inherited from his father. It is no longer flocks which are gained for a father-in-law, or for himself, but nations, with all their possessions, which he knows how to purchase for a king. Very charming is this story in its naturalness, only it appears too short, and one feels impelled to elaborate it in detail.

Such an amplified account of characters and events of which the Biblical narrative furnished the outline was already familiar to the Germans. The personages of both the Old and New Testaments had lived again in Klopstock's vivid and sympathetic portraiture, very attractive to the boy as well as to many of his contemporaries. Of Bodmer's efforts in this line he knew little or nothing; but *Daniel in the Lions' Den,* by Moser, made a great impression on his youthful mind. In that work an upright courtier and man of business, after passing through manifold tribulations, arrives at high honours, and the piety which threatens to be his undoing proves early and late his shield and buckler. I had long cherished a wish to work out the history of Joseph, but I could not come to any satisfactory conclusion with regard to the form, particularly as I was not conversant with any kind of versification adapted to such a work. But I now thought a treatment of it in prose very suitable, and devoted all my energies to its execution.[1] I endeavoured to differentiate and elaborate the characters, and by the interpolation of incidents and episodes, to make the old simple history a new and independent work. I did not consider, what, indeed, youth cannot consider, the necessity for some underlying meaning, and that this could only be obtained by the teaching of experience. Suffice it to say, that I pictured all the incidents down to the minutest details, and narrated them carefully to myself in order. (vol. I, pp. 120-122)

"Natural Religion" and the Bible

Now, though matters of taste stood on a very uncertain footing, there could be no denying that within the Protestant part of Germany and of Switzerland, what is generally called common-sense showed signs of vigorous life at the epoch. The scholastic philosophy—which at any rate has the merit of treating everything of interest to men accord-

---

[1] *This work was never published. See Thomas Mann's reference to it, pp. 232-233.*

ing to accepted principles, on accredited lines, under definite headings
—had, by the frequent obscurity and apparent unprofitableness of its
teaching, by its unseasonable application of a method in itself esti-
mable, and by its too great comprehensiveness, become alien, dis-
pleasing, and, finally, superfluous to the majority. Many a man became
convinced that nature had endowed him with the modicum of good
plain sense requisite for forming a clear conception of things, such as
would enable him to cope with them and conduct himself in relation
to them to his own advantage and that of others, without necessarily
troubling himself about ultimate principles, and without inquiring
into the connection of the most remote things, which do not particularly
concern us. Men made the experiment, opened their eyes, looked
straight before them, were observant, industrious, active, and believed
that if they reasoned and acted rightly in their own sphere, they might
venture to have an opinion on other matters, less close at hand.

In accordance with this theory, everyone was now entitled, not only
to philosophize, but also in course of time to consider himself a
philosopher. Philosophy was, therefore, a more or less sane and practical common-sense, which ventured to discuss general principles and
dogmatize about inner and external experiences. The clear-sighted
discrimination and decided moderation of writings and oral pronounce-
ments of this sort—for the *via media* and fairness towards all opinions
was deemed the only right course—inspired esteem and confidence;
and thus eventually philosophers were to be found in all the professions,
nay more, in all classes and trades.

In this way the theologians inevitably tended towards what is called
natural religion, and when the question was discussed how far the light
of nature may suffice to advance us in the knowledge of God and the
improvement and ennobling of man, they usually ventured to decide
in its favour without much hesitation. From the same principle of
moderation, they assigned equal rights to all positive religions, with
the result that they all became equally unimportant and uncertain. For
the rest, everything was allowed to stand, and since the Bible is so
full of meaning, that it surpasses every other book, in offering material
for reflection and opportunity for meditation on human affairs, it
could still, as before, be made the foundation of all sermons and other
religious treatises.

But a singular fate, which, in course of time, was not to be averted,
was awaiting this book as well as the whole body of profane literature.
Hitherto it had been accepted as a matter of implicit faith, that this

book of books was composed in one spirit; nay, more, that it was inspired, and, as it were, dictated by the Divine Spirit. But for a long time the discrepancies of the different parts had been now criticized, now defended, by believers and unbelievers. Englishmen, Frenchmen, and Germans had attacked the Bible with more or less violence, acumen, audacity, and maliciousness; and again and again it had been taken under the protection of earnest, high-minded men of each nation. As for myself, I loved and valued it; for to it almost alone did I owe my moral education, and the events, the doctrines, the symbols, the similes, had all impressed themselves deeply upon me, and had influenced me in one way or another. These unjust, scoffing, and perversive attacks, therefore, displeased me; but people were already sufficiently advanced to be glad to assume, partly as a cogent ground of defence for many passages, that God had accommodated himself to human modes of thought and powers of comprehension; that even those moved by the Spirit had not on that account been able to renounce their individuality; and that Amos, a cowherd, does not use the language of Isaiah, who is said to have been a prince.

From such views and convictions, aided by the constantly increasing knowledge of languages, there naturally developed that branch of study which attempted to investigate more accurately oriental localities, nationalities, natural products, and phenomena, and so make it possible to picture that ancient time. Michaelis applied the whole strength of his talents and his knowledge to this subject. Descriptions of travels contributed greatly to the interpretation of the Holy Scriptures, and later travellers were supplied with numerous questions, so that, by the answers to them, they might bear witness for the prophets and apostles.

In this way an effort was being made on all hands to bring the Holy Scriptures into a natural light, and to render modes of thought and representation peculiar to them more generally intelligible, so that by this historico-critical aspect many objections might be removed, much that was offensive effaced, and all shallow scoffing be made ineffective. At the same time a tendency in the opposite direction was apparent: there were men who chose the darkest, most mysterious writings as the subject of their meditations, and wished, not to elucidate them, but to corroberate them by internal evidence, by conjectures, calculations, and other ingenious and strange combinations, and so far as they contained prophecies, to confirm them by the events, and thus to justify a faith in what was to be expected in the near future.

. . . Hence arose controversies, hatred, persecution, and much that was unpleasant. I adhered to the partisans of enlightenment, and sought to appropriate to myself their principles and advantages, although I ventured to forebode, that by this extremely praisworthy, intelligent method of interpretation, the poetic value of the writings would eventually be lost, together with their prophetic significance. (vol. I, pp. 242-246)

Goethe's Attitude to the Bible in Maturity

But though now, partly from inclination, partly for literary and other purposes, I eagerly studied the antiquities of my country, and tried to render them present to my imagination, I was from time to time distracted from this subject by biblical studies and religious sympathies, since Luther's life and deeds, which shine out so gloriously in the sixteenth century, always brought me back to the Holy Scriptures, and to the consideration of religious feelings and opinions. To look upon the Bible as a compilation, dating from various periods, and having undergone revision at different times, was flattering to my smallminded vanity, since this view was then by no means predominant, much less received in the circle in which I lived. With regard to the main interpretation, I adhered to Luther's rendering; in matters of detail, I referred to Schmidt's literal translation, and made the best use I could of my smattering of Hebrew. That there are contradictions in the Bible, no one will now deny. These interpreters sought to reconcile by laying down the clearest passage as a foundation, and endeavouring to conform to its meaning those that were contradictory and less clear. I, on the contrary, wished to find out, by examination, which passage best expressed the real sense. To this I adhered, and rejected the rest as interpolated.

For a fundamental opinion had already formed definitely in my mind, without my being able to say whether it had been suggested, or inspired, or had arisen from my own reflection. It was this,—that in anything which is handed down to us, especially in writing, the real point is the groundwork, the inner meaning, the sense, the tendency of the work; that here lies all that makes it original, divine, effective, unassailable and indestructible; and that neither time, nor outward influences or vicissitudes, can in any degree affect this inner primitive nature, at least no more than sickness of the body affects a healthy soul. Thus, according to my view, the language, the dialect, the characteristics, the style, and finally the writing, were to be regarded as the mere body of every creation of the mind; this body, although nearly akin to the inner spirit, was yet exposed to deterioration and corruption; as, indeed, no tradition can be handed down in its original purity; nor, indeed, if so delivered, could it be perfectly intelligible in every succeeding epoch,—the former on account of the imperfection of those organs through which the tradition is delivered,—the latter on account of the differences of time and place, but especially the diversity of human capacities and modes of thought; for which reason the interpreters will never be able to agree.

Hence it is everyone's duty to try to discover the inner, essential nature of a book which particularly interests us, and at the same time, above all things, to consider in what relation it stands to our own inner nature, and how far, by its vitality, our own is stirred and rendered fruitful. On the other hand, everything external that exercises no influence on us, or is subject to doubt, is to be handed over to criticism, which, even if able to disintegrate and dismember the whole, would never succeed in depriving us of the essential foundation to which we cling, nor even in shaking us for a moment in the confidence we have once felt.

This conviction, born of faith and sight, which is applicable and strengthening in all those cases which we recognize as most vital, underlay the moral as well as the literary structure of my life, and may be regarded as a well-invested and richly productive capital, although in particular instances we may be led astray into making erroneous applications. It was by such an attitude of mind that the Bible first became really accessible to me. As is usually the case in a Protestant up-bringing, I had run through it many times, and by reading separate portions here and there I was perfectly familiar with it from beginning to end. The blunt realism of the Old Testament, and the tender simplicity of the New, had attracted me in many parts; it is true it never presented itself to me as a whole; but now the diversity of character of the different books no longer perplexed me; I knew how to grasp their significance correctly and in due order, and had expended too much feeling upon the book to be ever able to do without it. This emotional aspect was of itself sufficient to protect me against scoffing spirits, because I saw their dishonesty at once. I not only detested them, but they even prompted me to rage; and I still perfectly remember that in my childish fanatical zeal I could have throttled Voltaire, for his *Saul,* if I could only have got at him. On the other hand, every kind of honest investigation pleased me; I was delighted to gather any information as to the localities and costumes of the East, and so to gain more light on these subjects, and I continued to exercise all my powers of discrimination in the study of such valuable traditions. (vol. II, pp. 56-58)

NOVEMBER BOUGHS

(excerpt)

WALT WHITMAN

I SUPPOSE ONE cannot at this day say anything new, from a literary point of view, about those autochthonic bequests of Asia—the Hebrew Bible, the mighty Hindu epics, and a hundred lesser but typical works; (not now definitely including the Iliad—though that work was certainly of Asiatic genesis, as Homer himself was—considerations which seem curiously ignored.) But will there ever be a time or place—ever a student, however modern, of the grand art, to whom those compositions will not afford profounder lessons than all else of their kind in the garnerage of the past? Could there be any more opportune suggestion, to the current popular writer and reader of verse, what the office of poet was in primeval times—and is yet capable of being, anew, adjusted entirely to the modern?

All the poems of Orientalism, with the Old and New Testaments at the centre, tend to deep and wide, (I don't know but the deepest and widest,) psychological development—with little, or nothing at all, of the mere aesthetic, the principal verse-requirement of our day. Very late, but unerringly, comes to every capable student the perception that it is not in beauty, it is not in art, it is not even in science, that the profoundest laws of the case have their eternal sway and outcropping.

In his discourse on "Hebrew Poets" De Sola Mendes said: "The fundamental feature of Judaism, of the Hebrew nationality, was religion; its poetry was naturally religious. Its subjects, God and Providence, the covenants with Israel, God in Nature, and as reveal'd, God the Creator and Governor, Nature in her majesty and beauty, inspired hymns and odes to Nature's God. And then the checker'd history of the nation furnish'd allusions, illustrations, and subjects for epic display—the glory of the sanctuary, the offerings, the splendid ritual, the Holy City, and lov'd Palestine with its pleasant valleys and wild tracts." Dr. Mendes said "that rhyming was not a characteristic of Hebrew poetry at all. Metre was not a necessary mark of poetry. Great poets discarded it; the early Jewish poets knew it not."

Compared with the famed epics of Greece, and lesser ones since, the spinal supports of the Bible are simple and meagre. All its history, biography, narratives, etc., are as beads, strung on and indicating the eternal thread of the Deific purpose and power. Yet with only deepest faith for impetus, and such Deific purpose for palpable or impalpable theme, it often transcends the masterpieces of Hellas, and all masterpieces. The metaphors daring beyond account, the lawless soul, extravagant by our standards, the glow of love and friendship, the fervent kiss—nothing in argument or logic, but unsurpass'd in proverbs, in religious ecstacy, in suggestions of common mortality and death, man's great equalizers—the spirit everything, the ceremonies and forms of the churches nothing, faith limitless, its immense sensuousness immensely spiritual—an incredible, all-inclusive non-worldliness and dew-scented illiteracy (the antipodes of our Nineteenth Century business absorption and morbid refinement). . . .

I remember how enthusiastically William H. Seward, in his last days, once expatiated on these themes, from his travels in Turkey, Egypt, and Asia Minor, finding the oldest Biblical narratives exactly illustrated there to-day with apparently no break or change along three thousand years—the veil'd women, the costumes, the gravity and simplicity, all the manners just the same. The veteran Trelawney said he found the only real *nobleman* of the world in a good average specimen of the mid-aged or elderly Oriental. In the East the grand figure, always leading, is the *old man,* majestic, with flowing beard, paternal, etc. In Europe and America, it is, as we know, the young fellow. . . .

Strange, but true, that the principal factor in cohering the nations, eras and paradoxes of the globe, by giving them a common platform of two or three great ideas, a commonalty of origin, and projecting cosmic brotherhood, the dream of all hope, all time—that the long trains, gestations, attempts and failures, resulting in the New World, and in modern solidarity and politics—are to be identified and resolv'd back into a collection of old poetic lore, which, more than any one thing else, has been the axis of civilization and history through thousands of years—and except for which this America of ours, with its polity and essentials, could not now be existing.

No true bard will ever contravene the Bible. If the time ever comes when iconoclasm does its extremest in one direction against the Books of the Bible in its present form, the collection must still survive in another, and dominate just as much as hitherto, or more than hitherto, through its divine and primal poetic structure. To me, that is the living and definite element-principle of the work, evolving everything else. Then the continuity; the oldest and newest Asiatic utterance and character, and all between, holding together, like the apparition of the sky, and coming to us the same. Even to our Nineteenth Century here are the fountain heads of song. (pp. 396-398)

BOOKS THAT HAVE INFLUENCED ME

FRANCIS THOMPSON

YOUNG MR. OSBALDISTONE, you remember (if you are a reader of Scott's *Rob Roy*), grievously scandalised that devout rascal, Andrew Fair-

From *Literary Criticisms* by Francis Thompson, ed. Rev. Terence L. Connolly, S.J., Ph.D.; copyright 1948 by E. P. Dutton & Co., Inc. Reprinted by permission.

service, by talking about the poetry of the Psalms. Yet apart from the direct religious value of the Scriptures, they may also enter into the category of books which, by their literary greatness, profoundly modify a writer's mind, or style, or both. And by "literary greatness" I mean not simply beauty of external form, but the whole content and soul of the book, approached from the literary rather than the moral and dogmatic side. In the one case you read to be taught, in the other you are taught, often insensibly, through the book's appeal to the sensitive side of your nature. Unlike most English writers, the Bible as an influence (from this standpoint) has a late but important date in my life. As a child I read it, but for its historical interest. Nevertheless, even then I was greatly, though vaguely, impressed by the mysterious imagery, the cloudy grandeurs, of the *Apocalypse*. Deeply uncomprehended, it was, of course, the pageantry of an appalling dream: insurgent darkness, with wild lights flashing through it; terrible phantasms, insupportably revealed against profound light, and in a moment no more; on the earth hurryings to and fro, like insects of the hearth at a sudden candle; unknown voices uttering out of darkness, darkened and disastrous speech; and all this in motion and turmoil like the sands of a fretted pool. Such is the *Apocalypse* as it inscribes itself on the verges of my childish memories. In early youth it again drew me to itself, giving to my mind a permanent and shaping direction. In maturer years *Ecclesiastes* (casually opened during a week of solitude in the Fens) masterfully affected a temperament in key with its basic melancholy. But not till quite later years did the Bible as a whole become an influence. Then, however, it came with decisive power.

But not as it has influenced most writers. My style being already formed could receive no evident impress from it: its vocabulary had come to me through the great writers of our language. In the first place its influence was mystical. It revealed to me a whole scheme of existence, and lit up life like a lantern. Next to this, naturally, I was attracted by the poetry of the Bible, especially the prophetic books.

But beyond even its poetry, I was impressed by it as a treasury of *gnomic* wisdom. I mean its richness in utterances of which one could, as it were, chew the cud. This, of course, has long been recognised, and Biblical sentences have passed into the proverbial wisdom of our country. But the very finest, as too deep for popular perception, have remained unappropriated. Such is that beautiful saying in Proverbs :"As in water face answereth to face, so the heart of man to man." It is own sister to the lovely image in Rossetti's "Rose Mary."

The mirrored souls shook each to each
As the cloud-moon and the water-moon
Shake each to each.

Again, that profound aphorism, also in Proverbs, "Wisdom is before him that hath understanding; but the eyes of a fool are in the ends of the earth." I associate it with Blake's pregnant utterance: "The fool sees not the same tree that a wise man sees." But the Biblical saying is deeper. The *Book of Wisdom,* which Protestants reject, is full of beauty and profundity of this kind. None of the Eastern and other heathen "sacred volumes" sometimes brought into comparison with it have anything like the same grave dignity of form or richness of significance in their maxims. Upon this single quality, I think, I finally would elect to take my stand in regard to the Bible; and by this it has firmest hold of me. And whoever opens it, learned or simple, equally finds something of this kind appropriate to his understanding; it is—and that is perhaps the final word about it—the most elastic of all books. (pp. 542-544)

THE AUTHORIZED VERSION OF THE BIBLE

GEORGE SAINTSBURY

THERE IS NO REASON to believe that John Selden was not a good man; he certainly was an uncommonly clever one, and he came not far off being great. But one of the things, probably, which most hindered him from greatness was his possession of what has been called a 'cross-bench mind.' Thus, when he had said that 'the English translation of the Bible is the best translation in the world, and best renders the sense of the original,' he must needs say, a few lines lower, that the Bible is 'translated into English words rather than into English phrase.' To the first round declaration there is nothing to say but 'Hear, hear!' As to the second, one has to retort that a great deal of distinction is necessary. No doubt the translators followed upon but bettered the examples of Wyclif and Tyndale and Coverdale, of the 'Great' and the 'Bishops' ' versions, nay of Geneva and of Rheims, for there was plenty of humour in the time of Shakespeare, and it is not impossible that the grave divines winked as they borrowed jewels of silver and jewels of gold from Egyptian and Amalekite at once. No doubt they enriched 'English phrase' enormously. But at what point would the excellent author of *Mare Clausum* have fixed his original and exclusive 'English Phrase'? Ought the translators to have stuck to Anglo-Saxon (which has some capital Biblical versions) and called an astrologer a 'star-witty' man? Should they have passed to the part-French, part-Latin phraseology of the *Ancren Riwle?* was Wyclif himself to be the standard? Or the curious scholastic English of Reginald Peacock? Or the Latinized and rhetoricized clauses of Bishop Fisher?

The fact is that part of the reason of the extraordinary success of the Authorized Version, and of its unparalleled literary influence is the way in which the translators have (unconsciously no doubt) followed the secular course of the language and the literature as wholes, in sucking into themselves, building themselves up out of, the most diverse materials. They added a good deal, an immense deal to English phrase, but they did so on the general lines on which English phrase itself had grown up, and with the special advantage of having a catena of interpretations of their actual texts before them.

Hebrew and Septuagint and Vulgate all gave them turns of word and thought. The Wyclif versions had of course never been printed, and though there are resemblances they probably come oftenest either directly from the Vulgate or from the Rheims-Douai version. But Tyndale's New Testament had been printed nearly a century before the appearance of the Authorized Version, and though our authors are supposed to have taken the 'Bishops' ' for actual basis, it is pretty certain that all the intervening attempts were known to more or fewer of King James's men. The astounding skill with which they took the best from everything, and added better of their own, can only be appreciated by actual comparison of the different texts. But it may perhaps need some additional acquaintances with literature from the historical side to see the hold which the result obtained upon the national and literary mind. It is said (though I should think the statement rather difficult to prove satisfactorily) that the various editions of the Geneva version were not readily ousted from at least popular reading by the Authorized, and the learned English writers of the early seventeenth century to a great extent kept up the habit of quoting the Bible in Latin. But what Selden as well as others saw from the literary side other people must soon have seen from the other sides, and it must be remembered that the 'reading' of the Bible 'in churches' meant a very great deal. Neglect of divine service was a positively dangerous thing for some time, and attendance at it continued to be a matter almost as much of fashion as of duty for generations. Long after this ceased, and before it was revived, in at least some classes, by the Oxford Movement in England, every grammar- and public-school boy and every undergraduate in that country constantly heard it if he did not mark and inwardly digest it, while almost the whole population in Scotland and a very large proportion (adding the majority of the Nonconformists) in England read very little else. The phraseology and style of the Bible in the Version, which by no very slow degrees superseded all the others, supplied as it were a *publica materies,* a universally known common stock and ground of literary expression to which there is, if any parallel at all in literature, only that supplied by Homer in the flourishing times of Greek. An early, an odd, but a convincing proof of this universal diffusion may be found in Izaak Walton's grave disapproval of the merry companion whose jests were all either Scripture jests or something worse. Matter of popular jest must be matter of popular knowledge.

It is, however, probably of a rather higher class and range of influence than this that we should speak here, though it must be remembered that nothing is a handier weapon in the literary man's hand, nothing a more convenient and inexhaustible store of material for him, than what is common knowledge. The extraordinary merit of the Authorized Version as literature, and the variety of accomplishment displayed in it, could not escape such an age as that which followed its appearance. The Stuart period, from the first James to Anne, was one long Donnybrook Fair in political, ecclesiastical, and other matters, and the height of the diversion has been kept up fairly ever since in controversy about its doings. But one thing can be said safely, that never has the country seen a hundred years in which production of literature and interest in literature were more widely diffused among the upper and better educated classes. And such literature as the English Authorized Version could not fail to catch the ear of such a time.

Only those who, as was said above, have combined some study of its immediate antecedents with a wider one of the history of English prose literature can appreciate, though all who have any ear must feel, the extraordinary felicity of its phrase and movement. The indebtedness to previous translators in the matter of particular 'word-and-clause' renderings has been freely acknowledged, but it may be asserted with equal positiveness that in the architectonic of paragraph, passage and general context the borrowers leave their creditors far behind. The preference sometimes expressed, as far as the Psalms are concerned, for the version of the Book of Common Prayer, is a fallacy partly of familiarity, partly of failure to distinguish. This version is better to 'sing or say'; it is not better to read. It has been customary to attribute the discovery of the indefinable but at once recognizable 'Biblical cadence' to Tyndale; and it may be fairly granted that he was actually the first to "glimpse the panther,' which is the less surprising in that he was actually the first man of literary talent to apply a tolerably accomplished stage of English to the particular text and task. But neither in him (indeed he does not seem to have had time to attempt the greatest books) nor in any follower or set of followers, will be found anything like the astounding finish, fulness, and variety of the Authorized Version in dealing with matter like the Days of Creation, and the Exit of Israel, with Job and Ecclesiastes and the great passages at the beginning and end of Isaiah, with the visions of Ezekiel and the preaching of Amos, with the narrative quality of the Gospels and the Acts, with the more purple passages of the Epistles, and with the hues of sunset and eclipse that colour the Book of Revelation.

Nor, great as is purely Elizabethan prose, will anything similar or second be found in it. Hooker is, indeed, very nearly perfect in his own way of rhythm and of clause-and-sentence architecture, but it is a way rather strictly limited in its direction, and capable of seeming a little monotonous if you walk too long in it at one time. There are passages in Donne and Greville and Raleigh of higher excellence still, but it is by no means certain that most of these were not written later than the Authorized Version. And though the beauty of earlier English prose has been too little recognized, though as far back as Aelfric (not in his over-alliterated attempts), you may find prose which is real prose and yet cunningly rhythmed, it would on the whole be idle to expect, before the actual period of the Version, such accomplishment as this. It was almost impossible that it should come before; it was quite impossible that it should fail to diffuse its strong contagion on good wits when it came.

And it did not fail. That Milton should be full of Biblical phrase may seem not to go for much, because his subjects, after his early poems, are almost entirely Biblical or connected with ecclesiastical controversy. Jeremy Taylor is a divine, and quotes and paraphrases the Version. Bunyan, though it is very doubtful whether his study was so exclusively Biblical as has been thought, is equally a specialist. But a moment's thought will show that these assignments of cause are quite beside the question. Here you have, as a matter of fact, the greatest poet, the greatest orator, and the most popular writer for the lower classes soaked in this book, adapting their phrase to it, and it to their phrase, undergoing, continuing, transmitting its influence as second hand, while it maintains itself (in the ways above mentioned) at first.

The same partial but not real disability may seem to attach to Fuller and some others, so nothing need be said of them; and Walton has been glanced at. But take Sir Thomas Browne, whom some think the very greatest of all English prose writers, and whom few of any competence put far below the greatest. He again is soaked in the Bible, is constantly quoting it, now exactly and literally, now by floating and half-dissolving its phrasing into his own style after a fashion which some pundits have reprobated but which most great writers have practised with regard to authorities both sacred and profane. This is most obvious in the *Religio* of course, and side notes call the reader's attention to it in well-furnished editions; but it is hardly less noticeable elsewhere.

Yet the influence becomes hardly less extensive, more really remarkable, and in a sense more effectual still, when we leave the actual age of the Version itself and of the men who were alive (even though only children) when it was published. Their successors developed a strikingly different general temperament, occupied themselves with very different subjects, and consciously laboured at the creation of a style as different as possible from the figurative and highly coloured phraseology transmitted from Hebrew and Greek, from Latin and English itself. Yet we find such a man as Dryden (whether owing to his Puritan education or not does not matter; we are looking at the fact, not the cause), a layman, a practiser of definitely profane styles, and, if all tales are true, during part of his life no very orthodox person, as much soaked in the Bible as Browne and almost more so. Put *Absalom and Achitophel* out of the question (though this is an exceedingly generous and indeed rather quixotic concession) and you will find from *Astraea Redux* to the Fables, in poem and play and preface alike, Scriptural reference, Scriptural phrases, Scriptural rhythm leavening and permeating the whole range of composition. The practice of his (in some ways) pupil Addison is less glaring but even more decisive. His piety and his fastidious niceness combined make him chary of sowing Scriptural phrase broadcast; but it is constantly, as it were, at his ear and not far from his tongue. His best verse almost consists of Scriptural paraphrase or mosaic. His most exalted prose attempts are inspired and heightened by it.

When we come to the eighteenth century proper (of which, let it be remembered, Addison saw not a fifth part), the influence instead of failing, rather grows: it would seem as if, the more the general prose style tended towards drab in colour and pedestrian monotony in sound, the more the sumptuous palette and the endless resource in word-fugue and symphony, which the Authorized Version presents, suggested themselves as a refuge and relief. Smart's *Song to David* may be said to be in more senses than one a result of Furor Poeticus; but nobody now doubts that if the poet was mad the poem is a great one, and its whole stuff and substance, in expression as well as subject, come from the Book of 1611. It would be superfluous to speak of men like Cowper, but how great is the influence they show and how much greater that which they pass on! Johnson no doubt avoided Biblical phrase, but this was a matter partly of religious scruple, partly of specially literary critical view. A few Freethinkers may have disdained it. But, sometimes in the most unexpected places, it keeps presenting itself, now as a fortifier of style, now as a curiously contrasted set-off to it: but always the same; always at once gracious and magnificent; always recalling, maintaining, supplying, the best qualities and possibilities of English prose.

It would have been strange indeed if, when the partially (not wholly) dry tree of the eighteenth century sprang and burst once more into leaf and flower and fruit, a little before the beginning of the nineteenth, this supremely and constantly fertilizing influence has failed to exercise its power. Not even in the seventeenth century has the influence of the English Bible been more powerful in literature (whatever it may have been in life) than in that other, now dead, century which saw Newman's magnificent and pathetic panegyric of regret. At the beginning you will find it hardly less strong on such a man as Byron than on such a man as Southey, though the two were separated by gulfs of personal enmity, differences of political and other thought, views of morality, habit of life, everything almost that can make for difference between man and man. It is a great question whether Shelley's deliberate ætiology keeps it out: the fact is rather that Shelley's peculiar power of transforming every influence that he felt applies here also. Wordsworth and Coleridge require merely the mention of their names, as does Scott.

Turning for a moment from poetry to prose, the greatest prose writer of the second quarter of the century and the greatest of the third, Carlyle and Ruskin, once more exhibit the soaking—indeed, with Carlisle, 'Houndsditch' or no 'Houndsditch,' you could not eliminate the Biblical element without destroying the substance of style and thought alike. In fact, until quite recently, selection is equally impossible and unnecessary. The whole list, or almost the whole, of the greater men of letters passes the test, while there is no more remarkable instance in the whole three centuries than that of Mr. Swinburne, who made perhaps the most direct, abundant, and felicitous use of the phrase of our Version that English Literature has seen, and also derived from it the style—that is to say, the body—of many of his finest passages.

To prove all this by chapter and verse would merely require a brazen-bowelled scholar of tolerable wits, with a life-time before him, a proper supply of books, pens, and paper and ink in the first place, and money to finish a few dozen folio volumes of quotation when excerpted and arranged. But the fact would not be more certain after the collection of this evidence than it is now. Here are the best words of the best period of English in the best order. It would have been singular if the best writers had not taken advantage of them, and they have. Some say (unfortunately not without an appearance of truth) that the pitcher does not go to this well of English undefiled as it used to do; others, no doubt with the best intentions, try to puddle the well itself with incongruous admixture of modern and cacophonous phrase. The result in either case must be to some extent disastrous; but fortunately the well itself is indestructible, and always open. Every reader and writer of English can, and every wise reader and writer of English always will, come to its waters and drink. (pp. 124-131)

THE BIBLE AS LITERATURE—THE OLD TESTAMENT

JOHN COWPER POWYS

THE APPEARANCE of *The Bible Designed to Be Read As Living Literature,* with Ernest Sutherland Bates as the editor, has been a final proof—considering the huge response this edition has found on both sides of the Atlantic—of the truth of Matthew Arnold's words about the eternal value to humanity of what he called *Hebraism.*

The great critic's declaration that the two fountain-heads of all that is most precious in our Western civilization are the genius of the Hebrews and the genius of the Greeks, was one of those simple sayings that dive to the very bottom of the tossing and wavering ocean of ethnological values.

But it was Matthew Arnold who went on to add the more questionable remark that since three-fourths of human life are conduct, and since the Hebrew Scriptures deal preeminently with conduct, their influence, at any rate on the English-speaking portion of our Western civilization, is three times as important as the influence of the Greeks.

This latter remark of Matthew Arnold's is of course calculated to arouse the most angry controversy; it being exactly the sort of airy generalization that stings our Western temperament as if with the flick of a whip, but the very turmoil it excites in us all—some of us stirred to one reaction, some of us to another—is proof that our British Socrates, whether we agree with him or not, touched the quick of one of the most jumpy of our human nerves.

It appears that few of the Reformed Dutch, or the Lutheran Germans either, went to the lengths of Bible-worship to which our English and American Puritans went; nor can it I think be disputed that of all the Western literatures it is our own that has been most deeply influenced by the Bible.

But not only in "conduct"! For although both our English and our American ancestors *were* affected in that practical sense—and their Bible-inspired "conduct" was by no means always charitable or desirable—an equally powerful influence was exerted over their emotions, over their imagination, over their most secret feelings.

Mr. Bates' *Bible as Literature* has certainly appeared at the right moment in our English-speaking countries; for I am old enough to have seen in the last half-century a tremendous change in the reading of the Hebrew Scriptures. I cannot tell whether the same change has passed over the habits of the less orthodox Hebrews themselves, but certainly when I was a child all my Gentile elders were saturated with Bible-reading; and their imagination as well as their conduct both for good and evil showed Biblical influence at every turn.

But now, after fifty years, it is not so any more. Neither in England nor in America do people read the Bible as they used to do. In fact, I would go further than that and say that apart from educational compulsion, the professional studies of ministers and school-teachers and the devotion of a few religious eccentrics and men of letters, it is unusual for a young modern person to read the Bible at all. Think of the working-men you know; do any of *them* read the Bible? Think of the doctors, lawyers, manufacturers, and gentlemen of leisure you know; do any of *them* read the Bible? When I was a child, from almshouse pensioners to admirals of the fleet, from bargemen and engine-drivers to great merchants of the City, all elderly people read the Bible.

When I was young it was only the most extreme of free-thinkers who dared to express disbelief in this book; whereas to-day some of the most sensitive and spiritual-minded among my friends actually detest it, and do so on moral, aesthetic, and psychological grounds, quite apart from questions of science and philosophy!

The African population of the United States still, I fancy, read the Bible; but the great Middle West, which is the part of the country I know best and the part of the country least affected by European influence, has completely given up the custom; and I confess, though I so obstinately indulge in the habit myself I would take a malicious pleasure in assuring Matthew Arnold that though the great American

Middle West no longer reads the Bible, no region in the world, in all the essential human charities, has a more *naturally Christian soul*.

But though the post-war generation may not read the Bible as its ancestors did, none of us can escape its influence. The thing has gone too deep. Humanity cannot saturate itself for centuries with a book like the Old Testament, and throw off the spell in a couple of generations. Writers of our race, on both sides of the water, especially the more prophetic ones, have always used the Scriptures to noble account; and now with this new tendency, encouraged by Mr. Bates' excellent version, to treat these books in a new, fresh, and secular manner, it seems likely enough that this underlying influence inherited from our fathers may take on a new and living meaning.

Undoubtedly such a revival of interest in the Bible cannot restore all the good that our ancestors got out of it. And let us hope it will not restore the evil! But we have to pay for our enjoyment of it in this new, fresh, secular spirit by the loss of something that, both for good and evil, can never return.

I am thinking of those who come back to it after a real lapse of the habit. There are, of course, many of my own generation who, like their fathers in the time of Matthew Arnold, have gone on reading the book, though with minds free of the old gloomy and illiberal temper, and such have lost nothing. But when there *has* been this break in the atmospheric continuity those who return to it are apt to find that just in proportion as they have got rid of the old, evil, Puritan sanctimoniousness and sinister gloom, so also they have lost and can never quite get back that mysterious continuity of emotional atmosphere which, like those "happy pieties" spoken of by Keats, carries with it such magical and indefinable power.

And it is to the Puritans that we owe, both in Great Britain and America, this powerful *Biblical tradition,* from which, as I have hinted, so many individual free spirits from the time of Wycliffe down to the time of William Blake have drawn human inspiration.

For though plenty of evangelical gospel-men, both within and without the Church, have "preached Christ and Him crucified," it has been on the strength of the less amiable, less peaceable, less mystical, but not less poetical Old Testament that so many men of the old breed on both sides of the Atlantic have sustained in perils of land and in perils of water, in the face of tyrants and in the teeth of penury and disaster, their indomitable endurance.

And it is from the stern spirits of these stout soldiers of fortune that a protest must always rise when our mystical interpreters would fain expurgate, prune, soften, and allegorize away, for the sake of "purer" conceptions, the human wisdom, the human sensuality, the human anger, the human justice, the human magnanimity, the human triumph, of this old shameless *literature of the Old Testament.*

What both the sacerdotal and the evangelical churches are apt to forget, in their apologies for the Christian hope, is the innumerable company—for if the magical Christ is the God of youth, Jehovah is the God of old age—of old shepherds, old herdsmen, old hedgers and ditchers, old stonemasons, old carpenters, old sailors, old soldiers, old miners, old pioneers, old fishermen, together with their old wives, who have managed to dispense with all such airy expectations, whether Christian or otherwise, in the stoical consciousness of an "Eternal, not themselves, who makes for righteousness," but whose ways, alas, are not their ways nor His thoughts their thoughts!

But whether forgotten or not by the livelier and more sociable children of the mystery, it is these isolated and taciturn "stoics of the Scriptures" who alone, save for a few old-fashioned Miltonic scholars, do real justice to the Old Testament. These are they who take life for that troubled and brief thing that the wisdom of the Lord declares it to be.

> Man that is born of a woman is of few days and full of trouble. He cometh forth like a flower, and is cut down; he fleeth also as a shadow, and continueth not. . . . For there is hope of a tree, if it be cut down that it will sprout again and that the tender branch thereof will not cease. Though the root thereof wax old in the earth and the stock thereof die in the ground, yet through the scent of water it will bud and bring forth boughs like a plant. But man dieth and wasteth away; yea, man giveth up the ghost, and where is he?

The Gospels are radiant with youthful joy and with fresh hope; and although Jesus frequently threatens His Father's enemies with "wailing and gnashing of teeth" the general feeling of the New Testament, though it is too serious to be called buoyant, is certainly the opposite of pessimistic.

The Old Testament has a beautiful and poetic light shining from it, but it is the light of a sunset that is streaked with human blood; whereas the light that shines from the New Testament is the light of the dawn; and though it also is streaked with blood, it is the blood of a god, not the blood of men. The whole atmosphere of the New Testament is completely different from that of the Old, and our

English translators have observed this difference, giving to the English words a correspondent tone, so that, in comparison with the Old, the style of the New resembles a picture in water-colours as compared with one in oils.

In spite of a few desperate ejaculations, the general drift of the Old Testament is against any life after death.

> Wilt thou shew wonders to the dead? Shall the dead arise and praise thee? Shall thy loving kindness be declared in the grave? or thy faithfulness in destruction?

And save for a certain vein in the Prophet Ezekiel which must have influenced William Blake, and an apocalyptic tone in Daniel that must have influenced the author of the Book of Revelation, the Old Testament is singularly free from what we usually call mysticism.

To speak plainly, the Old Testament is anything but a spiritual book; but on the other hand it is a profoundly religious one, and although the Hebraic attitude to the Creator, whether under His name Elohim, or El Shaddai, or Yahweh, or the Lord of Hosts, is the propitiation of a jealous, revengeful, and cruel deity, yet so passionately emotional towards the Unseen, so furiously faithful to the God of Abraham, Isaac, and Jacob, of Sarah, Rebekah, and Rachel, was the Hebrew spirit that by the sheer intensity of its poetic imagination it transformed this tribal Demiurge, first into the Creator of heaven and earth, and then into the High and Holy One who inhabiteth Eternity— in other words, into the Nameless Tao or indefinable Absolute.

Spinoza's sublime conception of God—though he was excommunicated for holding it—was really implicit in the Old Testament from the start; not philosophically implicit, for the ancient Hebrews and the modern English resemble each other in their suspicion of philosophy, but emotionally, dramatically, and imaginatively so.

As one reads the story of Jacob in the first book of the Bible, and is forced against one's will to respect and more than respect this tenacious thief of blessings, one feels that as he gathered together one of his "heaps" of desert stones, under those far-off stars, he would not have been *emotionally* staggered or surprised, though he would have certainly been puzzled, had one of his "angels of the Lord," anticipating history, instructed him in the philosophy of Spinoza.

But what we discover in reading the King James Bible, when once by the help of our modern English commentary edited by Dr. Peake and the *Bible As Literature* edited by Mr. Bates we use the book as we

use Homer, is the surprising fact that instead of finding our religious
awe in the presence of life undermined—that awe which Goethe said
was the highest privilege of man—we find it intensified a hundred-
fold!

Liberated in this manner from that sinister, gloomy, morbid, and
wicked-pious atmosphere which the hypocrisy of human frailty has
thrown over this work we get a new and fresh inspiration; an inspiration not only from its literary beauty but from its real religious significance. One comes to feel as one gets older that intellectual persons
make too much of the philosophic distinctions at which they arrive
with so much pains, whereas the value of the literary or poetic approach
is that we realize with more and more clearness that, in this matter of
reverence for the mystery of life, "feeling is all in all," while the precise
philosophic groove through which this feeling expresses itself is of
relatively small importance.

Thus our response to the Bible as poetry rather than as doctrine
does not imply less emotional and imaginative feeling but more; because
it is by great literature rather than by great doctrine that we save our
souls alive.

For Catholics the miracle of the Mass is greater than all theological
doctrine about the Mass; and in the same way for us, as devoted Lollards, the poetry of the Bible is beyond all doctrines about the Bible.

And in truth the Bible, as we enjoy it to-day in this astounding
translation, in which all that is deepest in the Hebrew nature mingles
with all that is deepest in our Anglo-Celtic nature, is not a book for
one, but a book for all. Never was such a melting pot of all those
beautiful, natural inevitable contradictions, with which, from its "mis-
sing-link" ancestors down to this day, humanity has contradicted itself!

Whatever this dubious entity "truth" is *not*, we know one thing that
it certainly *is*, namely, a monstrous container of insoluble contradictions.

And what proves the Bible to be a greater book than any other in
the world except Homer and Shakespeare is the huge gamut of contradictory moods that mount up in its cresting tide.

In King James' Authorized Version we have a beautiful proof of the
power of both the Hebrew race and the Anglo-Celtic race to "contain,"
as Walt Whitman said he himself did, "multitudes." In fact, in this
unique book can be found the literary equivalent to that power of
adapting themselves to so many various climates which is the mark of
both your wandering Jew and your wandering Englishman.

It seems incredible that the same blending of old Hebrew and old

British scholarship could pass from narration as perfect as that when Joseph in Egypt first sees Benjamin among their brothers:

> And he lifted up his eyes and saw his brother Benjamin, his mother's son, and said, "Is this your younger brother of whom he spake unto me?" And he said, "God be gracious unto thee, my son."
>
> And Joseph made haste; for his bowels did yearn upon his brother: and he sought where to weep; and he entered into his chamber, and wept there.

—could pass, I say, from narration like that to poetry like this:

> O that thou wert as my brother, that sucked the breasts of my mother! when I should find thee without, I would kiss thee yea, I should not be despised, I would lead thee, and bring thee unto my mother's house, who would instruct me, I would cause thee to drink of spiced wine of the juice of my pomegranate. His left hand should be under my head and his right hand should embrace me. . . .
>
> Set me as a seal upon thine heart, as a seal upon thine arm; for love is strong as death; jealousy is cruel as the grave; the coals thereof are coals of fire, which hath a most vehement flame. Many waters cannot quench love, neither can the floods drown it; if a man would give all the substance of his house for love, it would utterly be contemned.

No! the power of the Bible does not lie in its doctrine, does not lie in its spirituality, does not even lie in its righteousness. It lies in its supreme emotional contradictions, each carried to its uttermost extreme, and each representing, finally and for all time, some unchanging aspect of human life upon earth.

What an individual needs so as to deepen the poetry of his life, what a race needs so as to deepen the poetry of its life, are various ritualistic and traditional sets of words in its own tongue, but in a heightened and dignified example of its own tongue, like some noble old piece of domestic furniture, a thousand years old, smooth with the touches of generations.

Up-to-date editions of the Bible may be examples of lively cleverness and sincere piety. But what I personally feel about them is that they are simply *not the Bible*. They have their place. They belong to the category of pious experiments and revivalistic movements; whereas *the Bible,* our Authorized Jewish-British classic, is part of our normal daily life. We taste it with our bread. We drink it with our beer. We smoke it—as John Milton used to do—with our tobacco. To the tune of its words we are born and die. To the tune of its homely grossness we enjoy the pleasures of bed and board. It blesses the spade with which our garden is dug, the plough that ploughs our fields, the keel of the boat from which our fish are caught.

Nor is there a natural and normal *sin*—among those which we all of us commit every day—that cannot be sinned, and punished, and repented of, to the accompaniment of these ancient words!

The Bible is to us what Homer was to the Greeks. Its words have become more than words. They have become a magic touch that throws across the passing details of each individual life the undying beauty of the life of humanity. And into the actual words themselves of the Authorized Version the life of humanity has now passed; so that when we hear the Revised Version translate that clue-word of the secret of Jesus—the word *agapé*—as "love" in place of the familiar "charity" we get an uncomfortable shock. Nor does "love" mean the same thing. Technically it may. Actually it *does not!*

The Bible, as we read it now in the Authorized Version, has for its main theme the ways of man to the Eternal and the ways of the Eternal to man. Man's ways to man, and man's feeling for Nature, are the warp and the woof between which this dominant thread moves. It is as illogical to say that there is no God because Jehovah acts in an arbitrary and immoral manner, as to say that there is no civilization because man used to dress in skins and fight with weapons of flint.

Jehovah was the name that the old Hebrews applied to the Nameless Power behind our astronomical universe; and when the Hebrews describe their Jehovah as at once infinitely merciful and infinitely cruel I cannot for my own part see that in this He differs very much from the Ultimate Mystery before whom we must all bow.

Too well do we know that the laws of the Nameless for human life upon earth are like its laws for the lives of beasts and birds and reptiles and fishes—dark and strange and utterly inscrutable! We must needs trust in Him, for He is all there is. He is life. He is death. He is pleasure. He is pain. He is the Whole; and He is beyond the whole. He is the Great Tao of whom to say nothing is the best wisdom. He is Being. He is Not-Being. He is Matter and He is Mind. He is the One and He is the Many. We mortal creatures of a day, conceived in darkness and acquainted with tribulation, born to trouble as the sparks fly upward, who are we to do more than dodge His thunder and enjoy His sunshine, until our dust returns to the earth as it was, and our spirit unto Him who gave it?

And the strange thing about the Old Testament is that it is so easy, I might say so *inevitable,* to feel in this tribal God of Israel, this Lord of Hosts, this Yahweh, this Jehovah, this Elohim, the deeper, more mysterious presence of the nameless Sustainer and Absorber of all things.

This is the gist of the whole business; this is the sum and meaning of all. We feel awe in the presence of *that* which we cannot name, of *that* which, judging by the cruelty and indifference of nature, seems to us—as It did to Job—no more good than It is evil; and yet with this very awe, and in proportion as we experience this awe, there rises in us the feeling that what we have come to call *goodness* is the one thing alone that in the last resort really matters.

That is the point. "Feeling is all in all. The name is sound and smoke, obscuring Heaven's clear glow." Names are nothing and everything. They are nothing, because their sounded syllables are but breath and air and custom. They are everything, because behind this breath, behind this custom, is the *feeling of awe,* the awe that points to simple goodness as the needle points to the north! Our ship goes down; we are gathered to our fathers; but "the word of the Lord"— that is to say the goodness that survives us—"endureth from genera-tion to generation."

The Nameless Power that excites this awe, seems Itself, judging by the ways of Its universe, to be no whit less wayward than Yahweh or Elohim, but the awe It excites in us is an atmosphere, say what you will, that suits the good better than it suits the evil.

What we call "morality" changes with epoch and place. It is a thing of custom and convention, and is often both cowardly and wicked; but the spirit of goodness is the same "yesterday, to-day, and for ever."

And it is this awe excited by the Nameless, that is to say by what the prophets of Israel called "God," that the merciful man—in spite of the ways of Nature—feels to be *with* him, while the unmerciful man feels it to be *against* him.

The Old Testament is the inspiration of the race which, of all races, has felt the *awe of the Nameless* most powerfully; and when some un-sophisticated Uncle Tom, or some simple-minded John Bunyan broods over this book, it doesn't matter how "anthropomorphic," as we call it, his own image of the Nameless is, or how immoral the ways of Jehovah were. What matters is that he feels the "awe of God" and the "presence of God" and comforts and sustains his soul amid the flow of the things that pass away by the feeling of being in touch—and what right have we to call such a feeling an illusion?—with That which was, and is, and is to come.

The Old Testament gives us no assurance about life after death, no commands to be spiritual or chaste. It conveys to us no delicate scruples about lying and fighting and eating and drinking and being revenged on our enemies. It suggests no ascetic suspicion that the accumulation of riches is wrong, no implication that the pleasures of sex are unlawful.

Jacob, or Israel, the father of the Twelve Tribes, is fully as crafty and tricky as the Homeric Odysseus, and bargains and argues and pleads with his jealous God, just as Odysseus does with Athene.

Wherein then, it may be asked, lies the greatness of this Patriarch's character? Wherein, for all the patient and humble and much-enduring men and women who have learnt by heart this tale "of our Father Jacob," is to be found the secret of the attraction that holds them? Does it not lie, as in all exciting stories from the beginning, in the protagonist's intense *awareness of his destiny,* his intense self-consciousness in everything he does, the unconquerable tenacity of his purpose? Isn't the whole secret of the Old Testament's attraction for egoists like ourselves to be found in that remark of Goethe's, "Earnestness alone makes life eternity"? The crafty, amorous, patient, unswerving, unwarlike Jacob takes his life with a gravity, with an awareness, with a sense of responsibility that is overwhelming, that is sublime, that is something before which all obstacles melt, as if by a slow, resistless magic!

Think of what the man must have felt when he awoke that morning after that tricky marriage—*"and behold it was Leah"!* But to serve another seven years for the woman he loved was as inevitable to his incorrigible tenacity as it was to steal Esau's birthright. Every sunrise that smote red into his tent found him, metaphorically speaking, wrestling with his angel, found him with his obstinate head on some sacred stone.

"How mysterious, how memorable," he is always thinking, "is this godlike spot, this godlike dawn, this godlike hour!" And with his "ladder" always ascending from time and space into the Nameless, Jacob naturally, inevitably, becomes Israel, the father of multitudes!

The most stirring and dramatic part of the four books that follow this patriarchal Genesis, namely Exodus, Leviticus, Numbers, and Deuteronomy, which are by far the least inspiring and the least interesting books in the whole Bible, have to do with the extraordinary personality of Moses, furious leader and far-sighted lawgiver, who must have been a sort of inspired Hebraic Merlin with his neurotic moods of "meekness," his fits of blind wrath, his black magic, and his terrifying intimacies with Jehovah.

Certain stories we are told about Moses carry upon their face, casually though they are related, the very seal of psychological truth. Such is the story, for instance, of how Aaron and Miriam, his brother and sister, revolted against him, because he, the great eugenic medicine man, took to wife an Ethiopian woman.

But do we not get the whole secret of the magnetic ascendancy of Moses in the effect of his appeal to his divine friend against these jeering purists, this high priest and this priest-loving lady; an appeal that was so effective that the great soothsaying Miriam had to flee from the face of that Ethiopian, and from the face of the whole camp, literally sick with terror!

In this single sentence it can be seen why it is that the English, the most individualistic of all races, had until yesterday such a mania for this Hebrew book.

> And the Lord came down in the pillar of the cloud and stood in the door of the tabernacle, and called Aaron and Miriam and they both came forth. And he said, "Hear now my words: if there be a prophet among you I the Lord will make myself known unto him in a vision and will speak unto him in a dream. My servant Moses is not so, who is faithful in all my house. With him will I speak mouth to mouth, even apparently, and not in dark speeches; and the similitude of the Lord he shall behold; wherefore then were ye not afraid to speak against my servant Moses?"

From the disappearance of Moses—for none knoweth his sepulchre unto this day—to the establishment of the kingdom under Saul and David the Old Testament intensifies its awe-inspiring drama.

The main theme of this great accumulative symphony is still the relation between man and the Nameless; and still does the Nameless, as in the stories of Samson and of Saul, find in Jehovah exactly what Jehovah found in Moses, an erratic, wayward, cantankerous, but faithful mouthpiece of its mysterious will.

And after all, as we know from bitter experience neither Milton's pure and eternal Spirit, who "Dove-like sat'st brooding on the vast abyss and mad'st it pregnant," nor the "loving Father" of Jesus, fills up or completes altogether the characteristics of the Power that governs the cosmos.

There has always been found, in its ways to men, and to animals and birds and fishes too, an element that is different from both these qualities, an element neither spiritual nor loving, an element indeed that has not only cruelty in it but an unmistakable touch of satanic malice.

It was St. Paul who made of Jesus—"but we have the mind of Christ"—what Aeschylus lacked the penetration to make of Prometheus, that is to say a God of *pure goodness,* to stand between us and this devilish element in the Nameless; for it was no more concealed from St. Paul than it was concealed from Dostoievsky how impossible it is to justify "the ways of God to man."

Certain figures in the Old Testament stand forth with dramatic outlines as distinct and with intensity of feeling as tragic as any figures in classic or Nordic literature. Such are the figures of Samson the Nazarite and Elijah the Tishbite. Both these gigantic personalities were peculiarly dear to the heart of the Nameless, who, as we read, inspired them with something of Its own cruel violence as well as with Its own creative spirit.

How often must the Hebrew race, and many another race, too, in their hour of subjection, have pondered, as Milton under the "barbarous dissonance" of the Restoration, upon the death of this hero of the Eternal!

The description of the death of Samson, as our King James Version translates it, is indeed a perfect example of how when we treat the Bible "as literature" we neither lessen its grandeur nor diminish its inspiration.

Treated as "the word of God," as our fathers treated it, how easily by taking it all for granted in one monotonous level of consecrated gloom can we lose altogether that poetry which is the highest "word" of all, and which is without any question the very inspiration of the Nameless!

And it came to pass, when their hearts were merry, that they said, "Call for Samson, that he may make us sport." And they called for Samson out of the prison house; and he made them sport: and they set him between the pillars. And Samson said unto the lad that held him by the hand, "Suffer me that I may feel the pillars whereupon the house standeth that I may lean upon them . . ." And Samson called upon the Lord and said, "O Lord God, remember me, I pray thee, and strengthen me, I pray thee, only this once, O God, that I may be avenged of the Philistines for my two eyes. . . ." And Samson said, "Let me die with the Philistines."

And he bowed himself with all his might; and the house fell upon the lords and upon all the people that were therein. So the dead which he slew at his death were more than they which he slew in his life.

But that Elijah its prophet made an even deeper impression on the Hebrew mind than Samson its champion is proved by the words of Jesus himself who hesitates not to declare that His great herald, John the Baptist, was actually a reincarnation of Elijah.

But unquestionably the favourite book of the Old Testament with average philosophistic Nordics is the Book of Job. And how significant it is of the manner in which Jehovah so effectively represents the Nameless, that God's only reply to our outraged indictment of his extraordinary ways should be a thundering description of our weakness compared with His strength!

It would be difficult to find anything more different from the tender and desperate piety of the Psalms than the sly worldly wisdom of the Proverbs; and how characteristic it is of the particular genius of our English translators that just as they can respond to the revolutionary spirit of these old writings, so they can convey in their version of the Proverbs that particular tone of what might be called *moderation in virtue,* which is the chief characteristic of our English Prayer Book!

"Be not over-righteous, nor take upon thyself to be too wise. Why should'st thou destroy thyself?" And certainly in their power of catching the poetic cynicism of *Ecclesiastes* side by side with the desperate humilities of the Psalms the King James scholars were not less than inspired. My own favourite book in the Bible is the Psalms, and it gives me a peculiar satisfaction to know that this was the feeling of our most sophisticated of all secular critics, Walter Pater. And what a book for the lonely and the unhappy the Psalms is!

Rationalist opponents of religion speak sometimes as if the organized churches were responsible for the Bible's hold over people. Nothing could be more untrue! The Old Testament, as cannot be repeated too often, remains the grand revolutionary arsenal for the individual's weapons against all constituted authority; and if, as William Blake says, Jesus Christ was the greatest revolutionary of all time, was indeed the supreme anarchist, who—

His seventy disciples sent
Against Religion and Government!

it is from the prophetic books of the Old Testament that Jesus drew, as so many others have done, the spirit of divine revolt against "the Powers of this World."

The *Biography* of our English Bible is, as Mr. Bates so admirably sums it up, the story of the resistless demand of the masses of the people, *against the will of constituted authority,* to possess this dangerous book.

We have, however, as the editor of *The Bible As Literature* willingly admits, to give the credit for our unequalled Authorized Version to one of our most eccentric rulers, namely to "the wisest fool in Christendom," King James the First! Making use of the earlier labours of William Tyndale and Miles Coverdale, this learned monarch's committee of scholars, headed by Dr. Reynolds of Corpus Christi, Oxford, and Dr. Lancelot Andrews, dean of Westminster, brought out this work—the greatest translation ever made— in the year 1611. Ardent as he was in this noble undertaking and assiduously pushing his churchmen on, James, Mr. Bates reminds us, insisted that no return should be made to the Tyndale-Coverdale translation of the Greek word *ecclesia* in the proper, classical, democratic sense of an "assembly" or "congregation," but that the sacerdotal expression "church," used in the so-called "Bishops' Bible," should be the word employed.

But never has the peculiar genius of English scholars, and never has, one must add, the peculiar genius of the English language, been displayed to grander effect than in this book, the actual words of which, even in the case of sundry expressions that cleverer and smarter revisions have "improved upon," have sunk so deeply into our popular consciousness that they have become for many of us the inveterate form through which our love, our hate, our happiness, our lust, our greed, our pity, our pride, our humility, our despair, our ecstasy, yea! and even our cursing of life, must be expressed, if they are to be expressed from the bowels of our soul!

And the curious thing is that, while for those who instinctively respond to the prelatical translation of *ecclesia* as "church," our English Prayer-Book offers its unequalled counterpart to the Latin of authority, of tradition, of order, of *organization,* King James's Bible has remained to this day the inexhaustible inspiration of heretics, outlaws, and rebels!

From the time of the Lollards this book has been the book of those who, like Walt Whitman, are critical of institutions, critical of priesthoods, critical of states and governments. The culmination of the Old Testament is in the spirit of prophecy; and the prophet, from the beginning of time unto this day, has been the despised of the rich, the trouble of the priests, and the mad terror of the ruler.

If any unwearied reader of the Bible were asked why after racing through this book from cover to cover he proceeds to repeat this singular performance, his answer would in essence be the same as that of Uncle Tom, the same as that of Tom o' Bedlam, the same as that of a vast anonymous multitude of Toms and Johns; namely, that it gives him the will, the tenacity, the cunning, even if it cannot give him the strength or the courage, *to put the world's values in their place!*

The greatest literary works of our Western world, and I cannot help suspecting of the whole round earth, are three in number. They are the Hebrew Scriptures, Homer, and Shakespeare. It was the greatest of Germans who said, "How can I hate the French when I owe to them my intellectual culture?" and it is hard not to feel that this Goethean idea of the power of literature to destroy race-prejudice is destined to outlive all that an inhuman and illiterate science can do in its eager desire to put weapons of destruction into the hands of oppressors.

And how ironical it is that any bold free-thinker among us with any real imaginative response to life should, out of his "intolerance of intolerance," give up enjoying this shameless, passionate, poetical, earth-loving Old Testament, in which there is no illusion about personal immortality, no illusion about ethical idealism, no illusion about the friendliness of the universe, no false hopes about this "thinking reed" so preposterously made in the image of God!

How ironical that such persons should say in their hearts: "The Bible is so obscure, so inconsistent, so full of sweet mirages and pleasant lies; let us therefore put in its place the simple, indubitable utterances of speculative psychology and the profound never-to-be-changed revelations of experimental physics!"

Many attempts have been made to explain the secret of the peculiar beauty of this great translation. One feels at once that the essential quality both of its prose and its poetry is at the opposite pole from the prevailing stylistic manner of modern writers.

The form of the ancient Hebrew poetry, as the Authorized Version catches its spirit, depends chiefly upon two elements—imaginative exaggeration and musical repetition.

It is in its subject-matter, however, that its power chiefly lies and

this consists in the inter-blending of three dominant motifs—the glory
and shame of man, the beauty and terror of nature, and the sometimes
appalling and sometimes consoling mystery of the First Cause. Each
of these recurrent motifs is constantly appearing and disappearing, as
the wild music of the ocean of life flows forward; while it is always
with this life, and never with any attempt to attain another life, that
the Old Testament is concerned. Nor does the ancient prose style of
the Hebrews, as King James's scholars render it, differ very much from
that of their poetry, save that the rhythmic repetition is less pronounced,
and the majestic realism of the simple narration holds the subject
even yet closer to the earth.

The Eternal must help us, *at least by the feeling of His Presence,* in
this actual life; for it is unlikely—so runs the constant refrain of the
Old Testament—that we shall hear His voice out of the dust.

It is impossible, for persons who love reading the Bible from beginning to end, not to feel thankful that the canonical order of the books
it contains, so artfully different from the chronological conclusions of
scientific research, has been allowed, by the deep dramatic sense of
those who arranged it and those who translated it, to mount up, exactly
as we have it to-day, from Genesis to Malachi.

The Book of Genesis contains, as it should contain, the simplest
narrations of all; monumental vignettes of human pathos and drama,
only equalled by Homer.

> And Isaac his father said unto him, "Who are thou?" And he
> said, "I am thy son, thy first-born Esau," And Isaac trembled
> very exceedingly, and said, "Who? where is he that hath taken
> venison, and brought it to me, and I have eaten of all before thou
> camest, and have blessed him? yea and he shall be blessed."
> And when Esau heard the words of his father, he cried with a
> great and exceeding bitter cry, and said unto his father, "Bless
> me, even me also, Oh my father."

But then, as we read on, following this totally unscientific but surely
inspired canon, though it be but the canon of a multitude of anonymous Hebrew scholars, and pass from Moses to the Judges, and from
the Judges to Saul and David and the Kings, the tone of the writing
grows steadily more subjective, more lyrical, more cosmic.

> And he came thither unto a cave, and lodged, there; and behold,
> the word of the Lord came to him and he said unto him, "What
> doest thou here, Elijah?" And he said, "I have been very jealous
> for the Lord God of hosts; for the children of Israel have forsaken

thy covenant, thrown down thine altars, and slain thy prophets with the sword; and I, even I only, am left; and they seek my life to take it away."

And he said, "Go forth, and stand upon the mount before the Lord." And behold, the Lord passed by, and a great and strong wind rent the mountains, and brake in pieces the rocks before the Lord; but the Lord was not in the wind; and after the wind an earthquake; but the Lord was not in the earthquake; and after the earthquake a fire; but the Lord was not in the fire; and after the fire a still small voice . . . "yet have I left me seven thousand in Israel, all the knees which have not bowed unto Baal, and every mouth which hath not kissed him."

Still following the canonical order handed down to us from these old nameless Jewish sages, an order charged with the *amor fati* of the most fate-conscious of all races, we arrive at the Book of Job, where, *de profundis* indeed, the soul of man turns upon the Manager of his World-Show, and, as Ivan Karamazov says, "returns Him the ticket."

And Job spake and said, "Let the day perish wherein I was born, and the night in which it was said, 'There is a man child conceived.' Let that day be darkness; let not God regard it from above, neither let the light shine upon it. Let darkness and the shadow of death stain it; let a cloud dwell upon it; let the blackness of the day terrify it. . . . Lo, let that night be solitary, let no joyful voice come therein. . . . Let it look for light, but have none; neither let it see the dawning of the day: because it shut not up the doors of my mother's womb, nor hid sorrow from mine eyes. . . . For now should I have lain still and been quiet, I should have slept; then had I been at rest . . . as an hidden untimely birth, I had not been; as infants which never saw light. There the wicked cease from troubling; and there the weary be at rest. There the prisoners rest together; they hear not the voice of the oppressor.

"The small and great are there; and the servant is free from his master.

"Wherefore is light given to him that is in misery, and life unto the bitter in soul . . . which rejoice exceedingly, and are glad when they can find the grave?"

And thus having reached the uttermost depths, and peradventure like Job, finding ourselves still alive, still going to and fro upon the earth, what chord, in this great ancient world-tragedy, will be struck after the second act, struck as the orchestra plays for the intermission?

Which of us who have lasted it out to middle age and tested the nature of the world cannot respond to the voice of the Preacher, that low-pitched paean of the second-best, whose disillusionment no Horace, no Voltaire, no Anatole France can surpass, but which by some dra-

matic instinct in humanity has fallen into its place in the very centre
of the Bible?

> For to him that is joined to all the living there is hope: for a
> living dog is better than a dead lion. For the living know that they
> shall die: but the dead know not any thing, neither have they
> any more a reward; for the memory of them is forgotten. . . .
> Whatsoever thy hand findeth to do, do it with thy might; for there
> is no work, nor device, nor knowledge, nor wisdom, in the grave,
> whither thou goest.
> I returned, and saw under the sun, that the race is not to the
> swift, nor the battle to the strong, neither yet bread to the wise,
> nor yet riches to men of understanding, nor yet favour to men of
> skill; but time and chance happeneth to them all.

Thus we hear the voice of the Preacher—"And behold! all is vanity
and vexation of spirit."

"All," as the greatest of the Greek philosophers said, "all flows
away and nothing abides."

Nothing? Faint and low, as if upon the wind of space, outside all
our egoistic cravings, outside all our inevitable frustrations, comes still
the voice of the Psalmist, that voice from "the God," as Emily Brontë
says, "within our breast," the God within us and yet beyond us, that is
our real "being and breath."

> My days are like a shadow that declineth; and I am withered
> like grass. . . . Of old hast thou laid the foundations of the earth;
> and the heavens are the work of thy hands. They shall perish,
> but thou shalt endure; yea, all of them shall wax old like a
> garment, as a vesture shalt thou change them, and they shall be
> changed: But thou art the same, and thy years shall have no
> end.

When Matthew Arnold said that the power of the Bible lay in its
appeal to mercy and justice, in its appeal to what we call "righteousness," he was not wrong; but there is more in it than that.

The culmination of the Old Testament is in the Prophets. All leads
up to the Prophets. Prose and poetry, lamentations and exultations,
despairs and resignations, to the Prophets it mounts up, and with the
Prophets it ends.

The poetry of the Psalms washes, like a cleansing air, over the
bitterness of every personal life; and its lyrical burden, soothing away
our personal griefs, is always the same. We as individuals are and
are not; but the Power by which we live, the Power into whose hands
we sink when we die, *That,* and That alone, abideth for ever; and in
That, and not in the self that perishes, is immortal life.

Lord, thou hast been our dwelling-place in all generations. Before the mountains were brought forth, or ever thou hadst formed the earth and the world, even from everlasting to everlasting thou art God.

Thou turnest man to destruction; and sayest, "Return, ye children of men." For a thousand years in thy sight are but as yesterday when it is past, and as a watch in the night. Thou carriest them away as with a flood; they are as a sleep: in the morning they are like grass which groweth up. In the morning it flourisheth and groweth up; in the evening it is cut down and withereth. . . .

The days of our years are three-score years and ten; and if by reason of strength they be fourscore years, yet is their strength labour and sorrow; for it is soon cut off, and we fly away.

Some will say, "What comfort is it to the individual who perishes that God, that the Nameless, should live for ever?" I think the answer is that for all its tragic finality there remains a strange beauty, a deep feeling of peace and calm and infinite escape, in the thought of the death of the individual self and the eternity of something that is not individual.

The greatest of modern American poets, Edgar Lee Masters, has expressed this feeling, the feeling that comes over us again and again as we give ourselves up to the ebb and flow of this Psalm-music, a music like a sad and tender night-wind passing over the roofs of the world and over the "window'd raggedness" of the outcasts of the world, giving us not hope but peace.

> *Ice cannot shiver in the cold,*
> *Nor stones shrink from the lapping flame.*
> *Eyes that are sealed no more have tears;*
> *Ears that are stopped hear nothing ill;*
> *Hearts turned to silt are strange to pain;*
> *Tongues that are dumb report no loss;*
> *Hands stiffened, well may idle be;*
>
>   .   .   .   .
>
> *Work is, but folded hands need work not;*
> *Nothing to say is for dumb tongues.*
>   *The rolling earth rolls on and on*
> *With trees and stones and winding streams—*
> *My dream is what the hill-side dreams!*

Yes, there is a strange satisfaction, mysterious as death, a satisfaction that the music of poetry alone can give in this feeling of the troubles of time being over, and the timeless "hill-side" of the Eternal alone continuing.

The individual passes; but there come moments when we are content that it should be so; for we feel that the thoughts of the most abject among us are not altogether lost. In the Eternal they still live—those thoughts and the labours of those hands.

> Let thy work appear unto thy servants, and thy glory unto their children. And let the beauty of the Lord our God be upon us, and establish thou the work of our hands upon us, yea the work of our hands establish thou it.

It is easy enough—alas, we all know that!—to lay so much stress upon the loss of our personal identity—this Jack and Tom and Bob and Bill, this Bess and Nell and Sue and Kate which is all we feel ourselves to be—that such talk as this about our "thoughts," or our "work," or some unearthly de-personalized "essence" surviving in the Eternal, sounds like a mockery of wordy rhetoric.

But living men are we, lively particles of dust and vapour, not algebraic equations, and if in everything else we get comfort from faint, vague, dim, flickering chances, and intimations of chances, such as when you press too hard upon them flit away like smoke, surely it is no mere priestly trick but a natural motion of the soul, as inevitable as the clutch of an embryo's fingers, that we should make the most of these old dim paleolithic hints of immortality.

But if the poetry of the Psalms is like the music of a long-drawn wind in the night, in the beauty of which we accept the passing of that which most certainly passes and the abiding of that which we may hope abides, when we come to the Prophets a different note is heard.

It is obscurer, it is wilder, it is more irrational. There is that in it that struggles to find an utterance for an inspiration that rolls away the great stone that all our reasonable and all our natural, and all our logical conclusions have placed upon the wishing-well of the heart's desire, the well of "our father Jacob," in the great desert.

In a new and unpredictable direction does this prophetic cry carry us. Hitherto, in the books of the Old Testament, it has been by tenacity of purpose, by heroic endurance, by strength and courage and faith, by the proud fulfilling of the Law, by the magnanimous practice of benevolence and righteousness, that the will of the Eternal was obeyed.

But in the Prophets the mystery of the universe is approached from a totally different direction. It is in fact not "approached" at all. *It is found within ourselves.* Yes, this great thundering and undying Eternal whose only answer to Job was to shout him down, is now discovered to be a living part, the only living part, of the individual soul that perishes!

"For my thoughts are not your thoughts, neither are your ways my ways," saith the Lord. . . . "Can a woman forget her sucking child, that she should not have compassion on the son of her womb? Yea, they may forget, yet will I not forget thee. . . ." For thus saith the high and lofty One that inhabiteth eternity. . . .

"I dwell in the high and holy place with him also that is of a contrite and humble spirit, to revive the spirit of the humble, and to revive the heart of the contrite."

It is as though the poetry of the Psalms had brought an echo out of infinite space.

For what is the "high and lofty One" doing here except answering the cry of that familiar Psalm that quivers through the chords of man's betrayed nerves like the wind through telegraph-wires?

Create in me a clean heart, O God, and renew a right spirit within me. . . .
For thou desirest not sacrifice, else would I give it; thou delightest not in burnt offering. The sacrifices of God are a broken spirit; a broken and a contrite heart, O God, thou wilt not despise. . . .

There is certainly nothing like this in Homer, and not very much resembling it in Shakespeare; nor, to confess the truth, is it very common in the Old Testament. It belongs rather to that particular aspect of the New Testament whereof Dostoievsky is the greatest modern exponent.

But rare though it be, it is the climax towards which the whole of the Old Testament moves, since Cain, the first-born went forth a wanderer over the face of the earth. It is nothing less than that psychological emptiness in the heart's abyss, which, when it is filled by the spirit of the Nameless, becomes what Emily Brontë calls "the God within my breast."

The difference, between this Hebrew emptiness in the soul that can only be filled by the Spirit beyond all worlds—dark and strange though that Nameless be—and the metaphysical selflessness advocated by Buddhism, is that the former treats the Nameless as a Person.

It was none other than Goethe who said, "and there is room for this also"; and for myself, as a sworn irrationalist, I can only say that I am proud to follow William Blake in placing this Semitic Book above all our Aryan metaphysic.

After all, the only thing I know *for certain* is my own personal mind; and *that* I know to be a Being that loves and hates and feels pleasure

and pain. Why then must I interpret the Eternal in terms of mathematical symbols of which I know nothing and of chemical forces which
I only know from the outside, while I reject as a childish analogy the
living identity which I know so intimately *and from the inside?*

It is true that these subtle intellectual systems in dealing with the
Self and "the escape from the self" call upon us to enter upon a cold-
blooded scientific "process of salvation" in which by a premeditated
method we craftily drop the part of the self that anyway is doomed,
in order to hitch some evasive fragments of what is left, as securely
as we can, to the slippery spirals of the Absolute.

But the reason why the Jewish Bible has so completely beaten off
the field—at any rate as far as our Anglo-Celtic soul is concerned—
all this Aryan metaphysic, is because it interprets the world in terms
of the heart rather than in terms of the head; and because it finds, as
indeed the great Kant himself found, that the secret of things lies in
the inspiration of the human conscience rather than in the cunning
decrees of the human intellect.

And here again I cannot see why humility *before* the Eternal, and
an escape from ourselves *into* the Eternal in the simple emotional
manner of the Psalms and the Prophets, should not lift us into the
Timeless quite as effectively as any mental concentration.

Jesus was only carrying the Psalms and Prophets a "fathom and a
half" further when he used his famous expression about losing your
life to save it; and the mere fact that the imaginative tone in the
Psalms and the Prophets turns the relations between the temporal and
the eternal into a poetic one rather than a chemical or a mathematical
one is from my point of view all to its advantage.

Few impassioned readers of the Bible have been dutiful adherents of
organized sacerdotal religion; for the spirit of both Old and New Testament is a spirit of revolt against organization of every kind.

Certainly in Great Britain, from the time of the Lollards to the
present hour, the strongest Bible-lovers have been anything but meek
adherents of either Church or State. Very often, as with the old inde-
pendents, they have been fierce opponents of them both. This is where
the spirit of the Bible differs from the spirit of the Prayer-Book; and I
am tempted to think that whereas the more docile and more feminine
piety in these islands cleaves to the Prayer-Book the Bible is still the
inspirer of the greater number of solitary souls who prefer to worship
in the "House not made with Hands."

For myself I lean to the view that if our survival after death depends, as some maintain, upon the measure of our detachment from self-absorption, there is a stronger liberating magic in the psychological humility of the Semitic method than in the metaphysical humility of the Aryan method, the former being spontaneous and imaginative, the latter premeditated and scientific.

In any case I am sure that the growing prejudice which so large a segment of our younger generation feels against the Bible is due to the fact that they link it with the disgusting hypocrisy, the sly maliciousness, the half-suppressed goatishness, of so many among its official champions.

But to hate the Bible because many of its adherents are repulsive is as absurd as to hate Homer because you had an unpleasant teacher at school. Herein lies the advantage of coming fresh to this book as if it were heathen literature. It puts back the heart into it, the heart that has been destroyed by the repulsive hypocrisies and odious cruelties of the past.

Written in the East, and made the supreme Sacred Book in the West, this living projection of the soul of Israel will no doubt have its rebirths and its revaluations to the end of time.

And we have to face the fact that our Anglo-Celtic race has come to find its *individual religion* in Jewish emotion and in Jewish imagination as nowhere else. This when you come to think of it is a very strange thing. I doubt if even the practical Romans allowed themselves to be dominated by the genius of the poetical Greeks to such a tune as this!

How has this come about? For it is clear that in the Latin of the Catholic Church the Hebrew element is not preserved to anything like the extent it is in our English Bible. Is it because we are the most unphilosophic and individualistic of all races and the race above all others to exalt the prophet at the expense of the thinker and the priest? Or was there, perhaps, in the ancient Iberian aboriginals of these islands a pre-Celtic strain that was not Aryan at all, and that is stirred in its atavistic depths by this Semitic book?

It is at any rate significant that just as the Irish were strengthened in the struggle to retain their racial identity by the Roman Church, so have the Welsh been strengthened in a similar struggle by the Welsh Bible.

Anyway, the whole of this Authorized Version, wherein the religious spirit of England is wedded to the religious spirit of the Jews, is inspired by what we call the *religious idea,* namely, the idea, defined by Goethe at the end of *Faust,* that all transitory things are symbols of what is beyond time.

"The great globe itself," as Shakespeare says, "yea! all which it inherit, shall dissolve and . . . leave not a rack behind."

But how can there be this flowing away without some hidden permanence whereby in reality we measure the speed of the flow? But the existence of this permanence, beyond and beneath the universal flux, is rather an intimation that comes to us in moments of deep feeling than a scientific conclusion.

And its presence, the presence of something beyond the laws of cause and effect, not unfrequently presents itself—at least it did to the ancient Hebrews and old-fashioned Englishmen—in the form of what we now call the "miraculous."

Thus Matthew Arnold's contention that the Bible will survive by its "morality touched by emotion" does not cover the whole field. What the Bible lives by is its undying protest in imperishable poetry against a world wherein "miracles" cannot happen!

The Biblical attitude is that creation *implies* the "miraculous"; and when one thinks of the fantastic shifts to which science has been put to get life going without the miraculous ever since Democritus had to supply his atoms with fish-hooks it seems that the Biblical attitude still holds good.

The Bible is great literature; but it is literature that "has the peculiarity," as the ancient Welsh books would put it, of giving our earth-wisdom a wholesome shock; the sort of shock that Hercules gave Antaeus when he lifted him into the air. But "this kind goeth not forth" without inspiration; and is the prerogative of the prophet rather than of the philosopher.

The hand of the Lord was upon me and carried me out in the spirit of the Lord, and set me down in the midst of the valley which was full of bones. And caused me to pass by them, round about; and behold, there were very many in the open valley; and lo, they were very dry.

And he said unto me, "Son of man, can these bones live?"
And I answered, "O Lord God, Thou knowest." (pp. 3-34)

ODYSSEUS' SCAR

ERICH AUERBACH

READERS OF THE *Odyssey* will remember the well-prepared and touching scene in book 19, when Odysseus has at last come home, the scene in which the old housekeeper Euryclea, who had been his nurse, recognizes him by a scar on his thigh. The stranger has won Penelope's good will; at his request she tells the housekeeper to wash his feet, which, in all old stories, is the first duty of hospitality toward a tired traveler. Euryclea busies herself fetching water and mixing cold with hot, meanwhile speaking sadly of her absent master, who is probably of the same age as the guest, and who perhaps, like the guest, is even now wandering somewhere, a stranger; and she remarks how astonishingly like him the guest looks. Meanwhile Odysseus, remembering his scar, moves back out of the light; he knows that, despite his efforts to hide his identity, Euryclea will now recognize him, but he wants at least to keep Penelope in ignorance. No sooner has the old woman touched the scar than, in her joyous surprise, she lets Odysseus' foot drop into the basin; the water spills over, she is about to cry out her joy; Odysseus restrains her with whispered threats and endearments; she recovers herself and conceals her emotion. Penelope, whose attention Athena's foresight had diverted from the incident, has observed nothing.

All this is scrupulously externalized and narrated in leisurely fashion. The two women express their feelings in copious direct discourse. Feel-

From *Mimesis, the Representation of Reality in Western Literature,* by Erich Auerbach, translated from the German by Willard R. Trask; copyright 1953 by The Princeton University Press. Reprinted by permission.

ings though they are, with only a slight admixture of the most general considerations upon human destiny, the syntactical connection between part and part is perfectly clear, no contour is blurred. There is also room and time for orderly, perfectly well-articulated, uniformly illuminated descriptions of implements, ministrations, and gestures; even in the dramatic moment of recognition, Homer does not omit to tell the reader that it is with his right hand that Odysseus takes the old woman by the throat to keep her from speaking, at the same time that he draws her closer to him with his left. Clearly outlined, brightly and uniformly illuminated, men and things stand out in a realm where everything is visible; and not less clear—wholly expressed, orderly even in their ardor—are the feelings and thoughts of the persons involved.

In my account of the incident I have so far passed over a whole series of verses which interrupt it in the middle. There are more than seventy of these verses—while to the incident itself some forty are devoted before the interruption and some forty after it. The interruption, which comes just at the point when the housekeeper recognizes the scar—that is, at the moment of crisis—describes the origin of the scar, a hunting accident which occurred in Odysseus' boyhood, at a boar hunt, during the time of his visit to his grandfather Autolycus. This first affords an opportunity to inform the reader about Autolycus, his house, the precise degree of the kinship, his character, and, no less exhaustively than touchingly, his behavior after the birth of his grandson; then follows the visit of Odysseus, now grown to be a youth; the exchange of greetings, the banquet with which he is welcomed, sleep and waking, the early start for the hunt, the tracking of the beast, the struggle, Odysseus' being wounded by the boar's tusk, his recovery, his return to Ithaca, his parents' anxious questions—all is narrated, again with such a complete externalization of all the elements of the story and of their interconnections as to leave nothing in obscurity. Not until then does the narrator return to Penelope's chamber, not until then, the digression having run its course, does Euryclea, who had recognized the scar before the digression began, let Odysseus' foot fall back into the basin.

The first thought of a modern reader—that this is a device to increase suspense—is, if not wholly wrong, at least not the essential explanation of this Homeric procedure. For the element of suspense is very slight in the Homeric poems; nothing in their entire style is calculated to keep the reader or hearer breathless. The digressions are not meant to keep the reader in suspense, but rather to relax the tension.

And this frequently occurs, as in the passage before us. The broadly narrated, charming, and subtly fashioned story of the hunt, with all its elegance and self-sufficiency, its wealth of idyllic pictures, seeks to win the reader over wholly to itself as long as he is hearing it, to make him forget what had just taken place during the foot-washing. But an episode that will increase suspense by retarding the action must be so constructed that it will not fill the present entirely, will not put the crisis, whose resolution is being awaited, entirely out of the reader's mind, and thereby destroy the mood of suspense; the crisis and the suspense must continue, must remain vibrant in the background. But Homer—and to this we shall have to return later—knows no background. What he narrates is for the time being the only present, and fills both the stage and the reader's mind completely. So it is with the passage before us. When the young Euryclea (vv. 401ff.) sets the infant Odysseus on his grandfather Autolycus' lap after the banquet, the aged Euryclea, who a few lines earlier had touched the wanderer's foot, has entirely vanished from the stage and from the reader's mind.

Goethe and Schiller, who, though not referring to this particular episode, exchanged letters in April 1797 on the subject of "the retarding element" in the Homeric poems in general, put it in direct opposition to the element of suspense—the latter word is not used, but is clearly implied when the "retarding" procedure is opposed, as something proper to epic, to tragic procedure (letters of April 19, 21, and 22). The "retarding element," the "going back and forth" by means of episodes, seems to me, too, in the Homeric poems, to be opposed to any tensional and suspensive striving toward a goal, and doubtless Schiller is right in regard to Homer when he says that what he gives us is "simply the quiet existence and operation of things in accordance with their natures"; Homer's goal is "already present in every point of his progress." But both Schiller and Goethe raise Homer's procedure to the level of a law for epic poetry in general, and Schiller's words quoted above are meant to be universally binding upon the epic poet, in contradistinction from the tragic. Yet in both modern and ancient times, there are important epic works which are composed throughout with no "retarding element" in this sense but, on the contrary, with suspense throughout, and which perpetually "rob us of our emotional freedom"— which power Schiller will grant only to the tragic poet. And besides it seems to me undemonstrable and improbable that this procedure of Homeric poetry was directed by aesthetic considerations or even by an aesthetic feeling of the sort postulated by Goethe and Schiller. The effect, to be sure, is precisely that which they describe, and is, further-more, the actual source of the conception of epic which they themselves hold, and with them all writers decisively influenced by classical anti-quity. But the true cause of the impression of "retardation" appears to me to lie elsewhere—namely, in the need of the Homeric style to leave nothing which it mentions half in darkness and unexternalized.

The excursus upon the origin of Odysseus' scar is not basically dif-ferent from the many passages in which a newly introduced character, or even a newly appearing object or implement, though it be in the thick of a battle, is described as to its nature and origin; or in which, upon the appearance of a god, we are told where he last was, what he was doing there, and by what road he reached the scene; indeed, even the Homeric epithets seem to me in the final analysis to be trace-able to the same need for an externalization of phenomena in terms perceptible to the senses. Here is the scar, which comes up in the course of the narrative; and Homer's feeling simply will not permit him to see it appear out of the darkness of an unilluminated past; it must be set in full light, and with it a portion of the hero's boyhood—just as, in the *Iliad,* when the first ship is already burning and the Myrmidons finally arm that they may hasten to help, there is still time not only for the wonderful simile of the wolf, not only for the order of the Myrmidon host, but also for a detailed account of the ancestry of several subordinate leaders (16, vv. 155ff.). To be sure, the aesthetic effect thus produced was soon noticed and thereafter consciously sought; but the more original cause must have lain in the basic impulse of the Homeric style: to represent phenomena in a fully externalized form, visible and palpable in all their parts, and completely fixed in their spatial and temporal relations. Nor do psychological processes receive any other treatment: here too nothing must remain hidden and unex-pressed. With the utmost fullness, with an orderliness which even passion does not disturb, Homer's personages vent their inmost hearts in speech; what they do not say to others, they speak in their own minds, so that the reader is informed of it. Much that is terrible takes place in the Homeric poems, but it seldom takes place wordlessly: Polyphemus talks to Odysseus; Odysseus talks to the suitors when he begins to kill them; Hector and Achilles talk at length, before battle and after; and no speech is so filled with anger or scorn that the particles which express logical and grammatical connections are lacking or out of place. This last observation is true, of course, not only of speeches but of the presentation in general. The separate elements of a phenomenon are

most clearly placed in relation to one another; a large number of conjunctions, adverbs, particles and other syntactical tools, all clearly
circumscribed and delicately differentiated in meaning, delimit persons,
things, and portions of incidents in respect to one another, and at the
same time bring them together in a continuous and ever flexible connection; like the separate phenomena themselves, their relationships—
their temporal, local, causal, final, consecutive, comparative, concessive,
antithetical, and conditional limitations—are brought to light in perfect
fullness; so that a continuous rhythmic procession of phenomena passes
by, and never is there a form left fragmentary or half-illuminated, never
a lacuna, never a gap, never a glimpse of unplumbed depths.

And this procession of phenomena takes place in the foreground—
that is, in a local and temporal present which is absolute. One might
think that the many interpolations, the frequent moving back and forth,
would create a sort of perspective in time and place; but the Homeric
style never gives any such impression. The way in which any impression
of perspective is avoided can be clearly observed in the procedure for
introducing episodes, a syntactical construction with which every reader
of Homer is familiar; it is used in the passage we are considering, but
can also be found in cases when the episodes are much shorter. To the
word scar (v. 393) there is first attached a relative clause ("which once
long ago a boar . . ."), which enlarges into a voluminous syntactical
parenthesis; into this an independent sentence unexpectedly intrudes
(v. 396: "A god himself gave him . . ."), which quietly disentangles
itself from syntactical subordination, until, with verse 399, an equally
free syntactical treatment of the new content begins a new present
which continues unchallenged until, with verse 467 ("The old woman
now touched it . . ."), the scene which had been broken off is resumed.
To be sure, in the case of such long episodes as the one we are considering, a purely syntactical connection with the principal theme would
hardly have been possible; but a connection with it through perspective would have been all the easier had the content been arranged with
that end in view; if, that is, the entire story of the scar had been presented as a recollection which awakens in Odysseus' mind at this particular moment. It would have been perfectly easy to do; the story of the
scar had only to be inserted two verses earlier, at the first mention of
the word scar, where the motifs "Odysseus" and "recollection" were
already at hand. But any such subjectivistic-perspectivistic procedure,
creating a foreground and background, resulting in the present lying
open to the depths of the past, is entirely foreign to the Homeric style;

the Homeric style knows only a foreground, only a uniformly illuminated, uniformly objective present. And so the excursus does not begin
until two lines later, when Euryclea has discovered the scar—the possibility for a perspectivistic connection no longer exists, and the story
of the wound becomes an independent and exclusive present.

The genius of the Homeric style becomes even more apparent when
it is compared with an equally ancient and equally epic style from a
different world of forms. I shall attempt this comparison with the account of the sacrifice of Isaac, a homogeneous narrative produced by
the so-called Elohist. The King James version translates the opening
as follows (Genesis 22: 1): "And it came to pass after these things,
that God did tempt Abraham, and said to him, Abraham! and he said,
Behold, here I am." Even this opening startles us when we come to
it from Homer. Where are the two speakers? We are not told. The
reader, however, knows that they are not normally to be found together in one place on earth, that one of them, God, in order to speak
to Abraham, must come from somewhere, must enter the earthly
realm from some unknown heights or depths. Whence does he come,
whence does he call to Abraham? We are not told. He does not come,
like Zeus or Poseidon, from the Aethiopians, where he has been enjoying a sacrificial feast. Nor are we told anything of his reasons for
tempting Abraham so terribly. He has not, like Zeus, discussed them
in set speeches with other gods gathered in council; nor have the
deliberations in his own heart been presented to us; unexpected and
mysterious, he enters the scene from some unknown height or depth
and calls: Abraham! It will at once be said that this is to be explained
by the particular concept of God which the Jews held and which was
wholly different from that of the Greeks. True enough—but this constitutes no objection. For how is the Jewish concept of God to be explained? Even their earlier God of the desert was not fixed in form and
content, and was alone; his lack of form, his lack of local habitation,
his singleness, was in the end not only maintained but developed even
further in competition with the comparatively far more manifest gods
of the surrounding Near Eastern world. The concept of God held by
the Jews is less a cause than a symptom of their manner of comprehending and representing things.

This becomes still clearer if we now turn to the other person in the
dialogue, to Abraham. Where is he? We do not know. He says, indeed: Here I am—but the Hebrew word means only something like
"behold me," and in any case is not meant to indicate the actual place

where Abraham is, but a moral position in respect to God, who has called to him—Here am I awaiting thy command. Where he is actually, whether in Beersheba or elsewhere, whether indoors or in the open air, is not stated; it does not interest the narrator, the reader is not informed; and what Abraham was doing when God called to him is left in the same obscurity. To realize the difference, consider Hermes' visit to Calypso, for example, where command, journey, arrival and reception of the visitor, situation and occupation of the person visited, are set forth in many verses; and even on occasions when gods appear suddenly and briefly, whether to help one of their favorites or to deceive or destroy some mortal whom they hate, their bodily forms, and usually the manner of their coming and going, are given in detail. Here, however, God appears without bodily form (yet he "appears"), coming from some unspecified place—we only hear his voice, and that utters nothing but a name, a name without an adjective, without a descriptive epithet for the person spoken to, such as is the rule in every Homeric address; and of Abraham too nothing is made perceptible except the words in which he answers God: *Hinne-ni,* Behold me here—with which, to be sure, a most touching gesture expressive of obedience and readiness is suggested, but it is left to the reader to visualize it. Moreover the two speakers are not on the same level: if we conceive of Abraham in the foreground, where it might be possible to picture him as prostrate or kneeling or bowing with outspread arms or gazing upward, God is not there too: Abraham's words and gestures are directed toward the depths of the picture or upward, but in any case the undetermined, dark place from which the voice comes to him is not in the foreground.

After this opening, God gives his command, and the story itself begins: everyone knows it; it unrolls with no episodes in a few independent sentences whose syntactical connection is of the most rudimentary sort. In this atmosphere it is unthinkable that an implement, a landscape through which the travelers passed, the serving-men, or the ass, should be described, that their origin or descent or material or appearance or usefulness should be set forth in terms of praise; they do not even admit an adjective: they are serving-men, ass, wood, and knife, and nothing else, without an epithet; they are there to serve the end which God has commanded; what in other respects they were, are, or will be, remains in darkness. A journey is made, because God has designated the place where the sacrifice is to be performed; but we are told nothing about the journey except that it took three days, and even that we are told in a mysterious way: Abraham and his followers rose "early in the morning" and "went unto" the place of which God had told him; on the third day he lifted up his eyes and saw the place from afar. That gesture is the only gesture, is indeed the only occurrence during the whole journey, of which we are told; and though its motivation lies in the fact that the place is elevated, its uniqueness still heightens the impression that the journey took place through a vacuum; it is as if, while he traveled on, Abraham had looked neither to the right nor to the left, had suppressed any sign of life in his followers and himself save only their footfalls.

Thus the journey is like a silent progress through the indeterminate and the contingent, a holding of the breath, a process which has no present, which is inserted, like a blank duration, between what has passed and what lies ahead, and which yet is measured: three days! Three such days positively demand the symbolic interpretation which they later received. They began "early in the morning." But at what time on the third day did Abraham lift up his eyes and see his goal? The text says nothing on the subject. Obviously not "late in the evening," for it seems that there was still time enough to climb the mountain and make the sacrifice. So "early in the morning" is given, not as an indication of time, but for the sake of its ethical significance; it is intended to express the resolution, the promptness, the punctual obedience of the sorely tried Abraham. Bitter to him is the early morning in which he saddles his ass, calls his serving-men and his son Isaac, and sets out; but he obeys, he walks on until the third day, then lifts up his eyes and sees the place. Whence he comes, we do not know, but the goal is clearly stated: Jeruel in the land of Moriah. What place this is meant to indicate is not clear—"Moriah" especially may be a later correction of some other word. But in any case the goal was given, and in any case it is a matter of some sacred spot which was to receive a particular consecration by being connected with Abraham's sacrifice. Just as little as "early in the morning" serves as a temporal indication does "Jeruel in the land of Moriah" serve as a geographical indication; and in both cases alike, the complementary indication is not given, for we know as little of the hour at which Abraham lifted up his eyes as we do of the place from which he set forth—Jeruel is significant not so much as the goal of an earthly journey, in its geographical relation to other places, as through its special election, through its relation to God, who designated it as the scene of the act, and therefore it must be named.

In the narrative itself, a third chief character appears: Isaac. While God and Abraham, the serving-men, the ass, and the implements are simply named, without mention of any qualities or any other sort of definition, Isaac once receives an appositive; God says, "Take Isaac, thine only son, whom thou lovest." But this is not a characterization of Isaac as a person, apart from his relation to his father and apart from the story; he may be handsome or ugly, intelligent or stupid, tall or short, pleasant or unpleasant—we are not told. Only what we need to know about him as a personage in the action, here and now, is illuminated, so that it may become apparent how terrible Abraham's temptation is, and that God is fully aware of it. By this example of the contrary, we see the sign. cance of the descriptive adjectives and digressions of the Homeric poems; with their indications of the earlier and as it were absolute existence of the persons described, they prevent the reader from concentrating exclusively on a present crisis; even when the most terrible things are occurring, they prevent the establishment of an overwhelming suspense. But here, in the story of Abraham's sacrifice, the overwhelming suspense is present; what Schiller makes the goal of the tragic poet—to rob us of our emotional freedom, to turn our intellectual and spiritual powers (Schiller says "our activity") in one direction, to concentrate them there—is effected in this Biblical narrative, which certainly deserves the epithet epic.

We find the same contrast if we compare the two uses of direct discourse. The personages speak in the Bible story too; but their speech does not serve, as does speech in Homer, to manifest, to externalize thoughts—on the contrary, it serves to indicate thoughts which remain unexpressed. God gives his command in direct discourse, but he leaves his motives and his purpose unexpressed; Abraham, receiving the command, says nothing and does what he has been told to do. The conversation between Abraham and Isaac on the way to the place of sacrifice is only an interruption of the heavy silence and makes it all the more burdensome. The two of them, Isaac carrying the wood and Abraham with fire and a knife, "went together." Hesitantly, Isaac ventures to ask about the ram, and Abraham gives the well-known answer. Then the text repeats: "So they went both of them together." Everything remains unexpressed.

It would be difficult, then, to imagine styles more contrasted than those of these two equally ancient and equally epic texts. On the one hand, externalized, uniformly illuminated phenomena, at a definite time and in a definite place, connected together without lacunae in a perpetual foreground; thoughts and feeling completely expressed; events taking place in leisurely fashion and with very little of suspense. On the other hand, the externalization of only so much of the phenomena as is necessary for the purpose of the narrative, all else left in obscurity; the decisive points of the narrative alone are emphasized, what lies between is nonexistent; time and place are undefined and call for interpretation; thoughts and feeling remain unexpressed, are only suggested by the silence and the fragmentary speeches; the whole, permeated with the most unrelieved suspense and directed toward a single goal (and to that extent far more of a unity), remains mysterious and "fraught with background."

I will discuss this term in some detail, lest it be misunderstood. I said above that the Homeric style was "of the foreground" because, despite much going back and forth, it yet causes what is momentarily being narrated to give the impression that it is the only present, pure and without perspective. A consideration of the Elohistic text teaches us that our term is capable of a broader and deeper application. It shows that even the separate personages can be represented as possessing "background"; God is always so represented in the Bible, for he is not comprehensible in his presence, as is Zeus; it is always only "something" of him that appears, he always extends into depths. But even the human beings in the Biblical stories have greater depths of time, fate, and consciousness than do the human beings in Homer; although they are nearly always caught up in an event engaging all their faculties, they are not so entirely immersed in its present that they do not remain continually conscious of what has happened to them earlier and elsewhere; their thoughts and feelings have more layers, are more entangled. Abraham's actions are explained not only by what is happening to him at the moment, nor yet only by his character (as Achilles' actions by his courage and his pride, and Odysseus' by his versatility and foresightedness), but by his previous history; he remembers, he is constantly conscious of, what God has promised him and what God has already accomplished for him—his soul is torn between desperate rebellion and hopeful expectation; his silent obedience is multilayered, has background. Such a problematic psychological situation as this is impossible for any of the Homeric heroes, whose destiny is clearly defined and who wake every morning as if it were the first day of their lives: their emotions, though strong, are simple and find expression instantly.

How fraught with background, in comparison, are characters like

Saul and David! How entangled and stratified are such human relations as those between David and Absalom, between David and Joab!
Any such "background" quality of the psychological situation as that
which the story of Absalom's death and its sequel (II Samuel 18 and
19, by the so-called Jahvist) rather suggests than expresses, is unthinkable in Homer. Here we are confronted not merely with the psychological processes of characters whose depth of background is verita-
bly abysmal, but with a purely geographical background too. For David
is absent from the battlefield; but the influence of his will and his
feelings continues to operate, they affect even Joab in his rebellion
and disregard for the consequences of his actions; in the magnificent
scene with the two messengers, both the physical and psychological
background is fully manifest, though the latter is never expressed.
With this, compare, for example, how Achilles, who sends Patroclus
first to scout and then into battle, loses almost all "presentness" so
long as he is not physically present. But the most important thing is
the "multilayeredness" of the individual character; this is hardly to be
met with in Homer, or at most in the form of a conscious hesitation
between two possible courses of action; otherwise, in Homer, the complexity of the psychological life is shown only in the succession and
alternation of emotions; whereas the Jewish writers are able to express
the simultaneous existence of various layers of consciousness and the
conflict between them.

The Homeric poems, then, though their intellectual, linguistic, and
above all syntactical culture appears to be so much more highly developed, are yet comparatively simple in their picture of human beings;
and no less so in their relation to the real life which they describe in
general. Delight in physical existence is everything to them, and their
highest aim is to make that delight perceptible to us. Between battles
and passions, adventures and perils, they show us hunts, banquets,
palaces and shepherds' cots, athletic contests and washing days—in
order that we may see the heroes in their ordinary life, and seeing them
so, may take pleasure in their manner of enjoying their savory present,
a present which sends strong roots down into social usages, landscape,
and daily life. And thus they bewitch us and ingratiate themselves to
us until we live with them in the reality of their lives; so long as we are
reading or hearing the poems, it does not matter whether we know
that all this is only legend, "make-believe." The oft-repeated reproach
that Homer is a liar takes nothing from his effectiveness, he does not
need to base his story on historical reality, his reality is powerful

enough in itself; it ensnares us, weaving its web around us, and that suffices him. And this "real" world into which we are lured, exists for itself, contains nothing but itself; the Homeric poems conceal nothing, they contain no teaching and no secret second meaning. Homer can be analyzed, as we have essayed to do here, but he cannot be interpreted. Later allegorizing trends have tried their arts of interpretation upon him, but to no avail. He resists any such treatment; the interpretations are forced and foreign, they do not crystallize into a unified doctrine. The general considerations which occasionally occur (in our episode, for example, v. 360: that in misfortune men age quickly) reveal a calm acceptance of the basic facts of human existence, but with no compulsion to brood over them, still less any passionate impulse either to rebel against them or to embrace them in an ectasy of submission.

It is all very different in the Biblical stories. Their aim is not to bewitch the senses, and if nevertheless they produce lively sensory effects, it is only because the moral, religious, and psychological phenomena which are their sole concern are made concrete in the sensible matter of life. But their religious intent involves an absolute claim to historical truth. The story of Abraham and Isaac is not better established than the story of Odysseus, Penelope, and Euryclea; both are legendary. But the Biblical narrator, the Elohist, had to believe in the objective truth of the story of Abraham's sacrifice—the existence of the sacred ordinances of life rested upon the truth of this and similar stories. He had to believe in it passionately; or else (as many rationalistic interpreters believed and perhaps still believe) he had to be a conscious liar—no harmless liar like Homer, who lied to give pleasure, but a political liar with a definite end in view, lying in the interest of a claim to absolute authority.

To me, the rationalistic interpretation seems psychologically absurd; but even if we take it into consideration, the relation of the Elohist to the truth of his story still remains a far more passionate and definite one than is Homer's relation. The Biblical narrator was obliged to write exactly what his belief in the truth of the tradition (or, from the rationalistic standpoint, his interest in the truth of it) demanded of him—in either case, his freedom in creative or representative imagination was severely limited; his activity was perforce reduced to composing an effective version of the pious tradition. What he produced, then, was not primarily oriented toward "realism" (if he succeeded in being realistic, it was merely a means, not an end); it was oriented toward truth. Woe to the man who did not believe it! One can perfectly well entertain historical doubts on the subject of the Trojan War or of Odysseus' wanderings, and still, when reading Homer, feel precisely the effects he sought to produce; but without believing in Abraham's sacrifice, it is impossible to put the narrative of it to the use for which it was written. Indeed, we must go even further. The Bible's claim to truth is not only far more urgent than Homer's, it is tyrannical—it excludes all other claims. The world of the Scripture stories is not satisfied with claiming to be a historically true reality—it insists that it is the only real world, is destined for autocracy. All other scenes, issues, and ordinances have no right to appear independently of it, and it is promised that all of them, the history of all mankind, will be given their due place within its frame, will be subordinated to it. The Scripture stories do not, like Homer's, court our favor, they do not flatter us that they may please us and enchant us—they seek to subject us, and if we refuse to be subjected we are rebels.

Let no one object that this goes too far, that not the stories, but the religious doctrine, raises the claim to absolute authority; because the stories are not, like Homer's, simply narrated "reality." Doctrine and promise are incarnate in them and inseparable from them; for that very reason they are fraught with "background" and mysterious, containing a second, concealed meaning. In the story of Isaac, it is not only God's intervention at the beginning and the end, but even the factual and psychological elements which come between, that are mysterious, merely touched upon, fraught with background; and therefore they require subtle investigation and interpretation, they demand them. Since so much in the story is dark and incomplete, and since the reader knows that God is a hidden God, his effort to interpret it constantly finds something new to feed upon. Doctrine and the search for enlightenment are inextricably connected with the physical side of the narrative—the latter being more than simple "reality"; indeed they are in constant danger of losing their own reality, as very soon happened when interpretation reached such proportions that the real vanished.

If the text of the Biblical narrative, then, is so greatly in need of interpretation on the basis of its own content, its claim to absolute authority forces it still further in the same direction. Far from seeking, like Homer, merely to make us forget our own reality for a few hours, it seeks to overcome our reality: we are to fit our own life into its world, feel ourselves to be elements in its structure of universal history. This becomes increasingly difficult the further our historical environment is removed from that of the Biblical books; and if these nevertheless maintain their claim to absolute authority, it is inevitable that they themselves be adapted through interpretative transformation. This was for a long time comparatively easy; as late as the European Middle Ages it was possible to represent Biblical events as ordinary phenomena of contemporary life, the methods of interpretation themselves forming the basis for such a treatment. But when, through too great a change in environment and through the awakening of a critical consciousness, this becomes impossible, the Biblical claim to absolute authority is jeopardized; the method of interpretation is scorned and rejected, the Biblical stories become ancient legends, and the doctrine they had contained, now dissevered from them, becomes a disembodied image.

As a result of this claim to absolute authority, the method of interpretation spread to traditions other than the Jewish. The Homeric poems present a definite complex of events whose boundaries in space and time are clearly delimited; before it, beside it, and after it, other complexes of events, which do not depend upon it, can be conceived without conflict and without difficulty. The Old Testament, on the other hand, presents universal history: it begins with the beginning of time, with the creation of the world, and will end with the Last Days, the fulfilling of the Covenant, with which the world will come to an end. Everything else that happens in the world can only be conceived as an element in this sequence; into it everything that is known about the world, or at least everything that touches upon the history of the Jews, must be fitted as an ingredient of the divine plan; and as this too became possible only by interpreting the new material as it poured in, the need for interpretation reaches out beyond the original Jewish-Israelitish realm of reality—for example to Assyrian, Babylonian, Persian, and Roman history; interpretation in a determined direction becomes a general method of comprehending reality; the new and strange world which now comes into view and which, in the form in which it presents itself, proves to be wholly unutilizable within the Jewish religious frame, must be so interpreted that it can find a place there. But this process nearly always also reacts upon the frame, which requires enlarging and modifying. The most striking piece of interpretation of this sort occurred in the first century of the Christian era, in consequence of Paul's mission to the Gentiles: Paul and the Church Fathers reinterpreted the entire Jewish tradition as a succession of figures prognosticating the appearance of Christ, and assigned the

Roman Empire its proper place in the divine plan of salvation. Thus while, on the one hand, the reality of the Old Testament presents itself as complete truth with a claim to sole authority, on the other hand that very claim forces it to a constant interpretative change in its own content; for millennia it undergoes an incessant and active development with the life of man in Europe.

The claim of the Old Testament stories to represent universal history, their insistent relation—a relation constantly redefined by conflicts—to a single and hidden God, who yet shows himself and who guides universal history by promise and exaction, gives these stories an entirely different perspective from any the Homeric poems can possess. As a composition, the Old Testament is incomparably less unified than the Homeric poems, it is more obviously pieced together—but the various components all belong to one concept of universal history and its interpretation. If certain elements survived which did not immediately fit in, interpretation took care of them; and so the reader is at every moment aware of the universal religio-historical perspective which gives the individual stories their general meaning and purpose. The greater the separateness and horizontal disconnection of the stories and groups of stories in relation to one another, compared with the *Iliad* and the *Odyssey,* the stronger is their general vertical connection, which holds them all together and which is entirely lacking in Homer. Each of the great figures of the Old Testament, from Adam to the prophets, embodies a moment of this vertical connection. God chose and formed these men to the end of embodying his essence and will—yet choice and formation do not coincide, for the latter proceeds gradually, historically, during the earthly life of him upon whom the choice has fallen. How the process is accomplished, what terrible trials such a formation inflicts, can be seen from our story of Abraham's sacrifice. Herein lies the reason why the great figures of the Old Testament are so much more fully developed, so much more fraught with their own biographical past, so much more distinct as individuals, than are the Homeric heroes. Achilles and Odysseus are splendidly described in many well-ordered words, epithets cling to them, their emotions are constantly displayed in their words and deeds—but they have no development, and their life-histories are clearly set forth once and for all. So little are the Homeric heroes presented as developing or having developed, that most of them—Nestor, Agamemnon, Achilles—appear to be of an age fixed from the very first. Even Odysseus, in whose case the long lapse of time and the many

events which occurred offer so much opportunity for biographical development, shows almost nothing of it. Odysseus on his return is exactly the same as he was when he left Ithaca two decades earlier. But
what a road, what a fate, lie between the Jacob who cheated his father
out of his blessing and the old man whose favorite son has been torn
to pieces by a wild beast!—between David the harp player, persecuted
by his lord's jealousy, and the old king, surrounded by violent intrigues,
whom Abishag the Shunnamite warmed in his bed, and he knew her
not! The old man, of whom we know how he has become what he is,
is more of an individual than the young man; for it is only during the
course of an eventful life that men are differentiated into full individuality; and it is this history of a personality which the Old Testament presents to us as the formation undergone by those whom God
has chosen to be examples. Fraught with their development, sometimes even aged to the verge of dissolution, they show a distinct stamp
of individuality entirely foreign to the Homeric heroes. Time can
touch the latter only outwardly, and even that change is brought to
our observation as little as possible; whereas the stern hand of God
is ever upon the Old Testament figures; he has not only made them
once and for all and chosen them, but he continues to work upon
them, bends them and kneads them, and, without destroying them in
essence, produces from them forms which their youth gave no grounds
for anticipating. The objection that the biographical element of the
Old Testament often springs from the combination of several legendary personages does not apply; for this combination is a part of
the development of the text. And how much wider is the pendulum
swing of their lives than that of the Homeric heroes! For they are
bearers of the divine will, and yet they are fallible, subject to misfortune and humiliation—and in the midst of misfortune and in their
humiliation their acts and words reveal the transcendent majesty of
God. There is hardly one of them who does not, like Adam, undergo
the deepest humiliation—and hardly one who is not deemed worthy
of God's personal intervention and personal inspiration. Humiliation
and elevation go far deeper and far higher than in Homer, and they
belong basically together. The poor beggar Odysseus is only masquerad-
ing, but Adam is really cast down, Jacob really a refugee, Joseph really
in the pit and then a slave to be bought and sold. But their greatness,
rising out of humiliation, is almost superhuman and an image of God's
greatness. The reader clearly feels how the extent of the pendulum's
swing is connected with the intensity of the personal history—precisely

the most extreme circumstances, in which we are immeasurably forsaken and in despair, or immeasurably joyous and exalted, give us, if we survive them, a personal stamp which is recognized as the product of a rich existence, a rich development. And very often, indeed generally, this element of development gives the Old Testament stories a historical character, even when the subject is purely legendary and traditional.

Homer remains within the legendary with all his material, whereas the material of the Old Testament comes closer and closer to history as the narrative proceeds; in the stories of David the historical report predominates. Here too, much that is legendary still remains, as for example the story of David and Goliath; but much—and the most essential—consists in things which the narrators knew from their own experience or from firsthand testimony. Now the difference between legend and history is in most cases easily perceived by a reasonably experienced reader. It is a difficult matter, requiring careful historical and philological training, to distinguish the true from the synthetic or the biased in a historical presentation; but it is easy to separate the historical from the legendary in general. Their structure is different. Even where the legendary does not immediately betray itself by elements of the miraculous, by the repetition of well-known standard motives, typical patterns and themes, through neglect of clear details of time and place, and the like, it is generally quickly recognizable by its composition. It runs far too smoothly. All cross-currents, all friction, all that is casual, secondary to the main events and themes, everything unresolved, truncated, and uncertain, which confuses the clear progress of the action and the simple orientation of the actors, has disappeared. The historical event which we witness, or learn from the testimony of those who witnessed it, runs much more variously, contradictorily, and confusedly; not until it has produced results in a definite domain are we able, with their help, to classify it to a certain extent; and how often the order to which we think we have attained becomes doubtful again, how often we ask ourselves if the data before us have not led us to a far too simple classification of the original events! Legend arranges its material in a simple and straightforward way; it detaches it from its contemporary historical context, so that the latter will not confuse it; it knows only clearly outlined men who act from few and simple motives and the continuity of whose feelings and actions remains uninterrupted. In the legends of martyrs, for example, a stiff-necked and fanatical persecutor stands over against an

equally stiff-necked and fanatical victim; and a situation so complicated—that is to say, so real and historical—as that in which the "persecutor" Pliny finds himself in his celebrated letter to Trajan on the
subject of the Christians, is unfit for legend. And that is still a comparatively simple case. Let the reader think of the history which we
are ourselves witnessing; anyone who, for example, evaluates the behavior of individual men and groups of men at the time of the rise
of National Socialism in Germany, or the behavior of individual peoples and states before and during the last war, will feel how difficult it
is to represent historical themes in general, and how unfit they are for
legend; the historical comprises a great number of contradictory motives in each individual, a hesitation and ambiguous groping on the
part of groups; only seldom (as in the last war) does a more or less
plain situation, comparatively simple to describe, arise, and even such
a situation is subject to division below the surface, is indeed almost
constantly in danger of losing its simplicity; and the motives of all the
interested parties are so complex that the slogans of propaganda can
be composed only through the crudest simplification—with the result
that friend and foe alike can often employ the same ones. To write
history is so difficult that most historians are forced to make concessions to the technique of legend.

It is clear that a large part of the life of David as given in the Bible
contains history and not legend. In Absalom's rebellion, for example,
or in the scenes from David's last days, the contradictions and crossing
of motives both in individuals and in the general action have become
so concrete that it is impossible to doubt the historicity of the information conveyed. Now the men who composed the historical parts are
often the same who edited the older legends too; their peculiar religious concept of man in history, which we have attempted to describe
above, in no way led them to legendary simplification of events; and
so it is only natural that, in the legendary passages of the Old Testament, historical structure is frequently discernible—of course, not in
the sense that the traditions are examined as to their credibility according to the methods of scientific criticism; but simply to the extent that the tendency to a smoothing down and harmonizing of events,
to a simplification of motives, to a static definition of characters which
avoids conflict, vacillation, and development, such as are natural to
legendary structure, does not predominate in the Old Testament world
of legend. Abraham, Jacob, or even Moses produces a more concrete,
direct, and historical impression than the figures of the Homeric world

—not because they are better described in terms of sense (the contrary is the case) but because the confused, contradictory multiplicity of events, the psychological and factual cross-purposes, which true history reveals, have not disappeared in the representation but still remain clearly perceptible. In the stories of David, the legendary, which only later scientific criticism makes recognizable as such, imperceptibly passes into the historical; and even in the legendary, the problem of the classification and interpretation of human history is already passionately apprehended—a problem which later shatters the framework of historical composition and completely overruns it with prophecy; thus the Old Testament, in so far as it is concerned with human events, ranges through all three domains: legend, historical reporting, and interpretative historical theology.

Connected with the matters just discussed is the fact that the Greek text seems more limited and more static in respect to the circle of personages involved in the action and to their political activity. In the recognition scene with which we began, there appears, aside from Odysseus and Penelope, the housekeeper Euryclea, a slave whom Odysseus' father Laertes had bought long before. She, like the swineherd Eumaeus, has spent her life in the service of Laertes' family; like Eumaeus, she is closely connected with their fate, she loves them and shares their interests and feelings. But she has no life of her own, no feelings of her own; she has only the life and feelings of her master. Eumaeus too, though he still remembers that he was born a freeman and indeed of a noble house (he was stolen as a boy), has, not only in fact but also in his own feeling, no longer a life of his own, he is entirely involved in the life of his masters. Yet these two characters are the only ones whom Homer brings to life who do not belong to the ruling class. Thus we become conscious of the fact that in the Homeric poems life is enacted only among the ruling class—others appear only in the role of servants to that class. The ruling class is still so strongly patriarchal, and still itself so involved in the daily activities of domestic life, that one is sometimes likely to forget their rank. But they are unmistakably a sort of feudal aristocracy, whose men divide their lives between war, hunting, marketplace councils, and feasting, while the women supervise the maids in the house. As a social picture, this world is completely stable; wars take place only between different groups of the ruling class; nothing ever pushes up from below. In the early stories of the Old Testament the patriarchal condition is dominant too, but since the people involved are individual nomadic or half-nomadic tribal leaders, the social picture gives a much less stable impression; class distinctions are not felt. As soon as the people completely emerges—that is, after the exodus from Egypt—its activity is always discernible, it is often in ferment, it frequently intervenes in events not only as a whole but also in separate groups and through the medium of separate individuals who come forward; the origins of prophecy seem to lie in the irrepressible politico-religious spontaneity of the people. We receive the impression that the movements emerging from the depths of the people of Israel-Judah must have been of a wholly different nature from those even of the later ancient democracies—of a different nature and far more elemental.

With the more profound historicity and the more profound social activity of the Old Testament text, there is connected yet another important distinction from Homer: namely, that a different conception of the elevated style and of the sublime is to be found here. Homer, of course, is not afraid to let the realism of daily life enter into the sublime and tragic; our episode of the scar is an example, we see how the quietly depicted, domestic scene of the foot-washing is incorporated into the pathetic and sublime action of Odysseus' homecoming. From the rule of the separation of styles which was later almost universally accepted and which specified that the realistic depiction of daily life was incompatible with the sublime and had a place only in comedy or, carefully stylized, in idyl—from any such rule Homer is still far removed. And yet he is closer to it than is the Old Testament. For the great and sublime events in the Homeric poems take place far more exclusively and unmistakably among the members of a ruling class; and these are far more untouched in their heroic elevation than are the Old Testament figures, who can fall much lower in dignity (consider, for example, Adam, Noah, David, Job); and finally, domestic realism, the representation of daily life, remains in Homer in the peaceful realm of the idyllic, whereas, from the very first, in the Old Testament stories, the sublime, tragic, and problematic take shape precisely in the domestic and commonplace: scenes such as those between Cain and Abel, between Noah and his sons, between Abraham, Sarah, and Hagar, between Rebekah, Jacob, and Esau, and so on, are inconceivable in the Homeric style. The entirely different ways of developing conflicts are enough to account for this. In the Old Testament stories the peace of daily life in the house, in the fields, and among the flocks, is undermined by jealousy over election and the promise of a blessing, and complications arise which would be utterly incomprehensible to the Homeric heroes. The latter must have palpable and clearly expressible reasons for their conflicts and enmities, and these work themselves out in free battles; whereas, with the former, the perpetually smouldering jealousy and the connection between the domestic and the spiritual, between the paternal blessing and the divine blessing, lead to daily life being permeated with the stuff of conflict, often with poison. The sublime influence of God here reaches so deeply into the everyday that the two realms of the sublime and the everyday are not only actually unseparated but basically inseparable.

We have compared these two texts, and, with them, the two kinds of style they embody, in order to reach a starting point for an investigation into the literary representation of reality in European culture. The two styles, in their opposition, represent basic types: on the one hand fully externalized description, uniform illumination, uninterrupted connection, free expression, all events in the foreground, displaying unmistakable meanings, few elements of historical development and of psychological perspective; on the other hand, certain parts brought into high relief, others left obscure, abruptness, suggestive influence of the unexpressed, "background" quality, multiplicity of meanings and the need for interpretation, universal-historical claims, development of the concept of the historically becoming, and preoccupation with the problematic.

Homer's realism is, of course, not to be equated with classical-antique realism in general; for the separation of styles, which did not develop until later, permitted no such leisurely and externalized description of everyday happenings; in tragedy especially there was no room for it; furthermore, Greek culture very soon encountered the phenomena of historical becoming and of the "multilayeredness" of the human problem, and dealt with them in its fashion; in Roman realism, finally, new and native concepts are added. We shall go into these later changes in the antique representation of reality when the occasion arises; on the whole, despite them, the basic tendencies of the Homeric style, which we have attempted to work out, remained effective and determinant down into late antiquity.

Since we are using the two styles, the Homeric and the Old Testament, as starting points, we have taken them as finished products, as they appear in the texts; we have disregarded everything that pertains to their origins, and thus have left untouched the question whether their peculiarities were theirs from the beginning or are to be re-

ferred wholly or in part to foreign influences. Within the limits
of our purpose, a consideration of this question is not necessary; for
it is in their full development, which they reached in early times, that
the two styles exercised their determining influence upon the representation of reality in European literature. (pp. 3-23)

WHAT IS ART?
(excerpt)

LEV NIKOLAEVICH TOLSTOI

What is Art?, *written late in Tolstoi's life (1896-7), is a strong argument for considering art as a social and religious concern, "a human
activity having for its purpose the transmission to others of the highest
and best feelings to which men have risen." True art, Tolstoi asserts, is
universal for "a given time in a given society." (Time and society are
broad in scope here.) Tolstoi particularly deprecates aestheticism, partly
because it makes "beauty" the central concern of art and partly because
it is an activity of coteries.*

*"The highest and best feelings" which modern art should communi-
cate and foster are those rising out of and tending to human unity.
Tolstoi uses the Joseph story as an example of art which evokes in men
"those feelings which show them that they are already united in the
joys and sorrows of life," or "art transmitting the simplest feelings of
common life, but such, always, as are accessible to all men in the whole
world."*

From *What is Art?* in *The Novels and Other Works of Lyof N. Tolstoï,* New
York, Charles Scribner's Sons, 1899, vol. XIX.

Again, Tolstoi uses the Joseph story as an example of a story not marked by "imitation," here referring to the piling up of descriptive details in the attempt to impart "a semblance of art" to what is not genuine art.

Thus Tolstoi's criticism of the story of Joseph is part of his whole theory of art in his later years.

To GIVE EXAMPLES, from the modern art of our upper classes, of art of the second kind, good universal art or even of the art of a whole people, is yet more difficult, especially in literary art and music. If there are some works which by their inner contents might be assigned to this class (such as "Don Quixote," Molière's comedies, "David Copperfield" and "The Pickwick Papers" by Dickens, Gogol's and Pushkin's tales, and some things of Maupassant's), these works are for the most part—from the exceptional nature of the feelings they transmit, and the superfluity of special details of time and locality, and, above all, on account of the poverty of their subject-matter in comparison with examples of universal ancient art (such, for instance, as the story of Joseph)—comprehensible only to people of their own circle. That Joseph's brethren, being jealous of his father's affection, sell him to the merchants; that Potiphar's wife wishes to tempt the youth; that having attained the highest station, he takes pity on his brothers, including Benjamin, the favorite,—these and all the rest are feelings accessible alike to a Russian peasant, a Chinese, an African, a child, or an old man, educated or uneducated; and it is all written with such restraint, is so free from any superfluous detail, that the story may be told to any circle and will be equally comprehensible and touching to every one. But not such are the feelings of Don Quixote or of Molière's heroes (though Molière is perhaps the most universal, and therefore the most excellent, artist of modern times), nor of Pickwick and his friends. These feelings are not common to all men, but very exceptional; and therefore, to make them infectious, the authors have surrounded them with abundant details of time and place. And this abundance of detail makes the stories difficult of comprehension to all people not living within reach of the conditions described by the author.

The author of the novel of Joseph did not need to describe in detail, as would be done nowadays, the blood-stained coat of Joseph, the dwelling and dress of Jacob, the pose and attire of Potiphar's wife, and how, adjusting the bracelet on her left arm, she said, "Come to me," and so on, because the subject-matter of feelings in this novel is so strong that all details, except the most essential,—such as that Joseph went out into another room to weep,—are superfluous, and would only hinder the transmission of feelings. And therefore this novel is accessible to all men, touches people of all nations and classes, young and old, and has lasted to our times, and will yet last for thousands of years to come. But strip the best novels of our times of their details, and what will remain? (vol. XIX, pp. 490-491)

THE THEME OF THE JOSEPH NOVELS
(excerpt)

THOMAS MANN

. . . . I have often been asked what it actually was that made me turn to this remote and out-of-the way subject and induced me to transform the biblical legend of the Egyptian Joseph into a broad cycle of novels, requiring many years of work. In answering this question, there is little importance in the external and anecdotical circumstances which prompted me, almost a decade and a half ago when I was still in Munich, to re-read the story in my old ancestral Bible. Suffice it to say that I was delighted, and that immediately a preliminary probing and productive searching began in my mind as to what it would be like to renew and reproduce this charming story in fresh narrative and with modern means—with *all* modern means, the spiritual and the technical ones. Almost immediately, these inner experiments significantly associ-

From *The Theme of the Joseph Novels,* by Thomas Mann, (lecture delivered Nov. 7, 1942 at the Coolidge Auditorium); published by the Library of Congress and reprinted in the *Atlantic Monthly,* February, 1943. Reprinted with the permission of Frau Thomas Mann.

ated themselves with the thought of a tradition: the thought of Goethe, in fact, who relates in his memoires "Dichtung und Wahrheit" how he, as a boy, had dictated the Joseph story to a friend and, in doing so, had woven it into a broad narrative. However, it soon met the fate of destruction because, in the author's own judgement, it still lacked too much in "substance." As an explanation of this youthful and premature venture, the sixty year old Goethe observes: "This natural story is highly amiable; only, it seems too short, and one is tempted to carry it out in all its details."

How strange! Immediately, these words from "Dichtung und Wahrheit" came to my mind, in the midst of my reveries: they were in my memory; I did not have to re-read them,—and indeed, they seem most fitting as the motto for what I then undertook; they furnish the simplest and most plausible explanation for my venture. The temptation which the young Goethe had naively followed, namely to carry out the short legendary report of Genesis in "all its details," repeated itself in my case at a stage of my life when the poetic execution could definitely obtain human and spiritual substance as well. But what does that mean: to carry out in detail what has been briefly reported? It is exactness, realization; it is to draw into proximity something very remote and vague, so that you believe you see it with your eyes and grasp it with your hands, and you think, that, finally, you learn the definite truth about it after having so long entertained very uncertain ideas on the subject. . .

It is quite possible that such secret charms played their part at the time of the earliest conception of the work. But this does not answer the question as to how I came to select this archaic subject-matter from the dawn of mankind. Different circumstances, some of a personal and others of a general temporal character, contributed to it, and the personal ones were also of a temporal nature; they had something to do with those years, and with a stage of life that had been attained. The readiness is all. As a man, and as an artist, I must somehow have been in *readiness* to be productively attracted by such subject-matter, and my Bible-reading was not mere chance. The various stages of life have different inclinations, claims, tendencies of taste—as well as abilities and advantages. It is probably a rule that in certain years the taste for all purely individual and particular phenomena, for the individual case, for the "bourgeois" aspect, in the widest sense of the word, fades out gradually. Instead, the typical, the eternally-human, eternally-recurring, timeless, in short: the mythical steps into the foreground of the interest. For, after all, the typical is already the mythical, insofar as it is pristine pattern and pristine form of life, timeless model and formula of eld, into which life enters by reproducing its traits out of the unconscious. Definitely, the attainment of the mythical viewpoint is of decisive importance in the life of the narrator; it signifies a peculiar enhancement of his artistic mood, a new serenity in recognizing and shaping which, as said before, is ordinarily reserved for the later years of life: for the mythical, it is true, represents an early and primitive stage in the life of humanity, but a late and mature one in the life of the individual.

There the word humanity has been pronounced—in connection with the ideas of the timelessly-typical and the mythical it automatically made its appearance. I had been in readiness to feel productively attracted by a subject-matter like the Joseph legend, because of the turning of my taste away from the bourgeois toward the mythical aspect. But, at the same time, I was in readiness for it because of my disposition for generally human feeling and thinking,—I mean: a feeling and thinking in human terms,—a disposition which was not only the product of my individual time and stage of life, but that of the time at large and in general, of OUR time, of the historic convulsions, adventures and tribulations, by which the question of man, the very problem of humanity was presented to us as an indivisible whole, and imposed upon our conscience as hardly ever to a generation before us. . . .

How much of an adventure I considered this mythical enterprise of mine, is indicated by the introduction to the first volume of "Joseph and His Brothers," "The Stories of Jaacob," which forms the anthropological prelude to the whole work. Entitled "Descent into Hell" it is a fantastical essay which seems like the cumbersome preparation for a risky expedition—a journey down into the depths of the past, a trip to the 'mothers.' The overture was sixty-four pages long—that might have made me suspicious in regard to the proportions of the whole, and did so to a degree—especially as I had decided, that the personal story of Joseph alone would not do, but that the primeval and original story, the history of the world demanded to be included, at least in perspective. The stories of Jaacob filled a heavy volume: in mingled order, anticipating and reverting, I recited them, strangely entertained by the novelty of dealing with human beings who did not quite know who they were, or who knew it in a more pious, deeply exact way than the modern individual; beings whose identity was open in back and included the past with which they identified themselves, in whose steps they tread and which again become present through them. . . .

"Faust" is a symbol of humanity, and to become something like that in my hands was the clandestine tendency of the Joseph story. I told about beginnings, where everything came into being for the first time. That was the attractive novelty, the uncommon amusement of this kind of fable telling, that everything was there for the first time, that one foundation took place after the other, the foundation of love, of envy, of hatred, of murder, and of much else. But this dominant originality is, at the same time, repetition, reflection, image; the result of rotation of the spheres which brings the upper, the starlike into the lower regions, carries, in turn, the worldly into the realm of the divine, so that gods become men, men in turn become gods. The worldly finds itself pre-created in the realm of the stars, and the individual character seeks its dignity by tracing itself back to the timeless, mythical pattern, giving it presence.

I dwelled on the birth of the Ego out of the mythical collective, the Abrahamitic Ego which is pretentious enough to assume that man should serve only the Highest, from which assumption the discovery of God followed. The claim of the human ego to central importance is the premise for the discovery of God, and from the very first the pathos for the dignity of the Ego is connected with that for the dignity of humanity.

At the same time, these humans remain confined in the mythical, the collective, to a large extent of their being. What they call spirit and culture, is just the conviction that their lives are the embodiment of the myth, and their ego detaches itself from the collective in much the same way as certain figures of Rodin wrest themselves out of the stone and awaken from it. Jaacob, weighty with stories, is also such a half- detached figure: his solemnness is still mythical and already individual; the cult which he devotes to his feelings, and for which he is punished by the jealousy of the Highest is the bland but proud assertion of an ego, which loftily feels itself the subject and hero of its stories. It is still a patriarchal and respectable form of human individualization and emancipation, and it grows far more bold and daring in the complicated case of his son Joseph. There is one, who has not discovered God, but knows how to "treat" Him; one who is not only the hero of his stories, but also their director, indeed the one who poetically "adorns" them; one who, it is true, still participates in the collective and mythical, but in a banteringly spiritualized and playful, purposefully conscious manner. In short, we see how the ego, in the process of its emancipation, soon becomes an artistic ego, attractive, delicate and—endangered, a tender concern for the respectable father, but with inborn possibilities of development and maturing, as have not existed before. In its youth, the artistic ego is of inexcusable egocentricity: it lives under the dangerous assumption that everybody must love it more than himself. But due to a sympathy and friendliness which nonetheless it never renounces, it finds its way into the social, while it matures, and becomes the provider and benefactor of a foreign people and of its own: in Joseph the ego flows back from arrogant absoluteness into the collective, common; and, the contrast between artistic and civic tendencies, between isolation and community, between individual and collective is fabulously neutralized, —as according to our hopes and our will; it must be dissolved in the democracy of the future, the cooperation of free and divergent nations under the equalizing sceptre of justice.

A symbol of humanity—in a certain way my work was entitled to this secret opinion of itself. After all, from the original and simple, the typical and canonical it led to the complicated, involved, late: the way from Canaan to the Egypt of the New Kingdom is the way from the piously primitive, the God-creating, God-contemplative idyl of the archfathers to a highly developed and sophisticated culture with its luxuries and absurd snobberies, in a land of the grandchildren, a land whose atmosphere is so much to Joseph's taste because he is himself a grandchild and a late soul.

The feeling for the way, the advancement, the change, the development is very strong in the book, its whole theology is connected with it and derived from it: namely, from its conception of the old testamental "Bond" between God and man: from the conviction that God and man are mutually dependent upon each other in common aspiration for enhancement. For God, too, is subject to development, He, too, changes and advances: from the desert-like and demoniacal to the spiritual and holy; and He can do so without the help of the human spirit as little, as the human spirit can without Him.—Were I to determine what I, personally, mean by religiousness, I should say: it is *attentiveness* and *obedience;* attentiveness to the inner changes of the world, the mutation in the aspects of truth and right; obedience which loses no time in adjusting life and reality to these changes, this mutation, and thus in doing justice to the spirit. To live in sin is to live against the spirit, to cling to the antiquated, obsolete, and to continue to live in it, due to inattentiveness and disobedience. And whenever the book speaks about the "concern with God," it speaks about the just fear of this sin and folly. "Concern with God" is not alone the creating of God in one's thoughts, and determining and recognizing Him, but principally the concern with His will, with which ours must coincide; with the demands of the present, the postulate of the aeon, of the world hour. It is the intelligent listening to what the world spirit wants, to the new truth and necessity; and a special, religious concept of *stupidity* follows from that: the stupidity before God, which does not know this concern, or complies with it as clumsily as Laban who still believes that he must slaughter his little son and bury him in the foundation of his house, a custom which once was quite beneficial but is so no longer. (pp. 5-8, 9-10, 16-20.)

THE FIRST BIOGRAPHY

BROOKE PETERS CHURCH

The First Biography

WHEN, IN ABOUT 1000 B.C., the Israelites developed a national consciousness and set up a king over a united nation, the Greeks were still divided into innumerable small groups, some settled on the land and building up what would later be the city-states, some wandering the seas seeking new lands to conquer and colonize. The Greeks never did become a united nation, and it was partly the variant points of view, which resulted from their various experiments in government and from the keen rivalry between the cities, that made the difference between their later development and that of the Hebrews. Having overthrown the old Minoan culture which they found established, and having destroyed its manufactures and trade, they were now faced with the problem of finding a means of livelihood. To this end new manufactures and new trade routes must be developed; and since such enterprises take time and energy as well as co-operation, it was another two hundred years after the Hebrews were established in Palestine before the Greeks of the Mediterranean basin could turn their activities into artistic and intellectual channels.

These centuries were by no means wasted, for the wide contacts of travel, the intense rivalry between the centers of trade and industry, and the development of the rudiments at least of scientific research through the requirements of industrial competition did much to waken the Greek to the infinite possibilities of the world of art and science.

There seems to have been no similar development among the Israelites. After all, they had had no such contact with an alien stock nor felt the impact of an utterly foreign culture, for the Canaanites and Hebrews, as also their neighbors the Phoenicians and Syrians, and farther off the Babylonians, were all Semites, claiming a common ancestry and cherishing many of the same traditions. Their differences grew out of their variations in cultural development. The Phoenicians were a commercial people with wide-flung interests, the Babylonians were empire builders and a great world power. The Syrians, between Babylonia and Phoenicia, had early learned to profit by their strategic position and grew rich on their pickings. Palestine was poor in natural resources and off the beaten track, and except in the far north had little contact with the outside world. Handicrafts and manufacture the Hebrew never developed, and as a result the broadening influences of wide commercial interests never reached him. In the mountains of the south he lived the shepherd life of his ancestors, in the north he supported himself by agriculture and as middleman in the trade that passed over his roads.

What the cultural conditions in Palestine were that made it possible as early as the tenth century B.C. for the Hebrews to develop a written literature, and a literature, as we shall see, of such surprising maturity, is not clear. Their own account of the state of the country on the eve of the kingdom, an account contained in Judges and I Samuel, describes a state of confusion, in which the opportunity for artistic and literary activity is unthinkable. However, there must have been a considerable group of educated men among them, not only in the more culturally developed north, with its Egyptian and Babylonian contacts, but also in the poorer and more sparsely settled south. For it is from the south that our first writing comes. The north, which was preponderantly Canaanite and more exposed to alien cultures, was slow in accepting

Jahweh, and was always a backslider in matters of religion and morality. Of the great leaders of thought in Israel whose names have come down to us, very few came from the north, and judging by the high ethical tone and religious atmosphere that pervades this early literature, it seems probable that the authors of the early writings were drawn from the newcomers in the south.

The new religion introduced by the Hebrews acted as a civilizing and unifying influence throughout the land, and the men who guided the movement must have been men of force and vision. Under their influence and teaching the hundreds of little shrines to various gods and heroes scattered throughout the land gradually lost their local significance and become in one way or another sacred to Jahweh, and the stories and ritual centered about them became imbued with the spirit of the one god. There was probably no sudden pronounced break between past and present, merely a gradual development; and even in the final redaction of the Old Testament in the fifth century B.C., as we shall see, there are still discernible the roots of the early pre-Jahweh beliefs current in the land when the Hebrews entered it.

In time, as the worship of the one god prevailed, and the people became convinced of a common origin and tradition all imbued with the spirit of a god who ruled the entire land, the step to one king as his representative on earth was easy. The immediate reason for electing a king was the Philistine menace, which endangered the whole country by constant and increasing encroachments and forced it to a united stand. The first choice fell on Saul, perhaps famous as a warrior, since his section of the country, the frontier between north and south, had frequently been the scene of bloody warfare, and after his death in battle with the Philistines David, a popular leader from the south, was appointed to succeed him.

The kingdom of David marks the high spot in the political development of the Hebrews. The promises of Jahweh had been fulfilled, the Land of Canaan had been brought under his sway and was ruled in his name by a strong and popular king who had driven the Philistines back to the coastal plain, seized the hitherto impregnable city of the Jebusites, Jerusalem, made it the capital, and united north and south under one rule. David's reign lasted from 1000 to 973 B.C., and before his death he had his son Solomon crowned king to succeed him, hoping in this way to found a dynasty and ensure the continuance of the kingdom he had built. These two reigns, marking the widest extent of Hebrew rule, are the golden age of Hebrew literature. The country was prosperous, the people contented, wealth began to accumulate, leisure increased; there was time for cultivation of the mind and spirit. The memory of this short period has remained in the race consciousness of Israel from that day to this.

During the reign of David the first stirrings of the intellectual awakening took a practical form. The leaders of the people seem to have felt the need of centralizing and organizing the religious life of the nation to correspond with the government. Both north and south made collections of the poetry so long current throughout the land. Apparently there was then, as always, a marked difference and some rivalry between the two parts of the country. The northern collection, the Book of Jasher (Book of the Upright), was perhaps made at Shechem, a large and popular center of worship in Ephraim; the southern, known as the Wars of Jahweh, at Jerusalem. The liturgies from the various shrines were also collected for the use of the congregations at the great centers. The first book of Psalms, 3 to 41, may represent the southern collection; the second and possibly the third books, Psalms 42 to 89, the northern. It is more than likely that the authorship of the Psalms was traditionally ascribed to David because in his time they were introduced as the liturgy of the whole people; for this is what they originally were, liturgies composed for use at many local shrines. In David's reign too, official records of court and temple began to be kept by the priests and scribes.

What the early fragments of song and story were like we may gather from the bits that were later embodied in the Old Testament. The Song of Lamech, Genesis 4:23; the curse of Canaan, Genesis 9:25; the Blessing of Jacob, Genesis 49:3 ff.; the victory Song of Moses and Miriam, Exodus 15:1 ff.; the Song of the Well, Numbers 21:17 ff.; the Balaam prophecies, Numbers 23 ff.; the Song of Moses, Deuteronomy 32:1 ff.; and the episode of the Sun and Moon standing still for Joshua, Joshua 10:13 ff., are all such bits. Some are explicitly quoted from the Wars of Jahweh or Book of Jasher; all are of higher antiquity than the context in which we find them and were current long before the priests collected them for use in their project. Some, like the Song of Lamech, are crude and shapeless, and seem already to have lost most of their meaning; others, as for example the Song of Moses, show an advanced spiritual development. The Song of Deborah, another and perhaps the oldest of these excerpts, is a supreme example of a victory ode; the Song of Miriam is the usual antiphonal song of triumph such as is used by the Bedouins today. The material is fragmentary, unrelated to any central theme, the form is exclamatory and repetitive and unsuited to straight narrative.

The Greeks, as we have seen, for some reason developed early a certain conventional form suited to narrative and this form continued to develop until it reached the perfection of hexameter verse. Hebrew verse in the tenth century was still hundreds of years behind such development, if indeed it ever could have become a suitable medium for the priests' purposes. It needed literally an act of God to mold the collection of Hebrew antiquities into a connected narrative, and this, during these years of collecting, collating, and reshaping, the priests were preparing to implement. So, while the Greeks composed their verse for joy in creating beauty, and to entertain an audience that itself grew more and more conscious of beauty, the Hebrew priests withdrew from the people their heritage of folklore and tradition, to return it to them in a new form of their own making, as a sacred book.

One factor which I have not mentioned in discussing the sudden development of literary activity in Palestine at this time is the invention of the alphabet. This seems to have been of Semitic origin, and came into use in Hither Asia in about 1000 B.C. Hitherto writing had been slow and clumsy, and the results were intelligible to only a very small and highly educated group. The Egyptians used a cumbersome system of hieroglyphics, the Babylonians a kind of syllabic shorthand, known today as cuneiform. Much of the writing—especially the cuneiform—was done on clay or waxed tablets, and there has come down to us from both Egypt and Babylonia a considerable body of business and legal documents, accounts, contracts, temple records, annals, and so forth. Some examples of literary value also have survived, such as the Gilgamesh Epic from Babylon, and the stories of Sinuhe and of the Shipwrecked Sailor from Egypt. But on the whole there is surprisingly little real literature to show for the hundreds of years of highly developed culture in these lands before the alphabet came into use. True, much has undoubtedly been lost, but the impression remains that writing and reading were for the most part confined to a professional group composed of civil servants and temple scribes, among whom were few creative or vivid imaginations.

Easy to master and use, in comparison with earlier methods, the alphabet made written self-expression available to a greater number of people, and to people not necessarily of the official classes; and at the same time it must have increased the reading public. It had the same effect in Greece when it came into use there about 750 B.C. In fact, the coincidence of alphabet and written literature occurring at such widely separated times in both Palestine and Greece suggests the immense effect it had, an effect much like that of the printing press in Europe over two thousand years later.

This is the historic setting in which the Hebrew priests began their work of collection and reshaping. The work continued for centuries, and finally evolved the Old Testament as it exists today; but for the purposes of literature, I have gone back to what has been recovered of the text as it existed in the seventh century B.C. Among the many threads woven into this text were several dealing with the story of David and his kingdom, and of three of these I shall speak in some detail. Two of the three were more or less formal histories composed originally in the southern and northern shrines, respectively, the southern version in about 950 B.C. and the northern a century later. The third is a unique production, a true biography by an unknown hand, standing almost alone in early literature as a definite study of a man. It is of this biography that I shall speak first.

While the priests at Jerusalem and Shechem were collecting and sorting and writing down the nation's heritage of folklore and ritual—a task of great difficulty, which was destined to stretch over many generations—one man, apparently not of the priestly school, perhaps not even a priest, was trying his hand at an independent piece of writing, a sketch of David as he knew him. What remains of this sketch—for it is scarcely more than that—may be found in II Samuel 9 through 20 inclusive, and the first and second chapters of I Kings.

It has suffered editing. The story of David was worked over so often and by so many hands that it is hard, often indeed impossible, to distinguish accurately between the various sources. Even in the biography, therefore, there are apparently omissions, and there seem also to have been some additions. The document itself has been appended as a unit at the end of David's life story, whereas chronologically it plainly stretches over a much longer period. Then, between II Samuel 20 and the first chapter of I Kings, four chapters of miscellaneous and unrelated material have been inserted, ostensibly to cover a lapse of years; and the biography is resumed at the beginning of I Kings with an abrupt transition to David as a very old and feeble man. These four inserted chapters add nothing to the sequence of events in David's reign. Whether at this point a part of the biography had been lost or contained material which the editors deemed unsuitable, or whether the old biographer, having laid his foundation, deliberately passed on to his climax, we shall never know.

Aside from its occasional editing, the biography has none of the earmarks of the official writings. Though touched with religion, it is concerned with its ethical rather than its formal aspects, and makes no effort to instruct or propagandize. How it came to be written and why, we do not know. It obviously took shape while hope for Israel's future was still high, before the dissension which divided the kingdom after Solomon's time was in evidence, for it contains no hint of future trouble and ends on his entering upon a long and glorious reign. It therefore probably dates from the earlier years of that reign, which would place it at about 960 B.C.

The biography is in prose, and is true biography. We know of no precedent in Palestine for this kind of writing, and yet it seems probable that something of the sort had been done before, for this is not the work of a beginner but a finished product, so sure and easy as to argue that the form was well known. Prose is generally a late development in written literature. The Greeks did not use it until after they had been writing verse for two hundred years. A precedent to this development of the prose narrative is to be found in Egypt, but whether the Hebrew writer was familiar with it we have no means of knowing, and we are faced with a finished product at what seems to be the earliest period of Hebrew literature.

Our only clues to the personality of the author must be gathered from the story itself. He was probably close to David, for he seems to know the most intimate details of the king's personal and family life. He could not have been a young man when he wrote, for his personal experience of the events he recounts covers a span of fifty years. He does not seem to have been a fighting man, for he had none of the old soldier's love for battles and campaigns; certainly the account of Joab's campaign against the Syrians, II Samuel 10:6-19, is not in the biographer's usual vein, and the story moves easily and naturally without it. He is not interested in ritual and dogma, or in Jahweh's power as such, as the average priest or scribe would have been, and there is nothing didactic or narrowly denominational about his work. His point of view is broad and tolerant, and directed not toward the particular Hebrew aspects of his subject, but toward the human and personal problem of David the individual.

In its grasp of psychological cause and effect his treatment shows a maturity which is surprising in contrast to the environment and period in which it occurs. The Greek dramatists, writing five hundred years later, did not yet face the implications of the interaction of character and events with the frank and unerring touch of this unknown Hebrew writer, who uses no oracles or prophecies or divine whims to motivate his story. David's own character and development as expressed in his acts carry the narrative to the end.

Read separately, and perhaps shorn of minor interpolations, these fourteen chapters are seen to be an independent unit, different in form and content from the material about it, and leading to a well thought-out conclusion. For the biographer constantly presents the very human complex of David the keen judge of men and political situations and David the weakling in the management of his family. The contrast is never commented upon; it is merely set forth in narrative. And the weakness for his family leads inevitably to the climax, which is built around the blood succession to the kingship.

There may originally have been more of the story, not only in the apparent gap between II Samuel 20 and I Kings, but something also in the nature of an opening section taking up David's early life. As we have it today, however, the biography begins with his efforts to find some of Jonathan's descendants, in order to show them special favor, an instance of generosity which is far ahead of the time, when the descendants of a rival royal line usually receive little mercy from the man in power. More than once this extraordinary trait recurs, in his clemency to Shimei, for example, and in his treatment of Mephibosheth after Absalom's revolt. It is a remarkable characteristic for those primitive days, when Jahweh was still a god of battle to most of the nation, and battle was slaughter. Nor in the world of tribal warfare and political maneuvering does David seem to have suffered by it, for in that world he knew men. It was only in his family relationships that generosity became weakness.

Then follows the story of Bath-sheba, for which the war with the Ammonites serves as preparation, since it explains Uriah's absence and later supplies the background for his riddance. This is the episode, as we shall see, that so largely determined the future of the kingdom. The cold-blooded murder of Uriah is in sharp opposition to the generosities of David's political career and points the contrast of his private life. However, he knows that he has sinned. True, there is a scene in which Nathan brings the sin home to him, but this may conceivably be an interpolation; if II Samuel 11:27a is joined directly to 12:15b, the connection is good and the sense more in keeping with the period. Then, in the death of his child David sees the punishment for his sin, and joyfully accepts Solomon's birth as a token of forgiveness. It is in this mood that he promises Bath-sheba that Solomon shall rule after his death, and it is only now that the inevitable force of cause and effect begins to work out and the real results of the sin begin to appear; for henceforth the movement of the story turns on the succession, set against a background of the king's unforgivable weakness in dealing with his family.

The episode which follows of Amnon and Tamar again brings this weakness forward, for David though angry will not raise his hand against his son. It is Absalom who takes vengeance, and perhaps there is a curious echo of some early tribal matriarchy in the fact that Tamar is his sister by the same mother, whereas Amnon is a half brother on the father's side only. Here Joab interferes to have Absalom brought back from banishment, perhaps because the old soldier admired forcefulness and was even then seeking a successor to David stronger than Bath-sheba's child, for whom he seems never to have cared. But Absalom stirs up revolt, and Joab, true to the kingship which he always served, puts an end to him. Characteristically David, weak as ever where his family is concerned, is more grieved by his son's death than rejoiced by the crushing of the revolt.

When David's character has been outlined, without comment or criticism by the author, the story goes on to its final phase. The king is now an old man, and again the question of the succession comes up. Once more Joab takes the side of the man of force, this time Adonijah, brother of Absalom by the same mother. But Bath-sheba's power is still great, and David is persuaded to settle the succession on Solomon. Thus the consequences of the early weakness are still at work, and David and Joab come to the parting of the ways. The parting seems to awaken David to the dangers of the future, for he sees now that Solomon has neither the force nor the personal popularity to contend with all the conflicting forces that beset the kingdom. Joab has shown his hostility, Shimei will be a rallying point for the Saul faction, still alive in the land. In his dying words the king sacrifices his old loyalties and clemencies to his love for Bath-sheba's son, for he tries to ensure Solomon's rule by counseling him to put Joab and Shimei to death— Joab, who had devoted a lifetime to service of the house of David, and Shimei, whom David himself had spared more than once. And so, at the end of his life the king is finally brought face to face with the natural and inevitable consequences of his sin with Bath-sheba.

Did the author have this idea in mind when he wrote the story?

Perhaps his choice of episodes was a mere chance, a haphazard selection of an old man's memories. But the more I read and reread these chapters the more I feel the conscious art of the author. The contrast between David and Joab is clear and pointed; and twice Joab is shown favoring Haggith's sons, who seem to have been enterprising and vigorous men, popular among the younger men of the kingdom. Remember that it was Joab who had engineered Uriah's death at David's orders, and perhaps some of his aversion to Bath-sheba's son was due to this circumstance, or he may have resented her hold on the king. The author makes no comment, but he gives the facts which suggest the conclusion.

The sense of a strong visual imagination pervades the writing, and an intensity that makes the scenes stand out like pictures. Tamar, bowed and with her hand laid on her head, the figure of mourning, Shimei on the hillside cursing and throwing stones, Mephibosheth, untended and with his feet unbound, greeting David on his return, Joab's pursuit of Amasa: described not as an old and garrulous man would remember them, with wealth of irrelevant description, but with the artist's eye for the telling detail. All the characterization is developed in action. Two of the most striking examples of real literary skill are the speeches of the woman of Tekoa and of Hushai the Archite. Both speeches are meant to deceive, and the author has shown their speciousness in their unnecessary length and flowery language. Figures of speech are comparatively rare in Hebrew prose, and especially simile, which is more complex than the metaphor which comes naturally to the Oriental. In both of these passages, however, the speaker uses simile, homely simile which would be natural to the characters: "as water spilt on the ground, which cannot be gathered up again"; "as a bear robbed of her whelps in the field"; "we will light upon him as the dew falleth on the ground." As a result of this literary device a smooth persuasiveness is given to the arguments suggesting the insincerity of the speakers. To my mind these two speeches show clearly the conscious artistry of the writer.

Though the episodes he cites from David's life are carefully selected and do not by any means give a complete history of the man, they are quite in keeping with the other stories of the national hero, which we find in the longer history, and this leads us to believe that the biography was a true even if partial piece of characterization. We seem to have here the study of one aspect of David's development, to which all else is subordinated—a well thought-out argument, with a definite thesis leading inexorably to the unhealthy state of Solomon's kingdom, which must already have been apparent to the thinking man of the time.

How did such a biography come to be written? Was the author a propagandist commissioned by Solomon to write an apologia for the murder of Joab and Shimei, who undoubtedly had a following in the land? Or were the last two chapters added by another hand in justification of the murders? I am not inclined to accept either answer. There is in the story no sign of partisanship, not even a hint of the personal touch which special pleading requires. Instead, there is a simplicity and earnestness which suggest that the author was writing not for wide publication and not on order, but to satisfy an inner urge to set down the truth as he saw it, perhaps only for himself and a small group of friends. There must have been men of the older generation in the kingdom who saw even then that all was not well, that the new king was not the man his father had been, and but poorly fitted to cope with the problems that were arising. How such a state of affairs had arisen, why David should have chosen Solomon, of all his sons, to succeed him, why, when a strong adviser was necessary, Joab, who had so long been David's right-hand man, should have been executed: these were the questions they would ask, and these were questions which one of their number tried to answer in his eyewitness account of the sequence of events as he saw them. Without the last two chapters the argument is unfinished and pointless, and the end of the story of David and Bath-sheba, with its unforeseen and fatal consequences, left in mid-air; with those last chapters it is a rounded and purposeful whole, ending with the words "And the kingdom was established in the hands of Solomon." No one could take exception to such a conclusion, but one wonders what the author really thought of the future.

I doubt very much if the writer foresaw that his story would be given to the world and become a part of the history of the kingdom. To the average reader of the time the episodes he chose were not such as would show off the power and glory of the great king or enhance his prestige, and so the prestige of the kingdom. For the David of the biography was first a man, and only incidentally a king. As a king he used his power to rid himself of Uriah, but the sin and its consequences, as they are told, concern the man and might be true of anyone whether he wore a crown or no.

This biography has been called the "court history" of David, but the term is a misnomer, since in David's day there was actually no court in the accepted sense of the word. Class distinctions, rank and specialized functions, which are the prerequisites of a court, seem to have been nonexistent in Palestine until the latter part of David's reign. At the end of his history, II Samuel 8:16-18, and again in the biography, II Samuel 20:23-26, there appear short résumés of David's appointments. The two lists come from different sources, which accounts for occasional variant names, but in most respects they are the same, and both show the emergence of what was still, even toward the end of the reign, the simplest kind of governmental organization. David himself was still the final arbiter, commander in chief of the army, court of appeal, and probably high priest.

Neither Saul nor David came from a noble or privileged class. The early tribal society acknowledged no differences in birth. A man attained prominence and became a leader by dint of his own exploits. Saul was a farmer's son. In battle with the Ammonites he so distinguished himself that he was chosen king. At first his rule may have been only over his own tribe, gradually extending to others as the Philistine menace grew and the need for a united effort of the tribes became increasingly clearer. His popularity was greatest in the north, and on his death his son Ish-baal (later edited to read Ish-bosheth) was chosen to succeed him.

David was a shepherd boy from the mountains of the south, probably one of the many who, impressed by Saul's victories, enlisted in his army. His great personal charm attracted Saul's attention and won him a place of prominence and trust in the king's immediate circle. But Saul knew the precariousness of his position, and as David's popularity grew he became so hostile that David was forced to flee. Returning to his own people he took service with the Philistines, who still controlled the south and were in constant conflict with the kingdom of Saul on the north, as well as with the local tribes of the region. In time David was joined by other malcontents and adventurers, until he found himself leader of a trusted band of outlaws who lived on the country, raiding and plundering and often making inroads on the territory under Saul's rule. For, though he claimed to be king of all Israel, Saul's hold on the south was so tenuous as to be merely nominal, and he probably paid tribute to the Philistines for what power he claimed.

Israel offered by no means a cohesive and united front, but was composed of small and warring tribes, only beginning to grow conscious of a common heritage in the light of a common cause and, as the new religion of Jahweh spread, a common faith. David's reputation for valor and his personal magnetism, which all the chroniclers stress, were no doubt largely responsible for his rapid rise to power after Saul's death. Furthermore, his political astuteness led him to "build up" the idea of kingship and develop its sanctity among his followers. Repeated mention is made by the historians of his respecting Saul and sparing his life as the "Lord's anointed." Some of this was undoubtedly a sincere exercise of mercy, for David seems always to have tended toward clemency; but he may also have been consciously inculcating respect for the kingship in his followers. Every act points to this, up to his burial of Ish-baal with suitable honors. For it must be remembered that kingship is not an early development in a tribal society, and must have been new to the Hebrew of the time.

After Saul's death David became king of the south, where his fame and popularity were greatest. The band of outlaws who had shared his exile and who may perhaps have numbered six hundred men were by now experienced veterans, and with their help David was able to throw off the Philistine yoke and free the country from its encroachments. The capital of this new kingdom was Hebron, a hill town south of Jerusalem. After consolidating and organizing his holdings David turned to the north and seized Jerusalem, a stronghold of the Canaanites, to which he moved his capital and from which he extended his rule northward until he was king in fact as well as name of all Israel.

Undoubtedly as he gained in power and prestige and brought the country under an increasingly centralized rule, some machinery of government was established and a more formal and organized social and political life developed. But there is no suggestion in the early accounts of anything approaching the court life of the great rulers of the more strongly established neighboring kingdoms. David's was still a personal rule, in which the king himself mingled freely with his subjects hearing their complaints and even accepting their criticism.

He knew the insecurity of his hold, and nothing more vividly illustrates the simplicity of this tribal society than his quick acceptance of Absalom's revolt and his flight on foot with what was apparently a handful of followers. There was no standing army, no professional palace guard, not even a stronghold in which he could take refuge; the people had momentarily revolted, and the tribal chieftain was deposed.

To call this biography a "court history," therefore, seems to me to give a false impression to the reader, to whom the word "court" has become associated with titles and special functions and a display of wealth. It is rather, as I have said, an intimate study of David the man, and the effect of his character on the events of his life and on the future of the kingdom. (pp. 21-33)

THE FORMAL HISTORY OF DAVID AND HIS TIMES

BROOKE PETERS CHURCH

IT COULD NOT HAVE BEEN long after the biography of David was written that a longer and more complete history of his life and times was begun. There were many good reasons for such an undertaking at this time, chief among them being the need of some cohesive force to weld and hold together the loose amalgamation of tribes which composed the kingdom. The common danger from the Philistines having been removed, there was no longer the consciousness of an urgent need for a united front. Signs of basic differences between north and south appear in David's biography and must have grown apparent to all thinking men before the end of Solomon's reign.

David was a self-made man, with all the self-made man's assurance and independence. He needed no family tree or coat of arms to bolster him up, for time and again he had proved his valor on the field of battle, he had built himself a kingdom out of a group of warring tribes, had made his power felt even in neighboring lands, and was respected and feared by friends and enemies alike. But Solomon, who was brought up in a harem by a doting mother and had the Oriental's love of luxury and ease, seems to have been possessed of none of his father's character and ability. He had wealth which he had not earned, a position which he had not achieved, and probably showed early the traits of character which led to the unpopularity of the dynasty in the north. When, after Solomon's death, Jeroboam revolted and divided the kingdom, his rallying cry was "Back to the simple life of our fore-fathers!" Even in Solomon's time the dangers of dissension must have been evident, and there was need for some propaganda which would establish the house of David as the chosen representative of Jahweh. To satisfy this need an authoritative history was essential, not only of David but of the events leading up to his reign, and it was probably as a result that the history began to be written.

That Solomon himself felt the need of establishing his own personal prestige is evident in the early acts of his reign. Where the ark was kept in David's time we are not told, but certainly not in a temple, nor did David live in a palace surrounded by pomp and ceremony. The conditions during his reign were apparently crude and primitive and he seems to have lived like his people, sharing his soldiers' hardships in battle and living in the usual low flat-roofed house of mud or sun-baked brick when at home. It was from the roof of such a house, where probably most of the business of life went on, that he caught the glimpse of Bath-sheba bathing, the incident that was to have such importance to the future. It remained for Solomon, who inherited the kingdom, to build both temple and palace. In Solomon's reign we begin to hear also of a court, and a court of the utmost luxury and splendor. He was the "first generation," trying to impress the world with his importance and incidentally to compensate for his own feeling of inadequacy in the face of the storm clouds that gathered about the future. Thus, added to the national need for a common background there was also Solomon's need for a prop to support his shaky self-esteem. Some kind of history was urgently essential for both king and subjects, if the kingdom so laboriously knit together was to endure.

It was to the priests at Jerusalem, probably the largest group of educated men in the land, that the task of compiling the history fell, and fortunately for us they appended to their official account the short sketch of David discussed in the preceding chapter. This biography, emphasizing as it does the circumstances leading to Solomon's accession to the throne, and making clear his crowning by David himself, gave the very touch the priests needed to prove their point. Indeed, in both form and content, style and matter, their formal history is so tuned to the biography as to suggest a conscious effort to lead up to it. It may well be, therefore, that the use of prose for narrative writing was determined by the unknown biographer.

But before the history was completed the catastrophe so long dreaded came to pass. Solomon's son Rehoboam was unable to hold his father's realm, and it was divided into north and south, Israel and Judah. The south continued the work it had begun and the north took over the writing of its own account of events. But different as were the points of view the prose form seems already to have become the chosen medium of narrative writing for the priests of both sections, and when, after 721, the northern kingdom was overrun by the Assyrians and the priests of Shechem with their precious documents took refuge in Jerusalem the identity of the form made easier the task of combining the narratives of the two sections.

The combined historical narrative, distinct from the biography which has been dovetailed with it, constitutes a large part of the first and second Books of Samuel. So many successive generations of editors have worked over it, and additions and interpolations have been made from so many sources, that it is hard to disentangle the threads and determine with finality to what layer they belong. For the combined narrative there seem to have been two major sources, one from the south and one from the north, the southern almost contemporaneous with the events described, the northern written a hundred years or so later.

After the close of I Samuel, the burden of the tale is shifted largely to the southern chronicle and there are fewer signs of dual source. It is in the earlier part of the story, contained in I Samuel itself, that the double narrative is most striking. There are two accounts of Saul's selection as king, two of his rejection, two of David's appearance at court, two negotiations for Saul's daughters; and in none of these duplications does the one incident presuppose knowledge of the other. When the two threads are followed separately, there appear two consecutive narratives, each almost but not quite complete, and each very like the other in content but very different in emphasis and atmosphere, as well as in point of view. The southern document is a clear and concise account of the lives of Saul and David, with little of the religious element, but made to lead up to the biography with masterly skill. It ends with the deaths of Saul, Jonathan, and Abner, Saul's general, practically where the biography begins. The northern document is a piece of passionate special pleading by a propagandist writing from a later viewpoint, and motivating incidents and passing judgment on them in the light of later and very different conditions.

Comparing the two versions, it becomes clear that the northern must have been written at least a hundred years later than the southern. Its point of view bespeaks a dislike of kings, which suggests that it was written after the division of the kingdom. Furthermore, there had been time for legend to develop and become part of the story. The editors of the late eighth century, who combined the two accounts, were often hard put to it to harmonize the very divergent religious and political views expressed in what might be called the "royalist" version of the south and the antiroyalist, or "popular," version of the north. A history of Charles I's reign in England, written by a courtier of the time and then combined with a history of the same period written by a Puritan during the Commonwealth might offer a parallel. When the northern version was written, Judah, as the southern kingdom had come to be known, was still ruled by David's dynasty; but Israel, the northern kingdom, had suffered a succession of kings, and its historians had developed an aversion to kingship itself, which was characteristic of the priestly point of view. Whether, as kings go, these rulers of the northern kingdom were as bad as they are painted, we shall probably never know.

This priestly aversion finds expression through Samuel, who appears as the mouthpiece of God, speaking with divine authority and repeatedly warning the people of the abuse of kingly power. From early times seers of his type were familiar figures in Israel and were objects of veneration to the people and fear to the rulers. They were the "prophets," and at times they gained so much power from popular support that they were a menace to the rather shaky throne. Records were kept, presumably by their disciples, of their sayings and doings, and it may be that the account used in this history came from such a source. Samuel is pre-eminently the prophet of the northern chronicle, and there we shall find his figure towering over that of Saul, whereas in the southern version he is a minor character.

The southern, or royalist, account opens with Saul's expedition in search of his father's asses. When the search failed he followed the advice of one of his men and applied for help to a soothsayer, one Samuel, whose reputation was clearly local, for Saul had not previously heard of him. At Jahweh's command Samuel secretly anointed Saul king of Israel and sent him home with the news that the asses had been found. This incident is the historians' mechanism for establishing the divine sanction of the kingship and it is immediately followed in the text by Saul's victory over the Ammonites, which ended in his elevation to the kingship by the people and established the popular sanction also.

The story passes on to the Philistine wars, with which David was to be so closely identified, and it may be that the historians deliberately hurried on to the scenes that prepared his entrance. In any case there is a period of years here which is not accounted for. Jonathan, for example, suddenly appears as a figure already known to the reader, and it is quite possible that he was introduced in some lost portion of the southern text, perhaps omitted by the later editors.

The account of the raid on Michmash is one of the most vivid pieces of descriptive writing in the Old Testament, so vivid that, according to a story of the First World War, Allenby following the Bible account letter for letter was able to duplicate the episode at one of the critical points of his campaign. It is at this juncture that the southern chronicle brings David on the stage and almost at once involves him in a feud with Saul. It is interesting to note that this feud did not extend to Saul's children, who might reasonably have been expected to resent David as an interloper and possible rival. Both Jonathan and Michal at once conceived a deep love for the shepherd boy and repeatedly protected him from Saul's unreasoning rage.

I have included in the text one story which seems to come from neither the official northern nor southern version—the story of Jonathan signaling to David with the arrows. There is a Robin Hood touch to this episode which is quite in keeping with David's life as an outlaw, and so makes the story fit its context. The ballads of Robin Hood's exploits were sung and recited all over the English countryside for years before they were written down, and this and many other stories of David may have been preserved to posterity in the same way. The Song of the Bow (II Samuel 1:19), for example, seems to have been a popular song before it was incorporated into the history, much as was "John Brown's Body" in our own Civil War.

During his years as a fugitive from Saul, David's life was in many ways like Robin Hood's, and like Robin Hood he lived up to a well-defined set of self-imposed ideals even in his lawlessness. One of these was his respect for the person of the king. This characteristic the priests may have further emphasized in their history, since the sanctity of kingship was an important part of the southern, or royalist, propaganda. It is worthy of note at this point that David did not take part in the battle in which Saul and Jonathan met their ends. The Philistines, distrusting his loyalty, had sent him to fight the Amalekites, with whom they had a score to settle. As a result, David's respect for the "Lord's anointed" was kept intact, an object lesson for later generations.

From the time when, after Saul's death, David is chosen king, the royalist version carries the burden of the story, though here and there occasional episodes, and psalms gathered from various sources, were interpolated by successive editors.

This southern story grows more detailed and vivid as Saul sinks into the background and David takes the center of the stage, for it was David's life that the priests were considering and in which both they and their audience took most interest. Saul's history served merely as an introduction, to prove the institution of kingship and explain the circumstances that led to David's succession. Nevertheless, the writer never permitted his purpose to interfere with his accuracy of characterization. He was careful to do Saul justice and depicted him, not as a conscious villain, spurred on by blind jealousy, nor as a helpless tool of fate or of the power of Jahweh. He is shown as a victim of his own neurotic, almost schizophrenic temperament, and in his diseased brain love and admiration for David constantly war with fear and jealousy of the shepherd boy's growing popularity. With great skill and insight the narrator arouses enthusiasm for David while maintaining sympathy for Saul, and at the end the reader must mourn over Saul's death while rejoicing at David's triumph.

As in the biography, so in this southern chronicle, even the minor characters are brilliantly etched. Jonathan is perhaps best remembered, and his selfless friendship for David has become a byword for friendship itself, more often quoted than even the bond between the Greek Damon and Pythias. Contrary to his own best interests and despite his father's repeated warnings, Jonathan's devotion and loyalty to David never wavered.

In contrast to this strong bond of friendship is set Michal's infatuation for David as the hero of the moment. The king's spoiled and self-willed daughter was carried away by love at first sight for the handsome stranger, and married the man of her choice. This romance of princess and shepherd boy follows an old pattern, recurring in the fairy lore of every time and land, whether the father be king, sheik, or modern business magnate. On her wedding night David was forced to flee from her father's wrath and Michal was left a widow in fact if not in name.

There is an interesting sequel to Michal's story. After David's flight from court Saul, according to the custom of the times, again gave Michal in marriage to one Phaltiel, whether with or without her consent we are not told. After Saul's death, when David had become king of Judah and was haggling with Abner and Ish-bosheth·for the northern kingdom, he made the stipulation that before he would agree to any treaty Michal must be returned to him. So Michal was separated from her second husband and sent back to David, followed, we are told, by Phaltiel weeping. We hear no more of Phaltiel, nor are we told what Michal's feelings were, nor of David's reception and treatment of his former wife.

But in II Samuel 6:16 we meet Michal again. David, bringing home the ark, went before it leaping and dancing. Michal, who was watching from the window, greeted David with scorn and mockery for such unseemly behavior. Hers was the attitude of the conventional aristocrat, shocked at her lowborn husband's loss of dignity. Her upbraidings and David's contemptuous reply show how great the breach between them had become. One is tempted to think of another instance, that of the concubines whom David left in Jerusalem when he fled from Absalom (II Samuel 20:3). In demanding Michal's return he had merely satisfied his pride by recovering his property; the author simply says, 6:23, "Therefore Michal the daughter of Saul had no child unto the day of her death." This passage may be another example of reading history backwards, from effect to cause, but at least the picture is consistent; Michal's behavior was that of a frustrated woman, expressing her bitterness. The Hebrew narrator's accuracy of observation brings this out, and the later editor's rationalization merely proves the point.

In this southern version of David's life there is none of the supernatural element which crept into the later accounts, an added reason for supposing that it was written down shortly after the events. Had the anecdotes been passed around by word of mouth for many years they would have gathered to themselves a host of exaggerations and miracles, for the greater the hero the greater the liberties permitted imagination and fancy in telling his story. That there was such folklore current may be seen from the story of David and Goliath, which was included from some other source and probably bears the same relation to truth as does the story of Washington and the cherry tree.

There is, too, in this account an echo of a very early phase of religious development, before idols and images of any kind had become taboo. The teraphim (idol) which Michal substitutes in the bed for David to deceive Saul was apparently part of the usual house furnishing of the day and the writer is not conscious of any offense in its existence. This again indicates an early date for the document, for quite plainly the commandment against making any "graven images" has not yet prevailed in the land. Old customs and beliefs change slowly, and it must have taken generations of preaching and exhorting to wipe out idol worship in Israel.

Turning now to the northern history, which as we saw was written about one hundred years later than the southern, we see at once the more popular idea of David and his times. Samuel, not Saul, takes the center of the stage and is the chief actor up to Saul's death. To stress his importance, the circumstances of his birth were tinged with the miraculous. As an answer to prayer he was born to Hannah, long childless, and was dedicated to Jahweh from birth. He communed with Jahweh directly when he was but a child and after the death of Eli succeeded to the "judgeship" of Israel.

Apparently this succession was contrived as the connecting link with Sampson, who as judge of Israel had already been in conflict with the Philistines, as were Samuel and, later, Saul and David. So a certain continuity of events and succession was attained by the later editors, who sought to give a long and consecutive history to the people. The account of Samuel's birth is very reminiscent of Samson's birth in the Book of Judges. In fact, the one may well have been borrowed from the other. Another touch designed to enhance Samuel's importance was the episode of Saul and the witch of Endor. Though the editors probably expurgated this episode and indeed the whole narrative of many of the most objectionable elements of popular superstition, this incident survives to suggest that Samuel was credited with supernatural powers which even outlasted his lifetime.

This northern narrative takes for granted that there was a temple where Samuel served before the ark, but as we have seen there was no temple before Solomon's time and the ark was probably kept in a movable shrine. This is not the only anachronism of which the northern record was guilty, unless it was the later editors who were responsible. Certainly the descriptions of the court life and temple ritual are far more elaborate and formal than the early kingdom could have known. The reality was probably very crude and simple, more like the impression left by the biography, where the king was scarcely distinguishable from his subjects and court life was nonexistent. In this later account the kingdom is described as a theocracy ruled by Jahweh through his agent the king, as before Saul's time it had been ruled by Samuel as judge or high priest, speaking for Jahweh.

In Samuel's old age, when his sons, like Eli's, proved corrupt and therefore unable to assume the leadership of Israel after their father's death, the people demanded a king and he yielded to their request despite his own better judgment and repeated warning of disasters to follow. This again was a backward reading of historical facts. The followers of Jahweh in the north had suffered under the kingship, and the priests read their experiences back into the past.

Chapter 15 of I Samuel tells of the offense which led to Saul's downfall. It was obviously trumped up with some difficulty and certainly seems too trifling for the severity of the punishment. At Jahweh's command Samuel now sought a new candidate for the kingship and the choice fell on David. The process of choosing him is in the best fairy-tale manner, the Cinderella motif we might call it: all the likely candidates appeared and were rejected in favor of the youngest and least considered of the group. From now on, interest is centered on Saul's decline and David's gradual rise to power.

This later narrative lacks much of the simplicity and vigor of the earlier story, but it includes details lacking in the earlier version without which much would be lost. Still more details are supplied by the sections not identified with either the northern or the southern chronicle, and which with one exception have been omitted from the text as I have here given it. Wherever these came from, they seem to have been added by later editors and so are not strictly a part of the eighth century version. The story of David and Goliath in chapter 17, for instance, is quite contradictory to chapter 16, where David is already at court and in favor with Saul.

As time went on, and the power of the Hebrews declined until finally their very existence not only as a nation but as a race was threatened, David, who marked the high spot in their national life, became increasingly important. To regain a homeland and a position in the world became their dream, and was translated into the Messianic hope of postexilic Israel. It is, therefore, not surprising that the editors of succeeding generations enlarged upon the power and strength of the kingdom of David until the history was overlaid with layer after layer of emendations. In the biography and early history we can see clearly the original picture of the rude and struggling early kingdom; the picture in the northern version is somewhat more elaborate, as was natural, coming as it did from a richer section of the country and a later period. But superimposed on these accounts, and tangled among them, is the picture drawn from the point of view of the postexilic Jew, who had seen the courts of the great empires, who lived hundreds of years after the times he described, and who had every reason for trying to read power and wealth back into the kingdom of David.

In the English stories of King Arthur, much the same transference of the later conception into an earlier period took place. The historical Arthur lived long before the age of courts and tournaments and of the chivalry which pervades the stories as we read them. He was an ancient Briton, probably dressed in skins and painted with woad. He worshipped his tribal god in stone circles, one of which still stands at Stonehenge in southern England. In the late fifth and the early sixth century A.D. he fought valiantly and with some success against the invading Angles and Saxons, and probably because of his personal prowess became a legendary figure, kept alive in the memory of invader and invaded alike by song and story.

Through the years these legends changed and grew. When they were finally written down, Arthur had been changed into a Christian king fighting the pagan hordes and surrounded by the group of faithful knights who made up the Round Table. His background had come to be the background of an impossibly idealized age of chivalry, where knights in armor rode about the country redressing wrongs and succoring women in distress. He had a splendid court and the land was sprinkled with moated castles. Instead of skins the knights wore shining armor, and the ladies dwelt in bowers and were clad in silks and samites.

Later generations, unable to visualize the actual conditions of Arthur's life and times and desirous of increasing his stature and importance, had imbued his story with all the splendor and pomp they could imagine. And no doubt the early church, knowing his hold on the popular imagination, had much to do with introducing the religious element. By this means they hoped to reach a wider public with the teachings of Christianity.

The pagan Arthur of the sixth century A.D. becomes, in Malory's version, a powerful Christian monarch of about the twelfth century, and the original Arthur, appearing in England even three centuries after his death, and even more had it been six centuries, would have failed to recognize himself in the later hero of the Arthurian cycle. In the same way, David's setting changed over the ages. Even by the seventh century B.C. he had become the conventional monarch of that age, and when the latest editors of the fifth and fourth centuries B.C. took up the tale he was changed beyond recognition.

In spite of the widely divergent sources, and in spite of artificial piecing together of what at first seem such opposing elements, there is a basic unity in the history which makes it stand out as one of the finest pieces of sustained narrative writing in the Old Testament. It is the longest continuous narrative that has survived from the eighth century and approaches the historical novel rather than history. Its unity results from the circumstance that the variations between the original documents are due to different emphasis rather than to intrinsic differences in fact. The northern writer, for example, insists on the attitude of his characters toward Jahweh as of prime importance, while the southern is almost indifferent to the matter. It is the story itself and the actors that harmonize the treatment and make for the cohesion. The originals who sat for the portraits must have been singularly vivid, and have left lasting impressions on tradition, to emerge in such consistent form from all the vicissitudes of oral and written transmission. Samuel, whether he be regarded as local soothsayer or judge of Israel, is always the same remote, somewhat forbidding figure, so far absorbed in Jahweh that his own family affairs suffer neglect and his sons become renegades to their country and their god. His is a universal tragedy, constantly repeated in all ages and lands and therefore appealing to all mankind. Saul is the unstable neurotic, a type with which war familiarizes the world. He is capable of performing the ordinary functions of everyday life but unable to endure the stress and strain on his emotions that is inherent in every period of upheaval. David is the self-made man, simple, direct, impressive, and strong in personal magnetism. His development from the carefree boy, playing the harp for Saul, to the old man who has seen success and sorrow and drained the cup of life is one of the most poignant documents of history.

Reviewing the course of Western literature in succeeding centuries, the first thing that bears any resemblance to the Life and Times of David is again the Icelandic saga. Certainly Suetonius' gossipy lives of the Caesars, Cornelius Nepos' dull biographies, and Plutarch's Lives cannot be compared to this early history, which, in its human treatment of the subject, approaches the historical novel of later days. The same realism, the same emphasis on the hero as a man and not as a political figure, distinguish both Norse saga and Hebrew story. There is always the possibility that the Icelander had the Hebrew model before him when he wrote, but the impression left, especially by the earlier sagas such as *Burnt Njal,* is of something indigenous to the soil. I think it more probable that in both Iceland and Palestine we find at this early period the same set of circumstances—people in remote and isolated regions developing independently the same form of artistic expression. (pp. 34-44)

ON THE WRITING OF HISTORY

BROOKE PETERS CHURCH

IT IS INTERESTING TO CONSIDER how the history of the Western world might have been changed had the historical writing of the Hebrews developed slowly and after the pattern set by the biographer of David and followed by the compilers of the early royalist account of David's life and times. These men knew their subject and stuck to fact, letting events take their natural course. They had no thesis to prove, no religious or political doctrine to preach, necessitating a distortion of fact.

It seems probable that from David's time onward comparatively full chronicles of the kings' reigns were kept in both north and south. Frequent references in the Book of Kings to the "Book of the Chronicles of Judah" or "of Israel," as the case may be, are not to the First and Second Books of Chronicles listed in the Old Testament (which are books of a much later date), but to contemporaneous chronicles of the kings, perhaps official records of temple and palace. How full and accurate these were we can only guess from the fragments incorporated with extensive editing in the Book of Kings. They seem, however, to have been much fuller than the meager records that have come down to us, for they are the subject of constant mention in those records, which refer to them for further details now no longer extant. For at the time of one of the editings of Kings they were either lost or deliberately destroyed, so perhaps depriving us of priceless treasures of source material.

Had the Hebrews been content to record events as they were known either from personal experience or by common report at the time of their occurrence, they might have given to the world valuable eyewitness information from the past such as the Greek historian Thucydides gave of the Peloponnesian War. Such a record could, in the light of further experience, be accurately analyzed and evaluated. For, in writing of current events, the putting together of familiar everyday cause and effect is too instinctive to be ignored. The biography of David is based on this instinct, as is the early, or royalist, history of David's times, and it is partly this which gives them their peculiar value. But the promise of those early writings was not to be fulfilled, for the writing of Hebrew history fell into the hands of a group of men obsessed by a purpose which far outweighed accuracy of recording.

I do not mean by this that the later editors and historians deliberately falsified their facts. According to their lights they were strictly honest, and merely read into the past their own, and to them more enlightened, point of view. They were motivated by the highest ethical purpose—to show the power of Jahweh. He was the prime mover, and every event whether of the past or the present was caused by him. The only fault to be found with such a conception is that it necessitates writing history backwards, from effect to cause. Were we to adopt this method, we might reach some surprising conclusions.

Take, for example, the invasion of Greece in the Second World War. Seeing Greece crushed, the Hebrew priest would not have looked into the train of events that led to her fall. He would have disregarded the rest of the world and the general conflagration which enveloped it. His only comment would have been, "The Greeks sinned, and so were delivered into the hands of their oppressors."

An interpretation of this kind would give Greece a disproportionate importance in present-day world affairs. It would make the whole world suffer to punish one small and insignificant nation. Palestine was a very small corner of the ancient world, but according to the Hebrew writers all the forces of the great kingdoms of Mesopotamia were set in motion time and again solely to punish her idolatry.

This historical method is first evident in a part of the Hebrew record which we have not yet considered, that which deals with the centuries before the time of the kingdom. Two such ancient histories have come down to us, and, like the two histories of David and his times, one (finished by about 850 B.C.) is from the south, and the other, written about a hundred years after the first, is from the north. It may be that the priests were already busy at the work of reconstructing this earlier past when the biographer and the royalist historian of David were writing of their own times, or it may be that the work was undertaken at a somewhat later date.

It was the peculiar need which the Hebrew leaders felt for a past history comparable in some degree to the records of the nations round about—a history which would prove the long-established solidarity and importance of Israel and bring out the power and singularity of Jahweh —which precluded a slow and gradual evolution of historical writing such as took place among the Greeks. Furthermore, the need was urgent, for the religion of Jahweh, still not fully established, would be in danger if the divided kingdom were further to dissolve into its component tribes.

For this purpose the priests gathered every scrap of legend, folklore and tradition, all the flotsam and jetsam of song and story current in the land, and from it pieced together a continuous record of a people, chosen by God from the dawn of time and set apart from the rest of the world as a favored race. This is the history which, many times edited and amended, is contained in the Pentateuch and the books of Joshua and Judges.

Granted the urgent need for a past history, there was really nothing but the common tradition of the people to use as material. The agglutination of wandering tribes settled in Palestine had no outstanding features in their past, such as great wars or conquests or invasions; theirs was a centuries-long record of "moving on" under the driving force of persecution or hunger. They had not even moved as a people, but in small groups and at different times. In David's time they were—for the moment—united by loyalty to the king and by a growing faith in the one god, Jahweh, whose deeds and power were extolled in verse recited in the various local shrines on the occasions of feasts and fasts. But as the conviction grew that the kingdom would not last, and still more after the north broke away, a stronger binder became essential, something that would prove the essential oneness of the tribes and their ancient affinity to Jahweh. What was

better suited to this purpose than the traditional material at hand—
variations in one form or another of a record of wandering?

The first documents were probably very crude, especially that written in the southern kingdom. The combined version of north and
south that has come down to us from the seventh century B.C. was
compiled by a master hand, and the result is a continuous narrative
answering all requirements. It explains the origin of man, the power
of Jahweh, the peculiar relationship of Israel to Jahweh, and promises an assured future to Israel if she continues to obey Jahweh's laws.

At so early a stage of cultural development that acceptance of these
legends from the past as facts was to be expected. The Greeks kept
their folklore fluid for many years longer until wider contacts and
greater maturity of experience allowed them to evaluate it. From the
historical point of view it is unfortunate that the Hebrews did not also
wait before crystallizing folklore into historical record. Greek myth
and legend was eventually woven into the art and literature of Greece
but did not interfere with the fact-finding and speculations of her
thinkers. The Hebrew not only gave out this traditional folklore as
fact, but tied it up with his religion and so shut off any chance of change
or development. For when history and religion had once been tied
together and events made dependent on the will of Jahweh, any alteration in the events as they had been given out would have called in
question the power of Jahweh. To reject or doubt the truth of the
record of the past would have been to reject the religion of Jahweh
and vitiate the future of Israel.

During the three hundred years which elapsed between this early
history of the seventh century and its final editing of about 350 B.C.,
the Hebrew priests stuck to their original statements and any changes
or modifications they made were not in the line of evaluation but of
rationalization. As the Hebrew's conception of Jahweh and his power
increased until it had reached the magnificent proportions of univer-
sality, taking in the creation of the world and gathering all the nations
of the earth under his rule, the priests' historical perspective narrowed
and became more and more exclusive and sectarian. Shut off from
world events, acutely conscious of Israel's own political unimportance,
they made up for her national insignificance by inventing the totali-
tarian state ruled by Jahweh, with the priests as his vicegerents and
orthodox Jewry as the chosen race. That there were more broad-
minded and well-informed Hebrews, men who accepted the belief in
one god for all the world and the Jew as minister and not mentor of

mankind, is evident when one reads the final version of Job or the inspired verse sequence of Second Isaiah or the teachings of the New Testament, which are in the same line of development and reflect much of the spirit of Deutero-Isaiah. But the authors of these books were not the official historians of Judaism.

Perhaps such a development was inevitable with a revealed religion which seems to have sprung up with the miraculous suddenness of a desert plant after rain. Like so many forced growths, the first flowering of Hebrew history was astonishingly powerful, as may be seen in what is left of the old version in Genesis, Exodus, Numbers, Deuteronomy, Joshua and Judges. It gave great promise, but in its later development the promise was not fulfilled.

The Greek made his gods in his own image and had no fear of them. He called on them for help, built temples and sacrificed to them, but he never permitted them to interfere with his freedom of inquiry into the world about him. At the time when the Hebrew priests were starting their re-editing of the seventh century documents, say 500 B.C., the Greek philosophers, regardless of their tradition, were already seeking a first principle; and while the Hebrews described creation as the work of one mind in seven days, the Greeks took the first faltering steps toward an evolutionary theory. The Hebrew had the revelation of a god outside the scope of man's power to imagine. In primitive days he was the god of the storm, who spoke by the thunder, whose voice was terrible. None could look on his face and live. Later the conception of a spiritual force was developed, but the awe and fear of the storm-god lived on. Nor did the later conception permit any questioning, any search for first principles, any expansion of knowledge. What had been said was said and was forever true. In itself the idea of such a god has limitless possibilities, but with the priests it was always bound to revelation and they never developed the attitude of the Greek philosopher.

Everyone of course studies history backwards and all history was written in the same order. We must each approach the past from our own moment in time. For us of today, with a fixed system of chronology in which to place events, using dates as hooks on which to hang the past, a review of other times is not difficult until in our backward progress we come to a period when there were no such convenient hangers as dates. For early man had no dates at all. He could not say B.C. or A.D., and it was not until comparatively late Roman times that the letters A.U.C. (Ab Urbe Condita) came into use. The Hebrew historians, and even the early Greek historians Herodotus and Thucydides, had no system of chronology, no focal point from which to date past centuries. Much of the vague discursiveness of Herodotus is due to this difficulty, for he was trying to describe past events which preceded by generations anything that he knew. He could not even be sure whether the various trains of events he discussed took place synchronously or at widely different times. Thucydides chose a smaller canvas to work on and was therefore able to date his history according to the years of the war he chronicled and in which he was living. But when in his introductory chapter he dealt with the distant past he too had to place his events vaguely in time.

The Greeks accepted this limitation and made no attempt to force the past into a connected sequence or to establish exact time measurements. Furthermore, they wrote history not to prove a preconceived theory but to inquire into what actually took place. Herodotus traveled far and wide to gather his facts, and according to his own lights sifted and weighed the evidence. He was of course far too credulous and accepted much which even in his day his better judgment should have told him was untrue; one feels sometimes that he was tempted into this error by the love of a good story. Wherever he could, however, he made allowance for error by giving variants of a legend or a tradition for his hearers to choose from. Never did he consider his opinion final.

Thucydides, a far greater historian, almost approached the modern method in his research, and his discussion of the probability of the truth of the Homeric tales comes startlingly close to the theories of today. For the events of his own time he was so accurate and detailed that his history is still authoritative. Take for example his extraordinary account of the plague in Athens in chapter 7 and compare it with the descriptions of the plague in the Book of Exodus or in II Samuel 24. Thucydides discusses the plague in detail in the hope apparently that what he says may be of use in finding the causes and the cure at some later date. The Hebrew authors accepted the plague as a visitation from Jahweh and never considered the possibility that it might have natural causes. This point of view was permissible to the early uninformed writers, but not to the later editors. Even Thucydides' habit of making the speakers say "what was in my opinion demanded of them by the various occasions" to which he so naïvely admits never affects his honest chronicling of the course of events. But the Hebrew from the beginning had a thesis to prove. His history could never be a mere statement of fact, he could never seek the truth impartially. To him history was merely the means to the end of proving Jahweh's might and his people's own peculiar importance.

Since history must be written backwards there is always danger of confusing cause and effect, and this danger is greatly increased if everything must be referred to one predetermined cause. By making Jahweh the protagonist and determining factor of his whole past, the Hebrew relieved himself of all responsibility for his acts and incidentally reversed the whole causal train of events. He not only wrote history backwards but read it backwards, seeing the will of God and not the natural relationship of cause and effect in all that took place. This again would have been understandable and permissible in early folklore, but when, instead of revising this folklore to conform with wider knowledge and scientific advances, the Hebrew in his later revisions merely intensified his earlier errors, the results often approach the absurd.

In the story of Moses, for instance, it was the late version that changed the account of Moses' death to fit the priestly editors' historical standpoint. Moses died before reaching the Promised Land. In the seventh century version this fact is stated quite simply and without comment. Presumably he died of old age or exhaustion. But in the late priestly revision his death comes as a punishment for usurping Jahweh's power. The reasoning seems to have been that Moses never reached the Promised Land, therefore he must have in some way disobeyed or offended the god. The most probable offense with a jealous god like Jahweh would be a usurpation of his power. The sin thus triangulated back was by inference read into the text and proved the historian's point. History thus treated can have no natural sequence of events, but must become episodic and erratic.

Another result of the Hebrew method of writing is the lack of detail. Such particularized description as we get in Herodotus or in Thucydides we never find in Hebrew history. For one thing, the material was worked over too often, and whatever merely concerned men and did not redound to the glory of Jahweh tended more and more to be omitted. There was no need for any inquiry, since all the answers came from God himself. The purpose of the writing was didactic, not philosophical. In the case of a plague, for instance, the priestly theory was apparently that the people sinned, Jahweh sent a plague, so find the sin. This is pragmatism of the crudest kind and very different from the impartial analysis and weighing of cause and effect which began to show itself even in the earliest Greek historians and filled their histories with the most varied detail. No wonder the Calvinists who guided their lives by the Old Testament believed in predestination. The doctrine is implicit in the text. Granted an omnipotent and omniscient god, dictator of the world, the point of view is inescapable.

Perhaps because he had always been a wanderer and an alien seeking a home in other men's lands, the Hebrew gained a sense of stability by resting on an old and established tradition. Perhaps he needed a consciousness of divine support to compensate for the fact that he was never a power in the world nor even a real political entity. His contacts with other nations were always by way of trade, not of statecraft. He was excluded, and he was a separatist. Which came first who can say?

The Greek, perhaps because of his increasing political power and subsequent empire building, was at home and at ease in the world. By virtue of his position he met the great people of the earth, mixed with them freely, visited their courts. Herodotus, for example, was a wide traveler and seems to have come in contact with all sorts and conditions of men. The broad tolerance of his history is the result of a cosmopolitan background; the acceptable traveler must himself accept—he cannot be forever criticizing. Narrow sectarianism was impossible for such people. At no time do the Greeks seem to have been obsessed by their religious beliefs, at no time were they proselytizers. Herodotus, for example, expresses no intolerance of alien faiths and even tries to synthesize the gods of the various nations, his own included. He was not a scientific historian and there is probably as much fancy as fact in his history, and as much misinformation as there is in Hebrew history, but he was only the beginning, working on incomplete information and quite able to accept correction. The seeds of further development were in him.

In the beginning of this chapter I suggested that the course of Hebrew historical writing—its manner of development—changed the course of world history. It is true that later historians followed the Greek model, and that Thucydides is used as source material for his times even today. But the history of the past which the Hebrews put together had its own profound effect, for it influenced the development of science and delayed the inquiry into origins and evolution.

When Christianity was struggling for existence, the same need appeared which had worked, long before, to bring about the writing of the Old Testament. To the Jews who first preached the new faith there was no break between their own sacred book and the coming of the

Messiah which it heralded. But it was the Gentiles, not the Jews, who accepted the religion of Jesus, and to them the Hebrew book was new and strange. Yet some background and authority for the new faith seemed necessary, and so little by little the church fathers, by allegory and harmonization, reconciled the Christians to the use of the Old Testament as the basis of their faith. So, together with the New Testament, it became "The Book" of the Christian church.

When the barbarians overran Europe and destroyed the Greek and Roman cultures, Christianity for many centuries remained the one civilizing influence in the Western world. We owe it a tremendous debt for keeping alive the flame of learning and for helping to establish a new culture on the ruins of the old.

During these centuries Greece, the cultural source of the now decadent Eastern Empire, was forgotten. Her creative genius no longer enriched the world with discoveries of scientific value or sublime literary and artistic achievements. She too was struggling for survival and had little energy to spare for creation. In the West, where Latin became the lingua franca, the Bible, translated into Latin, became the one book which everyone was taught, and the story of creation, as contained in the first chapter of Genesis, was accepted as the inspired and therefore true account of the beginnings.

No doubt there were in every generation some few lonely spirits who doubted the finality of the account and made their solitary investigations in secret. But if they tried to publish their findings, torture and death were their reward or they were regarded as wizards and frowned upon by the church.

When Columbus propounded the startling notion of an actual voyage based on the theory that the earth is round, he was laughed at. And yet, in the second century B.C., the Greek mathematician Eratosthenes had already measured the earth's diameter, so taking the first step on the way to a true conception of the universe, with a spherical world revolving around the sun. Just as the Hebrew method of reading history backwards exaggerated the importance of Israel, so their picture of creation exaggerated the importance of the earth and distorted scientific truth.

The trial of Galileo, the persecution of heretics, which has taken place even in very recent times, the rise of Calvinism, the settlement of Plymouth, all hark back to the work of the early Hebrew priests.

Even today new archaeological discoveries are given to the general public not as further enlightenment about the past but as proofs of the truth of the Old Testament. No one tries to prove to us that the *Iliad* is true. We accept it as a great epic poem, a treasure of world literature. Why, then, do we need proof that the Old Testament is true and cast it aside when we find that it is not a scientific document? It contains some of the world's greatest prose narrative, and from the seventh century B.C. onward the world would have been, and would be today, the poorer for its loss. (pp. 45-53)

THE GREAT MASTERPIECE, JOB

HENRY THATCHER FOWLER

THE BOOK OF JOB is one of that group of five or six world poems that stand as universal expressions of the human spirit. The *Iliad,* the *Niebelungenlied,* the *Divina Comedia,* belong to no age or nation, yet each is a distinctive product of its own time and of the race that gave it birth; in any other age, or among any other peoples, neither could have arisen. Similarly, Job is a characteristic product of post-exilic Israel. Without the work of the earlier prophets, the Deuteronomic era, the soul agonies of Jeremiah, the downfall of the nation and its interpretation by the writers of the exile, the book of Job could not have been written.

Many students of Hebrew literature count this poem the immediate outgrowth of the exile; its relation to the whole development of Israel's literature suggests rather its composition in the latter part of the fourth century B.C., shortly before the end of the Persian rule, or soon after Alexander's conquest. The prologue and epilogue (1–2, 42$^{7-17}$) may have formed an earlier prose story of Job, and some portions of the poem are best interpreted as later accretions.

The prologue moves rapidly, giving a series of distinct pictures: the ancient sheik, perfect, upright, and prosperous; the heavenly council; the first series of catastrophes. In the description of the last, one feels a formal, artificial structure somewhat like that of the late, priestly prose. The hero, his name, his home, his character, his misfortunes, are all introduced in the one chapter. The brief second chapter pictures: a second heavenly council; a new catastrophe; Job after the new misfortune has fallen upon him; the arrival of the three friends and their seven days' watch with Job.

This prologue offers a curious interpretation of human suffering. It presents a man perfect, upright, scrupulous in his piety; when his sons have had their birthday feasts, he rises early and performs sacrifices for them all, lest they have sinned in some way. Jehovah himself declares that there is none like him in all the earth, perfect, upright, fearing God, and turning away from evil. Upon this one comes loss of property, loss of family, and loathsome disease. The old stories of Israel had taught that it was sin which brought suffering upon humanity; the prophets had developed the doctrine of a righteous God who rewarded virtue and punished sin in the nation and the individual; already the sages had formulated this idea into many a proverb. Here is a new conception! Among the superhuman beings, the sons of God, who from time to time present themselves before Jehovah, is one called the Satan, "the Adversary."[1] The same word occurs in 1 Samuel 29[4]—The princes of the Philistines are afraid that David will be an adversary (satan). The word is first met as applied to a superhuman being in Zechariah 3[1], where the high priest is clothed in the sins of the people with the Satan standing at his right hand to act as his adversary.[2] In Zechariah there is no further explanation of the Satan's functions; in Job it appears that this son of God goes to and fro in the earth as an adversary to man. He cannot believe that any man is really good, really loves goodness for its own sake; "Does Job fear God for nought?" is his sarcastic question, and when Job stands the first test, the satanic mind is not satisfied. The Satan, new as he is in the Biblical literature, is not the newest and strangest conception in this story; a God who, to satisfy this evil-minded

---

[1] This is translated as a proper name in the English Bible, but in the Hebrew it has the definite article.

[2] To *be* or *act as adversary* is a denominative verb formed from *satan*.

son of his, permits misery to come to a perfect and upright man, is the most astonishing element in the story. Is this the God of justice of whom Amos and Ezekiel spoke, or the God of love that Hosea and Jeremiah came to know?

Job and the friends, it is to be remembered, knew nothing of any such reasons for the misfortunes; the writer uses a kind of dramatic irony, putting the readers into possession of facts unknown to the actors in the tragedy that is to follow. Job, knowing of no reason for his misfortunes, accepts them with complete resignation—The Lord gave and the Lord hath taken away; blessed be the name of the Lord, is his word of submission. When his wife bids him to curse God and die, he answers, What? shall we receive good at the hand of God, and shall we not receive evil?

The friends come from distant regions; they do not know Job, so changed is he; in true oriental fashion, they lift up their voices and weep and rend every one his mantle and sprinkle dust upon their heads. Then they sit in silence seven days and nights, seeing Job's great grief. So the prologue, the prose narrative, closes.

The poem begins with Job's curse or lament. In a lyric of great pathos Job asks, Why was I ever born? Why died I not at birth? Why can I not die now? There is a strikingly similar passage in the *Œdipus Coloneus*.

> Happiest beyond compare
> Never to taste of life;
> Happiest in order next,
> Being born, with quickest speed
> Thither again to turn
> From whence we came.

It is difficult to account for the change in Job from complete resignation to bitter outcry, if the poem and prose prologue were originally one and do not represent two different stories awkwardly joined. It would seem, however, that there must have been something before the poem to make it intelligible at all, and either one of two explanations is suggested to account for the change: Job's fortitude has given way under the stress and progress of his disease; this is commonly held to have been elephantiasis, a form of leprosy, horrible in its physical effects and, if possible, even more terrible in its mental aspects; or Job is maddened by the silent, accusing presence of his friends. It becomes clear to the reader, as the poem advances, that the friends interpret Job's sufferings as the sure evidence of his sins; possibly he realized this in the seven days and nights of silence and so was driven to desperate outcry.

To Eliphaz there is no excuse for Job's words; such giving way to grief is quite unworthy of one who has been a counsellor and upholder of others. Job ought to be confessing his sin, instead of complaining in this fashion. In the sight of God, before whom no man can be just, Job is no doubt a great sinner; trouble does not come without a cause, though it is true that man is born to trouble as naturally as the sparks fly upward. If I were in your place, Eliphaz says to Job, I would seek unto God and commit my cause unto him; then he goes off into ascription of lofty praise to God, promising great blessings to Job if he accepts correction and does not despise the chastening of the Almighty.

On the strength of 4 [12ff], Eliphaz has sometimes been called a mystic.

> Now a thing was secretly brought to me,
> And mine ear received a whisper thereof.
> In thoughts from the visions of the night,
> When deep sleep falleth on men,
> Fear came upon me, and trembling,
> Which made all my bones to shake.
> Then a spirit passed before my face;
> The hair of my flesh stood up.
> It stood still, but I could not discern the appearance thereof;
> A form was before mine eyes:
> There was silence, and I heard a voice, saying,
> Shall mortal man be more just than God?
> Shall a man be more pure than his Maker?

Job's answer seems at first to have little reference to the words of Eliphaz, except as he admits that his words have been rash[3] because of his great calamity. He longs for death and has no hope for the future, his strength cannot last; he is ready to faint, and pity ought to be showed him.[4] The figure with which he describes his experience with his friends is an effective one in that land of streams which are dry in summer's heat.

> My brethren have dealt deceitfully as a brook,
> As the channel of brooks that pass away;
> Which are black by reason of the ice,
> And wherein the snow hideth itself:
> What time they wax warm, they vanish;
> When it is hot, they are consumed out of their place.[5]

[3] 6[3].   [4] 6 14   [5] 6 15-17.

Chapter 6 describes the horror of Job's sickness and, near the close, turns to bitter words toward the watcher of men.

If I have sinned, what do I unto thee, O thou watcher of men?
Why hast thou set me as a mark for thee,
So that I am a burden to myself?
And why dost thou not pardon my transgression, and take away mine
    iniquity?
For now shall I lie down in the dust;
And thou wilt seek me diligently, but I shall not be.[6]

Bildad speaks much more bluntly than Eliphaz has done. He is shocked at Job's impiety: Doth God pervert judgment? he indignantly asks and then he makes a maddening suggestion.

If thy children have sinned against him,
And he hath delivered them into the hand of their transgression;

At the close he holds out hope to Job, though it may be in sarcasm. On the ground especially of 8 [8ff], Bildad has been styled a traditionalist, in contrast to Eliphaz.

For inquire, I pray thee, of the former age,
And apply thyself to that which their fathers have searched out
(For we are but of yesterday, and know nothing,
Because our days upon earth are a shadow);
Shall not they teach thee, and tell thee,
And utter words out of their heart?

Job now feels the full injustice of his fate; his sufferings prove him guilty of sin. If it is true that God blesses the righteous and gives suffering to the wicked, then the man who has great misfortune must be peculiarly wicked; this was suggested in the words of Eliphaz and is made very clear by Bildad. — If thou wert pure and upright; surely now he would awake for thee, and make the habitation of thy righteousness prosperous; this is the irrefutable wisdom of the generations. While Job sees the power of God and describes it better than the friends can, it is that very power which is proving him guilty; therefore Job concludes that God destroys the perfect and the wicked. Since wickedness rules in the world, it must be that God is responsible for it.

The earth is given into the hand of the wicked;
He covereth the faces of the judges thereof:
If it be not he, who then is it?[7]

6 6 20-21.   7 9 24.

At length, Job returns to the thought of the opening lament and then pleads for a little respite before he goes to the land of midnight darkness.

> Are not my days few? cease then,
> And let me alone, that I may take comfort a little,
> Before I go whence I shall not return,
> Even to the land of darkness and of the shadow of death;
> The land dark as midnight, .
> The land of the shadow of death, without any order,
> And where the light is as midnight.[8]

Job's plea to God for mercy is pathetic indeed, but the third friend, Zophar, feels nothing of the pathos; he is hot on a theological controversy.

> Should not the multitude of words be answered?
> And should a man full of talk be justified?
> Should thy boastings make men hold their peace?
> And when thou mockest, shall no man make thee ashamed?
> For thou sayest, My doctrine is pure,
> And I am clean in thine eyes.[9]

He wishes that God would speak and show Job the secrets of wisdom, and he makes the direct charge that God is exacting of Job less than his iniquity deserves. How more could be exacted it is difficult to see; Job would welcome death. At the end, Zophar also holds out hope, if Job will reform.

The point of view of the friends is now clear. They have inherited the noble truths worked out by Israel's great prophets; they believe in a God of justice and mercy, and they are most ardent defenders of this belief. A vast mass of experience, in all ages, confirms the truth of the prophetic doctrine that sin brings suffering to the sinner, but Job has had an experience which has opened his eyes to the fact that justice does not prevail on the earth; it does not in his case, and, as he looks about, he sees that it does not in other cases.

In the reply that closes this cycle of the debate, Job is decidedly sarcastic at the beginning.

> No doubt but ye are the people,
> And wisdom shall die with you.
> But I have understanding as well as you;

8 10 20-22.   9 11 2-4.

> I am not inferior to you:
> Yea, who knoweth not such things as these?[10]

The friends had *inherited* noble truths, and Job recognizes that they know nothing but traditional truth, with which he is quite as familiar as they. To repeat such dogma to one in his condition is but a mockery.

> In the thought of him that is at ease there is contempt for misfortune;
> It is ready for them whose foot slippeth.

Euripides, in his *Alcestis,* expressed similar truth.

> 'Tis easier to advise, than suffering to endure.

Then Job gives a flash-light picture of life as it really is, not as theory paints it.

> The tents of robbers prosper,
> And they that provoke God are secure;
> Into whose hand God bringeth abundantly.[11]

You say wisdom is with the ancients, he cries; No, wisdom is with God, and *power,* too. Then he gives a splendid, terrible description of the power and wisdom of God manifest with injustice.

With aged men is wisdom,
And in length of days understanding.
With God is wisdom and might;
He hath counsel and understanding.
Behold, he breaketh down, and it cannot be built again;
He shutteth up a man, and there can be no opening.
Behold, he withholdeth the waters, and they dry up;
Again, he sendeth them out, and they overturn the earth.
With him is strength and wisdom;
The deceived and the deceiver are his.
He leadeth counsellors away stripped,
And judges maketh he fools.
He looseth the bond of kings,
And bindeth their loins with a girdle.

He leadeth priests away stripped,
And overthroweth the mighty.
He removeth the speech of the trusty,

10 12 2-3.　　　11 12 6.

And taketh away the understanding of the elders.
He poureth contempt upon princes,
And looseth the belt of the strong.
He uncovereth deep things out of darkness,
And bringeth out to light the shadow of death.
He increaseth the nations, and he destroyeth them:
He enlargeth the nations, and he leadeth them captive.
He taketh away understanding from the chiefs of the people of the earth,
And causeth them to wander in a wilderness where there is no way.
They grope in the dark without light;
And he maketh them to stagger like a drunken man.[12]

Job was face to face with the problem that has become so insistent in these latter days; power and wisdom we find in the wonderful evolution of which men talk so glibly, but where's the justice in the law of tooth and claw? Is not the survival of the fittest the right of mere might? Job is a very modern book; it brings time-honored theory to the test in the laboratory of life. He knows the theory just as well as his confident friends, and he knows that the facts do not harmonize with the theory. Job was at heart a scientist, and when the scientific test of loyalty to simple fact is applied, time-honored theories often come crashing down. The thirteenth chapter opens: —

> Lo, mine eye hath seen all this,
> Mine ear hath heard and understood it.
> What ye know, the same do I know also:
> I am not inferior unto you.
> Surely I would speak to the Almighty,
> And I desire to reason with God.[13]

There we begin to get at the heart of Job; he must come face to face with God. To him, these men who repeat pious platitudes are forgers of lies, thinking to defend and please God with that which is contrary to fact.

> Hear now my reasoning,
> And hearken to the pleadings of my lips.
> Will ye speak unrighteously for God,
> And talk deceitfully for him?
> Will ye show partiality to him?
> Will ye contend for God?
> Is it good that he should search you out?
> Or as one deceiveth a man, will ye deceive him?[14]

12 12 12-25.   13 13 1-3.   14 13 6-9.

He will start out on bold adventure, abandoning orthodox falsehood, and, taking his life in his hand, will face God and present his case before him.

> Wherefore should I take my flesh in my teeth,
> And put my life in my hand?
> Behold, he will slay me; I have no hope:
> Nevertheless I will maintain my ways before him.[15]

Then the human strength of the sick man fails; if only God would remove his hand from him, he could argue his case, man's life is so brief and at its end, oblivion! O that thou wouldst hide me in the grave till thy wrath is passed and then give me a hearing, is his prayer.

This line of thought brings Job to the great mystery of the ages—If a man die, shall he live again? If Job could believe in a life beyond the grave, he could wait all the days of his appointed time, but he cannot believe it—The water washes away the stones, and thou destroyest the hope of man. Not life, but oblivion is man's fate. Job sinks back in despair, and the first cycle of the debate is ended.

The discussion proceeds through two more cycles, in which the friends are able to add little to the strength of their position, though their accusations become more direct; Eliphaz charges that Job's own mouth condemns him and later accuses the sufferer of a long category of sins, such as one in his former position might have committed. Job's professed inability to find God is cleverly, though superficially, perverted into ground for accusing him of sinning, in the confidence that God could not see him. The blunt and brutal Bildad quite loses his temper because of Job's lack of respect for him and his friends; it must be confessed that Job gives some occasion in his scorn for the miserable comforters who have nothing new to offer in his perplexity.

In the third cycle Bildad interjects a few words only and Zophar's name does not appear. This has often been interpreted as an intentional indication that the friends have been silenced. It is probable, however, that a part of chapter 27 was originally assigned to Zophar, since the point of view is that of the friends; in the mouth of Job, the words could only be sarcastic. It is possible also that Bildad's speech was originally longer.[16] Without the rather inartistically obvious method of indicating the silencing of the friends by assigning a few words only to

---

[15] 13 14-15.

[16] Barton tentatively reconstructs Bildad's third speech: 25 1-6, 24 17, 18, 5-8, 30 3-8, 24 21, 22, 19, 31, 24. *Job, The Bible for Home and School.*

Bildad and omitting Zophar, it is evident that they have no more to say.

In the second cycle, it appears that all Job really asks of his friends is some comprehending sympathy, while he fights his lonesome battle of the soul. It is God with whom the hero of the poem is really concerned; that fact that God is his enemy without cause, rends Job's heart. Early in the second cycle, Job rises to the assurance that in heaven his case is clear; apparently this high faith lasts a moment only, and his thoughts turn to the grave as his only hope. A little later, he returns to the conviction that he must have a vindicator[17] in heaven and that ultimately he will see God. This much is clear, though the close of verse 26 is ambiguous; it may possibly mean, as the King James version has it, in my flesh I shall see God, or it may mean, as in the Revised versions, without my flesh. The latter is the preferable rendering, although it expresses a hope for the future life of the spirit quite foreign to Job's usual thought. Once more, in the third cycle, Job cries,

> O that I knew where I might find him!
> That I might come even to his seat!

and goes on to express his firm faith that then he would get a fair hearing. Though he cannot find God,[18] Job is confident that the hidden one knows the way he takes, and that, when he has been tried, he shall come forth as gold.

The debate closes with the friends silenced, though not convinced; perhaps Job himself would never have come to see the error in the current theology without the bitter experience that forced him to a new point of view.

Following the section that may have been Zophar's missing speech (27 [7-11, 13-23]), there comes a remarkable poem upon the unsearchableness of wisdom.[19] This is not assigned to any one of the speakers and probably was inserted by some one who felt that it added a thought to the subject under discussion; it is no real help to the working out of the plan of the book, but in itself is a precious memorial of one type of Israel's poetry. In the next three chapters, Job speaks at length, contrasting his former honor with his present dishonored condition, telling how he had been accustomed to give sympathy to the wretched, and

[17] 19 [25]. *Vindicator* (See R. V. margin) represents the idea of *goel* better than *redeemer*.

[18] 23 [3-7].

[19] Chapter 28.

defending himself against the charges of sin. Suddenly he thinks, What is the use of this long defence? The Almighty does not hear me, and I am defending myself without knowledge as to the nature of the indictment.

The doctrine of rewards and penalties, which counted misfortune as the sure mark of guilt, introduced a deep note of tragedy into the life of many an earnest soul in ancient Israel, a tragedy that we can only imperfectly realize. It finds expression in the psalmist's prayer,

> Who can understand his errors;
> Cleanse thou me from secret faults.

The Babylonian penitential psalms reflect the same anxiety concerning sin, the nature of which is unknown to the guilty one.

Following Job's conclusion of the debate[20] come the speeches of Elihu, prefaced by a prose statement. Elihu has kept silent while those older than he spoke, but now he bursts forth in indignation against Job and the friends who have not been able to answer; he describes himself as full of words, and so he proves to be. Despite his swelling promises, he adds little to the points the three have made. The entire section, 32 to 36, is best interpreted as an interpolation rather than the work of the master who composed the main part of the book.

Dropping out the Elihu section, immediately after Job finishes speaking Jehovah answers him out of the stormwind. It is the old, poetic conception of the God of Israel appearing in the storm cloud; he comes to speak of his wisdom and power as seen in the creation of the world and in the order and control of the mighty forces of nature. The poetry is fine, though the thought is that common to the Hebrew prophets and poets, at least of the post-exilic period.

> Where wast thou when I laid the foundations of the earth?
> Declare, if thou hast understanding.
> Who determined the measures thereof, if thou knowest?
> Or who stretched the line upon it?
> Whereupon were the foundations thereof fastened?
> Or who laid the corner-stone thereof,
> When the morning stars sang together,
> And all the sons of God shouted for joy?
>
> Or who shut up the sea with doors,
> When it brake forth, as if it had issued out of the womb;
> When I made clouds the garment thereof,

20 31 40.

And thick darkness a swaddling-band for it,
And marked out for it my bound,
And set bars and doors,
And said, Hitherto shalt thou come, but no further;
And here shall thy proud waves be stayed?[21]

When Jehovah is made to speak, later,[22] of his unsearchable wisdom and power as seen in animal life, it is to us less sublime and, at times, almost ludicrous, unless we recall that superficial observations upon the habits of the wild creatures seemed recondite wisdom among the ancients.

At length Job is called upon to answer this display of the divine wisdom, and he replies:—

Behold, I am of small account; what shall I answer thee?
I lay my hand upon my mouth.
Once have I spoken, and I will not answer;
Yes, twice, but I will proceed no further.[23]

Jehovah now goes on still more completely to humble Job with further descriptions of his power as seen in the semi-mythical behemoth and leviathan. From our point of view, this seems on a much lower level than the preceding words of Jehovah; perhaps it was a climax to those who lived in an age that believed in the creatures described.[24]

Job answers in words that give the real conclusion of his long struggle.

Then Job answered Jehovah, and said,
I know that thou canst do all things,
And that no purpose of thine can be restrained.
Who is this that hideth counsel without knowledge?
Therefore have I uttered that which I understood not,
Things too wonderful for me, which I knew not.
Hear, I beseech thee, and I will speak;
I will demand of thee, and declare thou unto me.
I had heard of thee by the hearing of the ear;
But now mine eyes seeth thee:
Wherefore I abhor myself,
And repent in dust and ashes.[25]

Viewed as a philosophical discussion of the problem of suffering, the closing chapters of the poem do not advance beyond the discredited argument of the friends, that God is too exalted to be understood or

21 38 4-11.   22 39.   23 40 4-5.

24Many regard 40 15 to 41 34 as a later addition. For a concise argument see Barton, *Job,* pp. 31-32.

25 42.1-6.

questioned; but the book of Job is not primarily a philosophical discussion; it is a poem in its essence, as well as in form. It has often been called a dramatic poem, and it can be acted. To be sure, the action is chiefly in the prologue; in the long debate, there is no change of scene or characters. In the early Greek dramas little happened on the stage, what had happened elsewhere being recounted to the audience. The lack of actors and action on the stage itself was largely supplied by the chorus which, with its constant movement and song, filled and gratified the eye and ear. The Greek drama grew out of a combination of the rhythmic movements of sacrificial ceremonies with lyric, narrative poetry, and dialogue. With all possible concessions made, we can hardly call Job a drama. It does not have even the action of religious ceremony or dance of any kind, and the dialogue is slow, though splendidly wrought out. In fact, the Semites did not develop a drama in the European sense. Job has more affinity with the drama than with any other form of European poetry, but we have already noted that Semitic literature has its own forms, and it is useless to try and bring these rigidly under our Greek categories.

The book has again been denominated an epic, *The Epic of the Inner Life*.[26] As Homer and Vergil wrote of wars and wanderings, deeds of martial heroes who strove and struggled with great strength or cunning to win success in ways that delighted the Greeks and Romans, so the author of Job wrote of a typical Jewish hero whose warfare was within the soul and whose wanderings were on the restless seas of religious doubt and hope. In literary form, the poem is less like an epic than a drama, yet the suggestion of its epic quality has greatly helped to an understanding of the true import of the book.

The friends have some individuality, at least Eliphaz and Bildad have, yet their chief service is to present current doctrine effectively and to goad Job on in his long struggle toward a God in whom his soul can rest. Viewing the book as the story of Job's inner life, one finds more progress in the cycles of speeches than when these are considered as a debate.

The God in whom Job has been taught to believe, no longer exists for him; Job does not question the existence of one who rules over the affairs of men, but he does deny that there is one who rules with justice. He even holds God responsible for the injustice done by human judges. When Job realizes that the friends are trying to please God by lying for

[26]See the volume of this title by Professor J. F. Genung.

him, the author gives us our first clear view of his hero's higher faith in God; he cannot believe that God loves a lie, even when it is told in his defence. That came out in the last speech of the first cycle; in the second cycle, this faith in truth which is the inalienable right of every fearless lover of truth, led Job to his fleeting, returning faith that the justice of his cause was recorded in heaven; it led him also to his momentary glimpses beyond the dark grave. At first there was only a question—If a man die shall he live again? If only Job could believe in that future chance, he could endure everything here. It is a wonderful, prophetic glimpse from a time when a clear faith in personal immortality had not yet come to man. After the Christian faith came clear, men learned to endure, as Job knew that he could, with joyous strength, through seeing the unseen. Again the hope returned to Job, and no longer as a mere question; it became, for the moment, a confident assurance that, though worms might destroy this body, he would come face to face with God.

Through the centuries since Job was written, philosophers and, especially, poets have struggled with the problem of Job. Browning is full of it, and so are the great dramatists from Æschylus to modern times. Partial solutions that go beyond the philosophy of Job have been offered; the full answer is not yet. The poet of the *Suffering Servant,* indeed, went far deeper than the author of Job into the mystery of suffering.

As an argument, Job is negative; it demolishes absolutely the theory that righteousness on the one hand and health, wealth, and honor on the other are always proportional. Perhaps that is all the intellectual achievement that ought to be demanded of any one writer, but that accomplishment is not what makes the book a great poem. Job, like all true literature, is an interpretation of life—"Life is deeper and wider than any particular lesson to be learned from it; and just when we think that we have at last guessed its best meanings, it laughs in our face with some paradox which turns our solution into a new riddle."[27] Job mirrors the struggles of brave, true men and women to-day, as well as in the fourth century before Christ. It proves itself peculiarly the college students' book among the writings of ancient Israel, for it tells the story of their inner life when they, like Job, are willing to venture all for faith in truth.

The last eight verses of the prose epilogue mark a sad reaction from the great poem. They give back to Job just double all his former wealth

[27]H. A. Beers, *Split Zephyr.*

and family and bring life down to the vulgar, account-book standards that the poem spurned and shattered. This must be a part of the older story of Job, which the poet allowed to remain, or else, an unfortunate accretion. As the book stands, the first part of the epilogue puts a noble seal of approval on the lesson of the poem. Jehovah condemns the friends who have not spoken the thing that was right as his servant Job has; they are to offer sacrifices and Job is to pray for them that they may escape the consequences of their folly. Without this sanction of Job's words, the poem itself indicates firm faith that God, though his ways are past finding out, will reveal himself to the one who seeks and in a measure that will satisfy and leave the soul at rest. (pp. 321-336)

THE WISDOM OF ECCLESIASTES

ROBERT GORDIS

The Man

AS NEARLY AS CAN BE TOLD, Koheleth, or Ecclesiastes, lived during the dark and shadowy age in Jewish history that preceded the vivid glory of the Maccabees, some time during the fourth or third century before the Christian Era. It was an age well described by an older contemporary as a "day of small things," with little to stir men's hearts either to ecstasy or wrath. For the period of the Second Temple was one when great dreams had turned into petty realities and the resplendent visions of the fathers had become the very real but colorless background against which the children lived.

True enough, on the self-same site where Solomon had built his Temple five centuries earlier, a replica now stood. But this was only a modest imitation of the older structure, which continued to grow ever more glorious in the national consciousness, as it receded further into the past. That earlier Temple had been burnt in 586 B.C.E. by the Babylonian conquerors, who exiled the most important classes of people. While many of the captives, no doubt, were absorbed by the surrounding population in Mesopotamia and elsewhere, not all had been assimilated by their foreign environment. There now arose gifted leaders of deep spirituality, like Deutero-Isaiah and Ezekiel, who sustained the courage of the Judean exiles and fortified their solidarity by painting glorious pictures of a Restoration to Zion.

That Restoration had indeed come, but on a scale far removed from the prophetic visions. A small band of settlers had been allowed to return to Palestine by the magnanimous and far-sighted Cyrus, founder of the Persian Empire. Instead of a mighty nation holding sway over distant lands, as the prophets had foretold, the Jewish people in its own homeland was a tiny island in a heathen sea. Centered in Jerusalem, the new community enjoyed at best a precarious autonomy in the religious and cultural spheres, while being completely subservient, politically and economically, to the Persian overlords. The Jewish settlement was also imperilled by internal discord. It had required the stern and heroic measures of an Ezra to stem the tide of intermarriage which was particularly prevalent among the priests and other leaders of the community. This tendency threatened to obliterate the Jewish identity completely within the space of a few generations. Moreover, there was the perpetual threat of enemies from without. Only the resourcefulness of the Jewish governor, Nehemiah, had succeeded in erecting a city wall around Jerusalem, in spite of the intrigues of the neighboring Ammonites, Samaritans and Arabs.

The next few centuries that followed Ezra and Nehemiah are among the most obscure in Jewish history. Only a few incidents are recorded by Josephus for the entire period, and these generally of the most disreputable kind. We hear of a high priest murdering his brother in the Temple precincts, and of the scion of an aristocratic family of Judea having an affair with a Greek dancer in Alexandria. Thus the upper classes were already showing signs of the moral disintegration that led them a little later into wholesale surrender to the blandishments of the Hellenistic world and the virtual abandonment of the Jewish way of life.

There were, to be sure, deeper spiritual currents among the people, which, inchoate and unrecognized until hundreds of years later, escaped the vigilant eyes of the chronicler. Due to the chastening influence of the Babylonian Exile and the Return, the long campaign of religious and ethical education waged by the prophets and legislators of the First Temple period was finally crowned with success. Scorned and vilified in their own day, the Prophets had now attained to wide authority, and were more truly alive centuries after their death than in their own lifetime.

Perhaps even more significant was the achievement of Ezra, who succeeded in establishing the Torah, or the Five Books of Moses, as the basic law of Judaism. At a great assembly, participated in by the heads of every family in the newly constituted community, it was publicly accepted as binding for all time. But the Torah, written in earlier days, could not become a living force in the new community without study and reinterpretation. This significant function was undertaken by the *Sopherim,* or Scribes, better rendered "the Masters of the Book." They expounded the letter of Scripture, amplified it where it was brief or unclear, and extended its provisions to meet new conditions as they arose. They not only preserved the Torah; they gave it new life.

The importance of their work can scarcely be over-estimated. Their activity made the Bible relevant to the needs of new generations and thus prepared it to serve as the eternal charter of humanity. Their discussions and decisions were incorporated into the Oral Law, constituting the oldest part of the Mishnah and the Talmud. Thus the *Sopherim* laid the foundations of Rabbinic Judaism. They gave to Jewish tradition some of its most noteworthy characteristics, its protean capacity for adjustment and its fusing of realistic understanding and idealistic aspiration. These nameless Scribes thus contributed in no small measure to the survival of the Jewish people. But their significance is not limited to the household of Israel. The Christian world, too, owes them a deep debt of gratitude, all too often left unacknowledged. As founders of Pharisaic Judaism, they helped create the background from which Christianity arose, and formulated many of the basic teachings that both religions share in common.

All this lay, however, within the lap of the unborn future. In their own day, the role of the Scribes and teachers of the Oral Law was unspectacular. Doubtless it attracted little attention, since they were drawn mainly from the lower and middle classes of society.

The upper classes also possessed a medium of intellectual activity which, like the dominant spirit of the age, was severely practical in purpose. These groups, even the high-priestly families among them, whose position and income derived from their service in the Temple, were concerned less with the will of God than with the way of the world. Their goal in education was the training of their youth for careers as merchant princes, landed gentry or government officials. To satisfy this need, a special type of preceptor arose, principally, if not exclusively, in Jerusalem, the capital. Like the Sophists in classical Hellas, who performed a similar function for the upper-class youth of Greek society, these Hebrew teachers taught what they termed "Wisdom" (Hebrew *Hokmah,* Greek *Sophia*).

This Hebrew Wisdom was a true Oriental product that had been cultivated for centuries throughout the lands of the Fertile Crescent—Egypt, Palestine, Syria and Babylonia—and for similar purposes, the preparation of youth for success in government, agriculture and commerce. Increasingly it is becoming clear that, even in Israel, the roots of Wisdom were very ancient, part of the cultural inheritance of the Orient, which the Hebrews shared with their neighbors and kinsmen. The tradition that King Solomon is the symbol of Wisdom is no longer airily dismissed by scholars as a figment of the folk imagination. It is seen to reflect the historical fact that the intensive cultivation of Wisdom goes back to his reign, when wide international contacts and internal prosperity contributed to the flowering of culture.

It was, however, during the first half of the Second Temple period that Hebrew Wisdom reached its apogee, for reasons that need not detain us here. Primarily, it was concerned with the arts and wiles of practical living. The Hebrew Wisdom teachers sought to inculcate the virtues of hard work, zeal, prudence, sexual moderation, sobriety, loyalty to authority and religious conformity—all the elements of a morality making for worldly success. What is more, they did not hesitate to urge less positive virtues on their youthful charges, such as holding one's tongue and distributing largesse, as aids in making one's way.

Where words abound, sin is not wanting,
But he that controls his tongue is a wise man. (Prov. 10: 19)
A man's gift makes room for him,
It brings him before great men. (Prov. 18: 16)
In brief, this practical Wisdom represented a hard-headed, matter-of-fact, "safe and sane" approach to the problems of living. Of this prac-

tical Wisdom the literary repositories are *Proverbs* in the Bible and *Ben Sira,* or *Ecclesiasticus,* in the Apocrypha.

Among the many preceptors of Wisdom, however, were some whose restless minds refused to be satisfied with these practical goals of what may be termed the lower Wisdom. They sought to penetrate to the great abiding issues: the meaning of life, the purpose of creation, the nature of death, the mystery of evil. In grappling with these ultimate problems they insisted on using the same instruments of observation and common sense they applied to daily concerns, rather than rely on tradition and conventional doctrines. Like so many rationalist minds since their day, however, they found the unaided human reason incapable of solving these issues. Some, no doubt, finally made their peace with the traditional religion of their day. But others, more tough-minded, refused to take on faith what their reason could not demonstrate. Hence their writings reveal various degrees and types of skepticism and heterodoxy. Several of these devotees of the higher or speculative Wisdom were highly fortunate. For it was given them to transmute the frustration and pain of their quest into some of the world's greatest masterpieces, notably *Job* and *Koheleth*. It is within this environment of economic well-being and intense intellectual activity that Koheleth arose and in terms of which he must be understood.

His brief book gives tantalizingly few hints about his personal life, and these have been seized upon and elaborated variously by his readers. Some have inferred from the detailed description of luxury in Chapter Two that he was a country gentleman, an aristocrat of the old school. In that passage, however, Koheleth is merely adopting the rôle of King Solomon as a literary device, in order to drive home his point on the futility of wealth and wisdom, for both of which the great King was renowned.

It seems much more likely that Koheleth was a teacher in one of the Wisdom academies in Jerusalem, which catered to the educational needs of upper-class youth. Not merely by vocation but probably also by birth, he was closely identified with this group. It seems clear that he never suffered poverty and want. Apparently he enjoyed the benefits of travel and other opportunities that were denied to the poor. While his range of knowledge may not have equalled that of the author of *Job,* who has been described as the most learned ancient before Plato, he was cultured and well-informed. He was able to draw upon history, contemporary affairs and the science of his day, in order to express his own world view. In strikingly independent fashion, he utilized at least the catchwords of Greek philosophy, as well as the Torah and Prophetic literature of his own people as the medium for his own original ideas.

Only one other fact may be inferred about his personal history. Koheleth was a bachelor, or at least a man without children. For he is considerably exercised by the fact that when a man dies he must leave his wealth to "strangers," and he betrays no shred of sentiment for kith and kin.

If we must forego any other details about the external events of his life, we are fortunately in a better position to reconstruct his spiritual odyssey. From earliest youth his intellectual and emotional faculties were exceptionally keen and they determined the entire course of his development.

Fundamental in the boy and the man was a passionate love of life, the universal heritage of the healthy mind and the healthy body. He loved the tang of living. The sight of the sun, the breath of the wind, the good things of the world held him enthralled:

Sweet is the light and it is good for the eyes to see the sun. (xi: 7)

The experience of life thrilled him to the core. Women he loved deeply, and knew well the world of sensation to which they beckoned.

Enjoy life with the woman you love. (ix: 9)

Nor was he a stranger to other sources of material comfort and beauty. The cool spaciousness of gardens and orchards, the nobility of fine houses, the cheer of good food and fine wine, the charm of music and the grace of the dance, Koheleth savored them all. Even after his joy in life had been tempered by later experiences, he still felt that merely to be alive was a boon:

For a living dog is better than a dead lion. (ix: 4)

Had Koheleth possessed no other elements in his spiritual constitution except his love of life, he would have been happy. Possessing the means of gratifying his desires, he might have spent his days in carousing and feasting or in the subtler forms of sensual enjoyment. He could have been a Philistine or an esthete, but in any event a happy man. That happiness eluded him was the result of other facets in his personality.

As a Jew, Koheleth was naturally reared in the rich religious and cultural tradition of his people. In his time, too, the three main strands of Hebrew thought were not mere ancient historical memories, but living and dynamic forces. As we have seen, the teachings of the Torah were being practiced in the Temple cult by the priests and being expounded in the academies by the scribes. The period of the Prophets was over, but their teachings were accepted as integral to Judaism. As for the third spiritual current, that of the *Hokmah,* or Wisdom, this was now at its height, richly creative and deeply influential.

All these were part of the educative influences brought to bear upon Koheleth. In particular, a spark of the prophetic spirit singed his soul, and he was never again the same carefree, lusty youth. The beauty of nature and the luxury of wealth could not blot out the marks of man's injustice to his fellows:

Furthermore, I saw under the sun, in the place of judgment, there
was wickedness, and in the place of righteousness, wrong. (iii:16)

Superimposed upon his innate love of life, there had come a second great motive power, the love of justice. But there was a cruel difference between the two. While the first could easily be gratified, he was doomed to failure in the second. As he grew older, and became aware of the tragic distance that yawned between the prophetic ideal and the real world, something snapped within him. The magnificent audacity of the Prophets, their unshakable faith in the ultimate triumph of the right, was not for him. He was too realistic, too sober, too narrow, if you will, for that. Too many years had elapsed since the Prophets had foretold the doom of evil and folly, and still the wicked prospered, and folly sat enthroned in the high places:

I have seen everything during my vain existence, a righteous man
being destroyed for all his righteousness, and a sinner living long
for all his wickedness. (vii: 15)
Folly is often enthroned on the great heights. I have seen slaves
on horses, while lords must walk on foot like slaves. (x:6, 7)

Nor did Koheleth possess the spiritual energy to grow indignant and reprove his God, as did the author of *Job.* At the spectacle of injustice, the Prophets had thundered and pleaded and proclaimed the day of doom, but Koheleth merely smiled. Wrong and corruption were eternal, inherent in the scheme of things:

If you observe the despoiling of the poor and the perversion of
justice and right in the state, do not be astonished at the fact, for
each guardian of the law is higher than the next, and there are
still higher ones above them! (v: 7)

Yet Koheleth did not react with a cheap and easy cynicism to human suffering. On other themes he might be light or sarcastic, but here, as a rule, he was in deadly earnest, with a fervor almost prophetic in its intensity:

Again, I saw all the acts of oppression that are done under the
sun. Here are the tears of the oppressed, with none to comfort

them, and power in the hand of their oppressors with none to com-
fort them. So I praise the dead who already have died, more than
the creatures who art still alive. (iv: 1, 2)

The happiness of a carefree and joyous existence was ever-more be-
clouded for Koheleth by the vision of a world in agony. Koheleth became
a cynic, not because he was callous to human suffering, but, on the contrary, because he was acutely sensitive to man's cruelty and folly.

But Koheleth had not yet plumbed the full depths of the despair that
life was to breed in him. Stronger even than his love of justice was his
love of truth. Possessing a keen mind and a lively curiosity, he eagerly
sought after the profounder *Hokmah,* the fundamental insight into the
world and its meaning. It was the Wisdom hymned by the Sage, after
which Koheleth strove:

The Lord by Wisdom founded the earth
By Understanding He established the heavens. (Prov. iii: 19)

Koheleth sought to probe these mysteries, which the more matter-of-
fact Ben Sira had advised leaving alone, perhaps because he knew of
the perils that lurked in the quest:

What is too wonderful for you do not seek,
Nor search after what is hidden from you,
Seek to understand what is permitted you,
And have no concern with mysteries. (Ecclus. iii: 20, 21)

Job, too, had sought this Wisdom in vain:

Where is Wisdom to be found?
And where is the place of Understanding? (Job. xxviii: 20)

Yet in this very unknowability of the world, Job had found an anodyne
for his suffering, a token that there was a rational and just world-order,
though incomprehensible to man. For Job, the grandeur and harmony
of the cosmos, created by Divine Wisdom, was an earnest of an equally
pervasive moral universe, founded on Divine justice. But that faith
was not for Koheleth. His fruitless search for justice in human life had
grievously wounded his personal happiness. Now came the tragic
realization that the all-inclusive Wisdom of the universe was also un-
attainable:

I saw that though a man sleep neither by day nor by night, he
cannot discover the meaning of God's work which is done under
the sun. Even if a man searches hard, he will not find it; and
though a wise man may think he is about to learn it, he will be
unable to find it. (viii: 17)

A deep woe now settled upon the youthful enthusiast, when the futility of his aspirations was borne in upon him. Justice he had sought, but it was nowhere; wisdom he had pursued, but the phantom had vanished. All life was meaningless and futile, and his judgement upon it was devastating:

> *Vanity of vanities, says Koheleth,*
> *Vanity of vanities, all is vanity.* (i: i; xii: 8)

> *Hence I hated life, for all the work that is done beneath the sun seemed worthless to me, and everything, vanity and a chasing of wind.* (ii: 17)

As the spectacle of human cruelty and suffering was revealed to him, he despaired of life:

> *More fortunate than both the living and the dead, is he who has not yet been born and so has never seen the deeds that are being done under the sun.* (iv: 3)

Three great ideas had lighted his way in the world. The love of life was rich with promise of happiness, but the yearning for justice and wisdom had brought him only sorrow and disillusion.

For a space, one can live in a state of complete intellectual nihilism, without values or activities. Few men, however, and Koheleth was not among them, can abide that emptiness indefinitely. The quest for certainty is not abandoned merely because two of its roads have proved blind alleys, Koheleth *had* to discover some definite basis for belief, some rationale of action, if his life was to go on. It could not be wisdom or justice, for these had been weighed and found wanting. He had to retrace his steps to the first great principle of his life, the only law that had not brought him to grief. In the striving for happiness lay the only reasonable goal for human existence.

So Koheleth returns to his first love, but with a difference. The whole-hearted, instinctive gladness of youth is gone. His love of life is now the result of reflection, the irreducible minimum of his life's philosophy. He chants a hymn of joy, but there are overtones of tragedy, the sad music of the inevitability of old age, the echo of the cruelty and ignorance of mankind:

> *For if a man live many years, let him rejoice in them all, and remember that the days of darkness will be many, and that everything thereafter is nothingness.* (xi: 8)

> *So I saw that there is nothing better for a man than to rejoice*

*in his works, for that is his lot, and no one can permit him to
see what shall be after him.* (iii: 22)

Koheleth sets up the attainment of happiness as the goal of human
striving, not merely because he loves life, but because he cannot have
justice and wisdom. Joy is the only purpose that he can find in a
monotonous and meaningless world, in which all human values, such
as wealth, piety and ability, are vanity, where all men encounter the
same fate and no progress is possible.

The modern reader might expect that Koheleth would be led by his
views to deny the existence of God, but that was impossible to an
ancient mind, and especially to a Jew. Even the Epicureans, who
denied divine intervention in human affairs, and who sprang from a
people to whom the gods never had the same burning reality as to the
Hebrews, did not deny their being. Koheleth, a son of Israel, a pupil
of the prophets and the sages, could not doubt the reality of God for an
instant. For him, the existence of the world was tantamount to the
existence of God.

It was on the question of God's relation to men that Koheleth parted
company with the conventional teachers of his time. For all the bar-
rage of platitudes of the sages, there was not a shred of proof that God
wished to reveal the true Wisdom, the secret of life, to men. Similarly,
there was tragic evidence to contradict the glib assertion of the
moralists:

*Say to the upright that it shall be well with him, for he shall
eat the fruit of his doings. Woe to the wicked! It shall be ill
with him, for the reward of his hands shall be given him.*

(Isa. iii: 10, 11)

The Psalmist had sung:

*I have been young, and now am old, yet I have never seen an
upright man forsaken, and his offspring begging bread.*

(Ps. xxxvii: 25)

His words might be a prayer or a pious hope; they were scarcely the
result of empirical observation!

All that is certain is that man has an innate desire for happiness.
Since God has created man, He has also created this impulse. It thus
becomes clear that God's fundamental purpose for mankind is the
furthering of man's pleasure.

We may put it another way: Koheleth's morality recognizes the
pursuit of happiness as the goal. His metaphysics postulates the ex-

istence of God. His religion is the combination of both. Koheleth recognizes God's creative power and His limitless sovereignty. His will He has revealed to his creatures in man's inborn desire for happiness. But beyond these attributes, Koheleth refuses to affirm anything about his God.

Accordingly, the basic note of the book is its insistence upon the enjoyment of life, of all the good things in the world. There is the love of woman—and the singular is noteworthy—

> *Enjoy life with the woman whom you love,*
> *Through all the vain days of your life,*
> *That God has given you under the sun,*
> *For that is your life's reward,*
> *For your toil under the sun.* (ix: 9)

With a moving sense of the transitoriness of life, he calls for the vigorous and full-blooded enjoyment of all it affords, food and drink, oil and fine clothes, beautiful homes and music:

> *Whatever you are able to do, do with all your might, for there is neither action nor thought nor knowledge nor wisdom in the grave toward which you are moving.* (ix: 10)

In practice Koheleth advocates a moderate course, not very different from the attitude of the Rabbis of the Talmud:

> *Three things bring a sense of ease and contentment to a man: a beautiful home, an attractive wife, and fine clothes.*
>
> *(Berakot: 57a)*

What set his standpoint apart from theirs, was that his attitude stemmed not from a full-hearted acceptance of the world, as preached by religion, but from a sense of frustration and resignation, induced by his philosophy. Nothing really counts if truth and righteousness cannot be attained. Yet man lives and God rules, and God's manifest will is man's happiness, not that it matters overmuch, but this at least is certain.

This skeptical outlook with which Koheleth faced life needs to be analyzed a little more closely, both for the understanding of his personality and the evaluation of his message. Basically, his skepticism was rooted in his personality, to be sure, but it was nurtured by his upper-class origin and bias. In essence, skepticism is an indisposition to accept conventional ideas merely because of the pressure of the mass. But there is also another element in the constitution of a skeptic—a psycho-

•

logical inability to *act* so as to modify conditions. In other words, skepticism is a state of mind possible only for those who, observing evil, are not its immediate victims. Direct sufferers are usually impelled either to change the conditions or to seek escape from them through some avenue of action. The Hebrew prophets, oppressed by the social iniquity of their day, utilized elements of the folk-religion of Israel to create the exalted conception of the "End-time," when the Kingdom of God would be ushered in on earth and a just order established for all men and nations. The mystics of all religions, faced by the same problem, have sought refuge in an independent existence of the spirit. The teachers of Pharisaic Judaism and early Christianity offered the hope of another world after death where justice would be vindicated. On the other hand, the reformers and revolutionaries in all ages have striven to transform society in their own life-time through practical action.

Koheleth, like the other teachers of Wisdom, adopted none of these alternatives—partly, at least, because he personally found life tolerable even under the conditions he deprecated. His failure to respond actively to injustice is doubtless a crucial defect, so that our age cannot find in him the motive power toward the building of a better world that is so abundant in the Hebrew prophets. In the face of the towering evils of our own day, and the breath-taking vision of a nobler order now for the first time within realization, Amos and Isaiah are incomparably more inspiring guides.

But this temperamental difference between Koheleth and the Prophets must not blind us to his enduring value in teaching men how to meet those ills that must be transcended because they cannot be transformed. It is true that nowhere does Koheleth preach the virtue of courage in so many words. For him courage is not a conscious ideal, nor even an idea—it is far more, an inborn, pervasive quality. Every line in his book is instinct with the spirit of clear-eyed, brave and joyous acceptance of life, for all its inevitable limitations.

And these limitations *are* inevitable, however unwilling a youthful and activistic generation may be to confess it. Though men be ever more successful in moulding the pattern of the world nearer hearts' desire, they will still meet pain and frustration in life, for which they will require dignity and courage and the saving grace of good humor. This need for resignation is independent of political and economic systems. It inheres in the character of the universe and man's nature. Man is a creature whose reach is always greater than his grasp, with a boundless imagination weaving hopes and desires far beyond the capacity of his brief, earth-bound existence to fulfill. As Koheleth observes, "All a man's toil is for his wants, but his desires are never satisfied." In teaching men to taste life's joys without self-deception and to face its sorrows without despair, Koheleth performs an everlastingly significant function.

To set forth these basic attitudes toward life, Koheleth writes his book in old age, recapitulating the stages of his spiritual history in the process. As he contemplates his past career, he has no complaint to make; life has been good to him. He has been spared the degradation of poverty and the terror of insecurity, nor has he ever had to taste the bitterness of personal tragedy. His charm, insight and skill have doubtless made him a successful teacher in the Wisdom academies and brought him tangible as well as intangible rewards. The competence he has acquired now makes it possible for him to enjoy the amenities of life—a fine house in Jerusalem, a sense of independence, and the blessing of unworried leisure. Thus he sits in the sunset hours of his life, a tiny island of ease and contemplation within the whirling currents of life in the capital city.

His is a comfortable old age, but there is a quiet loneliness about it. He has no wife to share either the simple happenings of ordinary existence or the rare moments of deeper experience. His home has never re-echoed with the voices of children at play. He has never been stirred to ecstasy by their laughter or driven to distraction by their tears. But perhaps, he muses, it is better so, as he recalls the fine brave rapture of youth and the febrile ambitions of maturity, all now revealed as emptiness and chasing of wind.

From time to time, his former pupils visit him, for Judaism declares it a duty to pay respect to one's former teachers by calling on them. He looks into the faces of these lads who have since gone forth to positions of prominence and dignity in the practical world. Some are important government officials, others are Temple dignitaries, while others have far-flung economic interests as merchant princes or landed gentry. As his wise, understanding eyes scan their faces, he notes that they have paid a high price for success. The shining, carefree countenances of youth, the sparkling eyes brimful with mischief, are gone. In their stead are worn faces, some drawn, others grown puffy with the years, and tired, unhappy eyes sagging beneath the weight of responsibility. Time was when his pupils were young and he was old, but now the tables are turned. True, Koheleth is a few paces before them in the inexorable procession toward the grave. But in a deeper sense, he is young and they are prematurely old. He knows what they have forgotten—that men's schemes and projects, their petty jealousies and labors, their struggles and heartaches, all are vanity and that joy in life is the one Divine commandment.

Before it is too late, he takes pen in hand to transmit the truth, as he sees it, concerning the incomprehensible and indescribably precious blessing called life. For it is his secret wish that men after him, whom his living voice will never reach, may face life with truth as their banner and with a song in their hearts.

> *Go, then, eat your bread with joy,*
> *And drink your wine with a glad heart,*
> *For God has already approved your actions.*
> *At all times let your clothes be white,*
> *And oil on your head not be lacking.*
>
> *Enjoy life with the woman you love*
> *Through all the vain days of your life,*
> *Which God has given you under the sun,*
> *Throughout your brief days,*
> *For that is your life's reward*
> *For your toil under the sun.*

Whatever you are able to do, do with all your might, for there is neither action nor thought nor knowledge nor wisdom in the grave toward which you are moving. (IX: 7-10)

Doubtless Koheleth would have been the first to confess that in taking such pains to urge the enjoyment of life upon man, at a time when he himself had already passed his prime and reached the days in which there is no pleasure, there lurked more than a little of vanity—in both senses. Fortunately, however, the need for self-expression triumphed over the dictates of logic, and so a masterpiece was born.

The Book

WHEN THE BOOK OF KOHELETH is read without preconceptions, its thoroughly natural reaction to life is completely intelligible. Yet it is not really strange that it has been widely misunderstood. Since the book is in the Bible, most readers turn to it with more devoutness than alertness, and expect to be edified rather than stimulated by its contents. In general, this attitude of mind, however praiseworthy in intent, is harmful to an adequate appreciation of the Bible. In the case of Koheleth, it is fatal. The time is long overdue for recognizing, as A. B. Ehrlich observed, that the Bible is not a collection of religious texts, but rather "a national literature upon a religous foundation." Only from this point of view can the reader savor fully the vitality, color and broad humanity of the Bible and comprehend its message without the distortions induced by dogma or prejudice.

For the religious spirit, the Bible is eternally the Revelation of God, but in no superficial and mechanical sense. Rather it must be understood in the spirit of the profound Rabbinic comment on two rival schools, "Both these and the others are the words of the Living God." When the Bible is approached in this spirit and recognized as the repository of men's deepest aspirations for the truth about life, it becomes clear that *Koheleth* belongs of right in the great collection. Unfortunately, however, this viewpoint is still far from being universally accepted.

Another difficulty in the understanding of Koheleth is that he was struggling to use Hebrew for quasi-philosophic purposes, a use to which the language had not previously been applied. A thousand years later, medieval translators still found that Hebrew had not yet fully developed the flexibility, precision and vocabulary necessary for the treatment of philosophic themes. Koheleth's comparative success in this respect is not the least element of his literary skill.

His task was rendered still more difficult by two other facts. The Hebrew language has a very simple structure and only a few syntactic devices are available to express all possible nuances of meaning. Thus, to cite two instances, the moods of verbs must be inferred from the context and subordinate clauses of all varieties are externally indistinguishable from coordinate clauses. Obviously, these and similar features complicate the understanding of a text where exactness is essential.

In addition, during Koheleth's day, Hebrew was steadily losing ground to Aramaic, which resembles it more closely than any other Semitic language. Aramaic was rapidly becoming the *lingua franca* of the entire Semitic world. Hebrew, to be sure, was still spoken in the schools, and was utilized in religious ritual and literature, besides being cultivated by the more educated groups. But the all-powerful Aramaic was being spoken by the common people and making inroads even among the scholars. As a result, Aramaic idioms and modes of expression are characteristic of the Hebrew in "Koheleth," as well as in later writings.

Principally, however, the book has been misinterpreted because of a number of special features in its style, which are themselves a reflection of the author's personality.

Like other writers since, who were raised in a religious tradition from which they have broken away in whole or in part, Koheleth uses a *traditional religious vocabulary* to express his own special vision. The modern reader will think of Ernest Renan, Anatole France and George Santayana as manifesting at times a somewhat similar trait. A few examples of this tendency may be cited. Traditional morality declared that he who fulfilled God's will, would be happy. Koheleth declares that he who is happy is fulfilling God's will!

> *Indeed, every man whom God has given wealth and possessions and granted the power to enjoy them, taking his portion, and rejoicing in his labor, that is the gift of God, for it is God who provides the joy in a man's heart.* (v:18)

The Wisdom writers call the sinner a fool. So does Koheleth, but he reserves the right to define his terms. A sinner is he who fails to work for the advancement of his own happiness. The Book of Proverbs promises that the righteous will ultimately inherit the wealth of the evildoer:

> *He who increases his wealth by usury and interest, is gathering it for him who befriends the poor.* (xxviii:8)

Koheleth promises the same to the man who is "pleasing to God," the man who obeys God's will, and seeks to achieve joy:

> *To the man God favors, He gives wisdom, knowledge and joy, but to the "sinner," he assigns the task of gathering and amassing, only to hand it over at last to the man who is pleasing to God.* (11: 26)

The Prophets, with unfailing insistence, call upon the people to hear the word of God. So does Koheleth. He, too, calls upon his reader to remember God and His purpose for man, before old age sets in and the time for joy is past:

> *Remember your Creator in the days of your youth,*
> *Before the evil days come and the years draw near,*
> *Of which you will say, "I have no pleasure in them."* (xii: 1)

This clothing of the hedonistic principle in religious guise is not without analogy in Hebrew literature. The Book of Proverbs counsels:

> *Hear, my son, and be wise,*
> *and walk in the ways of your heart.* (xxiii: 19)

Ben Sira, whose general moral system is conventional, makes the enjoyment of life a duty:

> *My son, if you have the means, treat yourself well,*
> *For there is no pleasure in the grave,*
> *And there is no postponement of death.* (xiv: 11)

Even more striking are the words of the Talmudic sage, Samuel, of the third century, cited in the Talmud:

> *Seize hold and eat, seize hold and drink, for this world whence we depart is like a wedding feast.* (Babli, Erubin 54a)

Samuel's great contemporary, Rab, expresses the same sentiment in typically religious language:

> *Every man must render an account before God for all the good things he beheld in life and did not enjoy.* (Jerusalem Talmud, Kiddushin, end)

No more perfect analogy could be found to Koheleth's words:

> *Rejoice, O young man, in your youth,*
> *And let your heart cheer you in your youthful days.*
> *Follow the impulses of your heart*
> *And the desires of your eyes,*
> *And know that for all this,*
> *God will call you to account.* (xi: 9)

Similarly, when Koheleth says, "Go, eat your bread in joy and drink your wine with a glad heart, for God has already approved your actions" (ix: 7), he is expressing his philosophy of life in a religious vocabulary congenial to his own temper and the spirit of his age.

The second unique characteristic of Koheleth's style which has not been adequately noted, with disastrous results for the understanding of the book, is *his use of proverbial quotations*. This is undoubtedly the result of his background and occupation as a Wisdom teacher. His speculations on life did not lead him to abandon his interest in the mundane concerns of the lower Wisdom; he merely went beyond them. As Koheleth continued to teach the practical Wisdom to his pupils, he doubtless contributed to its literature, most of which is couched in short, pithy maxims of a realistic turn. Hence, maxims very similar in form and spirit to those in the Book of *Proverbs* are frequently met with in *Koheleth*. These are not interpolations by more conventional readers, as generally assumed. They belong, as Mac-

Donald has well noted, to the author's method of keeping connection with the past, while leaving it behind.

Koheleth's use of this folk-material is so varied and individual that it may fairly be described as creative. It is beyond question one of the most charming features of his style. At times he cites a proverb simply because he agrees with it, and he may elaborate upon it with a characteristic comment. Thus the most confirmed cynic will agree that

> *Through sloth the ceiling sinks in,*
> *And through slack hands the house leaks* (Eccl. x: 18),

or suggest that it is wise to diversify one's business undertakings:

> *Send your goods overseas, so that you may get your return*
> *after many days.* (Eccl. xi: 1)

Frequently, however, Koheleth's comment on the proverb that he quotes subtly changes the meaning of the text, shifting the ground from the realm of the matter-of-fact and the practical to the uncharted regions where speculation and skepticism have free rein.

Examples of this use of a proverb as a text with ironic comment are plentiful. Thus one conventional maxim extols the virtues of cooperation. Koheleth approves the sentiment, but for reasons of his own:

> *"Two are better than one, because they have a reward in their labor." True, for if either falls, the other can lift his comrade, but woe to him who is alone when he falls, with no one else to lift him. Then also, if two sleep together, they will be warm, but how can one alone keep warm? Moreover, if some enemy attack either one, the two will stand against him, while a triple cord cannot quickly be severed.* (iv: 9-12)

The conventional teachers of morality emphasized that love of money does not make for happiness. This idea is expanded by Koheleth through the characteristic reflection that strangers finally consume the substance of the owner.

> *"He who loves money will never have enough of it and he who loves wealth will never attain it." This is indeed vanity. For as wealth increases, so do those who would spend it, hence what value is there in the owner's superior ability, except that he has more to look upon?* (v: 9)

In what may perhaps be described as the most "conservative" passage in the Bible, the Book of Proverbs counsels submission to political authority:

Fear, my son, God and king, and meddle not with those who seek change. (Prov. xxiv: 21)

Koheleth repeats this idea, but with his tongue in his cheek:

> *I say: keep the king's command,*
> *And that because of the oath of God.*

Submit to the king because of your oath of fealty, but also, he adds as an afterthought:

> *Since the king's word is law, who may say to him: "What are you doing?* (viii: 2-4)

because the king is powerful enough to crush you!

Koheleth would undoubtedly agree with the universal view that life on any terms is preferable to death. Yet his general intellectual conviction as to the futility of living impels him to a comment which ostensibly justifies, but actually undermines, the entire proposition.

> *"He who is attached to the living still has hope, for a living dog is better than a dead lion." The living know at least that they will die; but the dead know nothing, neither have they any reward; for their memory is forgotten. Their loves, their hates, their jealousies, all have perished—never again will they have a share in all that is done under the sun.* (ix: 4-6)

Another noteworthy device by which Koheleth expresses his divergence from commonly accepted views is the use of *contrasting proverbs*. As is well known, proverbs frequently contradict one another, since they summarize the empirical experience of the race. When faced by the need of making an important decision, a man may find himself in a quandary between the warning, "Look before you leap" on the one hand, and "to hesitate is to be lost" on the other. The beautiful sentiment "Absence makes the heart grow fonder" is bluntly negated by the callous saying, "Out of sight, out of mind."

The compiler of Proverbs was aware of this tendency, when he quoted these two maxims in succession:

> *Answer not a fool according to his folly, lest thou also be like unto him.*
> *Answer a fool according to his folly, lest he be wise in his own eyes.* (Prov. xxvi: 4, 5)

Koheleth uses the same device, but for his own purposes. He cites a proverb expressing a widely accepted point of view and then subtly registers his disagreement, not by a lengthy argument, but by citing another utterance diametrically opposed. Where Koheleth's sympathies lie in these debates is easy to determine. In each pair of contrasting proverbs, the latter represents his standpoint.

No theme was dearer to the hearts of the instructors of youth than the importance of hard work. Koheleth expresses his doubts on the subject by first quoting a proverb attacking laziness and then citing another which mocks the gospel of unceasing toil:

"The fool folds his hands and thus destroys himself."
"Better a handful acquired with ease, than both hands full gained through labor and chasing after wind." (iv: 5, 6)

Like all the Wise Men, conventional or otherwise, Koheleth has a "prejudice" in favor of wisdom against folly. He himself tells how the wisdom of one poor man proved more efficacious than a mighty army. Yet he knows, too, how little wisdom is honored for its own sake, and how one fool can ruin the efforts of many wise men. These ideas seem to be expressed in some reflections, couched in the form of brief proverbs contradicted by others:

I said "Wisdom is better than prowess," but "the poor man's wisdom is despised and his words go unheeded."
"Wisdom is better than weapons." But "one fool destroys much good." (ix: 16, 18)

Whether Koheleth is citing other Wisdom writers or is himself the author of these "quotations" can rarely be determined. As a teacher of Wisdom, trained in its schools, he would naturally formulate his own ideas, as well as those he wished to negate, in the accepted form of the *mashal,* or proverb. Sometimes a stylistic peculiarity seems to indicate that the utterance is his own; but even where this clue is lacking, the material may well be original with him.

Naturally these quotations are not as a rule marked by external signs; they must be inferred from a careful study of the text, often based upon technical considerations. To transmit the sense to a modern reader, a translator must use quotation marks or an introductory phrase.

From all that has been said, it is clear that the Book of Koheleth is not a debate, a dialogue, or a philosophical treatise. It is best described as a *cahier* or notebook, into which the author jotted down his reflections during the enforced leisure of old age. They differ in mood, in style, and in length. At times when he grows impassioned, he develops a subtle inner rhythm, as in the majestic opening section of Chapter I. At others, the rhythm is much more pronounced, as in the unforgettable "Allegory of Old Age" in Chapter 12. Generally, however, his medium is prose.

It is possible that these brief essays were collected and edited by Koheleth himself, since the book opens and closes with the theme, "Vanity of vanities, all is vanity," and the first and last sections are the most eloquent and moving of all. Very often, the end of a section can be recognized by Koheleth's reverting, after a discussion of his subject, whether it be wealth, wisdom or corruption, to one of his two fundamental themes—the tragedy of man's ignorance of ultimate truth, and his God-given duty to achieve happiness.

The author's fascinating personality is thus reflected in a style rich in nuance and eloquent in its reticence. Koheleth, to be sure, is a skeptic, but that merely emphasizes the fact that he is a child of an age of tradition, when one world-outlook is dying and another still unborn. The skeptic is essentially a complex personality, the product of diverse and contradictory forces, such as childhood training and education, remolded by adult experience and reflection. No man ever rejects *in toto* the entire heritage of his day. In the soul of every skeptic there are intermingled the completely conventional, the modified old, and the radically new. To simplify Koheleth means to destroy him, but to approach him with understanding means to possess the key to a fascinating personality.

Koheleth's characteristic style helps to explain how the book managed to enter the Biblical canon. Matter-of-fact readers, unaware of his unconventional use of a religious vocabulary or his citation of proverbs for his own special purposes, would find the book replete with sound orthodox sentiments. And all the more would they be predisposed to this conclusion by the fact that Koheleth, in the two opening chapters, calls himself the son of David. His obvious purpose in doing so was to offer reflections on the value of wisdom and wealth, for both of which Solomon was famous. But this literary device stood Koheleth in good stead; it provided his book with the necessary aura of sanctity and antiquity for inclusion in Scripture.

Nevertheless, there was much in the book that was a stumbling-block to the devout. Rabbinic literature, indeed, records many objections to its retention in the Biblical canon. That it was never dislodged may be due in part to the naiveté and lack of historical perspective of many of its readers. But, basically, it is a tribute both to the fascination of the book and to the catholic taste of the Librarian of the Synagogue, who saw in every honest seeker after truth a servant of the one Source of truth. Whatever the motives that led to the preservation of the book, we cannot be too grateful.

Koheleth would have been shocked, even amused, to learn that his note-book had been canonized as part of Holy Scripture. But the obscure instinct of his people was building more truly than it knew when it stamped his work as sacred. In the deepest sense, Koheleth's is a religious book, because it seeks to grapple with reality. The Psalmist had sung:

> *A broken and contrite heart,*
> *O God, Thou wilt not despise.*

This cry of a sensitive spirit, wounded by man's cruelty and folly, this distilled essence of an honest mind, unwilling to soar on the wings of faith beyond the limits of the knowable, remains one of man's noblest offerings on the altar of truth. (pp. 8-39)

THE LITERARY GENIUS OF JESUS

PERCY COOPER SANDS

Use of illustration and imagery—oratory, instances of; balanced style—art of story-telling—parables—allegory—great sayings; epigram.

PROPHETS LIKE ISAIAH AND AMOS were assisted by their use of illustration. They knew that concrete instances appeal more to the audience than abstractions and generalities, and that a long address must be varied by changes of tone and even of types of sentence. The secret of good teaching is apt illustration that wakes interest and makes clear. 'Jesus

From *The Literary Genius of the New Testament,* by Percy C. Sands; Oxford University Press, 1924. Reprinted by permission.

may have designedly imitated the prophets', says a commentator. 'Naturally imitated' would be more correct, as he followed Jewish native traditions in many ways.

He adopts all their resources, such as, their use of *metaphor*:

> 'Ye are the salt of the earth,' 'I am the Bread of life',

of *simile*:

> 'As a hen gathereth her chickens . . .'

of *allegory,* as in the talk of the Good Shepherd;
of *hyperbole*:

> 'if thy hand offend thee, cut it off . . .'

of *paradox*:

> 'he that findeth his life, shall lose it,'

of *rhetorical question* and *irony*:

> 'if he ask for bread, will he give him a stone?'

of *repetition*:

> 'If thy hand offend thee, cut it off; it is better for thee . . .(where their worm dieth not . . .), and if thy foot offend thee, cut it off: it is better for thee . . . (where their worm dieth not . . .), and if thine eye offend thee, pluck it out: it is better for thee . . . (where their worm dieth not).'[1]

of *parallelism*:

> 'Heaven and earth shall pass away.
>
> but my words shall not pass away.'

of *apostrophe*:

> 'O Jerusalem, Jerusalem, that killest the prophets . . .'

of *epigram*:

> 'the foxes have holes, and the birds of the air have nests, but the Son of man hath not where to lay his head.'

The cast of this epigram reminds us of Isaiah's

> 'The ox knoweth his owner, and the ass his master's crib, but Israel doth not know, my people do not consider.'

The *analogy,* the *balance,* and the *compactness* are similar in both.

How full were the talks of Jesus of illustration by metaphor and simile, using common concrete objects to make clear spiritual and moral ideas, will only be grasped if we look closely at the Sermon on the

---

[1] Mark ix, 42 ff. The 'triplet' used by Jesus to drive his lesson home is not kept by Matthew. He has the same passage twice, but shortens it by coupling 'hand' and 'foot' in one case (v. 29), and omitting 'foot' in the other (xviii.8).

Mount, in which illustration follows hard on illustration. After the Beatitudes in Matt. v, Jesus commences with common household objects, like *salt* and *lamps* and *corn measures,* to explain Christian influences. If they want to know what sort of goodness to aim at, it is not to be that of the *Pharisees.* Here he points to great figures of the time. *Parts of the body* are used next. *Hand* and *eye* are put for bad habits, Christian retaliation is to turn the other *cheek,* modesty is like one *hand* not knowing what the other does, hypocrisy is the same as not noticing a beam in your own eye. Then come objects of nature, to show worry unnecessary, lilies, birds, grass put in the oven, strengthened by an example from history, in the person of Solomon. Praying is like knocking at a door, or a son asking for a helping at meal-times. Pearls and swine, narrow gates and broad roads, grapes from thorns and figs from thistles —all these link the hearers' common everyday life with the moral life, and even Aesop's Fables are drawn upon for the hypocrisy of the *wolf in sheep's clothing,* while the talk closes with the fine illustration of sincerity taken from housebuilding. 'He thought in pictures.'[2] Herod he sees as a 'fox', Peter as a 'rock', his disciples as the 'children of the bride-chamber', and his own suffering as a 'cup' put to his lips by his Father.

'The two chief means of teaching', said Bishop Creighton, 'are exaggeration and paradox.' Hyperbole or exaggeration has the same force in words as caricature in drawing. It surprises or startles the hearer into interest. It puts an improbable or impossible case to persuade belief in the more probable cases of real life. 'The hairs of your head are all numbered' is a hyperbole, or, as the Greek word means, 'shoots beyond the mark', because numbering the hairs would be a useless procedure even for Providence. But it impresses the human mind as a vivid symbol. The different interpretations found for the 'camel going through a needle's eye', viz. that the needle's eye was a small side gateway at Jerusalem through which the camel could not go without unloading, or that the word for 'camel' is a misreading for a word meaning 'rope', are ingenious but unnecessary, if we remember our Lord's fondness for hyperbole.

'If any one smite thee on the right cheek, turn to him the other also' is a hyperbolical figure of what humility should achieve. One would not actually present the cheek, but take a second blow passively. But the hyperbole is dramatic and saves words. 'You strain at a gnat and swallow a camel', 'Thou considerest not the beam that is in thine owne eye',

[2]Kelman, *Dict. of Christ and the Gospels,* vol. ii (Poet).

help to explain some hard sayings of Jesus that seem contradictory; for example, 'If any man come to me and hate not his father and mother, he cannot be my disciple' (Luke xiv. 26), put less strongly in Matt. x. 37: 'He that loveth father or mother more than me, is not worthy of me', which came from the same lips that rebuked the Scribes and Pharisees for neglecting the Fifth Commandment.

Paradox startles by coupling a metaphorical idea with a literal one, as in: 'Let the dead (spiritually so) bury their dead (physically so)'; 'He that loseth his life for my sake shall find it', where life again has both senses, physical and spiritual, 'he that loseth his physical life shall gain spiritual life'. When Jesus had purged the Temple, and the Jews challenged him for a sign, and he said, "Destroy this temple, and in three days I will raise it up,' they thought he referred to the Temple building, but he 'spoke of the temple of the body'. The paradox is almost a play on words.

Crescendo and climax, as found in Isaiah and Amos, are still more remarkable in the longer utterances of Jesus. Take even the Beatitudes, as given in Matthew. The eighth one in v. 10, 'Blessed are the persecuted', is expanded into a more detailed one about persecution, which by its mere length after the eight shorter ones, and by the apostrophe, the change from 'Blessed are those . . .' to 'Blessed are ye . . .' provides a climax, especially with the aid of the dramatic and unexpected close —'for my sake'—and the emphasis laid on the joy that follows, 'Rejoice and be exceeding glad, for great is your reward in Heaven.'

The talks of Jesus never suffer from a weak ending; the argument moves in orderly and balanced phrase to an effective finish. Take one of the most beautiful instances of his talking, on worry:

Matt. vi. 25–34. (Luke has it practically identical, and we may suppose it has had very little editing.)

25 Therefore I say unto you, Take no thought for your life, what ye shall eat, or what ye shall drink; nor yet for your body, what ye shall put on. Is not the life more than meat, and the body than raiment?

Ver. 25. Note the *balance* 'soul' (or 'life') and 'body', . . . soul more than meat? . . . body more than raiment? Each of these, 'food' and 'raiment', is then illustrated from nature, by the birds and the lilies.

26 Behold the fowls of the air: for they sow not, neither do they reap, nor gather into barns; yet your heavenly Father feedeth them. Are ye not much better than they?

26. 'a minore' conclusion in each case, 'if the birds, much more you', 'if the grass, much more you'.

27 Which of you by taking thought can add one cubit unto his stature?

28 And why take ye thought for raiment? Consider the lilies of the field, how they grow; they toil not, neither do they spin:

25–8. Four times the argument is put as a question, as if Jesus were pleading with their common sense rather than laying down the law. The *questions* break pleasantly into the series of commands, and bring a tenderness of tone into the address.

29 And yet I say unto you, That even Solomon in all his glory was not arrayed like one of these.

30 Wherefore, if God so clothe the grass of the field, which to day is, and to morrow is cast into the oven, *shall he* not much more *clothe* you, O ye of little faith?

29. The introduction of Solomon, the highest type of human splendour, is masterly. The lilies exceed Solomon. Yet they are mere grass, and perish in a day.

31 Therefore take no thought, saying, what shall we eat? or, What shall we drink? or, Wherewithal shall we be clothed?

32 (For after all these things do the Gentiles seek:) for your heavenly Father knoweth that ye have need of all these things.

31. Then comes the summing up, repeating the original command. Note again the *triple* arrangement. 'What shall we *eat*? What . . . *drink*? Wherewithal . . . *clothed*?'

33 But seek ye first the kingdom of God, and his righteousness; and all these things shall be added unto you.

34 Take therefore no thought for the morrow: for the morrow shall take thought for the things of itself. Sufficient unto the day *is* the evil thereof.

34. Matthew alone has the general conclusion, which rounds off the whole talk so effectively, a striking maxim putting the talk in tabloid form:
'Worry not for the morrow; the morrow will worry for itself;
sufficient for the day is the evil thereof.'

The English diction and rhythm of the A.V. almost excel the original —especially the sentence, 'even Solomon in all his glory was not *arrayed* like one of these'. 'Array' is a fine word, always suggesting splendour, whether of battle or clothes. It makes, too, a fine rhythm in the sentence.

The passage which best shows the oratorical art used by our Lord, next after the parables, is the talk on John the Baptist:

Matt. xi. 7–19. (Cf. Luke vii. 24–35. Matthew's version is probably nearest to the original, as Luke interposes an editor's comment, vv. 29, 30, and also puts ver. 13 of Matthew in a different context, Luke xvi. 16).

7. And as they departed, Jesus began to say unto the multitudes concerning John, What went ye out into the wilder-

Ver. 7. The *question* to arrest attention. *Irony* here, a reed as a contrast to the unbending strength of John.

ness to see? A reed shaken with the wind?

8 But what went ye out for to see? A man clothed in soft raiment? behold, they that wear soft *clothing* are in kings' houses.

9 But what went ye out for to see? A prophet? yea, I say unto you, and more than a prophet.

10 For this is *he,* of whom it is written, Behold, I send my messenger before thy face, which shall prepare thy way before thee.

11 Verily I say unto you, Among them that are born of women there hath not risen a greater than John the Baptist: notwithstanding he that is least in the kingdom of heaven is greater than he.

12 And from the days of John the Baptist until now the kingdom of heaven suffereth violence, and the violent take it by force.

13 For all the prophets and the law prophesied until John.

14 And if ye will receive *it,* this is Elias, which was for to come.

15 He that hath ears to hear, let him hear.

16 But whereunto shall I liken this generation? It is like unto children sitting in the markets, and calling unto their fellows,

17 And saying, We have piped unto you, and ye have not danced; we have mourned unto you, and ye have not lamented.

18 For John came neither eating nor drinking, and they say, He hath a devil.

19 The Son of man came eating and drinking, and they say, Behold a man gluttonous, and a wine-bibber, a friend of publicans and sinners. But wisdom is justified of her children.

8. Three times the question is put. Orators love the *triplet*. Cicero's speeches are full of it.

Irony again, a contrast to the rough hair garment of John.

A *general truth* hinting at the luxury of Herod's court.

9. The third time the question is put in earnest. 'A prophet? Yea, I say, much more than a prophet' (gradually building up the effect). 'He was the special messenger of the Messiah. He was the greatest of all the prophets, yet . . . (*paradox* again) the least in the kingdom of heaven is greater than even John—', bringing into relief against the background of John's dispensation the greatness of the new Gospel. John's ended in repentance, that of Jesus began with the free grace of God.

12. 'the violent take it by force', almost 'pillage it', a strong *hyperbole* to show the enthusiasm roused by John for the new Gospel.

13. John was the culmination of the whole line of prophets, the second Elijah—no name made a greater appeal than Elias.

15. 'he that hath *ears*'. Cf. the striking effect of Shakespeare's 'Friends, Romans, Countrymen, lend me your *ears.*'

Contrast the weak effect of 'Listen to me', or 'Attend to these my words'.

16. Change of theme, the reception of John, introduced again in *question* form, and at once attention is secured by a *simile* from the common scene in the market, children playing at weddings and funerals, and some of them in a mood for neither, sulking. It is put in the tersest language.

'We piped, and you danced not, we mourned, and you lamented not.'

18, 19. Note the *vigour of the phrasing* here and its *simplicity;* 'neither eating nor drinking', an abstainer living on the simplest fare.

'He hath a devil.' 'A gluttonous man and a winebibber,' the enemy's exaggeration of eating and drinking.

The notable *conclusion,* as brief as weighty, to dismiss the subject.

The rest of the chapter is put by Luke in a different arrangement, and may not have been delivered on the same occasion. Note especially the words 'in that hour' and 'at that time' used by Luke and Mark, though they put the passage in different places and assign them to different occasions.

The *balance and dignity* of the Hebrew style, with its majestic repetitions and parallelism, is best seen in the talk on the Last Judgment.[3] This balance is more in evidence in Matthew than in the other Gospels, as we have seen, but it is a marked feature of our Lord's addresses, whoever reports them.

It will be seen how closely the address to the 'Goats' answers that to the 'Sheep'. It is the close correspondence that makes the whole passage so impressive. It is shortened in the second part by using one verb 'minister' for the several verbs used before, but to have shortened it further would have reduced the impressiveness.

One more instance may be given to show how Jesus gave life and vigour to his addresses by the use of simile, analogy, and imagery: the talk on 'the last things'—

'As the lightning cometh from the east, and shineth unto the west, so also shall the coming of the Son of man be.'	Simile.
'For where the carcase is, there the eagles will be gathered together.'	Metaphor.
'Immediately after the tribulation of those days, shall the sun be darkened, and the moon shall not give her light, and the stars shall fall from heaven, and the powers of the heavens shall be shaken."[4]	Imagery such as the prophets used.

Then there is a sudden 'apostrophe,' as he turns to the audience, and gives a simile of a fig-tree:

'Now learn a parable of the fig tree . . .'	Apostrophe.
'When his branch is yet tender, ye know that summer is nigh; So likewise ye . . . know. . . . '	Parable.

This is followed by a comparison from past history:

'As the days of Noah were, so shall also the coming of the Son of man be.'

This crisis is explained in balanced clauses cast in parallel form:

'Then shall two be in the field, The one shall be taken, and the other left. Two women shall be grinding at the mill, The one shall be taken, and the other left.'	Parallelism.

To keep interest from flagging, two *stories* follow, to show the need of watchfulness, the second of   Parables.

[3] Matt. xxv. 31-46.
[4] Matt. xxiv. 27ff.

which is introduced in *question* form. The device of *refrains* is also not forgotten:

Rhetorical question.
Use of Refrain.

'So shall also the *coming* of the Son of man be' (three times).[5]

'Of that *day* and that *hour knoweth* no man.'[6]

'Ye *know* not what *hour* your Lord doth *come*.'[7]

'In such an hour as ye think not, the Son of man *cometh*."[8]

'The Lord shall *come* in a *day,* when he looketh not for him.'[9]

For the *climax* of the address is fitly reserved the punishment, and put in the strongest terms.

'shall *cut him asunder* . . . there shall be weeping and *gnashing of teeth.'*　　Climax.

And with this piece of vigorous diction the discourse probably ended.

All the oratorical methods of the old prophets, and in fact of all good speakers, are here employed by Jesus. Like them, he kept his hold upon his audience by the arts that are necessary to retain their attention undivided, rousing them by questions and dramatic changes from third person to second, enlivening them by apt illustrations from life or nature or past history, driving the warning home by effective repetition (though never overdoing this), startling them by a hyperbole, charming them by the choicest because the simplest and most forceful words, never losing sight of his main point, and summing up with some epigram or saying that rang out like a proverb, which the audience could not help carrying away with them, reverberating in their ears as they unwillingly melted away or followed him to his lodging, because, as was said of a lesser orator, Pericles the Athenian, he had 'left his sting in his hearers'.

No wonder that a public speaker could say that he made a point of reading the Bible daily, not for its devotional side, primarily, but for the improvement of his style, especially alluding to the parables of Jesus.

The Art of Story-telling. Parables.

The literary genius of our Lord is, of course, felt most powerfully in his *parables.*

Take a short one first, from Matthew's version; Matthew seems to preserve it in its original form, and Luke to have adapted it to hearers not familiar with the conditions of Palestine.

---

[5] vv. 27, 37, 39.　　[6] ver. 36.　　[7] ver. 42.　　[8] ver. 44.　　[9] ver. 50.

The House built on the Rock:[10]

A man is prospecting for a site for his house, and comes to one of the valleys or ravines called 'wadys'. It looks sheltered and attractive, especially a flat piece of sandy ground nestling under the steep bank, with signs of a stream that will give him water part of the year. But he knows the country and chooses instead a site on the rocky bank overlooking the ravine, more bleak, but, as he knows, more permanent. For the rainy season is at hand, and the unwary prospector who chose the attractive sandy corner in the ravine itself finds the stream is a raging torrent when it comes, and it does come very suddenly with the rains.

Matthew preserves throughout the perfect balance and rhythm of sentence and phrase, on which the effect of contrast depends. He has one variation of construction and one of diction to avoid too much sameness.

A. 'Everyone who heareth these sayings of mine, and doeth them, I will liken him to a wise man, who built his house upon the rock.
And down came the rain,   (In the Greek the verb comes
and (along) came the floods,   first with stronger force, which
and (fierce) blew the winds,   one misses in the A.V. transla-
  and *fell* upon that house: tion.)
and it fell not, for it was founded upon the rock.'

B. 'And everyone that heareth these sayings of mine, and doeth them not, shall be likened unto a foolish man, who built his house upon the sand.
And down came the rain,
and (along) came the floods,
and (fierce) blew the winds,
  and smote upon that house:
and it fell, and the fall of it was great.'

The ending must be noticed for its restraint of diction, 'It fell, and the fall of it was great'.

In Luke the balance and rhythm are less perfect, and we miss the impressive arrangement of Matthew—
'and when the flood arose,
the stream beat vehemently
  upon that house . . .'[11]

The impressiveness is still further sacrificed in the second half (ver. 40). In recasting the parable Luke has also made it a question of deep foundations, going down to the rock, and of good building, not of a

[10]Matt. vii. 24 ff.
[11]vi. 47 ff.

choice of site. He wrote for people less familiar with the geography of Palestine. Jesus would deliver the parable in a form true to Jewish surroundings, and, as we may well believe, with the balance and strength that Matthew has preserved.

The Parables of Jesus have been so much the whole world's property for centuries that it may seem almost superfluous to point out any of their merits, even in a literary sense. But it may be worth while to lay stress on some special features of three of the most popular. The Good Samaritan illustrates their lifelike detail, and the completeness with which the main point of the parables is brought out in a few words. As for detail, the particular road from Jerusalem to Jericho was notorious for robberies, and Jesus thus, like all good teachers, introduces local interest into his story. Then, while the priest gives the body a wide berth, for fear of pollution, the Levite, a little less holy, as a lay priest, could afford to inspect the body. The distinction between the two is a fine point. The condemnation of both, or rather of the system that bound them and checked their humanity, is all the more effective because it is silent. The choice of a Samaritan for the hero shows that neighbourliness is no question of race. The completeness of the Good Samaritan's treatment of the victim is the second notable feature, the attention to the wounds, oil used to heal, wine as a homely disinfectant; the lifting of the victim on to his *own* beast, so that he himself had to walk, instead of riding; the nursing of the patient at the inn ('took care of him'); the instruction to the landlord to see the nursing continued; the arrangement for the payment; the resolve to look in again, and see the business through. That is how mercy should be shown, Jesus suggests. That is the real neighbour.

In 'the Rich Man and Lazarus' an admirable feature is the description of the two men in so few words, two or three powerful strokes to make a portrait: the rich man *in purple and fine linen*—faring *sumptuously every day*—and the beggar *laid at his gate* (he has to be carried to his pitch)—*anxious for morsels*—*full of sores*—*the scavenger dogs lick his sores.* The extremes of wealth and poverty could not be painted in fewer words, or more graphically. Points to notice are that the beggar's 'dead' body does not matter, but the rich man has a funeral ('the beggar died . . .', 'the rich man died and *was buried*'). The beggar is borne to Paradise, called by the Jews 'Abram's Bosom'. Further, the request of the rich man is put with surprising modesty, '*dip the tip* of his *finger* in water and cool my tongue'. He does not ask for a drink. He has sunk very low. The answer is made as gentle as possible, '*Son*, remember. . . .' That dramatic 'gulf' forbids even this being granted.

The characters in these and other parables are common types, not extreme cases. Their shortcomings are common faults—selfishness, thoughtlessness, pride.

The censure is implied, not expressed. The rich man is blamed, like the priest and Levite, only by implication, not in so many words. The parables take for granted powers of judgment in the audience. 'The rich man dies, and is buried. And in Hades . . . being *in torments*. . . .' The parable does not waste time in justifying the suffering, and in ver. 25 the principle of compensation is quietly assumed as known to the rich man.

The rich man has the grace to think of his brothers. Even the prodigal son is only thoughtless, and 'comes to himself' (his sound, normal self) and has the grace of humility. He blames himself, but his father cuts him short. These parables in fact take a high view of human nature. The tragedy of the Rich Fool (Luke xii. 16-21) also springs from thoughtlessness, and the rebuke is not without its tenderness, 'You senseless man (not the stronger term 'fool'), that soul which you call yours (cf. I will say to *my* soul, ver. 19) they are demanding back from you this night. Then to whom will your goods go?' In 'the Wedding Supper' the guests refuse through preoccupation, in 'the Foolish Virgins' the fault is again thoughtlessness. In fact Jesus held up the reddest light of danger not to criminals, but to the respectable for what they *don't* do. It is the man who did *not* use his talent, the virgins who did *not* take oil in their lamps, the rich man who did *not* notice Lazarus at his gate, the people who did *not* give the cup of water and visit the prisoner, who are held up as examples. Their punishment is to be left outside in the darkness, like children looking through the window-panes at the party inside, the music and dancing and good things, their desolation more terrible than physical pain, and even causing 'gnashing of teeth'.

To the question why the parables make such a universal appeal, the answer will be best seen from the longest of them, the Prodigal Son. We are dealing with its literary beauties; its other beauties have been the subject of thousands of addresses.

First, its *rapid movement* as a story keeps the interest at full pitch. The downfall of the young man is told in two phrases, 'he wasted his substance in riotous living, and when he had spent all . . .'; his return in one sentence, 'he arose and came to his Father', while the father's only reply to his son's confession is an order to his servants to do him honour.

Secondly, it is 'things' that make stories go well, not emotions and abstractions. One of the secrets of the story's appeal to all ages and intelligences is its *concreteness.* Everything in it is concrete and vigorous. Everything is described in solid terms.

It is a story of goods, and spending, of bread and husks, and hunger and swine, of journeys and hired servants, and a concrete welcome, with robes and rings and shoes, and fatted calf and music and dancing. The parables have been called earthly stories with heavenly meanings; as literature, they are concrete stories with an abstract meaning. Everything is tangible. The son's offense is described as 'wasting *goods*' or, as the elder brother puts it, 'devouring his *living*', and his lost, abandoned state described as a hunger that would 'fill itself with *husks*' contrasted with the '*bread* and to spare' of the servants—solid symbols every time.

The story is one of great moral issues, repentance, forgiveness, jealousy, but it is all expressed in incident and action. The younger son's feelings take concrete form: he 'comes to himself', he 'will go back and say "I have sinned".' The sin is not merely a personal disgrace; it goes out from him and hits against heaven itself, and hits his Father too ('sinned against heaven . . .'). The only phrases expressing feelings as feelings are 'he had compassion' used of the father, and 'he was angry' used of the brother. The brother's jealousy takes a concrete form: 'Thou gavest me no *kid.*' The father's welcome takes a concrete form, he 'falls on his neck and kisses him tenderly.' So does his joy: 'Bring forth the best *robe, a ring,* and *shoes* (to show recovered sonship, for slaves went barefoot), and *kill, eat,* and be merry' (start *dancing* and *music,* ver. 25). His son's sin was a concrete thing to him, 'he was *dead,* and is *alive*'. The feelings and emotions are not analysed, they are instantly turned into action.

The vivid *dialogue,* as usual, and the use of direct speech, keep the story lively and quick. Even in such a small detail as the informing of the elder brother, the brother calls a servant and receives the news in direct speech.

The *diction* is simple in the extreme: 'when he had spent all, he began to be in want'; 'no man gave unto him'; 'when he was a great way off, his Father saw him'; 'thou art ever with me, and all that I have is thine'; and yet it is vigorous, 'there arose a mighty famine'; 'longing to fill himself with husks'; 'devoured thy living with harlots'; 'sinned against heaven and in thy sight'; a clear, forceful phrase, worth much abstract theology. All sin is sin against God.

As in the Old Testament stories, *repetition* is purposely used to bring out the main points of the story: e.g. in vv. 18 and 21: 'Father, I have sinned . . .'; and in vv. 24 and 32: 'for this my son was dead and is alive again. . . .'

The final phrasing of the close is specially beautiful in its balance, rhythm, and vowel-sounds.

'it was meet to make merry and be glad;
for this thy brother was dead, and is alive again;
   and was lost.   and is found.'

What a range of vowel-sounds, and what a happy close on the more resonant ones!

Some other delightful touches have been pointed out: The prodigal fails to finish his speech to his father. He had meant to say, 'Make me a hired servant'. His father's welcome chokes him. He sees he cannot be anything but a son.

The change in the prodigal's attitude is simply expressed by 'give' and 'make'. The father is no longer 'the Governor', as a boy would say, who signs the cheque for the allowance, and whose company can be easily dispensed with. The prodigal wants now to be in any humble relationship so long as he can be with him.

The brother's attitude is shown by the use of the pronoun, 'as soon as this *thy son* was come' (thy 'precious' son), and the father's gentle correction, *'this thy brother'*. In the elder brother's conduct 'the injured air of the complacent, hidebound moralist is drawn to the life'.
Allegory.

The writers of the Old Testament used allegory with a very happy effect, blending the figurative language with the literal facts, as in Psalm 1xxx, a pathetic appeal to God to revive the Jewish nation, which he had *planted* in the country *like a vine,* 'which threw out its branches to river and sea, till the wild boar (Assyria) rooted it up and trampled it down'. Uninterrupted allegory would have been too artificial for such an intimate appeal, but the quick changes from people to vine and vine to people keep the reality always before one, and underneath the beauty of the allegory the hard case of the nation shows all the more effectively. It is like a sculptor's use of light drapery to express and set off the human form underneath. The fine mould of the limbs shows better veiled than when exposed—a paradox. In John x there is a talk of Jesus in allegorical form, introducing the figure of the Good Shepherd leading his sheep, as was common in the East, and the contrast of the hireling. As he recurs to the figure again and again—his voice known to the sheep and his readiness to risk his life for them—

the real meaning of his own relationship to his own 'flock' is obvious, and is all the more effective for the veil of allegory.

Another form of allegory also occurs. The figure called personification is the basis of it. This is the account of the temptation in Luke and Matthew. In Genesis the first temptation of humanity is related as an allegory, with abstract turned into concrete, sin and temptation personified—the fruit, the serpent, and the disgrace—a story to last for all time. Jesus selected this vivid figure of personification to present his own temptation. The disciples must have had it from his own lips, and when he described the experiences he had passed through, he used his favourite form of parable to stamp it on their minds.

Not that Jesus discouraged the idea of a personal Satan. He always speaks of him as a person. 'I have seen Satan as lightning fall from Heaven', 'Simon, Satan hath desired to have you. . . .', 'The enemy that sowed them is the devil'. But in the account of the temptation he scarcely wished his disciples to understand that Satan appeared in bodily form and carried him to a mountain top. He knew that accounts of our own feelings are dull to others, and he makes his own doubts as vivid and interesting as he did the idea of repentance in the Prodigal Son.

The figures then of this allegory are simple, yet striking pictures, grand in conception:

'Command that these stones be made bread.'

'He set him on a pinnacle of the temple, . . . "Cast thyself down, and the angels shall bear thee up".'

'He took him to the top of a high mountain and shewed him all the kingdoms of the world in a moment of time. . . . All these will I give thee, if. . . .'

How simply the issues are expressed, and how easy to remember in that form!

His Great Sayings.

The greatest sayings of Jesus are not merely moral maxims like those of the sages of antiquity: 'Know thyself', 'Do nothing in excess'; or philosophical reflections: 'A life without a feast is a long road without an inn', 'Speech is the shadow of action'. Jesus could coin proverbs too: 'Cast not your pearls before swine', 'let the dead bury their dead', but his greatest sayings were personal appeals and personal claims or manifestoes. Such appeals and manifestoes, never made before or since, no doubt helped to prompt the verdict of the officers, when they could not arrest him: 'Never man spake like this man.' They recognized a personal force that distinguished the sayings from empty

bombast. But beauty as well as power distinguishes them. At the heart
of them is usually some word that may be taken in two senses, or some
image drawn from some common word of far reaching import: bread,
water, light, door, vine, shepherd, yoke, a metaphor that all could
understand. Through these images Jesus claims to be the very necessity
of existence to all men.

Most of these sayings are in John's Gospel, and many think that they
are not as Jesus uttered them but have been moulded by John. But
take this one from Matthew, of equal power and of particular beauty,
and with as marked a personal claim:

> 'Come unto me, all ye that labour and are heavily *burdened,* and I will
> give you *rest.*
> Take my *yoke* upon you, and learn of me,
> for I am gentle and lowly in heart,
>   and ye shall find *rest* for your souls;
> for my *yoke* is easy,
> and my *burden* is light.' (Matt. xi. 28 f.)

The *strength* of the saying arises from the paradoxes, namely that
one who offers a yoke as master, is at the same time gentle and lowly;
and that this yoke will bring rest. Its *beauty* arises from the *simile,*
prompted perhaps by the sight of loaded baggage-animals passing by;
from the *balance* of phrases, which is obvious in lines 3 and 4, 6 and 7;
from the *diction,* the rhythm of the couplets 'labour' and 'heavy laden'
or 'heavily burdened', 'gentle and lowly'; and from the slight degree of
repetition which emphasizes the main thought, 'ye shall find rest'
echoing 'I will rest you', 'yoke' answering 'yoke', and 'burden' echoing
'heavily burdened'.

This echoing of the main thought is seen in other sayings and is a
main feature of the longer talks in John's Gospel. There is no doubt
that the above is an unedited saying of Jesus; it has the stamp of his
genius upon it and the same ring as all his sayings in the Synoptists.
Note how similar is the cast of the next saying from John's Gospel,
especially in the balance of the last part of it, if we omit lines 3 and 4
from the passage in Matthew:

> 'He that eateth my flesh and drinketh my blood,
> hath eternal life;
> and I will raise him up at the last day.
> For my flesh is true meat
> and my blood is true drink.' (John vi. 54.)

Very powerful through its simple vigour and the terrible shadow behind
the words is:

'I, if I be lifted up, will draw all men unto me' (John xii. 32).

Perhaps the best instance of all of the special style of these sayings is that in John xii. 35 f., with the favourite image of light and darkness:

'Yet a little while, the light is with you.
Walk while ye have light,
   that the darkness may not overtake you,
   and he that walketh in darkness, knows not where he is
   going.
While ye have light, *believe* in the light,
   that ye may become *sons* of light.'

This comprises in the smallest space the true psychology of *action,* followed by *belief,* and then a permanent state of *relationship,* sonship. It also contains the usual contrast (light and darkness), and the favourite structure of syntax, the usual play upon the same words, and the arresting expression to close the syllogism, 'sons of light'.

The list cannot be closed without the rhythm of the couplet:

'In the world ye shall have tribulation:
   but be of good cheer, I have overcome the world' (John xvi. 33).

which forms the fitting close to the last great address to the disciples. (pp. 75-92)

ST. PAUL AS A LETTER WRITER

WILLIAM LYON PHELPS

THE FACT THAT I have never studied theology or New Testament interpretation gives me a possible advantage in the darkness of ignorance. In one of the stories of Captain Marryat, an untrained man was compelled to fight a duel with swords against a trained opponent; his skillful antagonist, expecting the usual formal thrust and parry, was killed on the first lunge. So, in grasping the sword of the Spirit, I find myself unhampered by any theological or textual code. No one regrets my lacking of learning more than I; but my method at all events has the advantage of simplicity. I shall take up the letters of Paul as I take up the letters of Emerson, and read them as examples of epistolary literature. I have no theory to establish and no systematic doctrine. At what date each letter was written, what corruptions if any have corroded the text, whether Paul wrote all or only some of them, are for the moment questions of minor importance; what we know for certain is that we have before us, in the incomparable English of 1611, a collection of letters which discuss everything of human interest from God to overcoats, which reveal a brilliant, passionate personality, and which have had a prodigious effect on the development of the Anglo-Saxon race.

Dante, Milton, Bunyan have each and all helped to shape our conceptions of God, of the future, of sin and salvation; but the formative influence of Paul's letters has been and still is greater than that of these three writers combined. Paul arrived exactly on time to aid in the spread of the Christian religion; for he was both a philosopher and a man of action. He was a profound thinker and a persuasive advocate. He was devoted to introspection and liked to travel. His love of metaphysics did not prevent him from being a successful advance agent of Christianity, carrying with him everywhere an excellent sample of the article he wished to distribute. His letters are full of pure and applied religion. He deals especially with the practical problems that confront young students—the temptations of the mind and the temptations of the body. He has been well called the "college man's apostle."

The year of his birth is not known, but he was probably about the same age as Jesus, for at the stoning of Stephen, he is called a young man. That might mean anything from seventeen to thirty-five. The rather important rôle he played in persecutions would seem to indicate manhood. On the other hand, the fact that at the murder of Stephen he took care of the clothes, just as small boys to-day hold coats for their big brothers, would indicate youth; and his zeal in persecution would harmonise with mental immaturity. I like to think of him as younger than Jesus, and I think of Jesus as forever young.

Paul was born at Tarsus, in Cilicia, in Asia Minor. It was a city of importance, both for its commercial industry and for its learning. Paul has every mark of being city bred; there is nothing provincial about his way of thought. The union in Tartus of Greek culture with Yankee enterprise was typical of Paul's own temperament. His father was a Jew, and belonged to the narrowest sect of the Pharisees, so that probably Paul was educated as sternly and strictly as our Puritan ancestors in New England. In austerity and alertness, he was a combination of Jonathan Edwards and Benjamin Franklin. His father was a Roman citizen; and so Paul was a free-born Roman as well as a Jew, a privilege which gave him a trump card in the game of life.

He seems to have made a journey to Jerusalem, with the intention of becoming a Rabbi; and in order to maintain himself while studying— analogous to the modern custom of working one's way through college— he learned the trade of a tent-maker, at which he turned many an honest penny in later years. Thus early he displayed the passion for righteousness and the passion for business characteristic of his race.

Jerusalem was the centre of Jewish learning; and the ambitious boy was fortunate in studying under a famous professor, Gamaliel. Although this wise man had a reputation for tolerance, Paul became a narrow and bitter Jewish partisan. Yet as every good teacher sows seed that sometimes comes to fruition only after many years, who knows but that in the marvellous words of Paul on Charity, we behold the green leaves of old Gamaliel?

The curriculum, like that of Oxford and Cambridge in the eighteenth century, was not broad, but it was decidedly intensive. It knew little of the elective system. It consisted of a study of the Old Testament, with commentaries thereupon. Paul obtained a sound and accurate knowledge of the Scriptures, which he turned to account in his later work among the Jews. His Letters abound in Biblical quotations.

Paul was graduated from Jerusalem a zealous, learned Jew. What does this mean? It means that he believed the only way to righteousness was to keep in detail the Jewish law; not only its moral precepts, but its technical formalities. This explains why Paul was so bitter against the dead Jesus and His followers. Like an orthodox party man in church and politics, he viewed with alarm the teachings of the disciples of Jesus, for he believed them to be not only heretical, but subversive, revolutionary. And his instinct, whether commendable or not, was correct; they were exactly what he thought they were, irreconcilable with the religious and social order in which he was brought up. A cardinal idea in the teachings of Jesus is that righteousness is a matter of the heart; forms and ceremonies are relatively unimportant. The coolness with which the greatest Democrat of all time jettisoned the cargo of orthodox ordinances caused priests to hold up their hands in horror. Paul was convinced that the Christian sect must be exterminated; and he gazed admiringly at the torture of Stephen, feeling certain of the approval of Jehovah.

While seeking fresh worlds to conquer, he learned that the Christian disease had broken out in Damascus; he obtained credentials from the high priest, and started for that city, his object being to arrest and carry to Jerusalem all the criminals he could catch. When he came near Damascus, he saw a great light, and was converted. From the Christian point of view, what happened to him was natural enough; man does not always seek God, but God is forever seeking man, the sole object of the appearance of Christ on earth. The Hound of Heaven was on his trail, and caught him on the broad road to disaster.

Paul was not the man to do anything by halves. As soon as he was baptised, he became active, beginning with his neighbours in Damascus, preaching for the new cause with the old vigour. The Jews naturally regarded him as a traitor, the inevitable fate of one who changes his convictions on any question of general concern. He escaped to Jerusalem, and had to escape from it. After his flight, he went back to his native town and stayed there for years. He seems to have lived quietly, but was evidently not forgotten, because Barnabas came after him, brought him to Antioch, and there the two friends worked together for twelve months.

Antioch was a large and famous city, and the new faith took such hold there that the disciples in this place were first called Christians.

Paul now went on a missionary journey, with Barnabas. He meant to work mainly among the Jews, but he received such cold treatment that he turned more and more to others, and thus after this journey he became the great apostle to the Gentiles. When the two men started out, it was Barnabas and Paul; when they returned, it was Paul and Barnabas. Paul's supremacy as a Christian preacher has never been challenged from that day to this.

Not only were many individuals converted to Christianity, but churches were founded; and by visiting them again on the way home, Paul succeeded in establishing them more firmly. On the second missionary journey, Paul went over into Europe, planting the faith in Western civilisation. The result of this expedition exceeded his wildest dreams, for he actually changed the currents of Western thought, and we are all different to-day from what we should have been had he restricted his wanderings. It was on this trip that he met Dr. Luke, and thus we get our account of Paul in the Acts of the Apostles. Obtaining little success with either the Jews or the educated Athenians, he came more and more into contact with the poor and lowly Gentiles, giving him much valuable training in clear exposition, and in knowledge of human nature.

Paul's lack of success with the cultivated Greeks is only what might have been expected. Browning has dramatically voiced it in the poem *Cleon*. The intellectual poet is vexed at the king's curiosity about an itinerant pedlar of religion. Yet though Cleon's armour of culture is impenetrable, he is a witness to the rising tide of Christianity, making its way among the downtrodden and oppressed.

> Thou canst not think a mere barbarian Jew
> As Paulus proves to be, one circumcised,
> Hath access to a secret shut from us?
> Thou wrongest our philosophy, O King,
> In stooping to inquire of such an one,
> As if his answer could impose at all!
> He writeth, doth he? Well, and he may write.
> Oh, the Jew findeth scholars! certain slaves
> Who touched on this same isle, preached him and Christ;
> And (as I gathered from a bystander)
> Their doctrine could be held by no sane man.

During the second missionary journey, Paul wrote the two letters to the Thessalonians, which were probably composed at Corinth.

His third missionary journey included a fifth visit to Jerusalem. At Ephesus, the metropolis of Asia Minor, Paul remained three years, fighting Paganism. Here he met the orator Apollos, who was one of the disciples of John the Baptist; and whose vigour in preaching showed that John's influence had not been cut off so easily as his head. The difference between the eloquence of Apollos and the eloquence of Paul was the same that, according to Mommsen, separated the eloquence of Cicero from the eloquence of Cæsar. That of the former was characterised by rounded periods; that of the latter, by deeply-felt thought.

On his third journey Paul seems to have written the two letters to the Corinthians, the letter to the Galatians, and to the Romans.

Why he undertook the fifth journey to Jerusalem with such eagerness we hardly know. He had collected some money for the poor there, and perhaps wished to distribute it in person. Nearly sixty years old, worn out with almost incredible hardships, he met with prophets of evil along the road, who vainly tried to dissuade him from his purpose. He reached Jerusalem at the Feast of the Pentecost, a time when crowds of Jews had flocked to the Holy City. Excitement was running high; many of the pilgrims came from places where they had heard the new evangelist, and when they saw him in Jerusalem, their anger knew no bounds. Paul could not reasonably complain of their treatment; for that was just the method he had used with seditious Christians.

In Cesarea Paul remained two years in captivity, one of the best things that ever happened to him. He needed rest, and the only way he could get it was by going to jail. During this enforced idleness, his mind was active, as subsequent letters show. He might have been set at liberty at once, for Felix the Roman knew well enough that Paul was no criminal. Probably Felix hoped that a bribe would be offered, but Paul was not the kind of man to buy his way out of prison. If he had not been a Roman citizen, he would have been treated more harshly. His Jewish enemies watched him as a cat would watch a mouse in a cage. As soon as Felix was succeeded by Festus, they eagerly besought the new official to give him up. But Paul appealed to Cæsar, which left nothing for Festus to do but to send him to Rome. Paul had always wanted to go to Rome, and here was a chance to travel thither at the expense of the state.

It is interesting to remember what excellent and fair-minded Roman officials appear in the New Testament. Pilate displayed considerable wisdom and courage; Gallio refused to bother himself with sectarian controversies, being engaged in the business of governing the people, and having no time for petty affairs; Felix, Festus, and Lysias were sensible and humane.

King Agrippa, in whose presence Paul was tried, was what Bernard Shaw would call a rubber-stamp King; an empty title, for he had little power, and even his thinking was done for him, as is still the fortunate custom in constitutional monarchies. This was no judicial trial, but rather a parlour performance, which Festus arranged for the entertainment of his guest.

At Rome Paul remained two years, living in practical freedom, although accompanied always by one soldier, who, I dare say, was often an agreeable companion. He preached and conversed, making many conquests among the Gentiles, among the Roman soldiers who guarded him, and even among Cæsar's household. He lived in his own hired house, and seems to have passed his days in cheerful activity. What became of him after this experience, nobody knows.

Every now and then the course of literature is disturbed by the appearance of a man who is something more and something greater than a literary artist; some one is born who feels within him the voice of a prophetic mission. Such a person was Socrates: such a person was Thomas Carlyle. These men exert an influence on the history of thought merely by opening their mouths and talking. So great a master of oral speech was Carlyle that I feel sure that with a gifted amanuensis, he could have affected the modern world deeply had he never put pen to paper. Socrates talked to a few friends in Athens and people of all nations still listen to him eagerly. The supreme illustration is our Lord, whose brief addresses and intimate conversations have changed the history of the world. Everything must have a beginning; and the Christian religion began in the word made flesh and remade into the living word. Paul relied on oratory so long as the Church remained within narrow geographical limits; but when, owing to his various journeys, the new faith spread far and wide, he was naturally forced into epistolary activity.

No letters have ever been so influential as these; for although they were written to particular groups at particular times and for particular reasons, thousands and thousands of men and women in the twentieth century read them as if they were addressed directly to themselves.

In everything except length, these letters are more like letters of to-day than like the polished literary efforts of the eighteenth century. Gray, Walpole, Cowper wrote familiar epistles in beautifully elaborate English, and often with conscious rhetorical effort; to-day, as some one has said, we do not write letters, we write only telegrams. Very few business or personal letters show any care for mere style; even the many letters written to the newspapers show less interest in the art of phrasing than the private correspondence of our New England forefathers.

It is often said that cheap postage is the cause of the degeneration of epistolary style; but it is not cheap postage, it is rather the lack of time that makes it difficult to write a good letter. The reason why journalism is a synonym for bad writing is not because the journalists do not know how to write, it is because they never have time to consider their sentences; hence they dress thought in ready-made clothes, like "all was bustle and confusion," "dull, sickening thud," and that familiar headline

X LAUDS Y

containing a verb one never hears and seldom sees outside of the newspapers. It is an interesting fact that just as the invention of labour-saving machinery meant the employment of more men in production instead of less, so the invention of time-saving devices always leaves those who use them with less leisure than before. Man has never been so busy as he is now, when he talks through a telephone, dictates to a stenographer, and travels in an automobile.

Paul's literary style, except at moments of exaltation, lacks grace and finish; it is clumsy, involved, twisted. Sometimes it winds itself up in many folds, like a boa constrictor; sometimes it is as brittle as a Western Union night letter. These faults must be charged to him, and not to his English translators; the original loses nothing in the version of 1611.

Paul was too busy to spend much time on the style of these epistles; they were written at various places, in moments snatched from days and nights of chronic activity. Possibly when he wrote "The night is far spent, the day is at hand," the actual dawn was breaking, and from the streets sounded the songs of home-going drunken revellers. They are offhand and impromptu, composed under the exigency of some crisis in the particular church he was trying to strengthen in the new faith. His custom was to dictate, and then when he signed his name, to add a few words in his own writing. The letters form no distinct body of articulated doctrine; the theologians who came after him tried with more or less success to codify his rules. Paul evidently meant to settle special cases as they came up—and he settled them all, not by the old laws, but by the new idea of universal love.

What his style loses in finish and grace, it gains in vivacity and vigour. The style has behind it the impelling force of white-hot sincerity. Occasionally it rises to vertiginous heights. What are now called the thirteenth and the fifteenth chapters of the first letter to the Corinthians are peaks of such lofty grandeur that they tower above everything else in the world's literature except the actual words of Jesus in the Gospels. The eminence of Jesus in literary art is as unique as his eminence in morality.

After one has read all the letters of Paul, the character of the writer appears with clearness. Although he adapted each letter to the particular needs of the recipients, the letters taken together reveal a portrait vivid enough to arouse the envy of John Sargent. We get a better idea of the true nature of the apostle from these letters than we do from the account in the Acts written by Luke, and the doctor was an excellent chronicler. Schopenhauer said that we can obtain a more accurate conception of the character of a man by reading one of his letters than we can from a personal interview. Most men in Schopenhauer's day wore beards; and the great pessimist said the beard was intended by nature to conceal the mouth, the one feature of the face that betrayed the intentions of its owner. He added that with women beards were unnecessary; for with them, dissimulation was inborn.

The first letter to the Thessalonians was written at Corinth, during the second missionary journey, and perhaps either in the year 50 or 52. Thessalonica, or as it is more tragically known in the twentieth century, Saloniki, had been visited by Paul just before he made his visit to Athens and Corinth. In this latter city Silas and Timothy came to see him, bringing the latest news from Thessalonica; and he was prompted therefore to write the earliest of his letters which have come down to us. The second letter was probably written a few months after the first, while Paul was still at Corinth. He wrote it to correct some misunderstandings that had been caused by the preceding epistle, chiefly with regard to the Second Advent.

At that time Greece was divided into two parts—Macedonia and Achaia. Thessalonica was the capital and chief city of Macedonia. It was a highly important town, and particularly important then and now, as a seaport. One of the chief manufactures was and is the making of goat's-hair cloth. This enabled Paul to find steady employment during his sojourn there.

He begins the letter in his usual diplomatic fashion by congratulating them heartily on the excellence of their work, for which he thanks God. He exhorts them to refrain from sensuality, and to become good citizens; and then he speaks of the second coming of Christ, warning them to be ever on guard, like faithful sentinels. The all but universal antipathy to hard work caused the Thessalonians to argue, that if Christ was coming again so soon, there was no particular reason for industry of any sort; and a second letter became necessary, in which he told them not to be weary in well doing. After he had finished dictating the letter, he added in his own writing,

> The salutation of Paul with mine own hand, which is the token in every epistle: so I write. The grace of our Lord Jesus Christ be with you all.

The Thessalonians were not the only people who used the imminence of the second coming as an excuse for shirking work. During the famous Dark Day in Connecticut, May 19, 1780, a group of legislators were assembled in Hartford, to transact business for the Commonwealth. When the darkness deepened, most of the statesmen were terrified, and some fell on their knees. I have always admired one man, who spoke out loud and bold, saying, "This is either the second coming of Christ or it is not; if it is not, we are all making fools out of ourselves. If it is, the Lord cannot find us in any better attitude than attending to the work for which we are here. I move that the candles be brought in, and that we proceed to business."

The two letters to the Corinthians were probably written during the third missionary journey, in 57 or 58 or possibly earlier. The first he wrote at Ephesus, the second at Philippi or in some part of Macedonia. Only a few months came between the two, and there is apparently a third letter which is lost. As we have seen, Paul was at Corinth some five years previous to the composition of these epistles. In 57 and 58 he was at Ephesus, where he was visited by a deputation from Corinth, bringing him news from the local church; and he sent a letter back with them. In the missing letter, he had made a severe attack on sensuality, the besetting sin of Corinth, as everyone knows. This sin had actually been made a form of worship, and the church needed some rather emphatic language from Paul on the subject, and got it.

One of the most interesting things in this great letter is the picture it gives of the apostolic church, often held up by zealots as a model for twentieth-century imitation. This early church was no Paradise, and if it existed in New York to-day, would probably be suppressed by the police. Some of the church-members lived openly dissolute lives; they fought each other in the courts; they were quarrelsome, lustful, avaricious, and gluttonous; misunderstanding the institution of the Lord's Supper, some of them got drunk at the Communion table. *Nous avons changé tout cela,* and still there is room for improvement.

Those of us who, like myself, are sore distressed by the weaknesses and imperfections of the modern Church of Christ, and still more by its lack of the qualities of leadership in the world's social organisation, ought to remember that although the Founder of Christianity was divine, the Church is neither more nor less than human. It is as human as a political party. It is the result of human effort to follow and imitate a Divine Example, and is naturally therefore far from ideal. It contains, like any political combination, men and women of the highest type, and also some that help to disgrace it in the eyes of outsiders. If the majority of its members were not better than the average of those without its pale, and if its influence in society were not on the whole an elevating one, it would be a complete instead of a partial failure. But its history is inspiring. The Church has purged itself of many cruelties, sins, and follies as it has climbed upward through the centuries. Yet to-day it is true to say that the organisation still needs the teachings of Jesus and the letters of Paul; and the best thing about it is that both Jesus and Paul find in the hearts of priests, ministers, and lay-workers a more immediate response than in any other group of men or women. As Browning says,

>   This it is to have to do
> With honest hearts: they easily may err,
> But in the main they wish well to the truth.
> You are Christians; somehow, no one ever plucked
> A rag, even, from the body of the Lord,
> To wear and mock with, but, despite himself,
> He looked the greater and was the better.

We must not expect too much of the Church. When we remember that the teachings of its Founder and Chief Apostle are directly opposed to human instincts, the wonder is that any real progress has been made. And I believe that in some thousands of years the Christians may be in the majority instead of in their present minority.

The Corinthian Church submitted all sorts of questions to Paul as referee. How about marriage—the gift of tongues (I imagine there were many fakers)—the position of women—the relations of church-members with outsiders? It needed not only wisdom on Paul's part to settle these disputed points, it required some patience; and I suspect he wrote the famous words on Charity as much to help himself as for those who were just learning to walk in the new and difficult road. After a careful explanation of the situation, together with a persuasive plea for hearty coöperation in which he used the metaphor of the human body, he said he would show them a more excellent way. This way is not the way of the law; it is not based on a system of rules, or petty prohibitions; it is the way of the Gospel, the way of affectionate sympathy. It is a pity that the nineteenth-century revisers changed the old seventeenth-century word *charity* into the too general word *love*. They changed it because "charity" had come commonly to mean cheque-signing. For what Paul meant is clearly the necessity of charity for the minds of others, for their points of view, for their weaknesses, and misunderstandings. If we have this divine gift of charity, we shall have the key to human nature and the key to the religious life; we shall have the greatest thing in the world. As Henry Drummond used to say, it is significant that the thirteenth chapter of First Corinthians, was written, not by John, but by Paul. It gains in eloquence, it gains in intensity, by being the reasoned view of a man who had originally little of this article of charity in his nature, and who owed all he had to the grace of God. It was his experience of humanity that taught him the overwhelming necessity of this virtue.

What a pity that our Puritan ancestors, who exhibited so bravely the sterner sides of the Christian faith, never agreed with Paul that Charity was greater than either faith or hope! It would have saved their own souls—which in many cases acutely needed the remedy they so earnestly advertised—and it would have made their reverberating pulpit oratory resemble something other than sounding brass.

After advising the Corinthians to insist on decency and order—two things of which they had only an elementary conception—Paul suddenly rises to the heights of sublimity in speaking of the resurrection of Christ, and of our assured victory over death and the grave. A party in the church, under the influence of Greek teaching, had denied the Resurrection, even as some ministers deny it now. Paul showed that it was the fundamental basis of the Christian faith; without it, we are of all men most miserable, not because the Christian life is valuable only for its future reward, but because we should all have been gulled; and there is perhaps no man on earth more pitiable than one who is deluded.

To affirm no resurrection of the dead, wrote Paul, is to deny Christ's resurrection, and thus to destroy the edifice of Christianity. Gnostic speculation grew like a fungus around the trunk of the tree of faith; starting with the idea that matter had always evil in it, the Gnostics claimed that if the body rises again, it must still contain evil. Paul is replying to these objections in his remark about the spiritual body. He appeals also to the witnesses that actually saw Christ. All that he says is still persuasive, still eloquent, except his argument, "what shall they do which are baptised for the dead, if the dead rise not at all? Why are they then baptised for the dead?" It is to be hoped that this point seemed more important to Corinthians than it does to Americans; there then prevailed in the Corinthian church the curious, and as it seems to me, silly custom of baptising living persons for some who had died without baptism. Paul seems to have believed in the efficacy of this superstitious rite.

It is important to understand the meaning of the word *mystery* in the phrase, "Behold, I shew you a mystery." In the seventeenth century this word often meant *secret,*—and what Paul is saying is not "I am about to exhibit some hocus-pocus," but rather, as we say to an expectant child, "I'll tell you a secret."

The conclusion, as always with Paul, is practical rather than mystical. Don't let Greek philosophy and paganism unsettle your minds. Have solid convictions. Remain steadfast. Keep busy.

It is a good thing for the early churches that they had for leader one who was not only a man of God but a man of sense. What would have become of them if they had had as their spiritual adviser somebody like A. Bronson Alcott? Or the monk Rasputin? Think what a following Rasputin would have had in Corinth!

The second letter to the Corinthians was written immediately after meeting Titus in Macedonia, who brought him the latest news from Corinth. This letter is a hot defense against accusations that a faction in the church had made against Paul.

No one knows where the letter to the Galatians was written, but the time seems to have been during the third missionary journey, perhaps either in 57 or 58. This letter is unique among his works, being written not to one church, but to all the churches in Galatia. On the second missionary journey, Paul had traveled through that country, founding churches; on the next trip he went through Galatia again, and became alarmed at the fickleness and instability of the flock. Now while he was at Ephesus or at Corinth—it really doesn't matter which—he received news that the Jew faction had nearly ruined the Galatian churches, and were cleverly undermining Paul's teachings. This made him both alarmed and indignant, and he immediately dictated this fiery missive. It is an important letter, for its purpose—apart from relieving his mind—was not to give general advice, but to settle a fundamental question. Whether he settled it for the Galatians or not, we shall never know; but he certainly settled it for the general body of Christians from that day to this, whether they live in Cape Town or in Michigan. This letter therefore may be considered epoch-making in the development of Christianity—both in theory and in practice. The question was the same one that made trouble for Paul on his previous journeys and in all his early preaching. Should Gentiles who became converted be compelled to conform to the Jewish law, including circumcision and other details? Three different views were held: the Judaistic party insisted on the strictest conformation; the regular apostles took a middle course, following the law themselves, but not compelling the Gentiles to do so; Paul, who always belonged to the extreme left, insisted that the law was of no consequence whatever; believing in Christ fulfilled the law and hence made it obsolete. Paul's doctrine was so radical, so clear, and so influential that it ultimately enabled Thomas Carlyle to speak lightly of the Ten Commandments.

The attitude of the apostle explains the hatred which the Hebrew party had for him, and their persistent efforts toward undercutting his teaching in every church founded by him. No sooner had the sound of his eloquence ceased in the new communities, than the Jews began their countermine. It is not necessary to suppose that their work was done by men sent from Jerusalem; the Jew faction existed everywhere.

In the Galatian churches, the Jews had made an impression on the people chiefly by three arguments. First, that Paul was not a genuine apostle, but an unauthorised demagogue. They felt no more bound by him than a twentieth-century Episcopal bishop feels bound by the theology of Billy Sunday. Second, that the Jewish Law was sacred and divine—Christ himself being the Messiah, not of the Gentiles, but of the Jews. Third, that Paul's attitude toward the Law meant absolute license, the destruction of holiness. No doubt the Jews were sincere in this.

To these three powerful arguments the letter to the "foolish Galatians" was addressed. It is a masterpiece of force, knocking down every shelter his enemies erected. The epistle may be divided into three parts: a defense of his credentials, the exaltation of Christ over the law, a vindication of the ethical value of liberty. The world has yet much to learn about the value of this third idea, and has lately been engaged upon a universal war in the endeavour to settle it once for all.

Paul is so excited that he forgets or neglects his usual custom of beginning with congratulations; contrariwise, he rebukes the church-members sharply, pronouncing a curse on those who teach any other gospel than that of Christ. He said he had not hesitated to rebuke Peter face to face for his cowardly yielding to Jewish public opinion. Soon he tries to carry his own point by a brilliant flank attack. He starts with the premises of his antagonists, boldly claiming Abraham as a witness to his own side of the case, even as Lessing, in another controversy, claimed that the liberty-loving Shakespeare was really a better follower of Aristotle than the classicists who condemned him. If you belong to Christ, you are the true heir of Abraham; if you stand by the law, you are his bond-servant, not his free son.

The conclusion of the letter is a magnificent defense of spiritual liberty. Instead of freedom meaning license, it creates a better character than can be formed by the Law. The true sons of Christ need no set of rules; by following Him they will produce the fruits of the Spirit, which are love, joy, peace, longsuffering, kindness, goodness, faithfulness, meekness, self-control: with these Paul contrasts the fruits of the flesh, that is, the results of the condition of man before the truth has made him free; and we have an impressive but not exaggerated roll-call of deadly sins.

In a bitter sarcasm, the apostle says that he wishes the sticklers for circumcision would go a little farther, and cut themselves off the earth.

God is greater than the moral code; in releasing ourselves from a troublesome list of formalities, we are more than ever bound to obey the great natural law of life—whatsoever a man soweth, that will he also reap.

As usual, Paul closes the letter with a few words in his own writing. He is so deeply moved by the condition of the Galatians, regarding them as bewitched, that he writes the postscript as it were in capitals, making even the shape of the words emphatic. "See with how large letters I have written unto you with mine own hand." And then, with that superb combination of spirituality and common sense, he brushes away forever the cobwebs of ritualism, centering all his force on the one supreme thing, the thing that really makes the difference between slavery and freedom: "for neither is circumcision anything, nor uncircumcision, but a new creature."

The importance of the letter to the Galatians can hardly be overestimated; it settled forever what should be the essential element of Christianity. Paul's words are needed in the twentieth century: they still form the best answer to those who seek salvation through elaborate ceremonies or through elaborate dogmas. True character must be formed within, springing from cheerful obedience to the spirit of Christ's teaching.

The letter to the Romans was probably written in the year 58 and from Corinth, while he was on his third missionary journey. This great epistle was directed to a community that Paul had never seen. He had always wanted to go to Rome, and while at Corinth he was nearer to Rome than to Jerusalem. He regarded Rome as the centre of the civilised world, and wished to conquer this citadel for Christ. He contemplated making a long Western trip, including Spain, and wanted to make Rome a base of operations. His zest for Rome was sharpened by the fact that he was a free-born Roman citizen. It would have interested him considerably could he have looked into the future, and beheld Rome as the centre not merely of civilisation, but of the Church of Christ.

Phoebe, a Christian woman, was about to start for Rome, and she may have carried this letter. Paul dictated the epistle in Greek, the stenographer being Tertius, who naïvely added a line himself. At the close there are many individual greetings; a long list of names is given, and Tertius, not wishing to be omitted, inserted "I, Tertius, who write the epistle, salute you in the Lord."

This letter was to prepare the Roman Church for Paul's coming visit; but unfortunately we know nothing of the condition of the organisation, and the letter does not tell us definitely. Were they mainly Jews or Gentiles? We do not know. It is possible that the two parties were openly hostile, and Paul wished to unite them.

The main aim of the letter is fairly clear. Paul, knowing that he was about to reach the centre of the Western world, wished to make evident to the Gentiles the nature of his free Gospel. They must understand that they had fully as much right to Christianity as the Jews. His letter is accordingly a platform of Christianity, both in theory and practice.

He seems to have taken more pains than usual in composition; writing to those whom he had not seen, he studied the principles of clearness and conciliation. The keynote is Justification by Faith. All, both Jews and Gentiles, are equally justified by faith. The Jews may think themselves safe because they have the law: yet not *having* the law, but *keeping* it, is the important thing. Even in that there is no clean righteousness, hence Jews and Gentiles both stand in need of the grace of God. Considering Paul's rough treatment from the Jews, and the way they had insidiously attacked him in the Galatian churches, one might naturally expect that in this letter he would furiously assail them. On the contrary, his tone toward the Jews is affectionate. His heart bleeds for his brethren; he even says he could wish himself damned for their sakes. He writes that they have a great natural advantage over the Gentiles, because they have been entrusted with the oracles of God. But the core of the letter is this: all men are alike condemned by the advent of Christ in the world, and all must have faith in Him to be saved.

Have Paul's ideas undergone a process of development? Yes. He says little about the second coming, which occupied so much space in the letters to the Thessalonians. The seventh and eighth chapters reveal his amazing skill as an expounder of the theory of sin and redemption; the twelfth chapter reveals him as a master-guide toward the elevation of daily conduct.

Whatever may be thought of Paul's knowledge of the nature of Christ, there can be no doubt of his profound acquaintance with the nature of man. Every man, woman, and child will find the seventh chapter an accurate mirror of the human heart. When Faust told Wagner that he had two souls within him, one lifting him aloft and the other dragging him down, he was simply making a poetic paraphrase of the immortal analysis by Paul. The following words might serve as a truthful autobiography for anybody: "What I would, that do I not: but what I hate, that do I." It is just as certain that the human mind recognises Truth, Beauty, and Goodness as desirable goals, as it is certain that the instincts of human nature pull in the opposite directions.

The four letters to the Philippians, to the Colossians, to Philemon, and to the Ephesians, are sometimes called the Prison Epistles, because it is thought that they were written while Paul was under detention at Rome. His imprisonment there probably lasted from 62 to 64. Paul had visited Philippi during the second missionary journey in 51-54. It was the first city in Europe in which he preached, and although he had been persecuted, his work was highly successful. This was where Paul and Silas were jailed, and their conduct during the earthquake— like that of the Salvation Army on the sinking steamer—caused some immediate conversions. Philippi was then a Roman city: hence the famous remark by the writer, "Our citizenship is in Heaven." Paul's lively interest in this church had been quickened by a personal tribute. The members made up a collection of money and gifts for Paul, and sent them to him by Epaphroditus. Any loving remembrance touched Paul deeply—for he had plenty of the other kind—and immediately upon receipt of the presents he composed this letter. He lays no particular stress on any doctrinal or ethical point—a wide difference from the letter to the Galatians. Of all the epistles, this is the most affectionate, the most letter-like. He simply thanks them, talks over affairs in general, and gives such advice as happens to rise to the surface of his mind. This is one reason why the style is so disconnected and so human. The keynote is Joy. He says tranquilly that the presents are most acceptable, and adds, "not that I speak in respect of want; for I have learned in whatsoever state I am, to be content."

The church at Colossæ, a town in Southern Phrygia, southeast of Ephesus, Paul had never seen. A new heresy was poisoning the members—a combination of Judaism and Gnosticism. The object of the letter was to fight this peril. As we might guess from its name, Gnosticism taught the supremacy of Knowledge. Faith will do well enough for children, invalids, and old ladies, but the intelligentsia need only science. In this sense Bazarov, Turgenev's nihilistic hero, was a Gnostic. Like all philosophers, they concerned themselves with the problem of evil, because evil is the most evident fact of all the facts in the world. They tried to relieve God of the responsibility for it, like some later philosophers; God could not therefore have immediately created the world. They thus propounded the following theory, and let it always be remembered that no one can invent a theory so absurd but that some can be found who will believe it. I do not know which is the easier—to propound an absurdity, or to secure disciples for it. The Gnostic idea was that God produced one being, that another, and so on until the divine ingredient, becoming constantly weaker by dilution, like Puritanism in the New England twentieth-century blood, could scarcely be detected at all. Then one of these emanations was base enough to connect with matter and create the world. Thus there was a graduated series of Beings between God and the World; which gave the philosophers the welcome task of arranging a systematic hierarchy of angels. The origin of evil is not in man, but in matter; and as a necessary result, the way of salvation was through complete asceticism.

Mingled with this Gnosticism at Colossæ was Judaism, with all its ritual of laws, feasts, Sabbaths and other restrictions. News of these difficulties came to Paul. Apparently he first wrote a letter to Laodicea which has been lost, and then this one to the Colossians. His style, except for one grand outburst, is confused, possibly for two reasons. He is not very well up in Gnosticism, and he has never seen the people he is addressing. At the end of the letter he wrote in his own hand

Remember my bonds.

The letter to Philemon is the only one written to an individual on a private matter. This is no church affair. It is exactly such a letter as one man would write to another on business. Perhaps Paul wrote other similar letters which are lost. This one shows the apostle in a natural, intimate vein. Onesimus, the slave of Philemon, had run away, and, in leaving his master, like Jessica, he had taken care not to depart empty-handed. Escaping to Rome, he had been attracted by Paul's teaching, had become converted, and apparently wished to do the square thing. He had a dog-like devotion to Paul, and had evidently made himself useful in a thousand ways. The apostle wanted to keep him; but he naturally felt it was his duty to return him to his owner, and the whole letter is a tactful intercession for the slave. The style is marked by courtesy, refinement, and consideration for both master and man. It is needless to add that all attempts to make of this epistle a type of the plan of salvation are as absurd as to twist the passionate love lyrics of Solomon's Song into a symbol of Christ and the Church.

The epistle to the Ephesians, like that to the Colossians, is a circular letter: they are companion pieces. This is addressed wholly to the Gentiles. The subject is Church Unity. Reconcile all difficulties—both theological and social—and get together on the basis of devotion to the person of Christ. Observe how steadily Paul has grown in breadth of view, and in tenderness. Instead of scolding, he pleads. He grew in grace to the last day of his life.

This has sometimes been called the profoundest of his letters. He was writing to philosophic folk, who could understand deep thinking and metaphysical ideas. The style, like that of most philosophers, is confused and involved, much more so than in the letter to the Colossians; but it rises in a superb passage toward the close, where he enumerates the complete outfit for the Christian soldier.

The epistles to Timothy and to Titus are called the Pastoral Epistles, because they were written to these men in their capacity as Pastors of Churches. Many scholars think they were not written by Paul. Ignorant of New Testament interpretation as I am, it would be an impertinence for me to express an opinion on this point. All I can say is, I am glad we have them, and I hope Paul wrote them. They were intended to guide Titus and Timothy in fundamental matters concerning Church government. They differ in language from the known epistles of Paul; but it is possible that Paul, like some other writers, occasionally went outside of his customary vocabulary. It is difficult to fit them in to any known period of our apostle's career of which we have definite information; and it seems as though the Church spoken of here had been more completely organised than is supposed to have been the case in Paul's lifetime.

Perhaps Paul, in a visit to the island of Crete, had tried to consolidate and strengthen the young Church. He seems to have left Titus behind to complete this work, and the letter gives the necessary directions. Titus was not a Jew. He was a Gentile whom Paul had run across years before. He was a Greek, and was one of the first Christian converts not circumcised. On Paul's memorable visit to Jerusalem, when the question of circumcision was to be settled, Paul took Titus along as an example.

Titus seems to have had difficulties at Crete. The church was weak and filled with heretics and slackers and sensualists and scandalmongers. Even one of their own prophets had said, "The Cretians are always liars, evil beasts, slow bellies." Paul's advice is definite and sensible, and contains a phrase that many who read the Bible only when they are sick or in danger, greet with recognition mingled with surprise. "Unto the pure all things are pure."

Timothy had been intimately associated with Paul, and is first mentioned in the sixteenth chapter of the Book of the Acts. His mother was a Jew. She had brought up her son in a good knowledge of the Scriptures. His father was a Greek. Although addressed to an individual, the letters to Timothy are not at all private in the sense of the word which fits the letter to Philemon. Paul evidently meant to have his advice read to the Church.

I confess without shame that the reason why I hope they were written by Paul is not because of their admonitions but simply because of their personal allusions, which bring the great writer very close. I have always admired Montaigne's curiosity about the tastes and little peculiarities of men of genius. Winter was coming on; Paul was an old man, and felt the approaching frost in his bones. Thomas Gray wrote in one of his last letters, "Now I even tremble at an east wind." Paul wants his overcoat. "The cloke that I left at Troas with Carpus, when thou comest, bring with thee." He is not only cold, he is lonely. "Only Luke is with me." Perhaps Doctor Luke had occasion to employ his professional skill, for Paul writes under the shadow of death. "Take Mark, and bring him with thee." But above all, he wants to see Timothy again, and twice he implores him to hurry up. "Do thy diligence to come shortly unto me," and then, after much miscellaneous information, he writes again, "Do thy diligence to come before winter."

Instead of talking about the second coming of Christ, he talks about his own death, which he, like many other once hopeful adventists, finally is forced to face. But although there are moments of despondency and weakness in these last words, the trumpet blast in the presence of the angel of death is like the clear tone of the slughorn of Childe Roland. It is a noble farewell from an old veteran, who has fought a good fight; it is a valediction forbidding mourning. (pp. 47-88)

III
READING THE BIBLE
AS LITERATURE

THE LITERARY IMPACT OF THE AUTHORIZED VERSION

C. S. LEWIS

The following essay by C. S. Lewis has been kept to this place, rather than put in the section with other general treatments of the Bible as literature, because it forms such a valuable commentary on the way of reading the Bible which is the basis of most of the materials in Part II of this book, "The General Reader's Bible." The reader who has followed the selections chronologically will have observed how they tend to be an expression of the romantic temperament in literature, and further reading, as suggested on pp. 363 to 365, will bear out the observation. Whether Professor Lewis's conjectures as to the future of this way of reading the Bible are sound only time will tell. To my mind a most stimulating way of treating at least some parts of the Bible is that illustrated in Professor Auerbach's comparison of an episode from the Odyssey *and one from* Genesis, *in which the religious conception behind a story and the religious purpose for which it is told affect the manner of telling. Something similar can be seen in G. Wilson Knight's treatment of literary form in the Gospels, in the book listed under Further Reading, p. 364.*

NO TRANSLATION can preserve the qualities of its original unchanged. On the other hand, except where lyrical poetry is in question, the literary effect of any good translation must be more indebted to the original than to anything else. This is especially true of narrative and

The Literary Impact of the Authorized Version, by C. S. Lewis, the Ethel M. Wood Lecture at the University of London; copyright 1950 by the Athlone Press. Reprinted by permission of the Athlone Press and of the author.

of moral instruction. Where the originals are Hebrew it holds in an unusual degree even for lyrical poetry because the parallelism of the form is a translatable quality. There is therefore no possibility of considering the literary impact of the Authorised Version apart from that of the Bible in general. Except in a few passages where the translation is bad, the Authorised Version owes to the original its matter, its images, and its figures. Our aesthetic experience in reading any of the great Old Testament stories or, say, the liberation of St. Peter and the shipwreck of St. Paul, depends only to a small extent on the translator. That is why I hope I may be excused for prefacing what I have to say about the literary fortunes of our English Bible by some remarks on the literary fortunes of the Bible before it became English. · What is common, even from the literary point of view, to the originals and all the versions is after all far more important than what is peculiar. And by carrying the story a little further back we have more chance to be cured of our dangerous though natural assumption that a book which has always been praised has always been read in the same way or valued for the same reasons. Virgil's Homer was very different from Chapman's, Chapman's from Pope's, Pope's from Andrew Lang's, and Andrew Lang's from Mr. Rieu's.

There is a certain sense in which 'the Bible as literature' does not exist. It is a collection of books so widely different in period, kind, language, and aesthetic value, that no common criticism can be passed on them. In uniting these heterogeneous texts the Church was not guided by literary principles, and the literary critic might regard their inclusion between the same boards as a theological and historical accident irrelevant to his own branch of study. But when we turn from the originals to any version made by one man, or at least bearing the stamp of one age, a certain appearance of unity creeps in. The Septuagint, the Vulgate, Luther's Bible, or the Authorised Version, can each perhaps be regarded as a book. And in the minds of those who used these translations the impression, if you will the illusion, of unity was increased by the unity of the liturgical context in which they were heard, and also by the doctrine of Inspiration. A belief in strictly verbal inspiration will indeed make all Scripture a book by a single Author. Hence Donne in his Seventy-Ninth Sermon rather comically passes favourable judgement on the style of the Omnipotent, assuring us that 'the Holy Ghost is an eloquent author, a vehement and an abundant author, but yet not luxuriant'.

The Bible thus considered, for good or ill, as a single book, has been read for almost every purpose more diligently than for literary pleasure. Yet certain *testimonia* to it even on that score can be collected from earlier ages.

The oldest literary appreciation that I know is also the most modern in tone. When Longinus[1] praises the author of Genesis—in his language, 'the lawgiver of the Jews'—for sublimity of conception, he seems to express a literary experience very like our own. Genesis is placed beside Homer and in some respects preferred to him. The Bible is being ranked among the classics on purely secular grounds. But it would be difficult to cite strict parallels from the ages that follow.

The learned M. de Bruyne in his *Etudes d'esthetique medievale* (1946) has collected a mass of evidence about the literary appreciation of Scripture in the Middle Ages. Praise is not lacking; but we certainly find ourselves in an alien world. On the threshold of that period we meet St. Augustine's curious statement that the Bible uses *humillimum genus loquendi*.[2] If this referred to style in the narrower sense, if the Psalms and Prophets seemed to him to use 'the lowest language' it would be almost inexplicable. Almost, but not quite; the great, roaring machine of Latin rhetoric can, at times, deafen the human ear to all other literature. But from the context I suppose that St. Augustine is referring to something rather different—to that apparent naivety or simplicity of the literal sense which offended him until he had been taught that it was merely the outer shell, concealing the *sacramentorum altitudo*.[3] This distinction between the literal or historical sense and the allegorical senses—however these are classified by different doctors —is a fundamental factor in all medieval reading of the Bible. It is no doubt true, and must be insisted on, that no superstructure of allegories was allowed to abrogate the truth of the literal sense. Hugo of St. Victor urges upon his pupils the necessity of mastering the literal sense first. 'I think', he writes, 'you will never be perfectly subtle in the Allegory unless you are first grounded in the History.'[4] Yet this very passage reveals how inevitably the medieval exegesis belittled what we should regard as the actual literary quality of the text. It is clear that Hugo expects his pupils to hurry through the historical sense too quickly and perfunctorily. *Noli contemnere minima haec*[5] he adds,

[1]*De Sublim.*, IX
[2]*Conf.*, VI, v.
[3]*Ibid.*
[4]*Eruditionis Didascalicae*, VI, iii
[5]*Ibid.*

'Despise not these small things'. If you had despised the alphabet you
would not now be able to read. An appreciation for which the story of
Joseph and his brethren or David and Goliath was merely the alphabet,
a necessary preliminary to higher and more delightful studies, may have
been keen, but it was very unlike our own. Hence we are not surprised
to find him saying that the Scriptures are like a honeycomb. They
appear dry on the outside *per simplicitatem sermonis* but are *dulcedine
plena* within.[6] Notice how the *simplicitas sermonis* echoes St. Augustine's *humillimum genus loquendi*. Again, the Scripture may be compared to a lyre. The spiritual senses are like the strings: the historical
sense is like the wood which does not sound itself but keeps the strings
together.[7]

I do not wish in any way to deride the doctrine of multiple senses.
Our own age, steeped in the symbolism of dreams and in the allegorical
or semi-allegorical work of writers like Kafka and Mr. Rex Warner,
will not look/down on that doctrine with superiority. We may anticipate a revival of the allegorical sense in Biblical criticism. But it will
probably be dangerous, and in the Middle Ages I think it was dangerous, to appreciation of the Historical Books as plain heroic narrative.

St. Thomas Aquinas throws a little more light on the references
which we have already met to the 'lowness' or 'simplicity' of the Bible.
He explains why Scripture expresses divine truths not merely through
corporeal images but even through images of vile bodies rather than
noble.[8] This is done, he says, to liberate the mind from error, to reduce the danger of any confusion between the symbol and the reality.
It is an answer worthy of a profound theologian. At the same time, the
passage in which it occurs reveals attitudes most hostile to aesthetic
appreciation of the sacred text. It would seem, he says, that Scripture
ought not to use metaphors. For what is proper to the lowest kind of
learning *(infimae doctrinae)* does not seem suitable to the queen of the
sciences. But metaphor is proper to poetry, and poetry is the lowest
of all forms of learning—*est infima inter omnes doctrinas*. The answer,
so far as it concerns us here, is that poetry and Scripture use metaphor
for quite different reasons; poetry for delight and Scripture *propter
necessitatem et ultitatem*.[9] Where a nineteenth century critic might
have said that Scripture was itself the highest poetry, St. Thomas says

[6]*Ibid*, IV, i
[7]*Ibid*, V. ii
[8]*Summa Theol. Quaest*. I, Art. IX
[9]*Ibid*.

rather that the highest and the lowest *doctrinae* have, paradoxically, one point in common, but of course for different reasons.

From other medieval writers, notably Ulric of Strasbourg, de Bruyne has collected passages which seem, but perhaps not without illusion, to come nearer to the modern point of view. In general, however, I do not think we shall go too far if we say that medieval appreciation of the Bible is divided from modern by a very wide gulf.

If the medieval approach is alien, that of the Renaissance seems to me sometimes repellent. We reach the age of Ciceronianism, of Humanism, of that deadly classical dignity which so obscured and distorted (along with many other things) the classics themselves. It was an age in which Scaliger could tax Homer with vulgarity and complain that Andromache's lament over Hector smacked of an ill-bred woman— *plebiam mulierculam.*[10] Where an aesthetic like this prevailed the simple grandeur of *Kings* and *Judges* and the Gospels had little chance of being valued at its true worth. Hence Vida thought that the story of the Passion could be improved by the tinsel of his *Christiad.* In a sense, of course, it is only a literary counterpart to the religious paintings of the time: there too vast Vitruvian halls rise as the background to 'deep, abstracted, holy scenes'. I leave to others a problem I have failed to solve—why this offends in words so much more than it does in paint—and pursue our immediate subject, by tracing the effect of this movement even on so great a man as Sir Thomas More. In his late treatise *On the Passion* he ventures to put words into the mouth of Our Lord. The thing had been done before. In the *Imitation* it had been so done as to satisfy not only piety but our sense of the Dominical style. But More takes the words in Gethsemane, 'This is your hour and the power of darkness', and seems to think they can be strengthened by expansion into the following:

> Thys is the shorte whyle that is graunted yee, and the libertie geuen unto darknesse, that nowe ye maye in the night, which till this howre ye coulde neuer be suffered to bryng to passe in the daye, like monstruous rauenyinge fowles, lyke skryche owles and hegges, lyke backes, howlettes, nighte crowes, and byrdes of the hellye lake, goe aboute with your billes, your tallentes, your teeth, and your shryle shryching outerageouslye, but all in vayne thus in the darke to flee uppon me.[11]

[10]*Poet.*, V. iii.
[11]*Works* (London, 1557), p. 1397, D-E.

I ought to warn you that I am quoting a translation, that of More's granddaughter. But if anyone looks at the Latin and likes it much better than the English, I shall be surprised. I am not, of course, suggesting for one moment any spiritual flaw. The question is about More's taste. Indeed, the more we reverence him as a man, the more striking the example becomes. Even a man so steeped as he in the spirit of the Dominical utterances could be, by Humanistic rhetoric, so deafened to the majesty of their style.

With the first Protestant translators we get some signs of a changed approach. I would wish to take every precaution against exaggerating it. The history of the English Bible from Tyndale to the Authorised Version should never for long be separated from that European, and by no means exclusively Protestant, movement of which it made part. No one can write that history without skipping to and fro across national and religious boundaries at every moment. He will have to go from the Soncino Hebrew Bible (1488) to Reuchlin's Hebrew Grammar (1506), then to Alcala for Cardinal Ximenes' great Polyglot (1514) and north for Erasmus' New Testament in the same year, and then to Luther for the German New Testament in 1522, and pick up Hebrew again with Munster's Grammar in 1525, and see Luther worked over by Zwinglius and others for the Zurich Bible of 1529, and glance at the two French versions of '34 and '35, and by no means neglect the new Latin translations of Pagninus ('28) and Munster ('34-'35). That is the sort of background against which Tyndale, Coverdale, Geneva, and Rheims must be set. For when we come to compare the versions we shall find that only a very small percentage of variants are made for stylistic or even doctrinal reasons. When men depart from their predecessors it is usually because they claim to be better Hebraists or better Grecians. The international advance of philology carries them on, and those who are divided by the bitterest theological hatreds gladly learn from one another. Tyndale accepts corrections from More: Rheims learns from Geneva: phrases travel through Rheims on their way from Geneva to Authorised. Willy-nilly all Christendom collaborates. The English Bible is the English branch of a European tree.

Yet in spite of this there is something new about Tyndale; for good or ill a great simplification of approach. 'Scripture', he writes, 'speaketh after the most grossest manner. Be diligent therefore that

[12]*Parable of the Wicked Mammon,* in *Doctrinal Treatises,* ed. H. Walter (Cambridge, 1848), p. 59.

ner' we recognize an echo of Augustine's *humillimum genus* and Hugo
of St. Victor's *simplicitas sermonis*. That rusticity or meanness which
we find it so hard to discern in the Bible is still apparent to Tyndale.
The novelty is the rejection of the allegorical senses. That rejection he
shares with most of the Reformers and even, as regards parts of the
Bible, with a Humanistic Papist like Colet; and it is no part of my
business to decide whether it marked an advance or a retrogression in
theology. What is interesting is not Tyndale's negation of the allegories
but his positive attitude towards the literal sense. He loves it for its
"grossness'. 'God is a Spirit', he writes, 'and all his words are spiritual.
His literal sense is spiritual.'[13] This is very characteristic of Tyndale's
outlook. For him, just as God's literal sense is spiritual, so all life is
religion: cleaning shoes, washing dishes, our humblest natural functions, are all 'good works'.[14] The life of *religion,* technically so called,
wins no 'higher room in heaven . . . than a whore of the stews (if she
repent)'.[15] This would certainly seem to be an attitude more favourable
to the literary appreciation of much Scripture than any we have yet
encountered. On the other hand Mr. Gavin Bone, whose loss we still
deplore at Oxford, has said roundly that Tyndale 'hated literature.'
This is based on his fierce condemnation of medieval romance[16]; a trait
which is Humanistic as well as Puritanical. But I do not think he did
hate literature. Where he speaks of his own work as a translator he
sounds like a man with a sense of style; as when he says that Hebrew
and Greek go well into English whereas 'thou must seek a compass in
the Latin, and yet shall have much work to translate it well-favouredly,
so that it hath the same grace and sweetness.'[17] More important still
is the evidence of his own original works.

I wish I had time to digress on those works. Tyndale's fame as an
English writer has been most unjustly overshadowed both by the
greater fame of More and by his own reputation as a translator. He
seems to me the best prose writer of his age. He is inferior to More
in what may be called the elbow-room of the mind and (of course)
in humour. In every other respect he surpasses him; in economy, in
lucidity, and above all in rhythmical vitality. He reaches at times a

[13]*Obedience of a Christian Man* (Walter, *op. cit.,* p. 309).
[14]*Parable of the Wicked Mammon* (Walter, *op. cit.,* pp. 100, 102).
[15]*Pathway* (Walter, *op. cit.,* p. 21).
[16]*Obedience* (Walter, *op. cit.,* p. 161).
[17]*Ibid.,* pp. 148, 149.

piercing quality which is quite outside More's range: 'as a man feeleth God in himself, so is he to his neighbour'[18]—'I am thou thyself, and thou art I myself, and can be no nearer of kin'[19]—'be glad, and laugh from the low bottom of his heart'[20]—'that he might see love, and love again'[21] —'Who taught the eagles to spy out their prey? Even so the children of God spy out their Father'.[22] Though it is not strictly relevant, may I be excused, since the fact seems to be insufficiently known, for saying that Tyndale's social ethics are almost identical with those of More?— quite equally medieval and equally opposed to what some call the New Economics. The points on which these two brave and holy men agreed may have been few; but perhaps they were sufficient, if they had been accepted, to have altered the course of our history for the better.

It is not, of course, to be supposed that aesthetic considerations were uppermost in Tyndale's mind when he translated Scripture. The matter was much too serious for that; souls were at stake. The same holds for all the translators. Coverdale was probably the one whose choice of a rendering came nearest to being determined by taste. His defects as well as his qualities led to this. Of all the translators he was the least scholarly. Among men like Erasmus, Tyndale, Munster, or the Jesuits at Rheims he shows like a rowing boat among battleships. This gave him a kind of freedom. Unable to judge between rival interpretations, he may often have been guided, half consciously, to select and combine by taste. Fortunately his taste was admirable.

The history of the Authorised Version has been told so often that I will not attempt to re-tell it, and its beauties praised so lavishly that I will not praise them. Instead, I will proceed at once to its influence as an English book. I shall attempt to define that influence, for I think there has been misunderstanding about it and even a little exaggeration.

Let us begin by distinguishing the various senses in which one book can be said to influence the author of another book.

(1)   A book may be, in the familiar language of research, a *source.* Lydgate mentions the loves of Mars and Venus. The immediate source might be some book like Boccaccio's *De Genealogia,* the ultimate source is Homer. It would, I think, be quite good English to say

---

[18]*Wicked Mammon* (Walter, *op. cit.,* p. 58).

[19]*Obedience,* p. 296.

[20]*Pathway,* p. 9.

[21]*Obedience,* p. 136.

[22]*Answer to More,* ed. H. Walter (Cambridge, 1850), p. 490.

that Lydgate was here influenced by Homer. But that is not the most useful way of employing the word in literary history, nor is it generally so employed. If anyone wishes to call a Source an Influence, let him do so; but let him recognize a Source as a very special kind of Influence. Most of us, I expect, would prefer to distinguish Source from Influence altogether. A Source gives us things to write about; an Influence prompts us to write in a certain way. Homer is a Source to Lydgate, but Homer was an Influence on Arnold when he wrote *Sohrab and Rustum.* Firdausi's *Shah Nameh* was Arnold's Source, but not an Influence on that poem. Malory was both a Source and an Influence in Tennyson's *Morte Darthur;* elsewhere in the *Idylls* a Source but perhaps hardly an Influence.

If these terms are accepted, we can distinguish the Bible as a Source for English Literature from the Bible as a literary Influence. That it is a Source of immense importance is obvious. For several centuries its persons, scenes, and doctrines were familiar to every Englishman. They are constantly used for illustration and allusion. But, of course, when the Bible is a Source, there is usually nothing to show whether the Authorised Version is being used or not. The Bible is one Source for Dryden's *Absalom and Achitophel,* but his spelling of Achitophel's name is not derived from the Authorised. We may indeed assume that most authors, and all unlearned authors, after the sixteenth century derived their Biblical knowledge from that version. But this does not seem to be a fact of any importance. The persons and stories would be the same in whatever text they were known. On my view the huge mass of Biblical material in our literature has no place in an account of the Influence of the Authorised Version considered as an English book.

(2) It would, I suppose, be possible to say that we are influenced by a book whenever we quote it; but probably no literary historian would wish to use the word *influence* in that way. It would seem to me reasonable to say, for example, that my own habit of immoderate quotation showed the Influence of Hazlitt, but not the Influence of the authors I quote; or that Burton's habit of immoderate quotation might be influenced by Montaigne, not by the authors he quotes. Frequent quotation is itself a literary characteristic; if the authors whom we rifle were not themselves fond of quotation, then, in the very act of quoting, we proclaim our freedom from their influence. It is almost the difference between borrowing a man's clothes for a particular occasion and imitating his style of dress. If English literature is full

of Biblical quotation, I would not describe this as the influence of the Authorised Version, any more than I would call Virgilians all those who quote Virgil. I am not saying that to do otherwise would be necessarily an improper use of language: I only think mine useful for the purpose in hand.

(3) So far I have been speaking of what may be called flagrant quotation—quotation isolated and proclaimed by typographical devices. But besides this, there is of course the embedded quotation— sentences or phrases from the Authorised Version artfully worked into an author's own language so that an ignorant reader might not recognize them. Our literature is full of this, especially in the nineteenth and early twentieth centuries; in Trollope, Swinburne, and Kipling it becomes a positive nuisance; one contemporary American professor is very seriously infected. To this process the word Influence might much more naturally be applied. Yet even this does not seem to me to be Influence in the deepest sense, and I would prefer not to call it Influence at all. I will try to explain why.

Let us begin by laying side by side with it two other phenomena of the same sort: the ubiquitous embedded quotations from Homer in Plato's prose, or from Shakespeare in English prose. The scraps of Homer slip very artfully in and out of the orchestration of a Platonic period. But of course they are all marked out from their surroundings by their metre and their dialect. No one would maintain that Plato's own style grows out of, or was learned from, Homer's. And indeed the Homeric bits would not be doing their work unless they were felt to be different from the Attic prose that surrounds them. They are used either for solemnity or facetiously—and the facetious is only the solemn stood on its head. The very response they demand depends on our feeling them as aliens. There would be no point in them unless we did. Far from showing that Plato's style has assimilated Homer's, they show the irreducible difference between them. And are not the embedded Shakespearian quotations in English the same? Of course, not every hack who speaks of a man more sinned against than sinning, or a consummation devoutly to be wished, knows that he is quoting Shakespeare. He may think (significantly) that he is quoting the Bible. He may even think he is using a proverb. But he knows quite well, and he expects his readers to know, that he is borrowing from somewhere. He counts on recognition. He is decorating his style. He wants the phrase to stand out from his own composition as gold lace stands out from a coat. The whole pleasure, such as it is, depends

on the fact that the embedded quotation is different—in other words
that his own style is not influenced by Shakespeare.

I believe that our embedded quotations from the Authorised Version
are nearly always in exactly this position. They are nearly always
either solemn or facetious. Only because the surrounding prose is
different—in other words, only in so far as our English is not influenced
by the Authorised Version—do they achieve the effect the authors
intended.

(4) Here at last we reach what I would describe as Influence in
the full and strict sense—the influence of the Authorised Version on
vocabulary. I do not think we are being (in this sense) influenced by
Shakespeare when we speak of a consummation devoutly to be wished.
But I do think we are influenced by him (though the phonetic history
is complicated) whenever we use *weird* as an adjective. We do so with
no sense of quotation: the word has been really assimilated, has gone
into the blood-stream of our language. In the same way we are being
influenced by Van Helmont (and perhaps by Paracelsus) whenever
we use the word *gas*. In the same way we are being influenced by the
Authorised Version and its predecessors whenever we use the words
beautiful, long-suffering, peace-maker or *scapegoat*. Tyndale is our
ultimate creditor for all these. But even here I must plead for a distinction. Henry Bradley rightly mentioned *damsel, raiment, travail,*
and *quick* in the sense 'alive,' as words saved by the Authorised Version for archaic and poetical use. But only for such use. They are
not in the blood-stream. As for *loving-kindness* and *tender mercies,*
they are so generally confined either to religious contexts or to mockery
(which for our special purpose tells the same tale) that I almost classify
them as very short embedded quotations.

(5) Finally, we come to literary influence in the fullest sense, the
sense it bears when we say that *Paradise Lost* is influenced by Homer
and Virgil, or nineteenth century journalism by Macaulay or modern
English poetry by Mr. Eliot. You will perhaps remember that I have
defined Influence, in this sense, as that which prompts a man to write
in a certain way. But even within this definition further distinctions
break out. The influence may show itself in architectonics. That is
the most obvious, though by no means the only, manner in which
Virgil influences Milton. The whole plan of his epic is Virgilian. Very
few English writers have undergone an influence of that sort from any
book of the Bible. Tupper's *Proverbial Philosophy* and the *Book of
Mormon* are perhaps instances. Some would add Blake's *Prophetic*

Books. Again, Influence may show itself in the use of language—in the rhythm, the imagery, or (using that word in its narrowest sense) the style.

The influence of the rhythms of the Authorised Version seems to me to be very hard to detect. Its rhythms are in fact extremely various, and some of them are unavoidable in the English language. I am not at all sure that a resemblance in rhythm, unless supported by some other resemblance, is usually recognizable. If I say 'At the regatta Madge avoided the river and the crowd' would this, without warning, remind you of 'In the beginning God created the heaven and the earth'? Even if it did, is the common rhythm, thus separated from community of thought and temper, a matter of any importance? I believe that wherever an English writer seems to us to recall the scriptural rhythms, he is always recalling other associations as well. The influence of rhythm, isolated from imagery and style, is perhaps an abstraction.

In imagery I suppose the influence to be very great, though I must frankly confess that I have not been able to invent a method of checking it. If English writers in elevated contexts tend to speak of corn and wine rather than of beef and beer and butter, of chariots rather than chargers, of rain rather than sunshine as a characteristic blessing, of sheep more often than cows and of the sword more often than either the pike or the gun, if bread rather than mutton or potatoes is their lofty synonym for food, if stone is more poetical than brick, trumpets than bugles and purple and fine linen loftier than satin and velvet, I suspect that this is due to the Bible, but I have no rigorous proof. Nor, in this sphere, would it be easy to distinguish the Biblical influence from that generally Mediterranean and ancient influence which comes from the classics as well as the Bible. But I believe the Biblical influence is here very great.

But in our style, in the actual build of our sentences, I think the influence has possibly been less than we suppose. The perfect example of an influence in this field is that exercised on our prose by Dryden and his contemporaries (Tillotson and the like). You remember that he went all through the *Essay on Dramatic Poesy* and altered every sentence that ended with a preposition. This is, I say, a perfect example of Influence. No one can pretend that this curious taboo was inherent in the genius of the language and would have developed even without the action of Dryden and his fellow Gallicists. On the contrary, it is so alien from the language that it has never penetrated into the conversation of even the worst prigs, and serves no purpose but to increase those little bunches of unemphatic monosyllables that English was already prone to. On the other hand, it has so established itself in our formal style that thousands obey it unconsciously. It is, very precisely, a thing that prompts us to write in a certain way: even I, who detest it for a frenchified schoolroom superstition, often feel it plucking at my elbow. I doubt whether the Authorised Version has achieved any comparable dominance over our style. Indeed, what astonishes me here is the failure of some of its most familiar terms to get into our language at all. *It came to pass, answered and said, lo* —have these ever been used by any English writer without full consciousness that he was quoting? If we look into those authors who are usually said to be influenced by the style of the Authorised Version, we shall find that such influence is indeed present but that it is hardly dominant. I will consider Ruskin and Bunyan.

In Ruskin embedded quotation and imagery from the Bible are made great use of, but Homer and Spenser are used not very much less, Dante not infrequently. And all these are used consciously. What Ruskin tells us in *Praeterita*[23] about the formation of his own style is relevant:

> Had it not been for constant reading of the Bible, I might probably have taken Johnson for my model of English. To a useful extent I have always done so; in these first essays, partly because I could not help it, partly of set, and well set, purpose . . . The turns and returns of reiterated *Rambler* and iterated *Idler* fastened themselves in my ears and mind: nor was it possible for me, till long afterwards, to quit myself of Johnsonian symmetry, in sentences intended either with swordsman's or paviour's blow, to cleave an enemy's crest or drive down the oaken pile of a principle.

In his mature style—in this very passage—I think we can recognize the Johnsonian element: I cannot recognize the Biblical. Elsewhere, though I do not deny its presence—and especially in the images—it is one of many resources. I think *resources* is the best word. It is, so to speak, one of the colours in his paint box, used at his own discretion. He has many others. And what makes the total effect, for me, so very unlike the Authorised Version, is the periodic structure of Ruskin's prose. Already in the passage quoted, which is familiar and epistolary

[23]XII.

compared with the high passages in *Modern Painters* or *Stones of Venice,* you will have noticed the transition *nor was it possible.* That is learned from classical Latin. And so, in the long run, is the Ruskinian period as a whole. A structure descending from Cicero through the prose of Hooker, Milton, and Taylor, and then enriched with romantic colouring for which Homer and the Bible are laid under contribution—that seems to me the formula for Ruskin's style. If you could take away what comes from the Bible it would be impaired. It would hardly, I think, be crippled. It would certainly not be annihilated. This is real influence, but limited influence. The influence of Italian epic on Spenser would be a good contrast. If you took away from the *Faerie Queen* everything that is learned from Ariosto and Boiardo, what would be left would be either nothing or a radically different poem. This is quite consistent with the view that Spenser has added something of his own and even transmuted his originals. The alchemist may turn silver into gold: but he had to have the silver.

Bunyan, at first sight, will strike most of us as far more Biblical than Ruskin. But this impression is partly due to the fact that both are to us rather archaic and rather simple in syntax. To that extent any unlearned author of Bunyan's time would be bound to remind us of the Bible whether he had ever read it or not. We must discount that accidental similarity and look deeper. I take an example at random:

> So *Mistrust* and *Timorous* ran down the hill, and Christian went on his way. But thinking again of what he heard from the men, he felt in his bosom for his Roll, that he might read therein and be comforted: but he felt, and found it not. Then was Christian in great distress, and knew not what to do, for he wanted that which used to relieve him, and that which should have been his pass into the Celestial City. Here therefore he began to be much perplexed and knew not what to do. At last he bethought that he had slept in the Arbour.

The question is not how much of this might occur in the Authorised Version, but how much might be expected to occur in Bunyan if he had not read it. Much of it, of course, is quite unlike the Bible; phrases like *Then was Christian in great distress, he wanted that which used to relieve him, Here therefore he began to be much perplexed.* There remain *he went on his way, he felt and found it not,* and the use of *so* to introduce a new step in a narrative. These are in the manner of the Authorised Version—though this use of *so* is not very common there and is far commoner in Malory. But I do not feel at all certain that Bunyan is deriving them from his Bible. And if we look through his work we shall find that his best and most characteristic sentences often have a very unscriptural ring:

> But the man, not at all discouraged, fell to cutting and hacking most fiercely.
> So I looked up in my Dream and saw the clouds rack at an unusual rate, upon which I heard a great sound of a Trumpet . . .
> Why, he objected against Religion itself; he said it was a pitiful low, sneaking business for a man to mind Religion.
> Some also have wished that the next way to their Father's house were here, that they might be troubled no more with either Hills or Mountains to go over: but the way is the way, and there's an end.
> At last he came in, and I will say that for my Lord, he carried it wonderful lovingly to him. There were but a few good bits at the Table but some of it was laid upon his Trencher.

Such passages seem to me the essential Bunyan. His prose comes to him not from the Authorised Version but from the fireside, the shop, and the lane. He is as native as Malory or Defoe. The Scriptural images themselves take on a new homeliness in these surroundings: 'She said she was sent for to go to her Husband: and then she up and told us how she had seen him in a dream, dwelling in a curious place among Immortals, wearing a Crown, playing upon a Harp.' The Crown and Harp come no doubt from the Apocalypse, but the rest of the sentence comes from Bedfordshire and in their village setting they are somehow transformed. Just so his Delectable Mountains are Bedfordshire hills magnified, green to the top. Without the Bible he would not have written the *Pilgrim's Progress* at all, for his mind would have been utterly different; but its style might have been much the same without the Authorised Version.

If I am right in thinking that the Authorised Version as a strictly literary influence has mattered less than we have often supposed, it may be asked how I account for the fact. I think there are two explanations.

In the first place, we must not assume that it always gave so much literary pleasure as it did in the nineteenth century. Thanks to Professor Sutherland, most of us now know about the egregious Edward Harwood who in 1768 published his *Liberal Translation of the New Testament: Being an Attempt to translate the Sacred Writings with the same Freedom, Spirit and Elegance With which other English Translations of the Greek Classics have lately been executed.* Harwood wrote to substitute 'the elegance of modern English' for 'the bald and barbarous language of the old vulgar version'. And no doubt Harwood was, by our standards, an ass. But can he have been the only one of his kind? Or does he voice a widely spread feeling which only reverence concealed? 'Bald and barbarous', lacking in elegance . . . we have heard something not quite unlike this before: 'the most grossest manner', *simplicitas sermonis, humillimum genus loquendi.* It is not a charge anyone would be likely to bring against the Authorised Version or its originals to-day. Those who dislike Scripture are now more likely to call its style florid or inflated; those who like it would praise it for sublimity. When and how did this change occur?

The answer, I suggest, is that the modern approach, or what was till lately the modern approach, to the Bible is deeply influenced by the Romantic Movement; by which I here mean not the Lake Poets but that taste for the primitive and the passionate which can be seen growing through nearly the whole of the eighteenth century. The men who were engaged in exhuming the ballads, the Elder Edda, the Sagas, the *Nibelungenlied* and the *Kalevala,* the forgers of *Otranto* and *Ossian,* those who dreamed of bards and druids, must have heard the Bible with new ears. The primitive simplicity of a world in which kings could be shepherds, the abrupt and mysterious manner of the prophets, the violent passions of bronze-age fighting men, the background of tents and flocks and desert and mountain, the village homeliness of Our Lord's parables and metaphors now first, I suspect, became a positive literary asset. The 'vile bodies' which St. Thomas had to explain were no longer felt to be vile. Something of the same sort was happening to Homer. Scaliger had found him low. Chapman had reverenced him for his hidden wisdom. With Pope's preface we reach a different attitude. 'I would not be as delicate', he says, 'as those modern critics who are shocked at the servile offices and mean employments in which we sometimes see the heroes of Homer engaged. There is a pleasure in taking a view of that simplicity, in opposition to the luxury of succeeding ages; in beholding monarchs without their guards, princes tending their flocks, and princesses drawing water from the springs.' He significantly adds that he has admitted into his version 'several of those general phrases and manners of expression which have attained a veneration even in our language from being used in the Old Testament'.

I suggest, then, that until the Romantic taste existed the Authorised Version was not such an attractive model as we might suppose. That would be one cause limiting its influence. The second cause was, I believe, its familiarity.

This may sound paradoxical, but it is seriously meant. For three centuries the Bible was so well known that hardly any word or phrase, except those which it shared with all English books whatever, could be borrowed without recognition. If you echoed the Bible everyone knew that you were echoing the Bible. And certain associations were called up in every reader's mind; sacred associations. All your readers had heard it read, as a ritual or almost ritual act, at home, at school, and in church. This did not mean that reverence prevented all Biblical echoes. It did mean that they would only be used either with conscious reverence or with conscious irreverence, either religiously or facetiously. There could be a pious use and a profane use: but there could be no ordinary use. Nearly all that was Biblical was recognizably Biblical, and all that was recognized was *sacer,* numinous; whether on that account to be respected or on that account to be flouted makes very little difference. Mark what Boswell says under Sat. April 3d 1773:

> He (sc. Dr. Johnson) disapproved of introducing scripture phrases into secular discourses. This seemed to me a question of some difficulty. A scripture expression may be used like a highly classical phrase to produce an instantaneous strong impression.

'Like a highly classical phrase'—that is the point; and producing a strong impression. It is difficult to conceive conditions less favourable to that unobtrusive process of infiltration by which a profound literary influence usually operates. An influence which cannot evade our consciousness will not go very deep.

It may be asked whether now, when only a minority of Englishmen regard the Bible as a sacred book, we may anticipate an increase of its literary influence. I think we might if it continued to be widely read. But this is not very likely. Our age has, indeed, coined the expression 'the Bible as literature'. It is very generally implied that those who have rejected its theological pretensions nevertheless continue to enjoy it as a treasure house of English prose. It may be so. There may be people who, not having been forced upon familiarity with it by believing parents, have yet been drawn to it by its literary charms and remained as constant readers. But I never happen to meet them. Perhaps it is because I live in the provinces. But I cannot help suspecting, if I may make an Irish bull, that those who read the Bible as literature do not read the Bible.

It would be strange if they did. If I am right in thinking that the Bible, apart from its sacred character, appeals most easily to a Romantic taste, we must expect to find it neglected and even disliked in our own age. The Counter-Romantic movement is indeed so violent that those of us who do not share it almost wonder if there is not something pathological in the violence. The hatred of Romanticism has reached that stage at which it can see no differences of kind between the things hated. I read the other day an essay in which the author dismissed Chesterton's *Ballad of the White Horse* on the ground that 'Morris manages these things better than Chesterton ever did; and nobody wants to preserve William Morris'. I can understand, even if I deplore, the taste that does not want to preserve William Morris. What staggers me is the implication that Chesterton and Morris wrote the same sort of poetry. It is as if a man said 'Holbein does all these things better than Titian'. I can only conclude that the author's revulsion from Romantic poetry has reached a degree of violence at which the difference between the cool water-colour effects of Morris, his northern bareness, and his monotonous plashing melody cannot be distinguished from all the gold and scarlet and all the orgiastic drumbeats of Chesterton. Phobias make strange bedfellows. Perhaps to those who cannot endure the presence of a cat, the huge, square-headed tabby Tom and the little smoke-faced goblin from Siam are all one. But clearly in an age so anti-Romantic as this, all those qualities which once helped the Bible as literature will work against it. David weeping over Absalom, Moses at the Burning Bush, Elijah on Carmel, the Horror of Great Darkness, the Maniac among the Tombs—what have these passages to say to an unbeliever unless he is a Romantic or to a Counter-Romantic unless he is a believer?

What I am saying involves the view that an approach to the Bible which seemed to many of us in our youth to be simply human, was in reality the product of a particular period in the history of taste. I hope you will find this the more credible because of our brief glances at the

Bible's earlier history. The Medieval taste for which the literal sense was merely the dry crust of the honeycomb concealing the golden sweetness of the allegory, and the Humanistic taste which felt that the simplicity of Scripture would be improved by rhetoric, may each have seemed, in its own day, natural and eternal. Against that background we can see in proper perspective the eighteenth and nineteenth century taste. No doubt we may conclude that the Counter-Romantic taste of the twentieth will also prove ephemeral; indeed, whatever the hidden fuel may be, it can hardly blaze in its present fury for very long. It will be succeeded by other attitudes which we cannot predict.

Inevitably we ask whether any of these is likely to be favourable to a literary appreciation of the Bible. Stripped (for most readers) of its divine authority, stripped of its allegorical senses, denied a romantic welcome for its historical sense, will it none the less return on the wave of some new fashion to literary pre-eminence and be read? And of course we do not know. I offer my guess. I think it very unlikely that the Bible will return as a book unless it returns as a sacred book. Longinus could enjoy it without being a Christian. But then Longinus came as near to being a Romantic as a Greek could, and his view of the world and man was in its own way a religious one.[24] It would be rash to expect many more of his kind. Unless the religious claims of the Bible are again acknowledged, its literary claims will, I think, be given only 'mouth honour' and that decreasingly. For it is, through and through, a sacred book. Most of its component parts were written, and all of them were brought together, for a purely religious purpose. It contains good literature and bad literature. But even the good literature is so written that we can seldom disregard its sacred character. It is easy enough to read Homer while suspending our disbelief in the Greek pantheon; but then the *Iliad* was not composed chiefly, if at all, to enforce obedience to Zeus and Athene and Poseidon. The Greek tragedians are more religious than Homer, but even there we have only religious speculation or at least the poet's personal religious ideas; not dogma. That is why we can join in. Neither Aeschylus nor even Virgil tacitly prefaces his poetry with the formula 'Thus say the gods'. But in most parts of the Bible everything is implicitly or explicitly introduced with 'Thus saith the Lord'. It is, if you like to put it that way, not merely a sacred book but a book so remorselessly and continuously sacred that it does not invite, it excludes or repels, the merely aesthetic

[24]v. cap. XXXIV.

approach. You can read it as literature only by a *tour de force*. You are cutting the wood against the grain, using the tool for a purpose it was not intended to serve. It demands incessantly to be taken on its own terms: it will not continue to give literary delight very long except to those who go to it for something quite different. I predict that it will in the future be read, as it always has been read, almost exclusively by Christians.

If many critics, especially older critics, speak of it differently to-day, I suggest that they may be influenced by amiable but unliterary motives. A sacred book rejected is like a king dethroned. Towards either of them there arises in well-disposed minds a chivalrous compunction. One would like to concede everything except the thing really at issue. Having supported the deposition, one would wish to make it clear that one had no personal malice. Just because you cannot countenance a restoration, you are anxious to speak kindly of the old gentleman in his personal capacity—to praise his fund of anecdote or his collection of butterflies. I cannot help thinking that when a critic old enough to remember the Bible in its power prophesies for it a great future as literature, he is often unconsciously swayed by similar motives. But such courtesies will not preserve it. Neither the Bible nor those who still read it as believers invite them; and the generation which is now growing up will disregard them. For the Bible, whether in the Authorised or in any other version, I foresee only two possibilities; either to return as a sacred book or to follow the classics, if not quite into oblivion yet into the ghost-life of the museum and the specialist's study. Except, of course, among the believing minority who read it to be instructed and get literary enjoyment as a by-product.

FURTHER READING

REFERENCE WORKS REPRESENTING JEWISH, CATHOLIC, AND PROTESTANT VIEWS

The Universal Jewish Encyclopedia, edited by Isaac Landman. The Universal Jewish Encyclopedia, Inc., New York, 1940. Volume Two, article "Bible," pp. 280-346.

A Catholic Commentary on Holy Scripture, ed. Dom Bernard Orchard, O.S.B., Rev. Edmund F. Sutcliffe, S.J., Rev. Reginald C. Fuller, Dom Ralph Russell, O.S.B. Thomas Nelson and Sons, Ltd., 1953.

The Interpreter's Bible, New York, Abingdon Press, 1952-1957.
General Articles: On the whole Bible and the Old Testament, Vol. 2, pp. 3-346: On the New Testament, Vol. 7, pp. 3-227.

BACKGROUND IN GEOGRAPHY AND HISTORY

ALBRIGHT, W. Foxwell, *The Archaeology of Palestine,* Harmondsworth, Middlesex, Penguin Books, 1949.

ALBRIGHT, William Foxwell, *From the Stone Age to Christianity. Monotheism and the Historical Process.* Second Edition with a new introduction by the author. Doubleday Anchor Books, Doubleday & Company, New York, 1957.

BARTON, George Aaron, *Archaeology and the Bible,* Philadelphia, American Sundayschool Union, 1925. Seventh edition revised, 1941.

GLOVER, Terrot Reaveley, *The Ancient World,* New York, The Macmillan Company, Cambridge, England, The University Press, 1935.

PRITCHARD, James B. (ed.) *Ancient Near Eastern Texts relating to the Old Testament,* Princeton University Press, 1950.

VAN SICKLE, Clifton Edwin, *A Political and Cultural History of the Ancient World,* Boston, Houghton Mifflin Company, 1947-8.

Westminster Historical Atlas of the Bible, ed. George Ernest Wright and Floyd V. Filson, Philadelphia, The Westminster Press, 1956.

WRIGHT, G. Ernest, *Biblical Archaeology,* Philadelphia, The Westminster Press; London, Gerald Duckworth & Co., Ltd., 1957.

GENERAL INTRODUCTIONS

BEWER, J. A., *The Literature of the Old Testament in its Historical Development,* Columbia University Press, New York, Rev. ed., 1947.

GOODSPEED, Edgar J., *An Introduction to the New Testament,* University of Chicago Press, 1937.

HENSHAW, T., *New Testament Literature in the Light of Modern Scholarship,* London, George Allen and Unwin, 1952.

MCNEILE, A. H., *An Introduction to the Study of the New Testament,* Second Edition revised by C. S. C. Williams, Oxford, Clarendon Press, 1953.

PFEIFFER, Robert H., *Introduction to the Old Testament,* New York and London, Harper & Brothers, 1941.

ROWLEY, H. H., *The Old Testament and Modern Study,* Oxford, Clarendon Press, 1951.

RYPINS, Stanley, *The Book of Thirty Centuries.* An Introduction to modern study of the Bible, New York, The Macmillan Company, 1951.

SCOTT, Ernest Findlay, *The Literature of the New Testament,* Columbia University Press, New York, 1936.

WATTS, Harold H., *The Modern Reader's Guide to the Bible,* Harper & Brothers, New York, 1949.

WILLOUGHBY, Harold R. (ed.) *The Study of the Bible Today and Tomorrow,* University of Chicago Press, Chicago, Ill., 1947.

THE BIBLE AS LITERATURE: GENERAL

CHASE, Mary Ellen, *The Bible and the Common Reader.* Revised edition, New York, Macmillan, 1955.

CHASE, Mary Ellen, *Life and Language in the Old Testament,* New York, Norton, 1955.

CULLER, Arthur J., *Creative Religious Literature, a New Literary Study of the Bible,* New York, Macmillan, 1930.

ELIOT, Thomas Stearns, "Religion and Literature," in *Essays Ancient and Modern,* London, Faber and Faber, 1936.

MACDONALD, Duncan Black, *The Hebrew Literary Genius,* Princeton, Princeton University Press, 1933.

MOULTON, Richard G., Peters, John P., Bruce, A. B., etc., *The Bible as Literature,* New York, Thos. Y. Crowell, 1896.

QUILLER-COUCH, Sir Arthur, "On Reading the Bible," in *On the Art of Reading,* G. P. Putnam's Sons, New York and London, 1920.

THE BIBLE AS LITERATURE—TREATMENTS OF SPECIAL ASPECTS

BAROWAY, Israel, "The Bible as Poetry in the English Renaissance," *Journal of English and Germanic Philology,* Vol. 32 (1933), pp. 447-480.

CHESTERTON, G. K., "The Book of Job," in *G.K.C. as M.C.* Methuen & Co., Ltd., London, 1929.

FRIES, Charles C., "One Stylistic Feature of the 1611 English Bible," in *Fred Newton Scott Anniversary Papers,* Chicago, Ill., University of Chicago Press, 1929.

FROUDE, James Anthony, "The Book of Job," in *Short Studies on Great Subjects* (first series), New York, Charles Scribner and Company, 1869.

GARDINER, J. H., "The Father of English Prose Style," *Atlantic Monthly,* LXXXV (1900) 684-692.

GRIERSON, Sir Herbert J. C., "Prophetic Poetry, The Hebrew Prophets," in *Milton and Wordsworth. Poets and Prophets,* New York: The Macmillan Company; Cambrjdge, Eng.: at the University Press, 1937.

GUNKEL, Herman, *The Legends of Genesis.* Translated by W. H. Carruth, Chicago, The Open Court Publishing Company, 1901.

GUNKEL, Hermann, *What Remains of the Old Testament and other Essays.* Trans. by the Rev. A. K. Dallas. London, George Allen & Unwin, Ltd., 1928.

JASTROW, Morris, Jr., *A Gentle Cynic,* Philadelphia & London, J. B. Lippincott Company, 1919.

JASTROW, Morris, Jr., *The Book of Job,* Philadelphia and London, J. B. Lippincott Company, 1920.

JASTROW, Morris, Jr., *The Song of Songs,* Philadelphia and London, J. B. Lippincott Company, 1921.

KALLEN, Horace Meyer, *The Book of Job as a Greek Tragedy, Restored.* With an introductory essay on the Original Form and Philosophic Meaning of Job. New York, Moffat, Yard and Company, 1918.

KNIGHT, G. Wilson, "The New Testament as an Art-form," "Mankind in Glory: An Essay on St. Paul," "The Pioneer of Life: An Essay on the Gospels," in

The Christian Renaissance, Toronto, The Macmillan Company of Canada, Ltd., 1933.

Lowes, John Livingston, "The Noblest Monument of English Prose," in *Essays in Appreciation,* Boston & New York, Houghton Mifflin Company, 1936.

Samuel, Maurice, *Some Peoples of the Book,* New York, Knopf, 1955.

Stevenson, William Barron, *The Poem of Job.* A literary study with a new translation. The Schweich lectures of the British Academy, 1943. London. For the British Academy by G. Cumberlege, Oxford University Press, 1947.

Wilson, Edmund, "On First Reading Genesis," in *Red, Black, Blond and Olive,* New York, Oxford University Press, 1956.

AUTHORS

AUERBACH, Erich, 1892– (pp. 209-230)

Scholar in field of Romance and Mediaeval Latin philology. Professor in Romance Philology, Marburg, 1929–1935; Professor of French and Romance Philology, Yale University, 1950–. Author of:
Mediaeval Symbolism and Realism.
Mimesis, tr. Willard R. Trask, 1953.

CHURCH, Brook Peters, 1885–1955 (pp. 237-270)

Teacher and writer. Author of three books on the Bible:
The Israel Saga, 1932
The Golden Years, 1947
The Private Lives of the Prophets, 1953.

FOWLER, Henry Thatcher, Ph.D., 1867–1948 (pp. 270-284)

Professor of Biblical Literature and History, Brown University, 1901–1934. Author of many books on the literature and history of the Bible, including:
The Books of the Bible, with Relation to Their Place in History (with Dr. M. C. Hazard), 1903
Studies in the Wisdom Literature of the Old Testament, 1907
The Origin and Growth of the Hebrew Religion, 1916
History and Literature of the New Testament, 1925.

GOETHE, Johann Wolfgang von, 1749–1832 (pp. 165-174)

German poet, dramatist, novelist and philosopher.

GORDIS, Robert, 1908– (pp. 284-305)

Biblical scholar and rabbi. Associate Professor of Biblical Exegesis, Seminary College of Jewish Studies, 1940–. Associate editor, department of Bible, *Universal Jewish Encyclopedia.* Author of several books on Old Testament literature.
Wisdom to Ecclesiastes, 1945
Koheleth, the Man and his World, 1951
The Song of Songs, 1954.

HART, H. St. J., 1912– (pp. 3-23)

Fellow of Queens' College and University Lecturer in Divinity, Cambridge University, England.

HERDER, Johann Gottfried von, 1744–1803 (pp. 133-165)

German theologian, critic and poet.

HOWARD, Wilbert Francis, D.D., 1880–1952 (pp. 78-86)

Professor of New Testament Language and Literature, Handsworth College, Birmingham. Author of a number of books on the New Testament.
The Fourth Gospel in Recent Criticism and Interpretation, 1931
Christianity according to St. John.
Grammar of New Testament Greek, vol. II, (ed. and joint author), 1929
The Romance of New Testament Scholarship, 1949.

KRAPP, George Philip, 1872–1934 (pp. 86-112)

Professor of English, Columbia University, 1910-1934. Scholarly publications in English literature and language, including:
Modern English—Its Growth and Present Use, 1909
The English Language in America, 1925
Anglo-Saxon Reader, 1929
The Junius Manuscript, 1931.

LAKE, Kirsopp, 1872–1946 (pp. 24-34)

Theologian and historian. Professor of Early Christian Literature, Harvard, 1914–1919. Professor of Ecclesiastical History, 1919–1932, Professor of History, 1932–1938. Archaeologist, editor of New Testament texts, and author of books on the New Testament, early Christian literature and theology, including:
Text of the New Testament, 1898
The Historical Evidence for the Resurrection of Jesus Christ, 1905
The Earlier Epistles of St. Paul, 1910
The Beginnings of Christianity, Five Volumes, 1920–1933
Six Collations of New Testament Narratives, 1933
Paul, His Heritage and Legacy, 1934.

LEWIS, Clive Staples, 1898– (pp. 343-362)

Professor of Mediaeval and Renaissance English, Cambridge University. Publications on English literature and theology, and novels, including:
The Screwtape Letters, 1942
A Preface to Paradise Lost, 1942
Christian Behavior, 1943
English Literature in the Sixteenth Century, 1954
Surprised by Joy (autobiography), 1955.

MANN, Thomas, 1875–1955 (pp. 232-237)

German novelist and critic. Author of the monumental twentieth-century treatment of the story of Joseph:
Joseph and His Brothers (tr. T. H. Lowe-Porter), 1934
Joseph in Egypt (tr. T. H. Lowe-Porter), 1938
Joseph the Provider (tr. T. H. Lowe-Porter), 1944.

MILTON, John, 1608–1674 (pp. 125-128)

English poet and controversialist. Author of the three greatest English poems on Biblical subjects, and a fourth very fine one:
Paradise Lost, 1667
Paradise Regained, 1671
Samson Agonistes, 1671
On the Morning of Christ's Nativity, 1629.

MULLO-WEIR, C.J., B.C., D. Phil. (pp. 70-78)

Professor of Hebrew and Semitic Languages in the University of Glasgow.
A Lexicon of Accadian Prayers in the Rituals of Expiation, 1934.

OESTERLEY, William O. E., D.D., Litt. D., 1866–1950 (pp. 51-63)

Professor of Hebrew and Old Testament Exegesis, University of London, 1926–1936. Author of many books on ancient manuscripts of the Bible and the development of literature, including:
The Religion and Worship of the Synagogue, 1907
The Books of the Apocrypha, 1914
The Wisdom of Egypt and the Old Testament, 1927
Proverbs (in *Westminster Commentaries on the Bible*), 1929
The Gospel Parables in the Light of Their Jewish Background, 1936.

PHELPS, William Lyon, 1865–1943 (pp. 320-339)

Professor of English, Yale University, 1901–1933. Author of many books on English and American literature, particularly modern, and of several books on the Bible, including:
Reading the Bible, 1919
Human Nature in the Bible, 1922
Human Nature and the Gospel, 1925.

POWYS, John Cowper, 1872– (pp. 185-208)

Novelist, poet, philosopher, critic. Many publications, including:
The Religion of a Sceptic, 1925
Suspended Judgments, 1916
The Meaning of Culture, 1930
In Defence of Sensuality, 1930
A Philosophy of Solitude, 1933
Enjoyment of Literature, 1938.

ROBINSON, Theodore Henry, D.D. Litt. D., 1881– (pp. 51-63)

Lecturer and Professor in Semitic Languages, University College, Cardiff, Wales, 1915–1944. Editor of Biblical texts and author of many books on the Bible and Hebrew religion, including:
Prophecy and the Prophets in the Old Testament, 1923
The Decline and Fall of the Hebrew Kingdoms, 1926
The Genius of Hebrew Grammar, 1927
Hebrew Religion: Its Origin and Development, (with W. O. E. Oesterley), 1930
A History of Israel (with W.O.E. Oesterley), 1932
The Poetry of the Old Testament, 1947.

ROWLEY, Rev. Harold Henry, D.D., B. Litt. 1890– (pp. 45-51)

Professor of Hebrew Language and Literature, University of Manchester. Publication on Biblical languages, history and religion, including:
The Aramaic of the Old Testament, 1929
The Growth of the Old Testament, 1950
From Joseph to Joshua, 1950
The Zadokite Fragments and the Dead Sea Scrolls, 1952
The Faith of Israel, 1956.

SAINTSBURY, George Edward Bateman, 1845–1933 (pp. 178-184)

Professor of Rhetoric and English Literature, University of Edinburgh, 1895–1915. Long list of publications on French and English literature and English style, of which a few are:
Specimens of English Prose Style, 1888
A History of Criticism (three volumes), 1900–1904
A History of English Prosody (three volumes), 1906–1910
History of English Prose Rhythm, 1912.

SANDS, Percy Cooper, 1883– (pp. 305-320)

Headmaster, Pocklington School, 1915–1944
Gods and Heroes
The Literary Genius of the Old Testament, 1924
The Literary Genius of the New Testament, 1932
Modern Illustrations of the Gospel

SIDNEY, Sir Philip, 1554–1586 (pp. 117-119)

English poet, critic, and statesman. Sidney was not a Biblical scholar, his three books being a pastoral romance, a volume of sonnets and lyrics, and a critical treatise. It is the way he cites the Bible in the critical treatise that justifies his inclusion here.

SYPHERD, Wilbur Owen, 1866– (pp. 64-69)

Professor of English, University of Delaware, 1906–1946. Author of books in English literature and composition, and Biblical literature:
The Literature of the English Bible, 1938
The Book of Books, 1944
The English Bible—Selections, 1921
"The Place of Luke in Literature," *Schelling Anniversary Papers,* 1923
Jephtha and his Daughter, A Study in Comparative Literature, 1948.

THOMPSON, Francis, 1859–1907 (pp. 176-178)

English poet, critic and essayist.

TOLSTOÏ, Count Lev Nikolaevich, 1828–1910 (pp. 230-232)

Russian novelist, social reformer, and religious mystic.

WHITMAN, Walt, 1819–1892 (pp. 174-176)

American poet, journalist, and essayist.

WITHER, George, 1588–1667 (pp. 120-124)

English poet and satirist. His work on the Bible includes:
Exercises upon the First Psalm, 1620
The Songs of the Old Testament. Translated into English Measures . . . . (Tc every song is added a new and easy tune,) 1621
The Hymns and Songs of the Church (with music by Orlando Gibbons), 1623
The Psalms of David translated into Lyric Verse, 1632
Hallelujah, or Britain's Second Remembrancer, 1641.

WRIGHT, George Ernest, 1909– (pp. 35-45)

Professor of Old Testament History and Theology, McCormick Theological Seminary. Author of books on Biblical archaeology, including:

The Old Testament against its Environment, 1951

The Pottery of Palestine from the Earliest Times to the End of the Early Bronze Age, 1937

The Westminster Historical Atlas to the Bible (with Floyd Vivian Filson and William Foxwell Albright), 1945, 1956.

Biblical Archaeology, 1957.

INDEX

THE TYPOGRAPHY, PRINTING, AND BINDING
OF THIS BOOK WERE EXECUTED BY
JACKSON TYPESETTING COMPANY OF JACKSON, MICHIGAN
HOLLERITH-WHITELOCK, INC., OF JACKSON
AND THE DEAN-HICKS COMPANY OF GRAND RAPIDS
THE TEXT IS SET IN 10 POINT TIMES ROMAN

The Library of Congress has cataloged this book as follows:

Reid, Mary Esson, *ed.*
   The Bible read as literature, an anthology. ₁1st ed.₁
Cleveland, H. Allen ₁1959₁

   375 p. 25 cm.

   Includes bibliography.

   1. Bible as literature.   ɪ. Title.

BS535.R4   220.88   58–11714 ‡

Library of Congress   ₁5₁